P9-BUI-540

Periodic Table of the Elements

Group	1 / 1A	2 / 2A	3 / 3B	4 / 4B	5 / 5B	6 / 6B	7 / 7B	8 / 8B	9 / 8B	10 / 8B	11 / 1B	12 / 2B	13 / 3A	14 / 4A	15 / 5A	16 / 6A	17 / 7A	18 / 8A
1	1 H 1.008																	2 He 4.003
2	3 Li 6.941	4 Be 9.012											5 B 10.81	6 C 12.01	7 N 14.01	8 O 16.00	9 F 19.00	10 Ne 20.18
3	11 Na 22.99	12 Mg 24.31											13 Al 26.98	14 Si 28.09	15 P 30.97	16 S 32.07	17 Cl 35.45	18 Ar 39.95
4	19 K 39.10	20 Ca 40.08	21 Sc 44.96	22 Ti 47.88	23 V 50.94	24 Cr 52.00	25 Mn 54.94	26 Fe 55.85	27 Co 58.93	28 Ni 58.69	29 Cu 63.55	30 Zn 65.41	31 Ga 69.72	32 Ge 72.64	33 As 74.92	34 Se 78.96	35 Br 79.90	36 Kr 83.80
5	37 Rb 85.47	38 Sr 87.62	39 Y 88.91	40 Zr 91.22	41 Nb 92.91	42 Mo 95.94	43 Tc (98)	44 Ru 101.1	45 Rh 102.9	46 Pd 106.4	47 Ag 107.9	48 Cd 112.4	49 In 114.8	50 Sn 118.7	51 Sb 121.8	52 Te 127.6	53 I 126.9	54 Xe 131.3
6	55 Cs 132.9	56 Ba 137.3	57 La 138.9	72 Hf 178.5	73 Ta 180.9	74 W 183.8	75 Re 186.2	76 Os 190.2	77 Ir 192.2	78 Pt 195.1	79 Au 197.0	80 Hg 200.6	81 Tl 204.4	82 Pb 207.2	83 Bi 209.0	84 Po (209)	85 At (210)	86 Rn (222)
7	87 Fr (223)	88 Ra (226)	89 Ac (227)	104 Rf (267)	105 Db (268)	106 Sg (271)	107 Bh (272)	108 Hs (270)	109 Mt (276)	110 Ds (281)	111 Rg (280)	112 Cn (285)	113 – (284)	114 – (289)	115 – (289)	116 – (293)	117 – (294)	118 – (294)

Lanthanides (Period 6)

58 Ce 140.1	59 Pr 140.9	60 Nd 144.2	61 Pm (145)	62 Sm 150.4	63 Eu 152.0	64 Gd 157.3	65 Tb 158.9	66 Dy 162.5	67 Ho 164.9	68 Er 167.3	69 Tm 168.9	70 Yb 173.0	71 Lu 175.0

Actinides (Period 7)

90 Th 232.0	91 Pa 231.0	92 U 238.0	93 Np (237)	94 Pu (244)	95 Am (243)	96 Cm (247)	97 Bk (247)	98 Cf (251)	99 Es (252)	100 Fm (257)	101 Md (258)	102 No (259)	103 Lr (262)

The Elements

Element	Symbol	Atomic Number	Relative Atomic Mass*	Element	Symbol	Atomic Number	Relative Atomic Mass*
Actinium	Ac	89	(227)	Molybdenum	Mo	42	95.94
Aluminum	Al	13	26.98	Neodymium	Nd	60	144.2
Americium	Am	95	(243)	Neon	Ne	10	20.18
Antimony	Sb	51	121.8	Neptunium	Np	93	(237)
Argon	Ar	18	39.95	Nickel	Ni	28	58.69
Arsenic	As	33	74.92	Niobium	Nb	41	92.91
Astatine	At	85	(210)	Nitrogen	N	7	14.01
Barium	Ba	56	137.3	Nobelium	No	102	(259)
Berkelium	Bk	97	(247)	Osmium	Os	76	190.2
Beryllium	Be	4	9.012	Oxygen	O	8	16.00
Bismuth	Bi	83	209.0	Palladium	Pd	46	106.4
Bohrium	Bh	107	(272)	Phosphorus	P	15	30.97
Boron	B	5	10.81	Platinum	Pt	78	195.1
Bromine	Br	35	79.90	Plutonium	Pu	94	(244)
Cadmium	Cd	48	112.4	Polonium	Po	84	(209)
Calcium	Ca	20	40.08	Potassium	K	19	39.10
Californium	Cf	98	(251)	Praseodymium	Pr	59	140.9
Carbon	C	6	12.01	Promethium	Pm	61	(145)
Cerium	Ce	58	140.1	Protactinium	Pa	91	231.0
Cesium	Cs	55	132.9	Radium	Ra	88	(226)
Chlorine	Cl	17	35.45	Radon	Rn	86	(222)
Chromium	Cr	24	52.00	Rhenium	Re	75	186.2
Cobalt	Co	27	58.93	Rhodium	Rh	45	102.9
Copernicium	Cn	112	(285)	Roentgenium	Rg	111	(280)
Copper	Cu	29	63.55	Rubidium	Rb	37	85.47
Curium	Cm	96	(247)	Ruthenium	Ru	44	101.1
Darmstadtium	Ds	110	(281)	Rutherfordium	Rf	104	(267)
Dubnium	Db	105	(268)	Samarium	Sm	62	150.4
Dysprosium	Dy	66	162.5	Scandium	Sc	21	44.96
Einsteinium	Es	99	(252)	Seaborgium	Sg	106	(271)
Erbium	Er	68	167.3	Selenium	Se	34	78.96
Europium	Eu	63	152.0	Silicon	Si	14	28.09
Fermium	Fm	100	(257)	Silver	Ag	47	107.9
Fluorine	F	9	19.00	Sodium	Na	11	22.99
Francium	Fr	87	(223)	Strontium	Sr	38	87.62
Gadolinium	Gd	64	157.3	Sulfur	S	16	32.07
Gallium	Ga	31	69.72	Tantalum	Ta	73	180.9
Germanium	Ge	32	72.64	Technetium	Tc	43	(98)
Gold	Au	79	197.0	Tellurium	Te	52	127.6
Hafnium	Hf	72	178.5	Terbium	Tb	65	158.9
Hassium	Hs	108	(270)	Thallium	Tl	81	204.4
Helium	He	2	4.003	Thorium	Th	90	232.0
Holmium	Ho	67	164.9	Thulium	Tm	69	168.9
Hydrogen	H	1	1.008	Tin	Sn	50	118.7
Indium	In	49	114.8	Titanium	Ti	22	47.88
Iodine	I	53	126.9	Tungsten	W	74	183.8
Iridium	Ir	77	192.2	Uranium	U	92	238.0
Iron	Fe	26	55.85	Vanadium	V	23	50.94
Krypton	Kr	36	83.80	Xenon	Xe	54	131.3
Lanthanum	La	57	138.9	Ytterbium	Yb	70	173.0
Lawrencium	Lr	103	(262)	Yttrium	Y	39	88.91
Lead	Pb	82	207.2	Zinc	Zn	30	65.41
Lithium	Li	3	6.941	Zirconium	Zr	40	91.22
Lutetium	Lu	71	175.0			113**	(284)
Magnesium	Mg	12	24.31			114	(289)
Manganese	Mn	25	54.94			115	(289)
Meitnerium	Mt	109	(276)			116	(293)
Mendelevium	Md	101	(258)			117	(294)
Mercury	Hg	80	200.6			118	(294)

*Values in parentheses represent the mass number of the most stable isotope.

**The names and symbols for elements 113 through 118 have not been chosen.

Cabrillo College

Volume 1
CHEM 30A & CHEM 32

Materials from

Principles of General, Organic &
Biological Chemistry
Second Edition

Janice Gorzynski Smith
University of Hawai'i at Mānoa

Boston Burr Ridge, IL Dubuque, IA New York San Francisco St. Louis
Bangkok Bogotá Caracas Lisbon London Madrid
Mexico City Milan New Delhi Seoul Singapore Sydney Taipei Toronto

The McGraw·Hill Companies

Volume 1
CHEM 30A & CHEM 32
Cabrillo College

Copyright © 2013 by The McGraw-Hill Companies, Inc. All rights reserved. Printed in the United States of America. Except as permitted under the United States Copyright Act of 1976, no part of this publication may be reproduced or distributed in any form or by any means, or stored in a data base retrieval system, without prior written permission of the publisher.

This book is a McGraw-Hill Learning Solutions textbook and contains select material from *Principles of General, Organic & Biological Chemistry*, Second Edition by Janice Gorzynski Smith. Copyright © 2012 by The McGraw-Hill Companies, Inc. Reprinted with permission of the publisher. Many custom published texts are modified versions or adaptations of our best-selling textbooks. Some adaptations are printed in black and white to keep prices at a minimum, while others are in color.

2 3 4 5 6 7 8 9 0   KNG KNG   14 13 12

ISBN-13: 978-0-07-766280-6
ISBN-10: 0-07-766280-6

Learning Solutions Consultant: Jill Albracht
Production Editor: Jennifer Bartell
Printer/Binder: King Printing

About the Author

Janice Gorzynski Smith was born in Schenectady, New York, and grew up following the Yankees, listening to the Beatles, and water skiing on Sacandaga Reservoir. She became interested in chemistry in high school, and went on to major in chemistry at Cornell University where she received an A.B. degree *summa cum laude*. Jan earned a Ph.D. in Organic Chemistry from Harvard University under the direction of Nobel Laureate E. J. Corey, and she also spent a year as a National Science Foundation National Needs Postdoctoral Fellow at Harvard. During her tenure with the Corey group, she completed the total synthesis of the plant growth hormone gibberellic acid.

Following her postdoctoral work, Jan joined the faculty of Mount Holyoke College where she was employed for 21 years. During this time she was active in teaching chemistry lecture and lab courses, conducting a research program in organic synthesis, and serving as department chair. Her organic chemistry class was named one of Mount Holyoke's "Don't-miss courses" in a survey by *Boston* magazine. After spending two sabbaticals amidst the natural beauty and diversity in Hawai'i in the 1990s, Jan and her family moved there permanently in 2000. Most recently, she has served as a faculty member at the University of Hawai'i at Mānoa, where she has taught a one-semester organic and biological chemistry course for nursing students, as well as the two-semester organic chemistry lecture and lab courses. She has also served as the faculty advisor to the student affiliate chapter of the American Chemical Society. In 2003, she received the Chancellor's Citation for Meritorious Teaching.

Jan resides in Hawai'i with her husband Dan, an emergency medicine physician. She has four children: Matthew and Zachary (margin photo on page 477); Jenna, a 2011 graduate of Temple University School of Law; and Erin (married with one son, Max), a 2006 graduate of Brown University School of Medicine and co-author of the Student Study Guide/Solutions Manual for this text. When not teaching, writing, or enjoying her family, Jan bikes, hikes, snorkels, and scuba dives in sunny Hawai'i, and time permitting, enjoys travel and Hawaiian quilting.

Dedicated to my family

Brief Contents

Contents

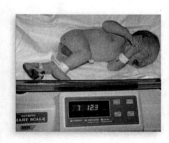

3 Ionic Compounds 67

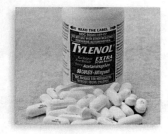

4 Covalent Compounds 94

7   Gases, Liquids, and Solids   198

8   Solutions   241

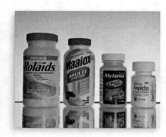

9 Acids and Bases 273

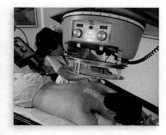

10 Nuclear Chemistry 315

Appendices

Preface

My goal in writing this text was to relate the fundamental concepts of general, organic, and biological chemistry to the world around us, and in this way illustrate how chemistry explains many aspects of everyday life. I have followed two guiding principles:

- use relevant and interesting applications for all basic chemical concepts
- present the material in a student-friendly fashion using bulleted lists, extensive illustrations, and step-by-step problem solving.

This text is different—by design. Since today's students rely more heavily on visual imagery to learn than ever before, this text uses less prose and more diagrams and figures to reinforce the major themes of chemistry. A key feature is the use of molecular art to illustrate and explain common phenomena we encounter every day. Each topic is broken down into small chunks of information that are more manageable and easily learned. Students are given enough detail to understand basic concepts, such as how soap cleans away dirt and why trans fats are undesirable in the diet, without being overwhelmed.

This textbook is written for students who have an interest in nursing, nutrition, environmental science, food science, and a wide variety of other health-related professions. The content of this book is designed for an introductory chemistry course with no chemistry prerequisite, and is suitable for either a two-semester sequence or a one-semester course. I have found that by introducing one new concept at a time, keeping the basic themes in focus, and breaking down complex problems into small pieces, many students in these chemistry courses acquire a new appreciation of both the human body and the larger world around them.

Building the Text

Writing a textbook is a multifaceted process. McGraw-Hill's 360° Development Process is an ongoing, never ending market-oriented approach to building accurate and innovative print and digital products. It is dedicated to continual large scale and incremental improvement, driven by multiple customer feedback loops and checkpoints. This is initiated during the early planning stages of new products, intensifies during the development and production stages, and then begins again upon publication, in anticipation of the next edition. This process is designed to provide a broad, comprehensive spectrum of feedback for refinement and innovation of learning tools, for both student and instructor. The 360° Development Process includes market research, content reviews, faculty and student focus groups, course- and product-specific symposia, accuracy checks, and art reviews.

The Learning System Used in *General, Organic, & Biological Chemistry*

▶ **Writing Style** A concise writing style allows students to focus on learning major concepts and themes of general, organic, and biological chemistry. Relevant materials from everyday life are used to illustrate concepts, and topics are broken into small chunks of information that are more easily learned.

▶ **Chapter Outline** The chapter outline lists the main headings of the chapter, to help students map out the organization of each chapter's content.

▶ **Chapter Goals, tied to end-of-chapter Key Concepts** The Chapter Goals at the beginning of each chapter identify what students will learn, and are tied numerically to the end-of-chapter Key Concepts, which serve as bulleted summaries of the most important concepts for study.

KEY CONCEPTS

❶ What do the terms in a chemical equation mean and how is an equation balanced? (5.1, 5.2)
• A chemical equation contains the reactants on the left side of an arrow and the products on the right. The coefficients tell how many molecules or moles of a substance react or are formed.
• A chemical equation is balanced by placing coefficients in front of chemical formulas one at a time, beginning with the most complex formula, so that the number of atoms of each element is the same on both sides. You must *not* balance the chemical equation by changing the subscripts in the chemical formulas of the reactants or products.

❷ Define the terms mole and Avogadro's number. (5.3)
• A mole is a quantity that contains 6.02×10^{23} atoms, molecules, or ions.
• Avogadro's number is the number of particles in a mole— 6.02×10^{23}.
• The number of molecules in a given number of moles is [b]'s number.

❸ [ ] molar mass calculated? (5.4)
[ ] sum of the atomic weights of all the [ ] ported in atomic mass units.
[ ] ss of one mole of a substance, [ ] olar mass is numerically equal to the [ ] ts are different (g/mol not amu).

[ ] stance and its number of moles
[ ] a conversion factor to determine [ ] ained in a given number of moles or [ ] e molar mass is used to determine [ ] stance are contained in a given

❺ How can a balanced equation and molar mass be used to calculate the number of moles and mass of a reaction product? (5.5, 5.6)
• The coefficients in a balanced chemical equation tell us the number of moles of each reactant that combine and the number of moles of each product formed. Coefficients are used to form mole ratios that serve as conversion factors relating the number of moles of reactants and products.
• When the mass of a substance in a reaction must be calculated, first its number of moles is determined using mole ratios, and then the molar mass is used to convert moles to grams.

❻ What is percent yield? (5.7)
• Percent yield = (actual yield/theoretical yield) × 100%.
• The actual yield is the amount of product formed in a reaction, determined by weighing a product on a balance. The theoretical yield is a quantity calculated from a balanced chemical equation, using mole ratios and molar masses. The theoretical yield is the maximum amount of product that can form in a chemical reaction from the amount of reactants used.

❼ What is the limiting reactant in a reaction? (5.8)
• The limiting reactant is the reactant that is completely used up in a reaction. The number of moles of limiting reactant determines the number of moles of product formed using mole ratios in the balanced equation.

❽ What are oxidation and reduction reactions? (5.9)
• Oxidation–reduction or redox reactions are electron transfer reactions.
• Oxidation results in the loss of electrons. Metals and anions tend to undergo oxidation. In some reactions, oxidation results in the gain of O atoms or the loss of H atoms.
• Reduction results in the gain of electrons. Nonmetals and cations tend to undergo reduction. In some reactions, reduction results in the loss of O atoms or the gain of H atoms.

❾ Give some examples of common or useful redox reactions. (5.9, 5.10)
• Common examples of redox reactions include the rusting of iron and the combustion of methane. The electric current generated in batteries used for flashlights and pacemakers results from redox reactions.

CHAPTER GOALS

In this chapter you will learn how to:
❶ Write and balance chemical equations
❷ Define a mole and use Avogadro's number in calculations
❸ Calculate formula weight and molar mass
❹ Relate the mass of a substance to its number of moles
❺ Carry out mole and mass calculations in chemical equations
❻ Calculate percent yield
❼ Determine the limiting reactant in a reaction
❽ Define oxidation and reduction and recognize the components of a redox reaction
❾ Give examples of common or useful redox reactions

▶ **Macro-to-Micro Illustrations** Because today's students are visual learners, and because visualizing molecular-level representations of macroscopic phenomena is critical to the understanding of any chemistry course, many illustrations in this text include photos or drawings of everyday objects, paired with their molecular representation, to help students understand the chemistry behind ordinary occurrences.

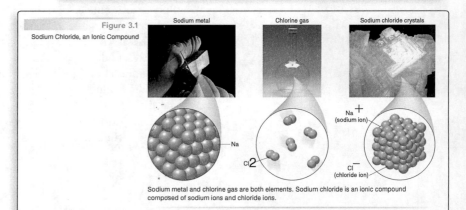

Figure 3.1
Sodium Chloride, an Ionic Compound

Sodium metal   Chlorine gas   Sodium chloride crystals

Na   Cl$_2$ Na$^+$ (sodium ion)   Cl$^-$ (chloride ion)

Sodium metal and chlorine gas are both elements. Sodium chloride is an ionic compound composed of sodium ions and chloride ions.

▶ **Problem Solving** Sample Problems lead students through the thought process tied to successful problem solving by employing Analysis and Solution parts. Sample Problems are categorized sequentially by topic to match chapter organization, and are often paired with practice problems to allow students to apply what they have just learned. Students can immediately verify their answers to the follow-up problems in the appendix at the end of the book.

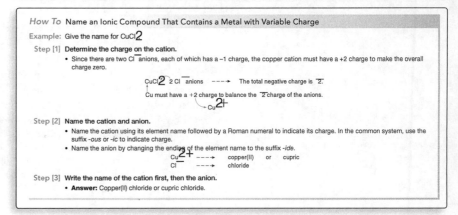

How To Name an Ionic Compound That Contains a Metal with Variable Charge

Example: Give the name for CuCl$_2$
Step [1] **Determine the charge on the cation.**
• Since there are two Cl$^-$ anions, each of which has a –1 charge, the copper cation must have a +2 charge to make the overall charge zero.

CuCl$_2$ → 2 Cl$^-$ anions ----→ The total negative charge is $\overline{2}$.
Cu must have a +2 charge to balance the $\overline{2}$ charge of the anions.
→ Cu^{2+}

Step [2] **Name the cation and anion.**
• Name the cation using its element name followed by a Roman numeral to indicate its charge. In the common system, use the suffix *-ous* or *-ic* to indicate charge.
• Name the anion by changing the ending of the element name to the suffix *-ide*.
Cu^{2+} ----→ copper(II) or cupric
Cl$^-$ ----→ chloride

Step [3] **Write the name of the cation first, then the anion.**
• **Answer:** Copper(II) chloride or cupric chloride.

▶ *How To's* Key processes are taught to students in a straightforward and easy-to-understand manner by using examples and multiple, detailed steps to solving problems.

▶ **Applications** Common applications of chemistry to everyday life are found in margin-placed Health Notes, Consumer Notes, and Environmental Notes, as well as sections entitled "Focus on Health & Medicine," "Focus on the Environment," and "Focus on the Human Body."

New to This Edition

Chapter Specific

- Atomic weights are now reported more systematically, using four significant digits for all weights. The periodic table of elements has also been revised accordingly in Chapter 2 and on the inside cover.
- Examples of ions with variable charge have been added to Chapter 3 to present a clearer discussion of the fact that some of the transition metals have a fixed charge while others are variable.
- A section on limiting reactants has been added to Chapter 5. This additional coverage instructs students on how to determine which reactant is limiting and how much product is formed using the mole ratios in a balanced equation.
- A more detailed discussion of the transition state in energy diagrams was added to Chapter 6.
- A discussion of heating and cooling curves was added to Chapter 7 in order to provide a more complete illustration of energy and phase changes.
- Material on optical activity and polarimetry has been added to Chapter 15.
- More photos have been added to Chapters 22 through 24 to aid students in visualizing and better relating to the concepts in the text.

General

- **Problem sets.** More problems with molecular art and 3-D models have been added to the text and end-of-chapter. A set of Challenge Problems has also been added at the end of each chapter.
- **Design.** The problem and sample problem headings have been moved out of the margin to leave more room for marginal photos and tables, allowing for photos and tables to be placed closer to relevant material in the text.
- **Photos.** About one-third to one-half of the chapter opening photos have been replaced with photos emphasizing relevance and student interest. More marginal photos of relevant applications have been added.
- **Art.** The representations of the human body have been given a much cleaner and androgynous appearance.

Our Commitment to Serving Teachers and Learners

TO THE INSTRUCTOR Writing a chemistry textbook is a colossal task. Teaching chemistry for over 20 years at both a private, liberal arts college and a large state university has given me a unique perspective with which to write this text. I have found that students arrive with vastly different levels of preparation and widely different expectations for their college experience. As an instructor and now an author I have tried to channel my love and knowledge of chemistry into a form that allows this spectrum of students to understand chemical science more clearly, and then see everyday phenomena in a new light.

TO THE STUDENT I hope that this text and its ancillary program will help you to better understand and appreciate the world of chemistry. My interactions with thousands of students in my long teaching career have profoundly affected the way I teach and write about chemistry, so please feel free to email me with any comments or questions at **jgsmith@hawaii.edu.**

P.A.V.E. the Way to Student Learning

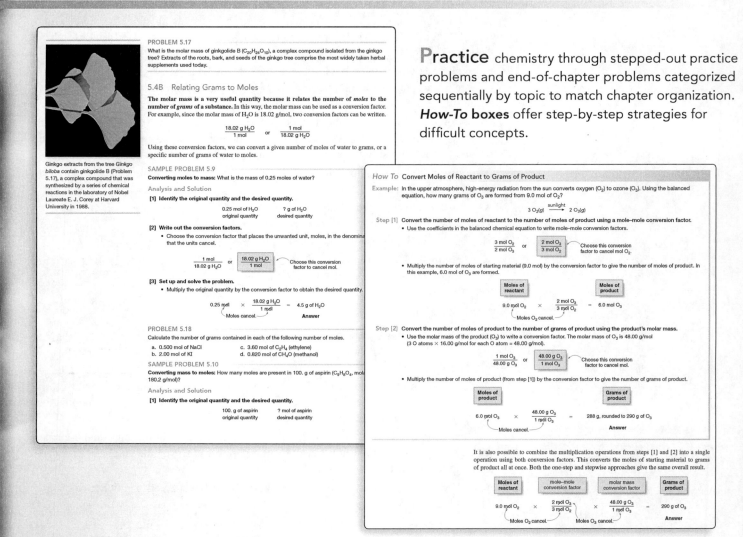

Practice chemistry through stepped-out practice problems and end-of-chapter problems categorized sequentially by topic to match chapter organization. *How-To boxes* offer step-by-step strategies for difficult concepts.

PROBLEM 5.17

What is the molar mass of ginkgolide B ($C_{20}H_{24}O_{10}$), a complex compound isolated from the ginkgo tree? Extracts of the roots, bark, and seeds of the ginkgo tree comprise the most widely taken herbal supplements used today.

5.4B Relating Grams to Moles

The molar mass is a very useful quantity because it relates the number of *moles* to the number of *grams* of a substance. In this way, the molar mass can be used as a conversion factor. For example, since the molar mass of H_2O is 18.02 g/mol, two conversion factors can be written.

$$\frac{18.02 \text{ g } H_2O}{1 \text{ mol}} \quad \text{or} \quad \frac{1 \text{ mol}}{18.02 \text{ g } H_2O}$$

Using these conversion factors, we can convert a given number of moles of water to grams, or a specific number of grams of water to moles.

SAMPLE PROBLEM 5.9

Converting moles to mass: What is the mass of 0.25 moles of water?

Analysis and Solution

[1] Identify the original quantity and the desired quantity.

0.25 mol of H_2O ? g of H_2O
original quantity   desired quantity

[2] Write out the conversion factors.
- Choose the conversion factor that places the unwanted unit, moles, in the denominator so that the units cancel.

$$\frac{1 \text{ mol}}{18.02 \text{ g } H_2O} \quad \text{or} \quad \frac{18.02 \text{ g } H_2O}{1 \text{ mol}}$$

Choose this conversion factor to cancel mol.

[3] Set up and solve the problem.
- Multiply the original quantity by the conversion factor to obtain the desired quantity.

$$0.25 \text{ mol} \times \frac{18.02 \text{ g } H_2O}{1 \text{ mol}} = 4.5 \text{ g of } H_2O$$

Moles cancel.   **Answer**

PROBLEM 5.18

Calculate the number of grams contained in each of the following number of moles.

a. 0.500 mol of NaCl   c. 3.60 mol of C_2H_4 (ethylene)
b. 2.00 mol of KI   d. 0.820 mol of CH_4O (methanol)

SAMPLE PROBLEM 5.10

Converting mass to moles: How many moles are present in 100. g of aspirin ($C_9H_8O_4$, molar mass 180.2 g/mol)?

Analysis and Solution

[1] Identify the original quantity and the desired quantity.

100. g of aspirin   ? mol of aspirin
original quantity   desired quantity

Ginkgo extracts from the tree Ginkgo biloba contain ginkgolide B (Problem 5.17), a complex compound that was synthesized by a series of chemical reactions in the laboratory of Nobel Laureate E. J. Corey at Harvard University in 1988.

How To Convert Moles of Reactant to Grams of Product

Example: In the upper atmosphere, high-energy radiation from the sun converts oxygen (O_2) to ozone (O_3). Using the balanced equation, how many grams of O_3 are formed from 9.0 mol of O_2?

$$3 O_2(g) \xrightarrow{\text{sunlight}} 2 O_3(g)$$

Step [1] Convert the number of moles of reactant to the number of moles of product using a mole–mole conversion factor.
- Use the coefficients in the balanced chemical equation to write mole–mole conversion factors.

$$\frac{3 \text{ mol } O_2}{2 \text{ mol } O_3} \quad \text{or} \quad \frac{2 \text{ mol } O_3}{3 \text{ mol } O_2}$$

Choose this conversion factor to cancel mol O_2.

- Multiply the number of moles of starting material (9.0 mol) by the conversion factor to give the number of moles of product. In this example, 6.0 mol of O_3 are formed.

Moles of reactant   Moles of product

$$9.0 \text{ mol } O_2 \times \frac{2 \text{ mol } O_3}{3 \text{ mol } O_2} = 6.0 \text{ mol } O_3$$

Moles O_2 cancel.

Step [2] Convert the number of moles of product to the number of grams of product using the product's molar mass.
- Use the molar mass of the product (O_3) to write a conversion factor. The molar mass of O_3 is 48.00 g/mol (3 O atoms × 16.00 g/mol for each O atom = 48.00 g/mol).

$$\frac{1 \text{ mol } O_3}{48.00 \text{ g } O_3} \quad \text{or} \quad \frac{48.00 \text{ g } O_3}{1 \text{ mol } O_3}$$

Choose this conversion factor to cancel mol.

- Multiply the number of moles of product (from step [1]) by the conversion factor to give the number of grams of product.

Moles of product   Grams of product

$$6.0 \text{ mol } O_3 \times \frac{48.00 \text{ g } O_3}{1 \text{ mol } O_3} = 288 \text{ g, rounded to } 290 \text{ g of } O_3$$

Moles cancel.   **Answer**

It is also possible to combine the multiplication operations from steps [1] and [2] into a single operation using both conversion factors. This converts the moles of starting material to grams of product all at once. Both the one-step and stepwise approaches give the same overall result.

Moles of reactant → mole–mole conversion factor → molar mass conversion factor → Grams of product

$$9.0 \text{ mol } O_2 \times \frac{2 \text{ mol } O_3}{3 \text{ mol } O_2} \times \frac{48.00 \text{ g } O_3}{1 \text{ mol } O_3} = 290 \text{ g of } O_3$$

Moles O_2 cancel.   Moles O_3 cancel.   **Answer**

Apply chemistry through **"Focus on Health & Medicine," "Focus on the Human Body,"** and **"Focus on the Environment"** sections woven throughout the text. Chemistry applications are also woven into marginal notes that cover topics on consumer, health, and environmental issues.

CONSUMER NOTE

Some anti-aging creams contain vitamin A.

11.7 FOCUS ON HEALTH & MEDICINE
Vitamins

Vitamins are organic compounds needed in small amounts for normal cell function. Our bodies cannot synthesize these compounds, so they must be obtained in our diet. Most vitamins are identified by a letter, such as A, C, D, E, and K. There are several different B vitamins, though, so a subscript is added to distinguish them—for example, B_1, B_2, and B_{12}.

Vitamins are classified on the basis of their solubility properties.

- A *fat-soluble vitamin* dissolves in an organic solvent but is insoluble in water. Fat-soluble vitamins have many nonpolar C—C and C—H bonds and few polar functional groups.
- A *water-soluble vitamin* dissolves in water. Water-soluble vitamins have many polar bonds.

Whether a vitamin is fat soluble or water soluble can be determined by applying the solubility principles discussed in Section 11.6. Vitamins A and C illustrate the differences between fat-soluble and water-soluble vitamins.

11.7A Vitamin A

Vitamin A, or **retinol,** is an essential component of the vision receptors in the eyes. It also helps to maintain the health of mucous membranes and the skin, so many anti-aging creams contain vitamin A. A deficiency of this vitamin leads to a loss of night vision.

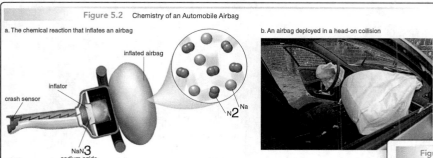

Figure 5.2 Chemistry of an Automobile Airbag

a. The chemical reaction that inflates an airbag

inflated airbag

inflator

crash sensor

N_2 Na

NaN$_3$
sodium azide

b. An airbag deployed in a head-on collision

A severe car crash triggers an airbag to deploy when an electric sensor causes sodium azide (NaN$_3$) to ignite, converting it to sod[...] and nitrogen gas (N_2). The nitrogen gas causes the bag to inflate fully in 40 milliseconds, helping to protect passengers from seri[...] The sodium atoms formed in this first reaction are hazardous and subsequently converted to a safe sodium salt. It took 30 years [...] reliable airbag system for automobiles.

Visualize chemistry through a dynamic art program that brings together macroscopic and microscopic representations of images to help students comprehend on a molecular level. Many illustrations include photos or drawings of everyday objects, paired with their molecular representation, to help students understand the chemistry behind ordinary occurrences. Many illustrations of the human body include magnifications for specific anatomic regions, as well as representations at the microscopic level, for today's visual learners.

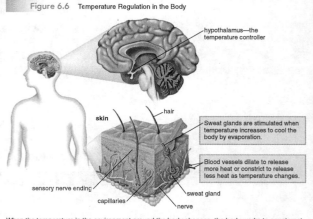

Figure 6.6 Temperature Regulation in the Body

hypothalamus—the temperature controller

hair

skin

Sweat glands are stimulated when temperature increases to cool the body by evaporation.

Blood vessels dilate to release more heat or constrict to release less heat as temperature changes.

sensory nerve ending

capillaries

sweat gland

nerve

When the temperature in the environment around the body changes, the body works to counteract the change, in a method similar to Le Châtelier's principle. The hypothalamus acts as a thermostat, which signals the body to respond to temperature changes. When the temperature increases, the body must dissipate excess heat by dilating blood vessels and sweating. When the temperature decreases, blood vessels constrict and the body shivers.

7.8A Vapor Pressure

HEALTH NOTE

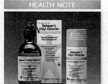

When a liquid is placed in an open container, liquid molecules near the surface that have enough kinetic energy to overcome the intermolecular forces, escape to the gas phase. This process, **evaporation,** will continue until all of the liquid has become gas. A puddle of water formed after a rainstorm evaporates as all of the liquid water is converted to gas molecules called water **vapor. Evaporation is an *endothermic* process**—it absorbs heat from the surroundings. This explains why the skin is cooled as sweat evaporates.

Chloroethane (CH$_3$CH$_2$Cl), commonly called ethyl chloride, is a local anesthetic. When chloroethane is sprayed on a wound it quickly evaporates, causing a cooling sensation that numbs the site of an injury.

H$_2$O
evaporation

In a closed container, some liquid molecules evaporate from the surface and enter the gas phase. As more molecules accumulate in the gas phase, some molecules re-enter the liquid phase in the process of **condensation. Condensation is an *exothermic* process**—it gives off heat to the surroundings. At equilibrium, the rate of evaporation and the rate of condensation are equal.

evaporation—molecules go from liquid to [...]

condensation—molecules go from gas to li[...]

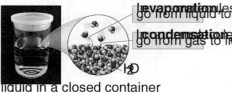

H$_2$O

liquid in a closed container

Engage students with a unique writing style that matches the method in which students learn. Key points of general, organic, and biological chemistry, along with attention-grabbing applications to consumer, environmental, and health-related fields, are woven together in a succinct style for today's to-the-point readers.

The gas laws we have already learned can describe the behavior of the gas molecules above a liquid. In particular, these gas molecules exert pressure, called **vapor pressure.**

- Vapor pressure is the pressure exerted by gas molecules in equilibrium with the liquid phase.

The vapor pressure exerted by a particular liquid depends on the identity of the liquid and the temperature. As the temperature is increased, the kinetic energy of the molecules increases and more molecules escape into the gas phase.

- Vapor pressure increases with increasing temperature.

When the temperature is high enough that the vapor pressure above the liquid equals the atmospheric pressure, even molecules below the surface of the liquid have enough kinetic energy to enter the gas phase and the liquid boils. **The *normal boiling point* of a liquid is the temperature at which its vapor pressure equals 760 mm Hg.**

Learning Resources for Instructors and Students

McGraw-Hill Connect® Chemistry

www.mcgrawhillconnect.com/chemistry

McGraw-Hill Connect® Chemistry is a web-based assignment and assessment platform that gives students the means to better connect with their coursework, with their instructors, and with the important concepts that they will need to know for success now and in the future. The chemical drawing tool found within Connect Chemistry is CambridgeSoft's ChemDraw, which is widely considered the "gold standard" of scientific drawing programs and the cornerstone application for scientists who draw and annotate molecules, reactions, and pathways. This collaboration of Connect and ChemDraw features an easy-to-use, intuitive, and comprehensive course management and homework system with professional-grade drawing capabilities.

With Connect Chemistry, instructors can deliver assignments, quizzes, and tests online. Questions from the text are presented in an auto-gradable format and tied to the text's learning objectives. Instructors can edit existing questions and author entirely new problems. They also can track individual student performance—by question, assignment, or in relation to the class overall—with detailed grade reports; integrate grade reports easily with Learning Management Systems (LMS) such as WebCT and Blackboard; and much more.

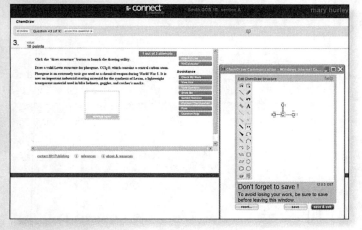

By choosing Connect Chemistry, instructors are providing their students with a powerful tool for improving academic performance and truly mastering course material. Connect Chemistry allows students to practice important skills at their own pace and on their own schedule. Importantly, students' assessment results and instructors' feedback are all saved online—so students can continually review their progress and plot their course to success.

McGraw-Hill ConnectPlus® Chemistry

Like Connect Chemistry, **McGraw-Hill ConnectPlus® Chemistry** provides students with online assignments and assessments, plus 24/7 online access to an eBook—an online edition of the text—to aid them in successfully completing their work, wherever and whenever they choose.

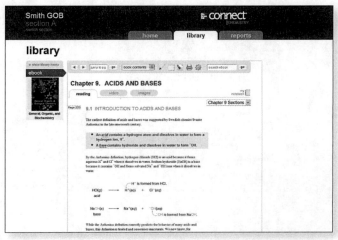

McGraw-Hill Higher Education and Blackboard®

McGraw-Hill Higher Education and Blackboard® have teamed up! What does this mean for you?

1. **Your life, simplified.** Now you and your students can access McGraw-Hill's Connect® and Create™ right from within your Blackboard course—all with one single sign-on. Say good-bye to the days of logging in to multiple applications.
2. **Deep integration of content and tools.** Not only do you get single sign-on with Connect and Create, you also get deep integration of McGraw-Hill content and content engines right in Blackboard. Whether you're choosing a book for your course or building Connect assignments, all the tools you need are right where you want them—inside of Blackboard.
3. **Seamless Gradebooks.** Are you tired of keeping multiple gradebooks and manually synchronizing grades into Blackboard? We thought so. When a student completes an integrated Connect assignment, the grade for that assignment automatically (and instantly) feeds your Blackboard grade center.
4. **A solution for everyone.** Whether your institution is already using Blackboard or you just want to try Blackboard on your own, we have a solution for you. McGraw-Hill and Blackboard can now offer you easy access to industry-leading technology and content, whether your campus hosts it, or we do. Be sure to ask your local McGraw-Hill representative for details.

McGraw-Hill LearnSmart™

This adaptive diagnostic learning system, powered by Connect Chemistry and based on artificial intelligence, constantly assesses a student's knowledge of the course material. As students work within the system, LearnSmart develops a personal learning path adapted to what each student has actively learned and retained. This innovative study tool

also has features to allow the instructor to see exactly what students have accomplished, with a built-in assessment tool for graded assignments. You can access LearnSmart for *General, Organic, & Biological Chemistry* at **www.mcgrawhillconnect.com/chemistry.**

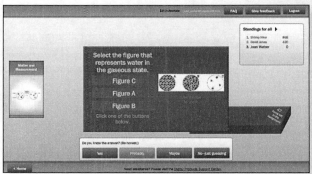

Customizable Textbooks: McGraw-Hill Create™

Create what you've only imagined. Introducing McGraw-Hill Create™—a new, self-service website that allows you to create custom course materials (print and eBooks) by drawing upon McGraw-Hill's comprehensive, cross-disciplinary content. Add your own content quickly and easily. Tap into other rights-secured third party sources as well. Then, arrange the content in a way that makes the most sense for your course, and if you wish, personalize your book with your course name and information. Choose the best delivery format for your course: color print, black-and-white print, or eBook. The eBook is now viewable for the iPad! And when you are finished customizing, you will receive a free PDF review copy in just minutes! Visit McGraw-Hill Create (**www.mcgrawhillcreate.com**) today and begin building your perfect book.

Presentation Center

Within the Instructor's Presentation Center, instructors have access to editable PowerPoint lecture outlines, which appear as ready-made presentations that combine art and lecture notes for each chapter of the text. For instructors who prefer to create their lecture notes from scratch, all illustrations, photos, and tables are pre-inserted by chapter into a separate set of PowerPoint slides.

An online digital library contains photos, artwork, animations, and other media types that can be used to create customized lectures, visually enhanced tests and quizzes, compelling course websites, or attractive printed support materials. All assets are copyrighted by McGraw-Hill Higher Education, but can be used by instructors for classroom purposes. The visual resources in this collection include:

- **Art** Full-color digital files of all illustrations in the book can be readily incorporated into lecture presentations, exams, or custom-made classroom materials.
- **Photos** The photo collection contains digital files of photographs from the text, which can be reproduced for multiple classroom uses.
- **Tables** Every table that appears in the text has been saved in electronic form for use in classroom presentations and/or quizzes.
- **Animations** Numerous full-color animations illustrating important processes are also provided. Harness the visual impact of concepts in motion by importing these files into classroom presentations or online course materials.

Digital Lecture Capture: Tegrity®

McGraw-Hill Tegrity® records and distributes your lecture with just a click of a button. Students can view anytime/anywhere via computer, iPod, or mobile device. Tegrity indexes as it records your slideshow presentations and anything shown on your computer, so students can use keywords to find exactly what they want to study.

Instructor's Solutions Manual

This supplement contains complete, worked out solutions for all the end-of-chapter problems in the text. It can be found within the Instructor's Resources for this text at **www.mcgrawhillconnect.com/chemistry**.

Computerized Test Bank Online

A comprehensive bank of test questions prepared by Jennifer Adamski is provided within a computerized test bank enabling you to create paper and online tests or quizzes in an easy-to-use program that allows you to prepare and access your test or quiz anywhere, at anytime. Instructors can create or edit questions, or drag-and-drop questions, to prepare tests quickly and easily. Tests may be published to an online course, or printed for paper-based assignments.

Student Study Guide/Solutions Manual

The Student Solutions Manual, prepared by Erin Smith Berk and Janice Gorzynski Smith, begins each chapter with a detailed chapter review that is organized around the chapter goals and key concepts. The Problem Solving section provides a number of examples for solving each type of problem essential to that chapter. The Self-Test section of each chapter quizzes chapter highlights, with answers provided. Finally, each chapter ends with the solutions to all in-chapter problems, as well as the solutions to all odd-numbered end-of-chapter problems.

Acknowledgments

Publishing a modern chemistry textbook requires a team of knowledgeable and hard-working individuals who are able to translate an author's vision into a reality. I am thankful to work with such a group of dedicated publishing professionals at McGraw-Hill. Much thanks goes to Sponsoring Editor Todd Turner and Senior Developmental Editor Mary Hurley, both of whom managed the day-to-day details of the project with timeliness and professionalism. Jayne Klein, Senior Project Manager, skillfully directed the production process, and Publisher Ryan Blankenship guided the project to assure that all the needed resources were available to see it to completion.

I am especially grateful to freelance Developmental Editor John Murdzek, whose unique blend of humor, chemical knowledge, and attention to detail were key ingredients at numerous stages in the creation of both the text and the student solutions manual. I have also greatly benefited from a team of advisors who helped guide me through the preparation of the first edition, as well as a panel of art reviewers who oversaw the creation of the beautiful figures present in the finished text.

Finally, I thank my family for their support and patience during the long process of publishing a textbook. My husband Dan, an emergency medicine physician, read the entire manuscript, took several photos that appear in the text, and served as a consultant for many medical applications. My daughter Erin co-authored the *Student Study Guide/Solutions Manual* with me, which was written while she was working as a full-time physician in emergency medicine.

Reviewers

The following people were instrumental in reading and providing feedback on the text and illustrations, which helped to shape my ideas into cohesive pages:

Madeline Adamczeski, *San Jose City College*
Karen Atkinson, *Bunker Hill Community College*
Dan Black, *Snow College*
Albert Bobst, *University of Cincinnati*
David Butcher, *Western Carolina University*
Ling Chen, *Borough of Manhattan Community College/CUNY*
Pam Clevenger, *Hinds Community College*
Rajeev Dabke, *Columbus State University*
William Daniel, *Bakersfield College*
Brahmadeo Dewprashad, *Borough of Manhattan Community College*
Pam Doyle, *Essex County College*
Coretta Fernandes, *Lansing Community College*
Zewdu Gebeyehu, *Columbus State University*
Arlene Haffa, *University of Wisconsin, Oshkosh*
Amy Hanks, *Brigham Young University, Idaho*
Blaine Harrison, *West Valley College*
John Haseltine, *Kennesaw State University*
Shirley Hino, *Santa Rosa Junior College*
Michael Hurst, *Georgia Southern University*
Tom Huxford, *San Diego State University*
Martina Kaledin, *Kennesaw State University*

Margaret Leslie, *Kent State University*
Julie Lowe, *Bakersfield College*
Ying Mao, *Camden Community College*
Craig McClure, *University of Alabama at Birmingham*
Mary Bethe Neely, *University of Colorado at Colorado Springs*
Felix Ngassa, *Grand Valley State University*
Amanda Norick, *Foothill College*
Kenneth O'Connor, *Marshall University*
Katherine Olsen, *Pierce College*
Johanna Petridou–Fisher, *Spokane Falls Community College*
Allan Pinhas, *University of Cincinnati*
Tomislav Pintauer, *Duquesne University*
Mike Ray, *California State University Fresno*
Jonathan Rhoad, *Missouri Western State University*
Jennifer Robertson–Honecker, *West Virginia University*
Paul Root, *Henry Ford Community College*
Raymond Sadeghi, *University of Texas at San Antonio*
Susan Marie Sawyer, *Kellogg Community College*
Colleen Scott, *Southern Illinois University Carbondale*
Nicholas Servis, *Vincennes University–Jasper Campus*
Heather Sklenicka, *Rochester Community and Technical College*
David Stanislawski, *Chattanooga State Technical Community College*
Denise Stiglich, *Antelope Valley College*
Susan Thomas, *University of Texas at San Antonio*
Lois Gilbert Waters, *Baltimore City Community College*
Lawrence Williams, *Wake Tech Community College*
Lawrence Yee, *Hartnell College*

McGraw-Hill Connect® Chemistry has been greatly enhanced by the efforts of Danae Quirk Dorr of Minnesota State University–Mankato, who worked to improve the content, author feedback and hints, and select problems for the second edition site; and Shirley Hino of Santa Rosa Junior College, who authored the interactive problem content, also authored feedback and hints, and performed accuracy checking of all Connect: Chemistry content. In addition, the following instructors also did a masterful job of authoring hints and feedback to augment all of the Connect: Chemistry homework problems: Eric Elisabeth of Johnson County Community College; Patrick Greco of Sinclair Community College; Paul Root of Henry Ford Community College; Emily Tansey of Otterbein College; John Tansey of Otterbein College; and Dave Tramontozzi of Macomb Community College. The following instructors performed accuracy checks of the Connect: Chemistry content to ensure the reliability and correctness: Jennifer Adamski (formally of Old Dominion University); Eric Elisabeth of Johnson County Community College; and Annise Goodman of Eastern Michigan University.

The following individuals helped write and review learning goal-oriented content for McGraw-Hill LearnSmart™ for *General, Organic, & Biological Chemistry:* Susan Bane, Binghamton University; Anne M. Distler, Cuyahoga Community College; Patrick Greco, Sinclair Community College; Lenore K. Hoyt, University of Louisville; David G. Jones, North Carolina Central University; Adam I. Keller, Columbus State Community College; Michael Koerner, University of Arizona; Jerry Mundell, Cleveland State University; Anne O'Connor, Cleveland State University; Shadrick I. Paris, Ohio University; Paul D. Root, Henry Ford Community College; Kathleen Thrush Shaginaw, Particular Solutions, Inc.; and David Tramontozzi, Macomb Community College.

We are also extremely grateful to the authors of the other ancillaries to accompany *General, Organic, & Biological Chemistry,* Second Edition: Lauren McMills of Ohio University–Athens for her authoring of the Instructor Solutions Manual; Andrea Leonard of the University of Louisiana at Lafayette for her authoring of the PowerPoint Lecture Outlines; and Jennifer Adamski for her authoring of the Test Bank.

List of *How To's*

List of Applications

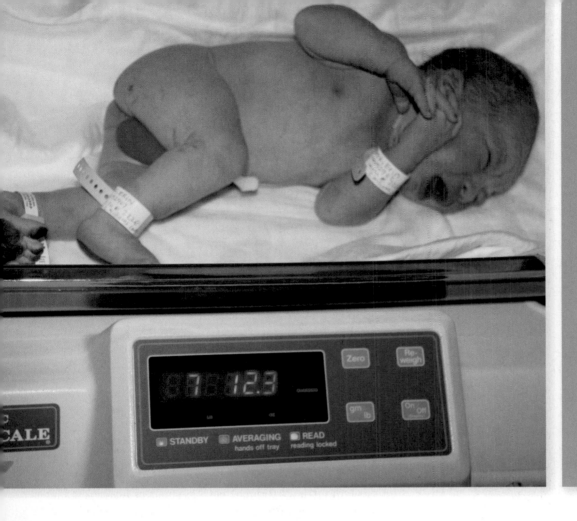

Determining the weight and length of a newborn are common measurements performed by healthcare professionals.

1

Matter and Measurement

CHAPTER GOALS

In this chapter you will learn how to:

1. Describe the three states of matter

2. Classify matter as a pure substance, mixture, element, or compound

3. Report measurements using the metric units of length, mass, and volume

4. Use significant figures

5. Use scientific notation for very large and very small numbers

6. Use conversion factors to convert one unit to another

7. Convert temperature from one scale to another

8. Define density and specific gravity and use density to calculate the mass or volume of a substance

Everything you touch, feel, or taste is composed of chemicals—that is, **matter**—so an understanding of its composition and properties is crucial to our appreciation of the world around us. Some matter—lakes, trees, sand, and soil—is naturally occurring, while other examples of matter—aspirin, CDs, nylon fabric, plastic syringes, and vaccines—are made by humans. To understand the properties of matter, as well as how one form of matter is converted to another, we must also learn about measurements. Following a recipe, pumping gasoline, and figuring out drug dosages involve manipulating numbers. Thus, Chapter 1 begins our study of chemistry by examining the key concepts of matter and measurement.

1.1 Chemistry—The Science of Everyday Experience

What activities might occupy the day of a typical student? You may have done some or all of the following tasks: eaten some meals, drunk coffee or cola, taken a shower with soap, taken notes in a class, checked email on a computer, watched some television, ridden a bike or car to a part-time job, taken an aspirin to relieve a headache, and spent some of the evening having snacks and refreshments with friends. Perhaps, without your awareness, your life was touched by chemistry in each of these activities. What, then, is this discipline we call **chemistry?**

- *Chemistry* is the study of matter—its composition, properties, and transformations.

What is **matter?**

- *Matter* is anything that has mass and takes up volume.

In other words, **chemistry studies anything that we touch, feel, see, smell, or taste,** from simple substances like water or salt, to complex substances like proteins and carbohydrates that combine to form the human body. Some matter—cotton, sand, an apple, and the cardiac drug digoxin—is **naturally occurring,** meaning it is isolated from natural sources. Other substances—nylon, Styrofoam, the plastic used in soft drink bottles, and the pain reliever ibuprofen—are **synthetic,** meaning they are produced by chemists in the laboratory (Figure 1.1).

> **Figure 1.1**   Naturally Occurring and Synthetic Materials

a. Naturally occurring materials   b. Synthetic materials

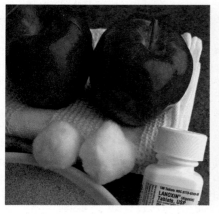 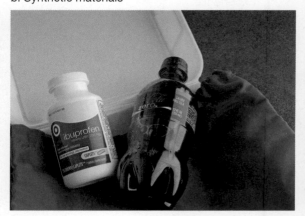

Matter occurs in nature or is synthesized in the lab. (a) Sand and apples are two examples of natural materials. Cotton fabric is woven from cotton fiber, obtained from the cotton plant. The drug digoxin (Trade name: Lanoxin), widely prescribed for decades for patients with congestive heart failure, is extracted from the leaves of the woolly foxglove plant. (b) Nylon was the first synthetic fiber made in the laboratory. It quickly replaced the natural fiber silk in parachutes and ladies' stockings. Styrofoam and PET (polyethylene terephthalate), the plastic used for soft drink bottles, are strong yet lightweight synthetic materials used for food storage. Over-the-counter pain relievers like ibuprofen are synthetic. The starting materials for all of these useful products are obtained from petroleum.

a.    b.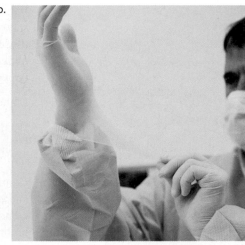

(a) Latex, the sticky liquid that oozes from a rubber tree when it is cut, is too soft for most applications.
(b) Vulcanization converts latex to the stronger, elastic rubber used in tires and other products.

Sometimes a chemist studies what a substance is made of, while at other times he or she might be interested in its properties. Alternatively, the focus may be how to convert one material into a new material with unique and useful properties. As an example, naturally occurring rubber exists as the sticky liquid latex, which is too soft for most applications. The laboratory process of vulcanization converts it to the stronger, more elastic material used in tires and other products (Figure 1.2).

Chemistry is truly the science of everyday experience. Soaps and detergents, newspapers and CDs, condoms and oral contraceptives, Tylenol and penicillin—all of these items are products of chemistry. Without a doubt, advances in chemistry have transformed life in modern times.

PROBLEM 1.1
Look around you and identify five objects. Decide if they are composed of natural or synthetic materials.

PROBLEM 1.2
Imagine that your job as a healthcare professional is to take a blood sample from a patient and store it in a small container in a refrigerator until it is picked up for analysis in the hospital lab. You might have to put on gloves and a mask, use a plastic syringe with a metal needle, store the sample in a test tube or vial, and place it in a cold refrigerator. Pick five objects you might encounter during the process and decide if they are made of naturally occurring or synthetic materials.

1.2 States of Matter

Matter exists in three common states—solid, liquid, and gas.

- A *solid* has a definite volume, and maintains its shape regardless of the container in which it is placed. The particles of a solid lie close together, and are arranged in a regular three-dimensional array.
- A *liquid* has a definite volume, but takes on the shape of the container it occupies. The particles of a liquid are close together, but they can randomly move around, sliding past one another.
- A *gas* has no definite shape or volume. The particles of a gas move randomly and are separated by a distance much larger than their size. The particles of a gas expand to fill the volume and assume the shape of whatever container they are put in.

For example, water exists in its solid state as ice or snow, liquid state as liquid water, and gaseous state as steam or water vapor. Blow-up circles like those in Figure 1.3 will be used commonly in this text to indicate the composition and state of the particles that compose a substance. In this molecular art, different types of particles are shown in color-coded spheres, and the distance between the spheres signals its state—solid, liquid, or gas.

Matter is characterized by its **physical properties** and **chemical properties.**

> • *Physical properties* are those that can be observed or measured without changing the composition of the material.

Common physical properties include melting point (mp), boiling point (bp), solubility, color, and odor. **A *physical change* alters a substance without changing its composition.** The most common physical changes are **changes in state.** Melting an ice cube to form liquid water, and boiling liquid water to form steam are two examples of physical changes. Water is the substance at the beginning and end of both physical changes. More details about physical changes are discussed in Chapter 7.

Figure 1.3   The Three States of Water—Solid, Liquid, and Gas

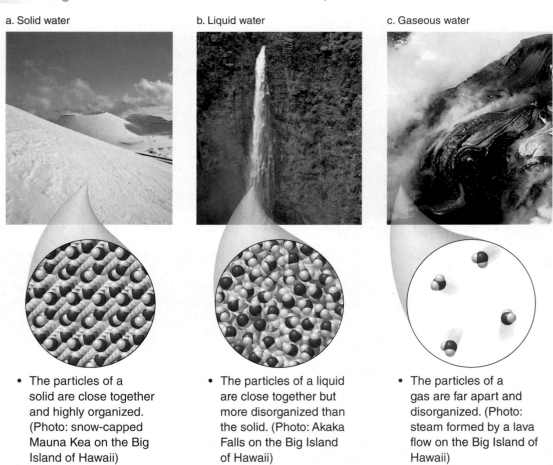

a. Solid water   b. Liquid water   c. Gaseous water

• The particles of a solid are close together and highly organized. (Photo: snow-capped Mauna Kea on the Big Island of Hawaii)

• The particles of a liquid are close together but more disorganized than the solid. (Photo: Akaka Falls on the Big Island of Hawaii)

• The particles of a gas are far apart and disorganized. (Photo: steam formed by a lava flow on the Big Island of Hawaii)

Each red sphere joined to two gray spheres represents a single water particle. In proceeding from left to right, from solid to liquid to gas, the molecular art shows that the level of organization of the water particles decreases. Color-coding and the identity of the spheres within the particles will be addressed in Chapter 2.

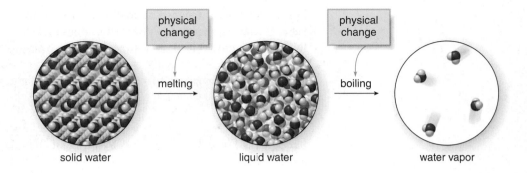

solid water   liquid water   water vapor

- *Chemical properties* are those that determine how a substance can be converted to another substance.

A *chemical change,* or a *chemical reaction,* **converts one material to another.** The conversion of hydrogen and oxygen to water is a chemical reaction because the composition of the material is different at the beginning and end of the process. Chemical reactions are discussed in Chapters 5 and 6.

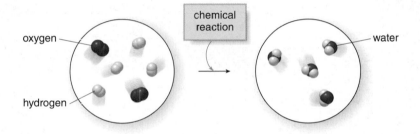

PROBLEM 1.3

Characterize each process as a physical change or a chemical change: (a) making ice cubes; (b) burning natural gas; (c) silver jewelry tarnishing; (d) a pile of snow melting; (e) baking bread.

PROBLEM 1.4

Does the molecular art represent a chemical change or a physical change? Explain your choice.

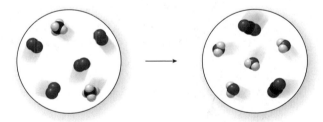

1.3   Classification of Matter

All matter can be classified as either a **pure substance** or a **mixture.**

- A *pure substance* is composed of a single component and has a constant composition, regardless of the sample size and the origin of the sample.

A pure substance, such as water or table sugar, can be characterized by its physical properties, because these properties do not change from sample to sample. **A pure substance cannot be broken down to other pure substances by any physical change.**

• A *mixture* is composed of more than one component. The composition of a mixture can vary depending on the sample.

The physical properties of a mixture may also vary from one sample to another. **A mixture can be separated into its components by physical changes.** Dissolving table sugar in water forms a mixture, whose sweetness depends on the amount of sugar added. If the water is allowed to evaporate from the mixture, pure table sugar and pure water are obtained.

sugar   water   sugar dissolved in water

pure substances   mixture

Mixtures can be formed from solids, liquids, and gases, as shown in Figure 1.4. The compressed air breathed by a scuba diver consists mainly of the gases oxygen and nitrogen. A saline solution used in an IV bag contains solid sodium chloride (table salt) dissolved in liquid water.

Figure 1.4   Two Examples of Mixtures

a. Two gases

b. A solid and a liquid

oxygen   nitrogen

water   sodium

chloride
(from chlorine)

Figure 1.5   Elements and Compounds

a. Aluminum foil

b. Nitrogen gas

c. Water

d. Table salt

aluminum   nitrogen   hydrogen   oxygen   chloride   sodium
                                                                (from chlorine)

- Aluminum foil and nitrogen gas are elements. The molecular art for an element shows spheres of one color only. Thus, aluminum is a solid shown with gray spheres, while nitrogen is a gas shown with blue spheres. Water and table salt are compounds. Color-coding of the spheres used in the molecular art indicates that water is composed of two elements—hydrogen shown as gray spheres, and oxygen shown in red. Likewise, the gray (sodium) and green (chlorine) spheres illustrate that sodium chloride is formed from two elements as well.

A pure substance is classified as either an **element** or a **compound.**

- An *element* is a pure substance that cannot be broken down into simpler substances by a chemical reaction.
- A *compound* is a pure substance formed by chemically combining (joining together) two or more elements.

An alphabetical list of elements is located on the inside front cover of this text. The elements are commonly organized into a periodic table, also shown on the inside front cover, and discussed in much greater detail in Section 2.4.

Nitrogen gas, aluminum foil, and copper wire are all elements. Water is a compound because it is composed of the elements hydrogen and oxygen. Table salt, sodium chloride, is also a compound since it is formed from the elements sodium and chlorine (Figure 1.5). Although only 118 elements are currently known, over 20 million compounds occur naturally or have been synthesized in the laboratory. We will learn much more about elements and compounds in Chapter 2. Figure 1.6 summarizes the categories into which matter is classified.

SAMPLE PROBLEM 1.1

Classify each example of molecular art as an element or a compound:

a.

b.

Analysis

In molecular art, an element is composed of spheres of the same color, while a compound is composed of spheres of different colors.

Solution

Representation (a) is an element since each particle contains only gray spheres. Representation (b) is a compound since each particle contains both red and black spheres.

PROBLEM 1.5

Classify each example of molecular art as a pure substance or a mixture:

a.
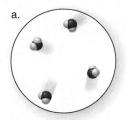

b.
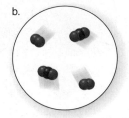

PROBLEM 1.6

Classify each item as a pure substance or a mixture: (a) blood; (b) ocean water; (c) a piece of wood; (d) a chunk of ice.

PROBLEM 1.7

Classify each item as an element or a compound: (a) the gas inside a helium balloon; (b) table sugar; (c) the rust on an iron nail; (d) aspirin. All elements are listed alphabetically on the inside front cover.

Figure 1.6   Classification of Matter

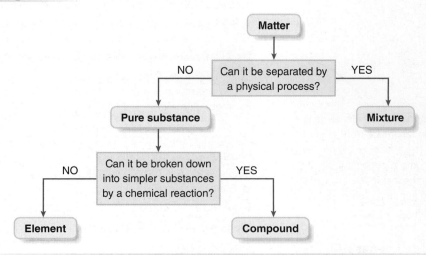

1.4 Measurement

Any time you check your weight on a scale, measure the ingredients of a recipe, or figure out how far it is from one location to another, you are measuring a quantity. Measurements are routine for healthcare professionals who use weight, blood pressure, pulse, and temperature to chart a patient's progress.

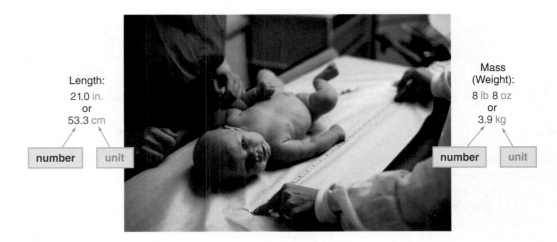

Length:
21.0 in.
or
53.3 cm

number   unit

Mass
(Weight):
8 lb 8 oz
or
3.9 kg

number   unit

In 1960, the **International System of Units** was formally adopted as the uniform system of units for the sciences. **SI units,** as they are called, are based on the metric system, but the system recommends the use of some metric units over others. SI stands for the French words, *Système Internationale.*

CONSUMER NOTE

The metric system is slowly gaining acceptance in the United States, as seen in the gallon jug of milk and the two-liter bottle of soda.

Table 1.1 The Basic Metric Units

Quantity	Metric Base Unit	Symbol
Length	Meter	m
Mass	Gram	g
Volume	Liter	L
Time	Second	s

- **Every measurement is composed of a *number* and a *unit.***

Reporting the value of a measurement is meaningless without its unit. For example, if you were told to give a patient an aspirin dosage of 325, does this mean 325 ounces, pounds, grams, milligrams, or tablets? Clearly there is a huge difference among these quantities.

1.4A   The Metric System

In the United States, most measurements are made with the **English system,** using units like miles (mi), gallons (gal), pounds (lb), and so forth. A disadvantage of this system is that the units are not systematically related to each other and require memorization. For example, 1 lb = 16 oz, 1 gal = 4 qt, and 1 mi = 5,280 ft.

Scientists, health professionals, and people in most other countries use the **metric system,** with units like meter (m) for length, gram (g) for mass, and liter (L) for volume. The metric system is slowly gaining popularity in the United States. The weight of packaged foods is often given in both ounces and grams. Distances on many road signs are shown in miles and kilometers. Most measurements in this text will be reported using the metric system, but learning to convert English units to metric units is also a necessary skill that will be illustrated in Section 1.7.

The important features of the metric system are the following:

- Each type of measurement has a base unit—the meter (m) for length; the gram (g) for mass; the liter (L) for volume; the second (s) for time.
- All other units are related to the base unit by powers of 10.
- The prefix of the unit name indicates if the unit is larger or smaller than the base unit.

The base units of the metric system are summarized in Table 1.1, and the most common prefixes used to convert the base units to smaller or larger units are summarized in Table 1.2. **The same prefixes are used for all types of measurement.** For example, the prefix *kilo-* means 1,000 times as large. Thus,

1 **kilo**meter = **1,000** meters	or	1 km = 1,000 m
1 **kilo**gram = **1,000** grams	or	1 kg = 1,000 g
1 **kilo**liter = **1,000** liters	or	1 kL = 1,000 L

The prefix *milli-* means one thousandth as large (1/1,000 or 0.001). Thus,

1 **milli**meter = **0.001** meters	or	1 mm = 0.001 m
1 **milli**gram = **0.001** grams	or	1 mg = 0.001 g
1 **milli**liter = **0.001** liters	or	1 mL = 0.001 L

Table 1.2 Common Prefixes Used for Metric Units

Prefix	Symbol	Meaning	Numerical Value[a]	Scientific Notation[b]
Mega-	M	Million	1,000,000.	10^6
Kilo-	k	Thousand	1,000.	10^3
Deci-	d	Tenth	0.1	10^{-1}
Centi-	c	Hundredth	0.01	10^{-2}
Milli-	m	Thousandth	0.001	10^{-3}
Micro-	μ[c]	Millionth	0.000 001	10^{-6}
Nano-	n	Billionth	0.000 000 001	10^{-9}

[a]Numbers that contain five or more digits to the right of the decimal point are written with a small space separating each group of three digits.
[b]How to express numbers in scientific notation is explained in Section 1.6.
[c]The symbol μ is the lower case Greek letter mu. The prefix *micro-* is sometimes abbreviated as **mc.**

The metric symbols are all lower case except for the unit **liter** (L) and the prefix **mega-** (M). Liter is capitalized to distinguish it from the number *one*. Mega is capitalized to distinguish it from the symbol for the prefix *milli-*.

PROBLEM 1.8

What term is used for each of the following units: (a) a million liters; (b) a thousandth of a second; (c) a hundredth of a gram; (d) a tenth of a liter?

1.4B Measuring Length

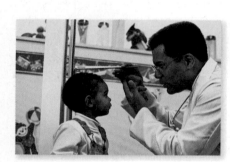

The base unit of length in the metric system is the *meter* (m). A meter, 39.4 inches in the English system, is slightly longer than a yard (36 inches). The three most common units derived from a meter are the kilometer (km), centimeter (cm), and millimeter (mm).

$$1,000 \text{ m} = 1 \text{ km}$$
$$1 \text{ m} = 100 \text{ cm}$$
$$1 \text{ m} = 1,000 \text{ mm}$$

Note how these values are related to those in Table 1.2. Since a centimeter is one *hundredth* of a meter (0.01 m), there are *100* centimeters in a meter.

PROBLEM 1.9

If a nanometer is one billionth of a meter (0.000 000 001 m), how many nanometers are there in one meter?

1.4C Measuring Mass

Although the terms mass and weight are often used interchangeably, they really have different meanings.

- *Mass* is a measure of the amount of matter in an object.
- *Weight* is the force that matter feels due to gravity.

The mass of an object is independent of its location. The weight of an object changes slightly with its location on the earth, and drastically when the object is moved from the earth to the moon, where the gravitational pull is only one-sixth that of the earth. Although we often speak of *weighing* an object, we are really *measuring its mass*.

The base unit of mass in the metric system is the *gram* (g), a small quantity compared to the English pound (1 lb = 454 g). The two most common units derived from a gram are the kilogram (kg) and milligram (mg).

$$1,000 \text{ g} = 1 \text{ kg}$$
$$1 \text{ g} = 1,000 \text{ mg}$$

PROBLEM 1.10

If a microgram is one millionth of a gram (0.000 001 g), how many micrograms are there in one gram?

1.4D Measuring Volume

The base unit of volume in the metric system is the *liter* (L), which is slightly larger than the English quart (1 L = 1.06 qt). One liter is defined as the volume of a cube 10 cm on an edge.

Note the difference between the units **cm** and **cm³**. The centimeter (cm) is a unit of length. A cubic centimeter (cm³ or cc) is a unit of volume.

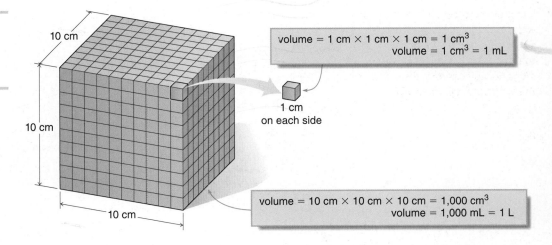

10 cm

10 cm

10 cm

1 cm on each side

volume = 1 cm × 1 cm × 1 cm = 1 cm³
volume = 1 cm³ = 1 mL

volume = 10 cm × 10 cm × 10 cm = 1,000 cm³
volume = 1,000 mL = 1 L

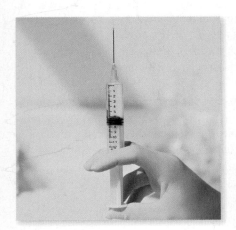

Three common units derived from a liter used in medicine and laboratory research are the deciliter (dL), milliliter (mL), and microliter (µL). **One milliliter is the same as one cubic centimeter (cm³), which is abbreviated as cc.**

$$1 \text{ L} = 10 \text{ dL}$$
$$1 \text{ L} = 1{,}000 \text{ mL}$$
$$1 \text{ L} = 1{,}000{,}000 \text{ µL}$$
$$1 \text{ mL} = 1 \text{ cm}^3 = 1 \text{ cc}$$

Table 1.3 summarizes common metric units of length, mass, and volume. Table 1.4 lists English units of measurement, as well as their metric equivalents.

PROBLEM 1.11

Using the prefixes in Table 1.2, determine which quantity in each pair is larger.

a. 3 mL or 3 cL

b. 1 ng or 1 µg

c. 5 km or 5 cm

d. 2 mL or 2 µL

Table 1.3 Summary of the Common Metric Units of Length, Mass, and Volume

Length	Mass	Volume
1 km = 1,000 m	1 kg = 1,000 g	1 L = 10 dL
1 m = 100 cm	1 g = 1,000 mg	1 L = 1,000 mL
1 m = 1,000 mm	1 mg = 1,000 µg	1 L = 1,000,000 µL
1 cm = 10 mm		1 dL = 100 mL
		1 mL = 1 cm³ = 1 cc

Table 1.4 English Units and Their Metric Equivalents

Quantity	English Unit	Metric–English Relationship
Length	1 ft = 12 in.	2.54 cm = 1 in.
	1 yd = 3 ft	1 m = 39.4 in.
	1 mi = 5,280 ft	1 km = 0.621 mi
Mass	1 lb = 16 oz	1 kg = 2.20 lb
	1 ton = 2,000 lb	454 g = 1 lb
		28.3 g = 1 oz
Volume	1 qt = 4 cups	946 mL = 1 qt
	1 qt = 2 pints	1 L = 1.06 qt
	1 qt = 32 fl oz	29.6 mL = 1 fl oz
	1 gal = 4 qt	

Common abbreviations for English units: inch (in.), foot (ft), yard (yd), mile (mi), pound (lb), ounce (oz), gallon (gal), quart (qt), and fluid ounce (fl oz).

1.5 Significant Figures

Numbers used in chemistry are either **exact** or **inexact.**

- An *exact* number results from counting objects or is part of a definition.

Our bodies have 10 fingers, 10 toes, and two kidneys. A meter is composed of 100 centimeters. These numbers are exact because there is no uncertainty associated with them.

- An *inexact* number results from a measurement or observation and contains some uncertainty.

Whenever we measure a quantity there is a degree of uncertainty associated with the result. The last number (farthest to the right) is an estimate, and it depends on the type of measuring device we use to obtain it. For example, the length of a fish caught on a recent outing could be reported as 53 cm or 53.5 cm depending on the tape measure used.

A container of 71 macadamia nuts weighs 125 g. The number of nuts (71) is exact, while the mass of the nuts (125 g) is inexact.

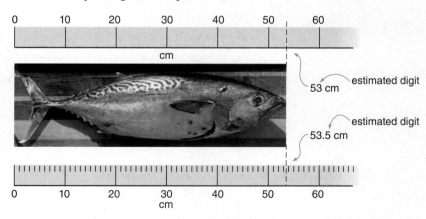

- *Significant figures* are all the digits in a measured number including *one* estimated digit.

Thus, the length 53 cm has two significant figures, and the length 53.5 cm has three significant figures.

1.5A Determining the Number of Significant Figures

How many significant figures are contained in a number?

> • **All nonzero digits are always significant.**

65.2 g	three significant figures
1,265 m	four significant figures
25 µL	two significant figures
255.345 g	six significant figures

Whether a zero counts as a significant figure depends on its location in the number.

Rules to Determine When a Zero is a Significant Figure

Rule [1] A zero *counts* as a significant figure when it occurs:

- Between two nonzero digits   29.05 g—four significant figures
  1.0087 mL—five significant figures

- At the end of a number with a decimal point   25.70 cm—four significant figures
  3.7500 g—five significant figures
  620. lb—three significant figures

Rule [2] A zero does *not* count as a significant figure when it occurs:

- At the beginning of a number   0.0245 mg—three significant figures
  0.008 mL—one significant figure

- At the end of a number that does not have a decimal point   2,570 m—three significant figures
  1,245,500 m—five significant figures

In reading a number with a decimal point from left to right, all digits starting with the first nonzero number are significant figures. The number 0.003 450 120 has seven significant figures, shown in red.

SAMPLE PROBLEM 1.2

How many significant figures does each number contain?

   a. 34.08   b. 0.0054   c. 260.00   d. 260

Analysis

All nonzero digits are significant. A zero is significant only if it occurs between two nonzero digits, or at the end of a number with a decimal point.

Solution

Significant figures are shown in red.

   a. 34.08 (four)   b. 0.0054 (two)   c. 260.00 (five)   d. 260 (two)

PROBLEM 1.12

How many significant figures does each number contain?

a. 23.45	c. 230	e. 0.202	g. 1,245,006
b. 23.057	d. 231.0	f. 0.003 60	h. 1,200,000

PROBLEM 1.13

How many significant figures does each number contain?

a. 10,040	c. 1,004.00	e. 1.0040	g. 0.001 004
b. 10,040.	d. 1.004	f. 0.1004	h. 0.010 040 0

PROBLEM 1.14

Indicate whether each zero in the following numbers is significant.

   a. 0.003 04   b. 26,045   c. 1,000,034   d. 0.304 00

1.5B   Using Significant Figures in Multiplication and Division

We often must perform calculations with numbers that contain a different number of significant figures. The number of significant figures in the answer of a problem depends on the type of mathematical calculation—multiplication (and division) or addition (and subtraction).

> • In multiplication and division, the answer has the same number of significant figures as the original number with the *fewest* significant figures.

Let's say you drove a car 351.2 miles in 5.5 hours, and you wanted to calculate how many miles per hour you traveled. Entering these numbers on a calculator would give the following result:

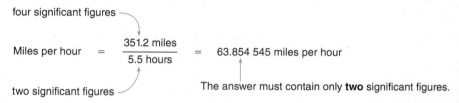

four significant figures

$$\text{Miles per hour} \quad = \quad \frac{351.2 \text{ miles}}{5.5 \text{ hours}} \quad = \quad 63.854\ 545 \text{ miles per hour}$$

two significant figures

The answer must contain only **two** significant figures.

The answer to this problem can have only *two* significant figures, since one of the original numbers (5.5 hours) has only *two* significant figures. To write the answer in proper form, we must **round off the number** to give an answer with only two significant figures. Two rules are used in rounding off numbers.

> • If the first number that must be dropped is 4 or less, drop it and all remaining numbers.
> • If the first number that must be dropped is 5 or greater, *round the number up* by adding one to the last digit that will be retained.

In this problem:

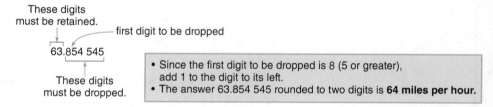

These digits must be retained.

first digit to be dropped

63.854 545

These digits must be dropped.

> • Since the first digit to be dropped is 8 (5 or greater), add 1 to the digit to its left.
> • The answer 63.854 545 rounded to two digits is **64 miles per hour.**

Table 1.5 gives other examples of rounding off numbers.

Table 1.5 Rounding Off Numbers

Original Number	Rounded To	Rounded Number
61.2537	Two places	61
61.2537	Three places	61.3
61.2537	Four places	61.25
61.2537	Five places	61.254

The first number to be dropped is indicated in red in each original number.
When this number is 4 or fewer, it and all other digits to its right are dropped.
When this number is 5 or greater, 1 is added to the digit to its left.

SAMPLE PROBLEM 1.3

Round off each number to three significant figures.

  a. 1.2735   b. 0.002 536 22   c. 3,836.9

Analysis

If the answer is to have *three* significant figures, look at the *fourth* number from the left. If this number is 4 or less, drop it and all remaining numbers to the right. If the fourth number from the left is 5 or greater, round the number up by adding one to the third digit.

Solution

  a. 1.27   b. 0.002 54   c. 3,840 (Omit the decimal point after the 0. The number
                                                     3,840. has four significant figures.)

PROBLEM 1.15

Round off each number in Sample Problem 1.3 to two significant figures.

SAMPLE PROBLEM 1.4

Carry out each calculation and give the answer using the proper number of significant figures.

  a. 3.81×0.046 b. $120.085 \div 106$

Analysis

Since these calculations involve multiplication and division, the answer must have the same number of significant figures as the original number with the fewest number of significant figures.

Solution

  a. $3.81 \times 0.046 = 0.1753$

- Since 0.046 has only two significant figures, round the answer to give it two significant figures.

    0.1753   Since this number is 5 (5 or greater), round the 7 to its left up by one.

Answer: 0.18

  b. $120.085 \div 106 = 1.132\ 877\ 36$

- Since 106 has three significant figures, round the answer to give it three significant figures.

    1.132 877 36   Since this number is 2 (4 or less), drop it and all numbers to its right.

Answer: 1.13

PROBLEM 1.16

Carry out each calculation and give the answer using the proper number of significant figures.

  a. 10.70×3.5 b. $0.206 \div 25,993$ c. $1,300 \div 41.2$ d. 120.5×26

1.5C Using Significant Figures in Addition and Subtraction

In determining significant figures in addition and subtraction, the decimal place of the last significant digit determines the number of significant figures in the answer.

- **In addition and subtraction, the answer has the same number of decimal places as the original number with the *fewest* decimal places.**

Suppose a baby weighed 3.6 kg at birth and 10.11 kg on his first birthday. To figure out how much weight the baby gained in his first year of life, we subtract these two numbers and report the answer using the proper number of significant figures.

                                               two digits after the decimal point
weight at one year = 10.11 kg   10.11 kg
                                       one digit after the decimal point
weight at birth =   3.6 kg   − 3.6 kg
                          weight gain = 6.51 kg

                            last significant digit

- The answer can have only **one** digit after the decimal point.
- Round 6.51 to 6.5.
- The baby gained 6.5 kg during his first year of life.

Since 3.6 kg has only one significant figure after the decimal point, the answer can have only one significant figure after the decimal point as well.

SAMPLE PROBLEM 1.5

While on a diet, a woman lost 3.52 lb the first week, 2.2 lb the second week, and 0.59 lb the third week. How much weight did she lose in all?

Analysis

Add up the amount of weight loss each week to get the total weight loss. When adding, the answer has the same number of decimal places as the original number with the fewest decimal places.

Solution

$$
\begin{array}{l}
3.52\ \text{lb} \\
2.2\ \text{lb} \quad \text{one digit after the decimal point} \\
0.59\ \text{lb} \\
\hline
6.31\ \text{lb} \quad \dashrightarrow \quad 6.3\ \text{lb} \\
\qquad\qquad\quad \text{round off}
\end{array}
$$

last significant digit

- Since 2.2 lb has only one digit after the decimal point, the answer can have only one digit after the decimal point.
- Round 6.31 to 6.3.
- Total weight loss: 6.3 lb.

PROBLEM 1.17

Carry out each calculation and give the answer using the proper number of significant figures.

a. 27.8 cm + 0.246 cm

b. 102.66 mL + 0.857 mL + 24.0 mL

c. 54.6 mg − 25 mg

d. 2.35 s − 0.266 s

1.6   Scientific Notation

Healthcare professionals and scientists must often deal with very large and very small numbers. For example, the blood platelet count of a healthy adult might be 250,000 platelets per mL. At the other extreme, the level of the female sex hormone estriol during pregnancy might be 0.000 000 250 g per mL of blood plasma. Estriol is secreted by the placenta and its concentration is used as a measure of the health of the fetus.

To write numbers that contain many leading zeros (at the beginning) or trailing zeros (at the end), scientists use **scientific notation.**

- In scientific notation, a number is written as $y \times 10^x$.
- The term y, called the coefficient, is a number between 1 and 10.
- The value x is an exponent, which can be any positive or negative whole number.

First, let's recall what powers of 10 with *positive* exponents, such as 10^2 or 10^5, mean. These correspond to numbers greater than one, and the positive exponent tells how many zeros are to be written after the number one. Thus, $10^2 = 100$, a number with two zeros after the number one.

The product has two zeros.

$$10^2 = 10 \times 10 = 100$$

The exponent 2 means "multiply two 10s."

The product has five zeros.

$$10^5 = 10 \times 10 \times 10 \times 10 \times 10 = 100{,}000$$

The exponent 5 means "multiply five 10s."

Powers of 10 that contain *negative* exponents, such as 10^{-3}, correspond to numbers less than one. In this case the exponent tells how many places (*not* zeros) are located to the right of the decimal point.

The answer has three places to the right of the decimal point, including the number one.

$$10^{-3} = \frac{1}{10 \times 10 \times 10} = 0.001$$

The exponent −3 means "divide by three 10s."

To write a number in scientific notation, we follow a stepwise procedure.

Hospital laboratory technicians determine thousands of laboratory results each day.

How To Convert a Standard Number to Scientific Notation

Example: Write each number in scientific notation: (a) 2,500; (b) 0.036.

Step [1] **Move the decimal point to give a number between 1 and 10.**

a. 2500.

Move the decimal point three places to the left to give the number 2.5.

b. 0.036

Move the decimal point two places to the right to give the number 3.6.

Step [2] **Multiply the result by 10^x, where x is the number of places the decimal point was moved.**

- If the decimal point is moved to the **left**, x is **positive.**
- If the decimal point is moved to the **right**, x is **negative.**

a. Since the decimal point was moved three places to the **left,** the exponent is +3, and the coefficient is multiplied by 10^3.

Answer: 2,500 = 2.5 × 10³

b. Since the decimal point was moved two places to the **right,** the exponent is −2, and the coefficient is multiplied by 10^{-2}.

Answer: 0.036 = 3.6 × 10⁻²

Notice that the number of significant figures in the coefficient in scientific notation must equal the number of significant figures in the original number. Thus, the coefficients for both 2,500 and 0.036 need two significant figures and no more. Figure 1.7 shows two more examples of numbers written in standard form and scientific notation.

$$2{,}500 = 2.5 \times 10^3 \quad \textit{not} \quad 2.50 \times 10^3 \text{ (three significant figures)}$$
$$\textit{not} \quad 2.500 \times 10^3 \text{ (four significant figures)}$$

two significant figures

Figure 1.7 Numbers in Standard Form and Scientific Notation

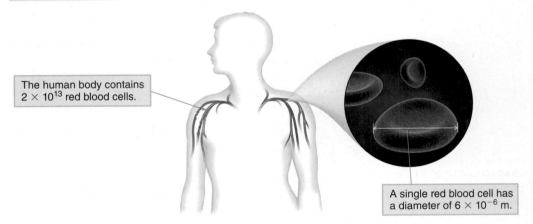

The human body contains 2×10^{13} red blood cells.

A single red blood cell has a diameter of 6×10^{-6} m.

Very large and very small numbers are more conveniently written in scientific notation.

Quantity	Number	Scientific Notation
Number of red blood cells	20,000,000,000,000	2×10^{13}
Diameter of a red blood cell	0.000 006 m	6×10^{-6} m

SAMPLE PROBLEM 1.6

Write the recommended daily dietary intake of each nutrient in scientific notation: (a) sodium, 2,400 mg; (b) vitamin B_{12}, 0.000 006 g.

Analysis

Move the decimal point to give a number between 1 and 10. Multiply the number by 10^x, where x is the number of places the decimal point was moved. The exponent x is (+) when the decimal point moves to the left and (−) when it moves to the right.

Solution

a.

$$2400. = 2.4 \times 10^3$$ the number of places the decimal point was moved to the left

Move the decimal point three places to the left.

- Write the coefficient as 2.4 (two significant figures), since 2,400 contains two significant figures.

b.

$$0.000\ 006 = 6 \times 10^{-6}$$ the number of places the decimal point was moved to the right

Move the decimal point six places to the right.

- Write the coefficient as 6 (one significant figure), since 0.000 006 contains one significant figure.

PROBLEM 1.18

Lab results for a routine check-up showed an individual's iron level in the blood to be 0.000 098 g per deciliter, placing it in the normal range. Convert this number to scientific notation.

PROBLEM 1.19

Write each number in scientific notation.

a. 93,200
b. 0.000 725

c. 6,780,000
d. 0.000 030

e. 4,520,000,000,000
f. 0.000 000 000 028

To convert a number in scientific notation to a standard number, reverse the procedure, as shown in Sample Problem 1.7. It is often necessary to add leading or trailing zeros to write the number.

- **When the exponent x is positive, move the decimal point x places to the *right*.**

$$2.800 \times 10^2 \qquad 2.800 \quad ---\rightarrow \quad 280.0$$

Move the decimal point to the right two places.

- **When the exponent x is negative, move the decimal point x places to the *left*.**

$$2.80 \times 10^{-2} \qquad 002.80 \quad ---\rightarrow \quad 0.0280$$

Move the decimal point to the left two places.

SAMPLE PROBLEM 1.7

As we will learn in Chapter 4, the element hydrogen is composed of two hydrogen atoms, separated by a distance of 7.4×10^{-11} m. Convert this value to a standard number.

Analysis

The exponent in 10^x tells how many places to move the decimal point in the coefficient to generate a standard number. The decimal point goes to the right when x is positive and to the left when x is negative.

Solution

$$7.4 \times 10^{-11} \qquad\qquad 000\ 000\ 000\ 07.4 \quad ---\rightarrow \quad 0.000\ 000\ 000\ 074 \text{ m}$$

Move the decimal point to the left 11 places.   **Answer**

The answer, 0.000 000 000 074, has two significant figures, just like 7.4×10^{-11}.

PROBLEM 1.20

There are 6.02×10^{21} "particles" called molecules (Chapter 4) of aspirin in 1.8 g. Write this number in standard form.

PROBLEM 1.21

Convert each number to its standard form.

a. 6.5×10^3
b. 3.26×10^{-5}

c. 3.780×10^{-2}
d. 1.04×10^8

e. 2.221×10^6
f. 4.5×10^{-10}

1.7 Problem Solving Using the Factor–Label M...

Often a measurement is recorded in one unit, and then it must be converted to a... example, a patient may weigh 130 lb, but we may need to know her weight in *kilo*... late a drug dosage. The recommended daily dietary intake of potassium is 3,500 m... For need to know how many grams this corresponds to.

1.7A Conversion Factors

To convert one unit to another we use one or more **conversion factors.**

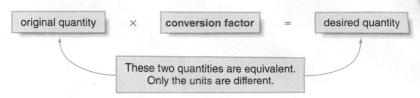

These two quantities are equivalent.
Only the units are different.

- A *conversion factor* is a term that converts a quantity in one unit to a quantity in another unit.

A conversion factor is formed by taking an equality, such as 2.20 lb = 1 kg, and writing it as a ratio. We can always write a conversion factor in two different ways.

$$\frac{2.20 \text{ lb}}{1 \text{ kg}} \quad \text{or} \quad \frac{1 \text{ kg}}{2.20 \text{ lb}} \quad \begin{array}{l} \text{numerator} \\ \\ \text{denominator} \end{array}$$

conversion factors for pounds and kilograms

> Refer to Tables 1.3 and 1.4 for metric and English units needed in problem solving. Common metric and English units are also listed on the inside back cover.

With pounds and kilograms, either of these values can be written above the division line of the fraction (the numerator) or below the division line (the denominator). The way the conversion factor is written will depend on the problem.

SAMPLE PROBLEM 1.8

Write two conversion factors for each pair of units: (a) kilograms and grams; (b) quarts and liters.

Analysis

Use the equalities in Tables 1.3 and 1.4 to write a ratio that shows the relationship between the two units.

Solution

a. Conversion factors for kilograms and grams:

$$\frac{1000 \text{ g}}{1 \text{ kg}} \quad \text{or} \quad \frac{1 \text{ kg}}{1000 \text{ g}}$$

b. Conversion factors for quarts and liters:

$$\frac{1.06 \text{ qt}}{1 \text{ L}} \quad \text{or} \quad \frac{1 \text{ L}}{1.06 \text{ qt}}$$

PROBLEM 1.22

Write two conversion factors for each pair of units.

a. miles and kilometers
b. meters and millimeters
c. grams and pounds
d. milligrams and micrograms

1.7B Solving a Problem Using One Conversion Factor

Using conversion factors to convert a quantity in one unit to a quantity in another unit is called the **factor–label method.** In this method, if a unit appears in the numerator in one term and the denominator in another term, the units *cancel*. **The goal in setting up a problem is to make sure *all unwanted units cancel.***

20

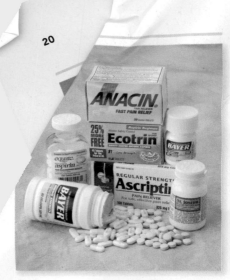

How many grams of aspirin are contained in a 325-mg tablet?

Let's say we want to convert 130 lb to kilograms.

$$\underset{\text{original quantity}}{130 \text{ lb}} \quad \times \quad \boxed{\textbf{conversion factor}} \quad = \quad \underset{\text{desired quantity}}{? \quad \text{kg}}$$

Two possible conversion factors: $\dfrac{2.20 \text{ lb}}{1 \text{ kg}}$ or $\dfrac{1 \text{ kg}}{2.20 \text{ lb}}$

To solve this problem we must use a conversion factor that satisfies two criteria.

- **The conversion factor must relate the two quantities in question—pounds and kilograms.**
- **The conversion factor must cancel out the unwanted unit—pounds.**

This means choosing the conversion factor with the unwanted unit—pounds—*in the denominator* to cancel out pounds in the original quantity. This leaves kilograms as the only remaining unit, and the problem is solved.

$$130 \text{ lb} \quad \times \quad \overset{\boxed{\textbf{conversion factor}}}{\dfrac{1 \text{ kg}}{2.20 \text{ lb}}} \quad = \quad \boxed{59 \text{ kg}} \quad \textbf{answer in kilograms}$$

Pounds (lb) must be the denominator to cancel the unwanted unit (lb) in the original quantity.

We must use the correct number of significant figures in reporting an answer to each problem. In this case, the value 1 kg is *defined* as 2.20 lb; in other words, 1 kg contains the exact number "1" with *no* uncertainty, so it does not limit the number of digits in the answer. Since 130 lb has two significant figures, the answer is rounded to two significant figures (59 kg).

As problems with units get more complicated, keep in mind the following general steps that are useful for solving any problem using conversion factors.

How To   Solve a Problem Using Conversion Factors

Example: How many grams of aspirin are contained in a 325-mg tablet?

Step [1] **Identify the original quantity and the desired quantity, including units.**

- In this problem the original quantity is reported in milligrams and the desired quantity is in grams.

$$\underset{\text{original quantity}}{325 \text{ mg}} \qquad \underset{\text{desired quantity}}{? \text{ g}}$$

Step [2] **Write out the conversion factor(s) needed to solve the problem.**

- We need a conversion factor that relates milligrams and grams (Table 1.3). Since the unwanted unit is in milligrams, **choose the conversion factor that contains milligrams in the denominator so that the *units cancel.***

$$\text{Two possible conversion factors:} \quad \dfrac{1000 \text{ mg}}{1 \text{ g}} \quad \text{or} \quad \boxed{\dfrac{1 \text{ g}}{1000 \text{ mg}}} \quad \text{Choose this factor to cancel the unwanted unit, mg.}$$

- Sometimes one conversion factor is all that is needed in a problem. At other times (Section 1.7C) more than one conversion factor is needed.
- If the desired answer has a single unit (grams in this case), **the conversion factor must contain the desired unit in the numerator and the unwanted unit in the denominator.**

Step [3] **Set up and solve the problem.**

- Multiply the original quantity by the conversion factor to obtain the desired quantity.

$$\underset{\text{original quantity}}{325 \text{ mg}} \quad \times \quad \overset{\boxed{\textbf{conversion factor}}}{\dfrac{1 \text{ g}}{1000 \text{ mg}}} \quad = \quad \underset{\text{desired quantity}}{0.325 \text{ g of aspirin}}$$

The number of mg (unwanted unit) cancels.

How To, continued . . .

Step [4] **Write the answer using the correct number of significant figures and check it by estimation.**

- Use the number of significant figures in each inexact (measured) number to determine the number of significant figures in the answer. In this case the answer is limited to three significant figures by the original quantity (325 mg).
- Estimate the answer using a variety of methods. In this case we knew our answer had to be less than one, since it is obtained by dividing 325 by a number larger than itself.

PROBLEM 1.23

The distance between Honolulu, HI, and Los Angeles, CA, is 4,120 km. How many frequent flyer miles will you earn by traveling between the two cities?

PROBLEM 1.24

Carry out each of the following conversions.

  a. 25 L to dL   b. 40.0 oz to g   c. 32 in. to cm   d. 10 cm to mm

---

1.7C   Solving a Problem Using Two or More Conversion Factors

Some problems require the use of more than one conversion factor to obtain the desired units in the answer. The same stepwise procedure is followed no matter how many conversion factors are needed. Keep in mind:

- **Always arrange the factors so that the denominator in one term cancels the numerator in the preceding term.**

Sample Problem 1.9 illustrates how to solve a problem with two conversion factors.

SAMPLE PROBLEM 1.9

An individual donated 1.0 pint of blood at the local blood bank. How many liters of blood does this correspond to?

Analysis and Solution

[1] **Identify the original quantity and the desired quantity.**

1.0 pt   ? L

original quantity   desired quantity

[2] **Write out the conversion factors.**

- We have no conversion factor that relates pints to liters directly. We do, however, know conversions for pints to quarts, and quarts to liters.

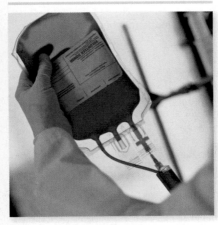

How many liters of blood does this pint of blood contain?

pint–quart conversion   quart–liter conversion

$$\frac{2\ pt}{1\ qt} \quad or \quad \boxed{\frac{1\ qt}{2\ pt}} \qquad\qquad \frac{1.06\ ct}{1\ L} \quad or \quad \boxed{\frac{1\ L}{1.06\ qt}}$$

Choose the conversion factors with the unwanted units—pt and qt—in the denominator.

[3] **Solve the problem.**

- To set up the problem so that unwanted units cancel, arrange each term so that the units in the numerator of one term cancel the units of the denominator of the adjacent term. In this problem we need to cancel both pints and quarts to get liters.
- The single desired unit, liters, must be in the **numerator** of one term.

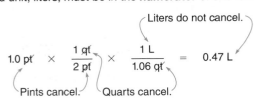

$$1.0\ \cancel{pt} \quad \times \quad \frac{1\ \cancel{qt}}{2\ \cancel{pt}} \quad \times \quad \frac{1\ L}{1.06\ \cancel{qt}} \quad = \quad 0.47\ L$$

Liters do not cancel.

Pints cancel.   Quarts cancel.

[4] Check.

- Since there are two pints in a quart and a quart is about the same size as a liter, one pint should be about half a liter. The answer, 0.47, is just about 0.5.
- Write the answer with two significant figures since one term, 1.0 pt, has two significant figures.

PROBLEM 1.25

Carry out each of the following conversions.

a. 6,250 ft to km   b. 3 cups to L   c. 4.5 ft to cm

1.8 FOCUS ON HEALTH & MEDICINE
Problem Solving Using Clinical Conversion Factors

Sometimes conversion factors don't have to be looked up in a table; they are stated in the problem. If a drug is sold as a 250-mg tablet, this fact becomes a conversion factor relating milligrams to tablets.

$$\frac{250 \text{ mg}}{1 \text{ tablet}} \quad \text{or} \quad \frac{1 \text{ tablet}}{250 \text{ mg}}$$

mg–tablet conversion factors

The active ingredient in Children's Tylenol is acetaminophen.

Alternatively, a drug could be sold as a liquid solution with a specific concentration. For example, Children's Tylenol contains 80 mg of the active ingredient acetaminophen in 2.5 mL. This fact becomes a conversion factor relating milligrams to milliliters.

$$\frac{80 \text{ mg}}{2.5 \text{ mL}} \quad \text{or} \quad \frac{2.5 \text{ mL}}{80 \text{ mg}}$$

mg of acetaminophen–mL conversion factors

Sample Problems 1.10 and 1.11 illustrate how these conversion factors are used in determining drug dosages.

SAMPLE PROBLEM 1.10

A patient is prescribed 1.25 g of amoxicillin, which is available in 250-mg tablets. How many tablets are needed?

Analysis and Solution

[1] Identify the original quantity and the desired quantity.

- We must convert the number of grams of amoxicillin needed to the number of tablets that must be administered.

1.25 g	? tablets
original quantity	desired quantity

[2] Write out the conversion factors.

- We have no conversion factor that relates grams to tablets directly. We do know, however, how to relate grams to milligrams, and milligrams to tablets.

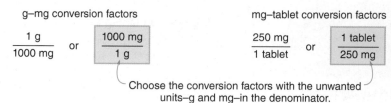

g–mg conversion factors   mg–tablet conversion factors

$$\frac{1 \text{ g}}{1000 \text{ mg}} \quad \text{or} \quad \boxed{\frac{1000 \text{ mg}}{1 \text{ g}}} \qquad\qquad \frac{250 \text{ mg}}{1 \text{ tablet}} \quad \text{or} \quad \boxed{\frac{1 \text{ tablet}}{250 \text{ mg}}}$$

Choose the conversion factors with the unwanted units–g and mg–in the denominator.

[3] Solve the problem.

- Arrange each term so that the units in the numerator of one term cancel the units in the denominator of the adjacent term. In this problem we need to cancel both grams and milligrams to get tablets.

- The single desired unit, tablets, must be located in the **numerator** of one term.

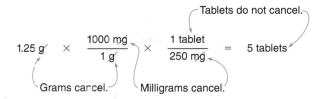

$$1.25 \text{ g} \times \frac{1000 \text{ mg}}{1 \text{ g}} \times \frac{1 \text{ tablet}}{250 \text{ mg}} = 5 \text{ tablets}$$

Tablets do not cancel.

Grams cancel.   Milligrams cancel.

[4] Check.

- The answer of 5 tablets of amoxicillin (not 0.5 or 50) is reasonable. Since the dose in a single tablet (250 mg) is a fraction of a gram, and the required dose is more than a gram, the answer must be greater than one.

SAMPLE PROBLEM 1.11

A dose of 240 mg of acetaminophen is prescribed for a 20-kg child. How many mL of Children's Tylenol (80. mg of acetaminophen per 2.5 mL) are needed?

Analysis and Solution

[1] Identify the original quantity and the desired quantity.

- We must convert the number of milligrams of acetaminophen needed to the number of mL that must be administered.

240 mg   ? mL

original quantity   desired quantity

[2] Write out the conversion factors.

mg of acetaminophen–mL conversion factors

$$\frac{80. \text{ mg}}{2.5 \text{ mL}} \quad \text{or} \quad \boxed{\frac{2.5 \text{ mL}}{80. \text{ mg}}}$$

Choose the conversion factor to cancel mg.

[3] Solve the problem.

- Arrange the terms so that the units in the numerator of one term cancel the units of the denominator of the adjacent term. In this problem we need to cancel milligrams to obtain milliliters.
- In this problem we are given a fact we don't need to use—the child weighs 20 kg. We can ignore this quantity in carrying out the calculation.

$$240 \text{ mg} \times \frac{2.5 \text{ mL}}{80. \text{ mg}} = 7.5 \text{ mL of Children's Tylenol}$$

Milligrams cancel.

[4] Check.

- The answer of 7.5 mL (not 0.75 or 75) is reasonable. Since the required dose is larger than the dose in 2.5 mL, the answer must be larger than 2.5 mL.

PROBLEM 1.26

If one teaspoon contains 5.0 mL, how many teaspoons of Children's Tylenol must be administered in Sample Problem 1.11?

PROBLEM 1.27

A patient is prescribed 0.100 mg of a drug that is available in 25-µg tablets. How many tablets are needed?

PROBLEM 1.28

How many milliliters of Children's Motrin (100 mg of ibuprofen per 5 mL) are needed to give a child a dose of 160 mg?

1.9 Temperature

Temperature is a measure of how hot or cold an object is. Three temperature scales are used: **Fahrenheit** (most common in the United States), **Celsius** (most commonly used by scientists and countries other than the United States), and **Kelvin** (Figure 1.8).

The Fahrenheit and Celsius scales are both divided into **degrees.** On the Fahrenheit scale, water freezes at 32 °F and boils at 212 °F. On the Celsius scale, water freezes at 0 °C and boils at 100 °C. To convert temperature values from one scale to another, we use two equations, where °C is the Celsius temperature and °F is the Fahrenheit temperature.

To convert from Celsius to Fahrenheit:

$$°F = 1.8(°C) + 32$$

To convert from Fahrenheit to Celsius:

$$°C = \frac{°F - 32}{1.8}$$

The Kelvin scale is divided into **kelvins (K)**, not degrees. **The only difference between the Kelvin scale and the Celsius scale is the zero point.** A temperature of –273 °C corresponds to 0 K. The zero point on the Kelvin scale is called **absolute zero,** the lowest temperature possible. To convert temperature values from Celsius to Kelvin, or vice versa, use two equations.

To convert from Celsius to Kelvin:

$$K = °C + 273$$

To convert from Kelvin to Celsius:

$$°C = K - 273$$

SAMPLE PROBLEM 1.12

An infant had a temperature of 104 °F. Convert this temperature to both °C and K.

Analysis

First convert the Fahrenheit temperature to degrees Celsius using the equation °C = (°F – 32)/1.8. Then convert the Celsius temperature to kelvins by adding 273.

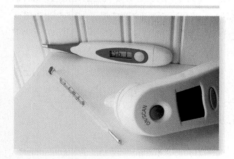

Although mercury thermometers were used in hospitals to measure temperature for many years, temperature is now more commonly recorded with a digital thermometer. Tympanic thermometers, which use an infrared sensing device placed in the ear, are also routinely used.

Figure 1.8   Fahrenheit, Celsius, and Kelvin Temperature Scales Compared

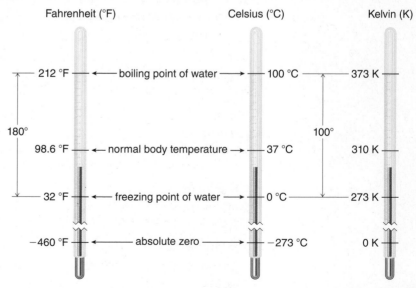

Fahrenheit (°F)	Celsius (°C)	Kelvin (K)
212 °F ← boiling point of water →	100 °C	373 K
180°		100°
98.6 °F ← normal body temperature →	37 °C	310 K
32 °F ← freezing point of water →	0 °C	273 K
–460 °F ← absolute zero →	–273 °C	0 K

Since the freezing point and boiling point of water span 180° on the Fahrenheit scale, but only 100° on the Celsius scale, a Fahrenheit degree and a Celsius degree differ in size. The Kelvin scale is divided into kelvins (K), not degrees. Since the freezing point and boiling point of water span 100 kelvins, one kelvin is the same size as one Celsius degree.

Solution

[1] Convert °F to °C:

$$°C = \frac{°F - 32}{1.8}$$

$$= \frac{104 - 32}{1.8} = 40.\ °C$$

[2] Convert °C to K:

$$K = °C + 273$$

$$= 40. + 273 = 313\ K$$

PROBLEM 1.29

When the human body is exposed to extreme cold, hypothermia can result and the body's temperature can drop to 28.5 °C. Convert this temperature to °F and K.

PROBLEM 1.30

Convert each temperature to the requested temperature scale.

a. 20. °C to °F   c. 298 K to °F

b. 150. °F to °C   d. 75 °C to K

1.10   Density and Specific Gravity

Two additional quantities used to characterize substances are **density** and **specific gravity.**

1.10A   Density

Density **is a physical property that relates the mass of a substance to its volume.** Density is reported in grams per milliliter (g/mL) or grams per cubic centimeter (g/cc).

$$density = \frac{mass\ (g)}{volume\ (mL\ or\ cc)}$$

The density of a substance depends on temperature. For most substances, the solid state is more dense than the liquid state, and as the temperature increases, the density decreases. This phenomenon occurs because the volume of a sample of a substance generally increases with temperature but the mass is always constant.

Water is an exception to this generalization. Solid water, ice, is *less* dense than liquid water, and from 0 °C to 4 °C, the density of water *increases*. Above 4 °C, water behaves like other liquids and its density decreases. Thus, water's maximum density of 1.00 g/mL occurs at 4 °C. Some representative densities are reported in Table 1.6.

The density (not the mass) of a substance determines whether it floats or sinks in a liquid.

• A less dense substance floats on a more dense liquid.

Table 1.6 Representative Densities at 25 °C

Substance	Density [g/(mL or cc)]	Substance	Density [g/(mL or cc)]
Oxygen (0 °C)	0.001 43	Urine	1.003–1.030
Gasoline	0.66	Blood plasma	1.03
Ice (0 °C)	0.92	Table sugar	1.59
Water (4 °C)	1.00	Bone	1.80

Although a can of a diet soft drink floats in water because it is less dense, a can of a regular soft drink that contains sugar is more dense than water so it sinks.

Ice floats on water because it is less dense. When petroleum leaks from an oil tanker or gasoline is spilled when fueling a boat, it floats on water because it is less dense. In contrast, a cannonball or torpedo sinks because it is more dense than water.

Knowing the density of a liquid allows us to convert the volume of a substance to its mass, or the mass of a substance to its volume.

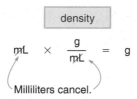

To convert volume (mL) to mass (g):

$$\text{mL} \times \frac{\text{g}}{\text{mL}} = \text{g}$$

Milliliters cancel.

To convert mass (g) to volume (mL):

$$\text{g} \times \frac{\text{mL}}{\text{g}} = \text{mL}$$

Grams cancel.

For example, one laboratory synthesis of aspirin uses the liquid acetic acid, which has a density of 1.05 g/mL. If we need 5.0 g for a synthesis, we could use density to convert this mass to a volume that could then be easily measured out using a syringe or pipette.

$$5.0 \text{ g acetic acid} \times \frac{1 \text{ mL}}{1.05 \text{ g}} = 4.8 \text{ mL of acetic acid}$$

Grams cancel.

SAMPLE PROBLEM 1.13

Calculate the mass in grams of 15.0 mL of a saline solution that has a density 1.05 g/mL.

Analysis

Use density (g/mL) to interconvert the mass and volume of a liquid.

Solution

$$15.0 \text{ mL} \times \frac{1.05 \text{ g}}{1 \text{ mL}} = 15.8 \text{ g of saline solution}$$

Milliliters cancel.

The answer, 15.8 g, is rounded to three significant figures to match the number of significant figures in both factors in the problem.

PROBLEM 1.31

Calculate the mass in grams of 10.0 mL of diethyl ether, an anesthetic that has a density of 0.713 g/mL.

PROBLEM 1.32

(a) Calculate the volume in milliliters of 100. g of coconut oil, which has a density of 0.92 g/mL.
(b) How many liters does this correspond to?

PROBLEM 1.33

Suppose we have two substances, **A** and **B,** and the density of **A** is greater than the density of **B.**
(a) If we have equal volumes of **A** and **B,** which one has the larger mass? (b) If we have equal masses of **A** and **B,** which one has the larger volume?

HEALTH NOTE

The specific gravity of a urine sample is measured to check if a patient has an imbalance in metabolism.

1.10B Specific Gravity

Specific gravity **is a quantity that compares the density of a substance with the density of water at 4 °C.**

$$\text{specific gravity} = \frac{\text{density of a substance (g/mL)}}{\text{density of water (g/mL)}}$$

Unlike most other quantities, specific gravity is a quantity without units, since the units in the numerator (g/mL) cancel the units in the denominator (g/mL). Since the density of water is 1.00 g/mL at 4 °C, **the specific gravity of a substance equals its density, but it contains no units.** For example, if the density of a liquid is 1.5 g/mL, its specific gravity is 1.5.

The specific gravity of urine samples is often measured in a hospital lab. Normal urine has a density in the range of 1.003–1.030 g/mL (Table 1.6), so it has a specific gravity in the range of 1.003–1.030. Consistently high or low values can indicate an imbalance in metabolism. For example, the specific gravity of urine samples from patients with poorly controlled diabetes is abnormally high, because a large amount of glucose is excreted in the urine.

PROBLEM 1.34

(a) If the density of a liquid is 0.80 g/mL, what is its specific gravity? (b) If the specific gravity of a substance is 2.3, what is its density?

CHAPTER HIGHLIGHTS

KEY TERMS

Celsius scale (1.9)	Fahrenheit scale (1.9)	Mixture (1.3)
Chemical properties (1.2)	Gas (1.2)	Physical properties (1.2)
Chemistry (1.1)	Gram (1.4)	Pure substance (1.3)
Compound (1.3)	Inexact number (1.5)	Scientific notation (1.6)
Conversion factor (1.7)	Kelvin scale (1.9)	SI units (1.4)
Cubic centimeter (1.4)	Liquid (1.2)	Significant figures (1.5)
Density (1.10)	Liter (1.4)	Solid (1.2)
Element (1.3)	Mass (1.4)	Specific gravity (1.10)
English system of measurement (1.4)	Matter (1.1)	States of matter (1.2)
Exact number (1.5)	Meter (1.4)	Temperature (1.9)
Factor–label method (1.7)	Metric system (1.4)	Weight (1.4)

KEY CONCEPTS

❶ **Describe the three states of matter. (1.1, 1.2)**
  • Matter is anything that has mass and takes up volume. Matter has three common states:
    • The solid state is composed of highly organized particles that lie close together. A solid has a definite shape and volume.
    • The liquid state is composed of particles that lie close together but are less organized than the solid state. A liquid has a definite volume but not a definite shape.
    • The gas state is composed of highly disorganized particles that lie far apart. A gas has no definite shape or volume.

❷ **How is matter classified? (1.3)**
  • Matter is classified in one of two categories:
    • A pure substance is composed of a single component with a constant composition. A pure substance is either an element, which cannot be broken down into simpler substances by a chemical reaction, or a compound, which is formed by combining two or more elements.
    • A mixture is composed of more than one component and its composition can vary depending on the sample.

❸ What are the key features of the metric system of measurement? (1.4)

• The metric system is a system of measurement in which each type of measurement has a base unit and all other units are related to the base unit by a prefix that indicates if the unit is larger or smaller than the base unit.

• The base units are meter (m) for length, gram (g) for mass, liter (L) for volume, and second (s) for time.

❹ What are significant figures and how are they used in calculations? (1.5)

• Significant figures are all digits in a measured number, including one estimated digit. All nonzero digits are significant. A zero is significant only if it occurs between two nonzero digits, or at the end of a number with a decimal point. A trailing zero in a number without a decimal point is not considered significant.

• In multiplying and dividing with significant figures, the answer has the same number of significant figures as the original number with the fewest significant figures.

• In adding or subtracting with significant figures, the answer has the same number of decimal places as the original number with the fewest decimal places.

❺ What is scientific notation? (1.6)

• Scientific notation is a method of writing a number as $y \times 10^x$, where y is a number between 1 and 10, and x is a positive or negative exponent.

• To convert a standard number to a number in scientific notation, move the decimal point to give a number between 1 and 10. Multiply the result by 10^x, where x is the number of places the decimal point was moved. When the decimal point is moved to the left, x is positive. When the decimal point is moved to the right, x is negative.

❻ How are conversion factors used to convert one unit to another? (1.7, 1.8)

• A conversion factor is a term that converts a quantity in one unit to a quantity in another unit. To use conversion factors to solve a problem, set up the problem with any unwanted unit in the numerator of one term and the denominator of another term, so that unwanted units cancel.

❼ What is temperature and how are the three temperature scales related? (1.9)

• Temperature is a measure of how hot or cold an object is. The Fahrenheit and Celsius temperature scales are divided into degrees. Both the size of the degree and the zero point of these scales differ. The Kelvin scale is divided into kelvins, and one kelvin is the same size as one degree Celsius.

❽ What are density and specific gravity? (1.10)

• Density is a physical property reported in g/mL or g/cc that relates the mass of an object to its volume. A less dense substance floats on top of a more dense liquid.

• Specific gravity is a unitless quantity that relates the density of a substance to the density of water at 4 °C. Since the density of water is 1.00 g/mL at this temperature, the specific gravity of a substance equals its density, but it contains no units.

PROBLEMS

Selected in-chapter and odd-numbered end-of-chapter problems have brief answers in Appendix B. The *Student Study Guide and Solutions Manual* contains detailed solutions to all in-chapter and odd-numbered end-of-chapter problems, as well as additional worked examples and a chapter self-test.

Matter

1.35 Classify each example of molecular art as a pure element, a pure compound, or a mixture.

a.
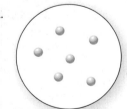

c.

b.

d.
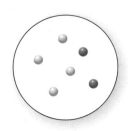

1.36 (a) Which representation(s) in Problem 1.35 illustrate a mixture of two elements? (b) Which representation(s) in Problem 1.35 illustrate a mixture of a compound and an element?

1.37 What is the difference between an element and a compound?

1.38 What is the difference between a compound and a mixture?

1.39 Describe solids, liquids, and gases in terms of (a) volume (how they fill a container); (b) shape; (c) level of organization of the particles that comprise them; (d) how close the particles that comprise them lie.

1.40 How do physical properties and chemical properties differ?

1.41 Classify each process as a chemical or physical change.
  a. dissolving calcium chloride in water
  b. burning gasoline to power a car
  c. heating wax so that it melts

1.42 Classify each process as a chemical or physical change.
  a. the condensation of water on the outside of a cold glass
  b. mixing a teaspoon of instant coffee with hot water
  c. baking a cake

1.43 When a chunk of dry ice (solid carbon dioxide) is placed out in the air, the solid gradually disappears and a gas is formed above the solid. Does the molecular art drawn below indicate that a chemical or physical change has occurred? Explain your choice.

solid   gas

1.44 The inexpensive preparation of nitrogen-containing fertilizers begins with mixing together two elements, hydrogen and nitrogen, at high temperature and pressure in the presence of a metal. Does the molecular art depicted below indicate that a chemical or physical change occurs under these conditions? Explain your choice.

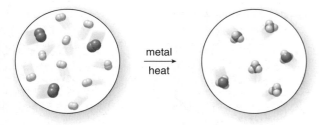

metal
heat

Measurement

1.45

a. What is the temperature on the given Fahrenheit thermometer?
b. How many significant figures does your answer contain?
c. Convert this temperature into °C.

1.46 (a) What is the length of the given crayon in centimeters? (b) How many significant figures does this value contain? (c) Convert this value to meters, and write the answer in scientific notation.

1.47 What is the difference between an exact number and an inexact number? Give an example of each type of number.

1.48 Label each quantity as an exact or inexact number.
   a. A recipe requires 10 cloves of garlic and two tablespoons of oil.
   b. A dog had five puppies whose combined weight was 10 lb.
   c. The four bicycles in the family have been ridden for a total of 250 mi.
   d. A child fell and had a 4-cm laceration that required 12 stitches.

1.49 Which quantity in each pair is larger?
   a. 5 mL or 5 dL   c. 5 cm or 5 mm
   b. 10 mg or 10 μg   d. 10 Ms or 10 ms

1.50 Which quantity in each pair is larger?
   a. 10 km or 10 m   c. 10 g or 10 μg
   b. 10 L or 10 mL   d. 10 cm or 10 mm

Significant Figures

1.51 How many significant figures does each number contain?
   a. 16.00   c. 0.001 60   e. 1.06   g. 1.060×10^{10}
   b. 160   d. 1,600,000   f. 0.1600   h. 1.6×10^{-6}

1.52 How many significant figures does each number contain?
   a. 160.   c. 0.000 16   e. 1,600.   g. 1.600×10^{-10}
   b. 160.0   d. 1.60   f. 1.060   h. 1.6×10^{6}

1.53 Round each number to three significant figures.
   a. 25,401   c. 0.001 265 982   e. 195.371
   b. 1,248,486   d. 0.123 456   f. 196.814

1.54 Round each number in Problem 1.53 to four significant figures.

1.55 Carry out each calculation and report the answer using the proper number of significant figures.
   a. 53.6×0.41 c. $65.2 \div 12$ e. 694.2×0.2
   b. $25.825 - 3.86$ d. $41.0 + 9.135$ f. $1,045 - 1.26$

1.56 Carry out each calculation and report the answer using the proper number of significant figures.
   a. $49,682 \times 0.80$ c. $1,000 \div 2.34$ e. $25,000 \div 0.4356$
   b. $66.815 + 2.82$ d. $21 - 0.88$ f. $21.5381 + 26.55$

Scientific Notation

1.57 Write each quantity in scientific notation.
   a. 1,234 g   c. 5,244,000 L   e. 44,000 km
   b. 0.000 016 2 m   d. 0.005 62 g

1.58 Write each quantity in scientific notation.
   a. 0.001 25 m   c. 54,235.6 m   e. 4,440 s
   b. 8,100,000,000 lb   d. 0.000 001 899 L

1.59 Convert each number to its standard form.
   a. 3.4×10^{8} c. 3×10^{2}
   b. 5.822×10^{-5} d. 6.86×10^{-8}

1.60 Convert each number to its standard form.
   a. 4.02×10^{10} c. 6.86×10^{9}
   b. 2.46×10^{-3} d. 1.00×10^{-7}

1.61 Which number in each pair is larger?
   a. 4.44×10^3 or 4.8×10^2 c. 1.3×10^8 or 52,300,000
   b. 5.6×10^{-6} or 5.6×10^{-5} d. 9.8×10^{-4} or 0.000 089

1.62 Rank the numbers in each group from smallest to largest.
   a. 5.06×10^6, 7×10^4, and 2.5×10^8
   b. 6.3×10^{-2}, 2.5×10^{-4}, and 8.6×10^{-6}

1.63 Write the recommended daily intake of each nutrient in scientific notation.
   a. 0.000 400 g of folate   c. 0.000 080 g of vitamin K
   b. 0.002 g of copper   d. 3,400 mg of chloride

1.64 A blood vessel is 0.40 μm in diameter. (a) Convert this quantity to meters and write the answer in scientific notation. (b) Convert this quantity to inches and write the answer in scientific notation.

Problem Solving and Unit Conversions

1.65 The average mass of a human liver is 1.5 kg. Convert this quantity to (a) grams; (b) pounds; (c) ounces.

1.66 A *grain* is a unit of measurement sometimes used in medicine to indicate the dose of a medication, where 1 grain = 65 mg. How many grains are contained in a typical 325-mg aspirin tablet?

1.67 Carry out each of the following conversions.
   a. 300 g to mg   d. 300 g to oz
   b. 2 L to μL   e. 2 ft to m
   c. 5.0 cm to m   f. 3.5 yd to m

1.68 Carry out each of the following conversions.
   a. 25 μL to mL   d. 300 mL to qt
   b. 35 kg to g   e. 3 cups to L
   c. 2.36 mL to L   f. 2.5 tons to kg

1.69 Carry out each of the following conversions.
   a. What is the mass in kilograms of an individual who weighs 234 lb?
   b. What is the height in centimeters of a child who is 50. in. tall?
   c. A patient required 3.0 pt of blood during surgery. How many liters does this correspond to?
   d. A patient had a body temperature of 37.7 °C. What is his body temperature in °F?

1.70 Carry out each of the following conversions.
   a. What is the mass in pounds of an individual who weighs 53.2 kg?
   b. What is the height in inches of a child who is 90. cm tall?
   c. How many mL are contained in the 5.0 qt of blood in the human body?
   d. A patient had a body temperature of 103.5 °F. What is his body temperature in °C?

1.71 (a) How many milliliters are contained in 1 qt of milk? (b) How many fluid ounces are contained in 1 L of soda?

1.72 The official distance of a marathon is 26 miles and 385 yards. Convert this value to kilometers.

Temperature

1.73 Carry out each of the following temperature conversions.
   a. An over-the-counter pain reliever melts at 53 °C. Convert this temperature to °F and K.
   b. A cake is baked at 350. °F. Convert this temperature to °C and K.

1.74 Methane, the main component of the natural gas used for cooking and heating homes, melts at −183 °C and boils at −162 °C. Convert each temperature to °F and K.

1.75 Which temperature in each pair is higher?
   a. −10 °C or 10 °F   b. −50 °C or −50 °F

1.76 Rank the temperatures in each group from lowest to highest.
   a. 0 °F, 0 °C, 0 K   b. 100 K, 100 °C, 100 °F

Density and Specific Gravity

1.77 What is the difference between density and specific gravity?

1.78 The density of sucrose, table sugar, is 1.56 g/cc. What volume (in cubic centimeters) does 20.0 g of sucrose occupy?

1.79 If a urine sample has a mass of 122 g and a volume of 121 mL, what is its density in g/mL?

1.80 A volume of saline solution had a mass of 25.6 g at 4 °C. An equal volume of water at the same temperature had a mass of 24.5 g. What is the density of the saline solution?

1.81 If milk has a density of 1.03 g/mL, what is the mass of one quart, reported in kilograms?

1.82 If gasoline has a density of 0.66 g/mL, what is the mass of one gallon, reported in kilograms?

1.83 Which is the upper layer when each of the following liquids is added to water?
   a. heptane (density = 0.684 g/mL)
   b. olive oil (density = 0.92 g/mL)
   c. chloroform (density = 1.49 g/mL)
   d. carbon tetrachloride (density = 1.59 g/mL)

1.84 Which of the following solids float on top of water and which sink?
   a. aluminum (density = 1.70 g/cc)
   b. lead (density = 11.34 g/cc)
   c. Styrofoam (density = 0.100 g/cc)
   d. maple wood (density = 0.74 g/cc)

1.85 (a) What is the specific gravity of mercury, the liquid used in thermometers, if it has a density of 13.6 g/mL? (b) What is the density of ethanol if it has a specific gravity of 0.789?

1.86 Why is specific gravity a unitless quantity?

Applications

1.87 A lab test showed an individual's cholesterol level to be 186 mg/dL. (a) Convert this quantity to g/dL. (b) Convert this quantity to mg/L.

1.88 Hemoglobin is a protein that transports oxygen from the lungs to the rest of the body. Lab results indicated a patient had a hemoglobin concentration in the blood of 15.5 g/dL, which is in the normal range. (a) Convert the number of grams to milligrams and write the answer in scientific notation. (b) Convert the number of grams to micrograms and write the answer in scientific notation.

1.89 A woman was told to take a dose of 1.5 g of calcium daily. How many 500-mg tablets should she take?

1.90 A soccer player weighed 70.7 kg before a match, drank 1.8 L of liquid (density 1.05 g/mL) during the match, and weighed 69.3 kg after the match. How many pounds of sweat did the soccer player lose?

1.91 A medium banana contains 451 mg of the nutrient potassium. How many bananas would you have to eat in one day to obtain the recommended daily intake of 3.5 g of potassium?

1.92 A single 1-oz serving of tortilla chips contains 250 mg of sodium. If an individual ate the entire 13-oz bag, how many grams of sodium would he ingest? If the recommended daily intake of sodium is 2.4 g, does this provide more or less than the recommended daily value, and by how much?

1.93 A bottle of liquid medication contains 300. mL and costs $10.00. (a) If the usual dose is 20. mL, how much does each dose cost? (b) If the usual dose is two tablespoons (1 tablespoon = 15 mL), how much does each dose cost?

1.94 The average nicotine content of a Camel cigarette is 1.93 mg. (a) Convert this quantity to both grams and micrograms. (b) Nicotine patches, which are used to help quit smoking, release nicotine into the body by absorption through the skin. The patches come with different amounts of nicotine. A smoker begins with the amount of nicotine that matches his typical daily intake. The maximum amount of nicotine in one brand of patch supplies a smoker with 21 mg of nicotine per day. If an individual smoked one pack of 20 Camel cigarettes each day, would a smoker get more or less nicotine per day using this patch?

1.95 A chemist synthesized 0.510 kg of aspirin in the lab. If the normal dose of aspirin is two 325-mg tablets, how many doses did she prepare?

1.96 Maalox is the trade name for an antacid and antigas medication used for relief of heartburn, bloating, and acid indigestion. Each 5.0-mL portion of Maalox contains 400. mg of aluminum hydroxide, 400. mg of magnesium hydroxide, and 40. mg of simethicone. If the recommended dose is two teaspoons four times a day, how many grams of each substance would an individual take in a 24-hour period? (1 teaspoon = 5.0 mL.)

1.97 A patient is prescribed 2.0 g of a medication to be taken four times a day. If the medicine is available in 500.-mg tablets, how many tablets are needed in a 24-hour period?

1.98 A patient receives an intravenous (IV) solution that flows at the rate of 150 mL per hour. (a) How much fluid does the patient receive in 20. min? (b) How long does it take for the patient to receive 90. mL of fluid? (c) If the IV bag holds 600. mL of fluid, how many minutes does it take to empty the bag? (d) If the solution contains 90. mg of glucose per mL, how long will it take to give the patient 2.0 g of glucose?

CHALLENGE PROBLEMS

1.99 Often the specific amount of a drug to be administered must be calculated from a given dose in mg per kilogram of body weight. This assures that individuals who have very different body mass get the proper dose. If the proper dosage of a drug is 2.0 mg/kg of body weight, how many milligrams would a 110-lb individual need?

1.100 Quinine, a drug isolated from the bark of the cinchona tree native to the Andes Mountains, is an effective treatment for malaria. Children typically receive a dose of 10. mg/kg three times a day for seven days. How many grams would a 28-kg child receive during the course of a treatment?

1.101 Children's Chewable Tylenol contains 80 mg of acetaminophen per tablet. If the recommended dosage is 10 mg/kg, how many tablets are needed for a 42-lb child?

1.102 Artemether, an antimalarial drug prepared from the Chinese antimalarial plant *Artemisia annua,* can be given either orally or by injection. When the drug is given in pill form, the patient receives 160 mg on the first day, and then 80. mg daily for the next four days. When the drug is given by injection, the patient receives 3.2 mg/kg of body weight on the first day, and then 1.6 mg/kg daily for the next four days. (a) Which method gives a 40.-kg individual the larger dose? (b) Which method gives a 100.-kg individual the larger dose?

1.103 Children's Liquid Motrin contains 100. mg of the pain reliever ibuprofen per 5 mL. If the dose for a 45-lb child is 1.5 teaspoons, how many grams of ibuprofen would the child receive? (1 teaspoon = 5.0 mL.)

1.104 If the proper dose of a medication is 10 µg/kg of body weight, how many milligrams would a 200-lb individual need?

2

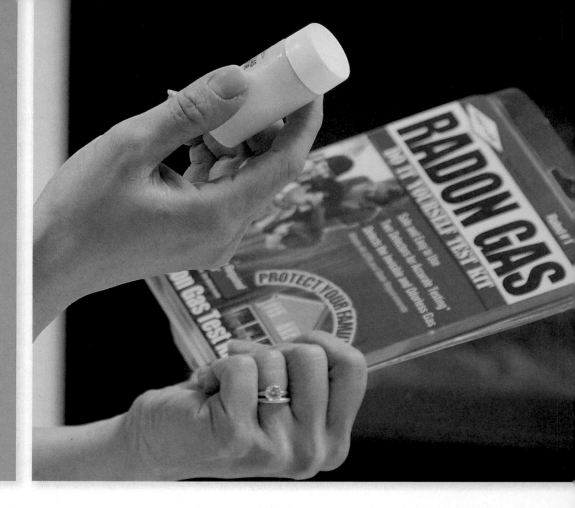

Radon detectors are used to measure high levels of radon, a radioactive noble gas linked to an increased incidence of lung cancer.

Atoms and the Periodic Table

CHAPTER GOALS

In this chapter you will learn how to:

1. Identify an element by its symbol and classify it as a metal, nonmetal, or metalloid
2. Describe the basic parts of an atom
3. Distinguish isotopes and calculate atomic weight
4. Describe the basic features of the periodic table
5. Understand the electronic structure of an atom
6. Write an electronic configuration for an element
7. Relate the location of an element in the periodic table to its electronic configuration
8. Draw an electron-dot symbol for an atom
9. Use the periodic table to predict the relative size and ionization energy of atoms

Examine the ingredients listed on a box of crackers. They may include flour, added vitamins, sugar for sweetness, a natural or synthetic coloring agent, baking soda, salt for flavor, and BHT as a preservative. No matter how simple or complex each of these substances is, it is composed of the basic building block, the **atom.** The word *atom* comes from the Greek word *atomos* meaning *unable to cut.* In Chapter 2, we examine the structure and properties of atoms, the building blocks that comprise all forms of matter.

2.1 Elements

You were first introduced to elements in Section 1.3.

• An *element* is a pure substance that cannot be broken down into simpler substances by a chemical reaction.

Of the 118 elements currently known, 90 are naturally occurring and the remaining 28 have been prepared by scientists in the laboratory. Some elements, like oxygen in the air we breathe and aluminum in a soft drink can, are familiar to you, while others, like samarium and seaborgium, are probably not. An alphabetical list of all elements appears on the inside front cover.

Each element is identified by a one- or two-letter symbol. The element carbon is symbolized by the single letter **C,** while the element chlorine is symbolized by **Cl.** When two letters are used in the element symbol, the first is upper case while the second is lower case. Thus, **Co** refers to the element cobalt, but CO is carbon monoxide, which is composed of the elements carbon (C) and oxygen (O). Table 2.1 lists common elements and their symbols.

While most element symbols are derived from the first one or two letters of the element name, 11 elements have symbols derived from Latin or German origins. Table 2.2 lists these elements and their symbols.

PROBLEM 2.1

Give the symbol for each element.

a. calcium, a nutrient needed for strong teeth and bones
b. radon, a radioactive gas produced in the soil
c. nitrogen, the main component of the earth's atmosphere
d. gold, a precious metal used in coins and jewelry

Elements are named for people, places, and things. For example, *carbon* (C) comes from the Latin word *carbo,* meaning *coal* or *charcoal; neptunium* (Np) was named for the planet Neptune; *einsteinium* (Es) was named for scientist Albert Einstein; and *californium* (Cf) was named for the state of California.

ENVIRONMENTAL NOTE

Carbon monoxide (CO), formed in small amounts during the combustion of fossil fuels like gasoline, is a toxic component of the smoggy air in many large cities. Carbon monoxide contains the elements carbon (C) and oxygen (O). We will learn about carbon monoxide in Section 12.8.

Table 2.1 Common Elements and Their Symbols

Element	Symbol	Element	Symbol
Bromine	Br	Magnesium	Mg
Calcium	Ca	Manganese	Mn
Carbon	C	Molybdenum	Mo
Chlorine	Cl	Nitrogen	N
Chromium	Cr	Oxygen	O
Cobalt	Co	Phosphorus	P
Copper	Cu	Potassium	K
Fluorine	F	Sodium	Na
Hydrogen	H	Sulfur	S
Iodine	I	Zinc	Zn
Lead	Pb		

Table 2.2 Unusual Element Symbols

Element	Symbol
Antimony	Sb (stibium)
Copper	Cu (cuprum)
Gold	Au (aurum)
Iron	Fe (ferrum)
Lead	Pb (plumbum)
Mercury	Hg (hydrargyrum)
Potassium	K (kalium)
Silver	Ag (argentum)
Sodium	Na (natrium)
Tin	Sn (stannum)
Tungsten	W (wolfram)

PROBLEM 2.2

An alloy is a mixture of two or more elements that has metallic properties. Give the element symbol for the components of each alloy: (a) brass (copper and zinc); (b) bronze (copper and tin); (c) pewter (tin, antimony, and lead).

PROBLEM 2.3

Give the name corresponding to each element symbol: (a) Ne; (b) S; (c) I; (d) Si; (e) B; (f) Hg.

2.1A Elements and the Periodic Table

A periodic table appears on the inside front cover for easy reference.

Long ago it was realized that groups of elements have similar properties, and that these elements could be arranged in a schematic way called the **periodic table** (Figure 2.1). The position of an element in the periodic table tells us much about its chemical properties.

Figure 2.1 The Periodic Table of the Elements

	1A 1	2A 2	3B 3	4B 4	5B 5	6B 6	7B 7	← 8B → 8	9	10	1B 11	2B 12	3A 13	4A 14	5A 15	6A 16	7A 17	8A 18	
1	1 **H** 1.008																	2 **He** 4.003	1
2	3 **Li** 6.941	4 **Be** 9.012											5 **B** 10.81	6 **C** 12.01	7 **N** 14.01	8 **O** 16.00	9 **F** 19.00	10 **Ne** 20.18	2
3	11 **Na** 22.99	12 **Mg** 24.31											13 **Al** 26.98	14 **Si** 28.09	15 **P** 30.97	16 **S** 32.07	17 **Cl** 35.45	18 **Ar** 39.95	3
4	19 **K** 39.10	20 **Ca** 40.08	21 **Sc** 44.96	22 **Ti** 47.88	23 **V** 50.94	24 **Cr** 52.00	25 **Mn** 54.94	26 **Fe** 55.85	27 **Co** 58.93	28 **Ni** 58.69	29 **Cu** 63.55	30 **Zn** 65.41	31 **Ga** 69.72	32 **Ge** 72.64	33 **As** 74.92	34 **Se** 78.96	35 **Br** 79.90	36 **Kr** 83.80	4
5	37 **Rb** 85.47	38 **Sr** 87.62	39 **Y** 88.91	40 **Zr** 91.22	41 **Nb** 92.91	42 **Mo** 95.94	43 **Tc** (98)	44 **Ru** 101.1	45 **Rh** 102.9	46 **Pd** 106.4	47 **Ag** 107.9	48 **Cd** 112.4	49 **In** 114.8	50 **Sn** 118.7	51 **Sb** 121.8	52 **Te** 127.6	53 **I** 126.9	54 **Xe** 131.3	5
6	55 **Cs** 132.9	56 **Ba** 137.3	57 **La** 138.9	72 **Hf** 178.5	73 **Ta** 180.9	74 **W** 183.8	75 **Re** 186.2	76 **Os** 190.2	77 **Ir** 192.2	78 **Pt** 195.1	79 **Au** 197.0	80 **Hg** 200.6	81 **Tl** 204.4	82 **Pb** 207.2	83 **Bi** 209.0	84 **Po** (209)	85 **At** (210)	86 **Rn** (222)	6
7	87 **Fr** (223)	88 **Ra** (226)	89 **Ac** (227)	104 **Rf** (267)	105 **Db** (268)	106 **Sg** (271)	107 **Bh** (272)	108 **Hs** (270)	109 **Mt** (276)	110 **Ds** (281)	111 **Rg** (280)	112 **Cn** (285)	113 – (284)	114 – (289)	115 – (289)	116 – (293)	117 – (294)	118 – (294)	7

6	58 **Ce** 140.1	59 **Pr** 140.9	60 **Nd** 144.2	61 **Pm** (145)	62 **Sm** 150.4	63 **Eu** 152.0	64 **Gd** 157.3	65 **Tb** 158.9	66 **Dy** 162.5	67 **Ho** 164.9	68 **Er** 167.3	69 **Tm** 168.9	70 **Yb** 173.0	71 **Lu** 175.0	6
7	90 **Th** 232.0	91 **Pa** 231.0	92 **U** 238.0	93 **Np** (237)	94 **Pu** (244)	95 **Am** (243)	96 **Cm** (247)	97 **Bk** (247)	98 **Cf** (251)	99 **Es** (252)	100 **Fm** (257)	101 **Md** (258)	102 **No** (259)	103 **Lr** (262)	7

metal | metalloid | nonmetal

- **Metals** are shiny substances that conduct heat and electricity. Metals are ductile, meaning they can be drawn into wires, and malleable, meaning they can be hammered into shapes.
- **Metalloids** have properties intermediate between metals and nonmetals.
- **Nonmetals** are poor conductors of heat and electricity.

The elements in the periodic table are divided into three categories—**metals, nonmetals,** and **metalloids.** The solid line that begins with boron (B) and angles in steps down to astatine (At) marks the three regions corresponding to these groups. All metals are located to the *left* of the line. All nonmetals except hydrogen are located to the *right*. Metalloids are located along the steps.

- *Metals* are shiny materials that are good conductors of heat and electricity. All metals are solids at room temperature except for mercury, which is a liquid.
- *Nonmetals* do not have a shiny appearance, and they are generally poor conductors of heat and electricity. Nonmetals like sulfur and carbon are solids at room temperature; bromine is a liquid; and nitrogen, oxygen, and nine other elements are gases.
- *Metalloids* have properties intermediate between metals and nonmetals. Only seven elements are categorized as metalloids: boron (B), silicon (Si), germanium (Ge), arsenic (As), antimony (Sb), tellurium (Te), and astatine (At).

PROBLEM 2.4

Locate each element in the periodic table and classify it as a metal, nonmetal, or metalloid.

a. titanium	c. krypton	e. arsenic	g. selenium
b. chlorine	d. palladium	f. cesium	h. osmium

2.1B FOCUS ON THE HUMAN BODY
The Elements of Life

Because living organisms selectively take up elements from their surroundings, the abundance of elements in the human body is very different from the distribution of elements in the earth's crust. **Four nonmetals—oxygen, carbon, hydrogen, and nitrogen—comprise 96% of the mass of the human body, and are called the** *building-block elements* (Figure 2.2). Hydrogen and oxygen are the elements that form water, the most prevalent substance in the body. Carbon, hydrogen, and oxygen are found in the four main types of biological molecules—proteins, carbohydrates, lipids, and nucleic acids. Proteins and nucleic acids contain the element nitrogen as well. These biological molecules are discussed in Chapters 19–22.

Figure 2.2   The Elements of Life

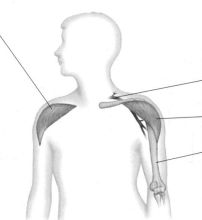

Building-Block Elements

Oxygen (O)
Carbon (C)
Hydrogen (H)
Nitrogen (N)

These four elements compose almost 96% of the mass of the human body. Muscle tissue contains all four building-block elements.

Trace Elements

Arsenic (As)	Fluorine (F)	Nickel (Ni)
Boron (B)	Iodine (I)	Selenium (Se)
Chromium (Cr)	Iron (Fe)	Silicon (Si)
Cobalt (Co)	Manganese (Mn)	Zinc (Zn)
Copper (Cu)	Molybdenum (Mo)	

Each trace element is present in less than 0.1% by mass. A small quantity (15 mg or less) of each element is needed in the daily diet.

Major Minerals

Potassium (K), sodium (Na), and chlorine (Cl) are present in body fluids.

Magnesium (Mg) and sulfur (S) are present in the proteins found in muscle.

Calcium (Ca) and phosphorus (P) are present in teeth and bones.

Each major mineral is present in 0.1–2% by mass. At least 100 mg of each mineral is needed in the daily diet.

CONSUMER NOTE

Nutrition Facts

Serving Size 3/4 cup (30g)
Servings Per Container about 17

Amount Per Serving	Cereal	Cereal with 1/2 cup Fat Free Milk
Calories	120	160
Calories from Fat	15	15
	% Daily Value**	
Vitamin A	15%	20%
Vitamin C	0%	0%
Calcium	0%	15%
Iron	60%	60%
Vitamin D	10%	25%
Thiamin	25%	30%
Riboflavin	25%	35%
Niacin	25%	25%
Vitamin B$_6$	25%	25%
Folic Acid	50%	50%
Vitamin B$_{12}$	25%	35%
Phosphorus	4%	15%
Magnesium	4%	8%
Zinc	2%	6%
Copper	2%	2%

INGREDIENTS: CORN, WHOLE GRAIN WHEAT, SUGAR, WHOLE GRAIN ROLLED OATS, BROWN SUGAR, HIGH OLEIC VEGETABLE OIL† (CANOLA OR SUNFLOWER OIL), RICE FLOUR, WHEAT FLOUR, MALTED BARLEY FLOUR, SALT, RICE, CORN SYRUP, WHEY (FROM MILK†), HONEY, MALTED CORN AND BARLEY SYRUP, CARAMEL COLOR, ARTIFICIAL FLAVOR, ANNATTO EXTRACT (COLOR). BHT ADDED TO PACKAGING MATERIAL TO PRESERVE PRODUCT FRESHNESS.
VITAMINS AND MINERALS: REDUCED IRON, NIACINAMIDE, VITAMIN B6, VITAMIN A PALMITATE, RIBOFLAVIN (VITAMIN B2), THIAMIN MONONITRATE (VITAMIN B1), ZINC OXIDE (SOURCE OF ZINC) FOLIC ACID, VITAMIN B12, VITAMIN D

Many breakfast cereals are fortified with iron to provide the consumer with this essential micronutrient.

Seven other elements, called the **major minerals** or **macronutrients,** are also present in the body in much smaller amounts (0.1–2% by mass). Sodium, potassium, and chlorine are present in body fluids. Magnesium and sulfur occur in proteins, and calcium and phosphorus are present in teeth and bones. Phosphorus is also contained in all nucleic acids, such as the DNA that transfers genetic information from one generation to another. At least 100 mg of each macronutrient is needed in the daily diet.

Many other elements occur in very small amounts in the body, but are essential to good health. These **trace elements** or **micronutrients** are required in the daily diet in small quantities, usually less than 15 mg. Each trace element has a specialized function that is important for proper cellular function. For example, iron is needed for hemoglobin, the protein that carries oxygen in red blood cells, and myoglobin, the protein that stores oxygen in muscle. Zinc is needed for the proper functioning of many enzymes in the liver and kidneys, and iodine is needed for proper thyroid function. Although most of the trace elements are metals, nonmetals like fluorine and selenium are micronutrients as well.

PROBLEM 2.5

Classify each micronutrient in Figure 2.2 as a metal, nonmetal, or metalloid.

2.1C Compounds

In Section 1.3 we learned that a *compound* **is a pure substance formed by chemically combining two or more elements together.** Element symbols are used to write chemical formulas for compounds.

- A *chemical formula* uses element symbols to show the identity of the elements forming a compound and subscripts to show the ratio of atoms (the building blocks of matter) contained in the compound.

For example, table salt is formed from sodium (Na) and chlorine (Cl) in a ratio of 1:1, so its formula is NaCl. Water, on the other hand, is formed from two hydrogens for each oxygen, so its formula is H_2O. The subscript "1" is understood when no subscript is written. Other examples of chemical formulas are shown below.

$$\overset{\displaystyle \frown \text{2 H's for each O}}{H_2O} \qquad \overset{\displaystyle \frown \text{2 O's for each C}}{CO_2} \qquad \overset{\displaystyle \frown \text{3 C's}}{C_3H_8}\,{\frown\text{8 H's}}$$

water   carbon dioxide (dry ice)   propane

As we learned in Section 1.2, molecular art will often be used to illustrate the composition and state of elements and compounds. Color-coded spheres, shown in Figure 2.3, are used to identify the common elements that form compounds.

For example, a red sphere is used for the element oxygen and gray is used for the element hydrogen, so H_2O is represented as a red sphere joined to two gray spheres. Sometimes the spheres will be connected by "sticks" to generate a **ball-and-stick** representation for a compound. At other times, the spheres will be drawn close together to form a **space-filling** representation. No matter

Figure 2.3   Common Element Colors Used in Molecular Art

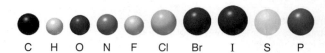

C   H   O   N   F   Cl   Br   I   S   P

how the spheres are depicted, H_2O always consists of one red sphere for the oxygen and two gray spheres for the two hydrogens.

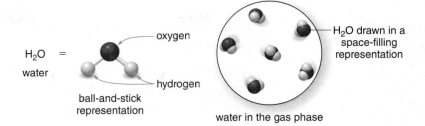

H_2O =

water

ball-and-stick representation

water in the gas phase

SAMPLE PROBLEM 2.1

Identify the elements used in each example of molecular art.

a.

b.

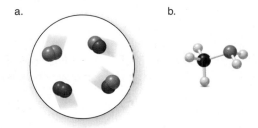

Analysis

Use Figure 2.3 to determine the identity of the color-coded spheres.

Solution

a. The blue spheres in this space-filling representation correspond to the element nitrogen and the red spheres correspond to the element oxygen. Thus, one "particle" contains two nitrogens, one contains two oxygens, and two contain one oxygen and one nitrogen.

b. This ball-and-stick representation contains the elements carbon (black), nitrogen (blue), and hydrogen (gray).

PROBLEM 2.6

Identify the elements used in each example of molecular art.

a.   b.   c.

PROBLEM 2.7

Identify the elements in each chemical formula, and give the number of atoms of each element.

a. NaCN (sodium cyanide)   c. C_2H_6 (ethane)   e. CO (carbon monoxide)
b. H_2S (hydrogen sulfide)   d. SnF_2 (stannous fluoride)   f. $C_3H_8O_3$ (glycerol)

PROBLEM 2.8

Halothane is an inhaled general anesthetic, commonly used since the 1950s. Identify the elements in the ball-and-stick representation of halothane.

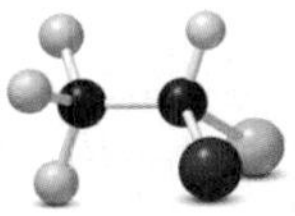

halothane

2.2   Structure of the Atom

All matter is composed of the same basic building blocks called *atoms*. An atom is much too small to be seen even by the most powerful light microscopes. The period at the end of this sentence holds about 1×10^8 atoms, and a human cheek cell contains about 1×10^{16} atoms. An atom is composed of three subatomic particles.

- A proton, symbolized by p, has a positive (+) charge.
- An electron, symbolized by e⁻, has a negative (–) charge.
- A neutron, symbolized by n, has no charge.

Protons and neutrons have approximately the same, exceedingly small mass, as shown in Table 2.3. The mass of an electron is much less, 1/1,836 the mass of a proton. These subatomic particles are not evenly distributed in the volume of an atom. There are two main components of an atom.

- The *nucleus* is a dense core that contains the protons and neutrons. Most of the mass of an atom resides in the nucleus.
- The *electron cloud* is composed of electrons that move rapidly in the almost empty space surrounding the nucleus. The electron cloud comprises most of the volume of an atom.

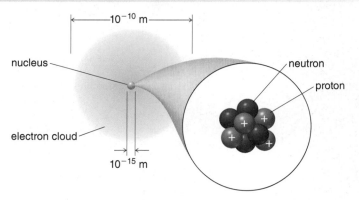

main components of an atom

While the diameter of an atom is about 10^{-10} m, the diameter of a nucleus is only about 10^{-15} m. For a macroscopic analogy, if the nucleus were the size of a baseball, an atom would be the size of Yankee Stadium!

The charged particles of an atom can either attract or repel each other.

- Opposite charges attract while like charges repel each other.

Thus, two electrons or two protons repel each other, while a proton and an electron attract each other.

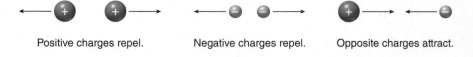

Positive charges repel.   Negative charges repel.   Opposite charges attract.

Table 2.3 Summary: The Properties of the Three Subatomic Particles

Subatomic Particle	Charge	Mass (g)	Mass (amu)
Proton	+1	1.6726×10^{-24}	1
Neutron	0	1.6749×10^{-24}	1
Electron	−1	9.1093×10^{-28}	Negligible

CONSUMER NOTE

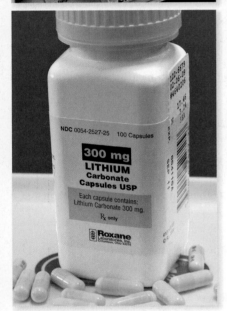

The element lithium is found in many consumer products, from long-lasting lithium batteries to the prescription medication lithium carbonate, used to treat individuals with bipolar disorder.

Since the mass of an individual atom is so small (on the order of 10^{-24} g), chemists use a standard mass unit, the **atomic mass unit,** which defines the mass of individual atoms relative to a standard mass.

- One atomic mass unit (amu) equals one-twelfth the mass of a carbon atom that has six protons and six neutrons; 1 amu = 1.661×10^{-24} g.

Using this scale, one proton has a mass of 1.0073 amu, a value typically rounded to 1 amu. One neutron has a mass of 1.0087 amu, a value also typically rounded to 1 amu. The mass of an electron is so small that it is ignored.

Every atom of a given type of element always has the *same* number of protons in the nucleus, a value called the *atomic number,* symbolized by Z. Conversely, two *different* elements have *different* atomic numbers.

- The *atomic number (Z)* = the number of protons in the nucleus of an atom.

Thus, the element hydrogen has one proton in its nucleus, so its atomic number is one. Lithium has three protons in its nucleus, so its atomic number is three. The periodic table is arranged in order of increasing atomic number beginning at the upper left-hand corner. The atomic number appears just above the element symbol for each entry in the table.

Since a neutral atom has no overall charge:

- Z = the number of protons in the nucleus = the number of electrons.

Thus, the atomic number tells us *both* the number of protons in the nucleus and the number of electrons in the electron cloud of a neutral atom.

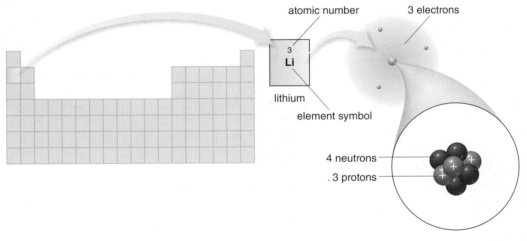

SAMPLE PROBLEM 2.2

For the given atom: (a) determine the number of protons, neutrons, and electrons in the neutral atom; (b) give the atomic number; (c) identify the element.

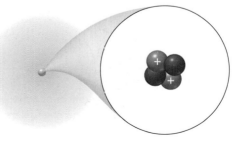

Analysis

- The number of protons = the number of positively charged particles = the atomic number.
- The number of neutrons = the number of uncharged particles.
- The number of protons = the number of electrons in a neutral atom.
- The atomic number determines the identity of an element.

Solution

a. The element contains two protons and two neutrons. Since a neutral atom has the same number of protons and electrons, the element has two electrons.

b. The two protons give the element an atomic number of two.

c. The element with two protons in the nucleus is **helium.**

PROBLEM 2.9

An element has nine protons and 10 neutrons in the neutral atom. (a) How many electrons are present in the neutral atom? (b) What is the atomic number of this element? (c) Identify the element.

SAMPLE PROBLEM 2.3

Identify the element that has an atomic number of 19, and give the number of protons and electrons in the neutral atom.

Analysis

The atomic number is unique to an element and tells the number of protons in the nucleus and the number of electrons in the electron cloud of a neutral atom.

Solution

According to the periodic table, the element potassium has atomic number 19. A neutral potassium atom has 19 protons and 19 electrons.

PROBLEM 2.10

Identify the element with each atomic number, and give the number of protons and electrons in the neutral atom: (a) 2; (b) 11; (c) 20; (d) 47; (e) 78.

Both protons and neutrons contribute to the mass of an atom. The **mass number,** symbolized by A, is the sum of the number of protons and neutrons.

- **Mass number (A) = the number of protons (Z) + the number of neutrons.**

For example, a fluorine atom with nine protons and 10 neutrons in the nucleus has a mass number of 19.

SAMPLE PROBLEM 2.4

For the given atom: (a) determine the number of protons and neutrons; (b) give the atomic number and the mass number; (c) identify the element.

Analysis

- The number of protons = the number of positively charged particles = the atomic number. The atomic number determines the identity of an element.
- The number of neutrons = the number of uncharged particles.
- The mass number = the number of protons + the number of neutrons.

Solution

a. The element contains six protons and seven neutrons.

b. The six protons give the element an atomic number of six. The mass number = the number of protons + the number of neutrons = 6 + 7 = 13.

c. The element with six protons in the nucleus is **carbon.**

PROBLEM 2.11

For the given atom: (a) determine the number of protons and neutrons; (b) give the atomic number and the mass number; (c) identify the element.

SAMPLE PROBLEM 2.5

How many protons, neutrons, and electrons are contained in an atom of argon, which has an atomic number of 18 and a mass number of 40?

Analysis

- In a neutral atom, the atomic number (Z) = the number of protons = the number of electrons.
- The mass number (A) = the number of protons + the number of neutrons.

Solution

The atomic number of 18 means that argon has 18 protons and 18 electrons. To find the number of neutrons, subtract the atomic number (Z) from the mass number (A).

$$
\begin{aligned}
\text{number of neutrons} &= \text{mass number} - \text{atomic number} \\
&= \quad 40 \quad - \quad 18 \\
&= \quad 22 \text{ neutrons}
\end{aligned}
$$

PROBLEM 2.12

How many protons, neutrons, and electrons are contained in each atom with the given atomic number and mass number?

a. $Z = 17, A = 35$ b. $Z = 14, A = 28$ c. $Z = 92, A = 238$

PROBLEM 2.13

What is the mass number of an atom that contains

a. 42 protons, 42 electrons, and 53 neutrons?   b. 24 protons, 24 electrons, and 28 neutrons?

2.3 Isotopes

Two atoms of the same element always have the same number of protons, but the number of neutrons can vary.

- *Isotopes* are atoms of the same element having a different number of neutrons.

2.3A Isotopes, Atomic Number, and Mass Number

Most elements in nature exist as a mixture of isotopes. For example, all atoms of the element chlorine contain 17 protons in the nucleus, but some of these atoms have 18 neutrons in the nucleus and some have 20 neutrons. Thus, chlorine has two isotopes with different mass numbers, 35 and 37. These isotopes are often referred to as chlorine-35 (or Cl-35) and chlorine-37 (or Cl-37).

An isotope symbol is also written using the element symbol with the atomic number as a subscript and the mass number as a superscript, both to the left.

The element hydrogen has three isotopes. Most hydrogen atoms have one proton and no neutrons, giving them a mass number of one. About 1% of hydrogen atoms have one proton and one neutron, giving them a mass number of two. This isotope is called **deuterium,** and it is often symbolized as **D.** An even smaller number of hydrogen atoms contain one proton and two neutrons, giving them a mass number of three. This isotope is called **tritium,** symbolized as **T.**

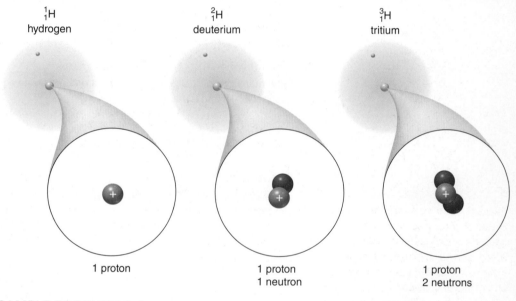

$^{1}_{1}H$
hydrogen

$^{2}_{1}H$
deuterium

$^{3}_{1}H$
tritium

1 proton

1 proton
1 neutron

1 proton
2 neutrons

SAMPLE PROBLEM 2.6

For each atom give the following information: [1] the atomic number; [2] the mass number; [3] the number of protons; [4] the number of neutrons; [5] the number of electrons.

   a. $^{118}_{50}Sn$ b. $^{195}_{78}Pt$

Analysis

- The superscript gives the mass number and the subscript gives the atomic number for each element.
- The atomic number = the number of protons = the number of electrons.
- The mass number = the number of protons + the number of neutrons.

Solution

	Atomic Number	Mass Number	Number of Protons	Number of Neutrons	Number of Electrons
a. $^{118}_{50}Sn$	50	118	50	118 − 50 = 68	50
b. $^{195}_{78}Pt$	78	195	78	195 − 78 = 117	78

PROBLEM 2.14

For each atom give the following information: [1] the atomic number; [2] the mass number; [3] the number of protons; [4] the number of neutrons; [5] the number of electrons.

   a. $^{13}_{6}C$ b. $^{121}_{51}Sb$

SAMPLE PROBLEM 2.7

Determine the number of neutrons in each isotope: (a) carbon-14; (b) ^{81}Br.

Analysis

- The identity of the element tells us the atomic number.
- The number of neutrons = mass number (A) – atomic number (Z).

Solution

a. Carbon's atomic number (Z) is 6. Carbon-14 has a mass number (A) of 14.

$$\text{number of neutrons} = A - Z$$
$$= 14 - 6 = 8 \text{ neutrons}$$

b. Bromine's atomic number is 35 and the mass number of the given isotope is 81.

$$\text{number of neutrons} = A - Z$$
$$= 81 - 35 = 46 \text{ neutrons}$$

PROBLEM 2.15

Magnesium has three isotopes that contain 12, 13, and 14 neutrons. For each isotope give the following information: (a) the number of protons; (b) the number of electrons; (c) the atomic number; (d) the mass number. Write the isotope symbol of each isotope.

ENVIRONMENTAL NOTE

Although gasoline sold in the United States no longer contains lead, leaded gasoline is still used extensively in Asia, Africa, and Latin America. Gasoline exhaust containing lead pollutes the air and soil, and individuals exposed to high lead levels can suffer from circulatory, digestive, and nervous disorders. Lead (Pb) is a metal with atomic number 82 and atomic weight 207.2, as shown in the periodic table.

2.3B Atomic Weight

Some elements like fluorine occur naturally as a single isotope. More commonly, an element is a mixture of isotopes, and it is useful to know the average mass, called the **atomic weight** (or **atomic mass**), of the atoms in a sample.

- The *atomic weight* is the weighted average of the mass of the naturally occurring isotopes of a particular element reported in atomic mass units.

The atomic weights of the elements appear in the alphabetical list of elements on the inside front cover. The atomic weight is also given under the element symbol in the periodic table on the inside front cover.

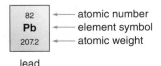

lead

To determine the atomic weight of an element, two quantities must be known: the mass of each isotope in atomic mass units, and the abundance with which each isotope occurs.

How To Determine the Atomic Weight of an Element

Example: What is the atomic weight of the element chlorine?

Step [1] List each isotope, along with its mass in atomic mass units (amu) and the percentage that each isotope occurs in nature.

- Chlorine has two isotopes—Cl-35 and Cl-37.
- To solve the problem, the masses and abundances of the isotopes must be known.

	Mass (amu)	Isotopic Abundance
Cl-35	34.97	75.78% = 0.7578
Cl-37	36.97	24.22% = 0.2422

- The mass of any isotope is very close to the mass number of the isotope.
- To convert a percent to a decimal, divide by 100%, which is the same as moving the decimal point two places to the left; thus,

$$75.78\% = 0.7578$$

—Continued

How To, continued . . .

Step [2] **Multiply the isotopic abundance by the mass of each isotope, and add up the products. The sum is the atomic weight for the element.**

Mass due to Cl-35: 0.7578×34.97 amu = 26.5003 amu

Mass due to Cl-37: 0.2422×36.97 amu = 8.9541 amu

Atomic weight = 35.4544 amu rounded to 35.45 amu

Answer

SAMPLE PROBLEM 2.8

Calculate the atomic weight of copper, which has two isotopes with the following properties: Cu-63 (62.93 amu, 69.17% natural occurrence) and Cu-65 (64.93 amu, 30.83% natural occurrence).

Analysis

Multiply the isotopic abundance by the mass of each isotope, and add up the products to give the atomic weight for the element.

Solution

Mass due to Cu-63: 0.6917×62.93 amu = 43.5287 amu

Mass due to Cu-65: 0.3083×64.93 amu = 20.0179 amu

Atomic weight = 63.5466 amu rounded to 63.55 amu

Answer

PROBLEM 2.16

Calculate the atomic weight of each element given the mass and natural occurrence of each isotope.

a. Magnesium	Mass (amu)	Isotopic Abundance	b. Vanadium	Mass (amu)	Isotopic Abundance
Mg-24	23.99	78.99%	V-50	49.95	0.250%
Mg-25	24.99	10.00%	V-51	50.94	99.750%
Mg-26	25.98	11.01%			

2.3C FOCUS ON HEALTH & MEDICINE
Isotopes in Medicine

Generally the chemical properties of isotopes are identical. Sometimes, however, one isotope of an element is radioactive—that is, it emits particles or energy as some form of radiation. Radioactive isotopes have both diagnostic and therapeutic uses in medicine.

As an example, iodine-131 is used in at least two different ways for thyroid disease. Iodine is a micronutrient needed by the body to synthesize the thyroid hormone thyroxine, which contains four iodine atoms. To evaluate the thyroid gland, a patient can be given sodium iodide (NaI) that contains radioactive iodine-131. Iodine-131 is taken up in the thyroid gland and as it emits radiation, it produces an image in a thyroid scan, which is then used to determine the condition of the thyroid gland, as shown in Figure 2.4.

Higher doses of iodine-131 can also be used to treat thyroid disease. Since the radioactive isotope is taken up by the thyroid gland, the radiation it emits can kill overactive or cancerous cells in the thyroid.

Other applications of radioactive isotopes in medicine are discussed in Chapter 10.

Figure 2.4 Iodine-131 in Medicine

a.

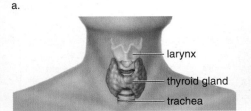

— larynx

— thyroid gland

— trachea

b.

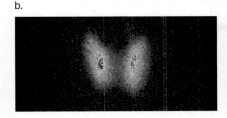

c.

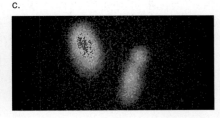

The thyroid gland is a butterfly-shaped gland in the neck, shown in (a). Uptake of radioactive iodine-131 can reveal the presence of a healthy thyroid as in (b), or an unsymmetrical thyroid gland with dense areas of iodine uptake as in (c), which may be indicative of cancer or other thyroid disease.

2.4 The Periodic Table

Every beginning chemistry text has a periodic table in a prominent location—often the inside front cover—because it is a valuable list of all known elements organized so that groups of elements with similar characteristics are arranged together. The periodic table evolved over many years, and it resulted from the careful observations and experiments of many brilliant scientists in the nineteenth century. Most prominent was Russian chemist Dmitri Mendeleev, whose arrangement in 1869 of the 60 known elements into groups having similar properties in order of increasing atomic number became the precursor of the modern periodic table (inside front cover and Figure 2.5).

2.4A Basic Features of the Periodic Table

The periodic table is arranged into seven horizontal rows and 18 vertical columns. The particular row and column tell us much about the properties of an element.

- A row in the periodic table is called a *period.* Elements in the same row are similar in size.
- A column in the periodic table is called a *group.* Elements in the same group have similar electronic and chemical properties.

The rows in the periodic table are numbered 1–7. The number of elements in each row varies. The first period has just two elements, hydrogen and helium. The second and third rows have eight elements each, and the fourth and fifth rows have 18 elements. Also note that two rows of 14 elements appear at the bottom of the periodic table. The **lanthanides,** beginning with the element cerium ($Z = 58$), immediately follow the element lanthanum (La). The **actinides,** beginning with thorium ($Z = 90$), immediately follow the element actinium (Ac).

Each column in the periodic table is assigned a **group number.** Groups are numbered in two ways. In one system, the 18 columns of the periodic table are assigned the numbers 1–18, beginning with the column farthest to the left. An older but still widely used system numbers the groups 1–8, followed by the letter A or B.

- The *main group elements* consist of the two columns on the far left and the six columns on the far right of the table. These groups are numbered 1A–8A.
- The *transition metal elements* are contained in the 10 short columns in the middle of the table, numbered 1B–8B.
- The *inner transition metal elements* consist of the lanthanides and actinides, and they are not assigned group numbers.

The periodic table in Figure 2.5 has both systems of numbering groups. For example, the element carbon (C) is located in the second row (period 2) of the periodic table. Its group number is 4A (or 14).

HEALTH NOTE

Administering a zinc tablet dissolved in water to a child with diarrhea can save his life. Diarrhea kills more children worldwide than malaria or AIDS. Zinc is a metal located in group 2B (12) in the periodic table.

Figure 2.5   Basic Features of the Periodic Table

Period	1A 1	2A 2												3A 13	4A 14	5A 15	6A 16	7A 17	8A 18	
1	1 **H** 1.008	Group number																	2 **He** 4.003	1
2	3 **Li** 6.941	4 **Be** 9.012	3B 3	4B 4	5B 5	6B 6	7B 7		8B		1B 11	2B 12		5 **B** 10.81	6 **C** 12.01	7 **N** 14.01	8 **O** 16.00	9 **F** 19.00	10 **Ne** 20.18	2
3	11 **Na** 22.99	12 **Mg** 24.31						8	9	10				13 **Al** 26.98	14 **Si** 28.09	15 **P** 30.97	16 **S** 32.07	17 **Cl** 35.45	18 **Ar** 39.95	3
4	19 **K** 39.10	20 **Ca** 40.08	21 **Sc** 44.96	22 **Ti** 47.88	23 **V** 50.94	24 **Cr** 52.00	25 **Mn** 54.94	26 **Fe** 55.85	27 **Co** 58.93	28 **Ni** 58.69	29 **Cu** 63.55	30 **Zn** 65.41	31 **Ga** 69.72	32 **Ge** 72.64	33 **As** 74.92	34 **Se** 78.96	35 **Br** 79.90	36 **Kr** 83.80	4
5	37 **Rb** 85.47	38 **Sr** 87.62	39 **Y** 88.91	40 **Zr** 91.22	41 **Nb** 92.91	42 **Mo** 95.94	43 **Tc** (98)	44 **Ru** 101.1	45 **Rh** 102.9	46 **Pd** 106.4	47 **Ag** 107.9	48 **Cd** 112.4	49 **In** 114.8	50 **Sn** 118.7	51 **Sb** 121.8	52 **Te** 127.6	53 **I** 126.9	54 **Xe** 131.3	5
6	55 **Cs** 132.9	56 **Ba** 137.3	57 **La** 138.9	72 **Hf** 178.5	73 **Ta** 180.9	74 **W** 183.8	75 **Re** 186.2	76 **Os** 190.2	77 **Ir** 192.2	78 **Pt** 195.1	79 **Au** 197.0	80 **Hg** 200.6	81 **Tl** 204.4	82 **Pb** 207.2	83 **Bi** 209.0	84 **Po** (209)	85 **At** (210)	86 **Rn** (222)	6
7	87 **Fr** (223)	88 **Ra** (226)	89 **Ac** (227)	104 **Rf** (267)	105 **Db** (268)	106 **Sg** (271)	107 **Bh** (272)	108 **Hs** (270)	109 **Mt** (276)	110 **Ds** (281)	111 **Rg** (280)	112 **Cn** (285)	113 – (284)	114 – (289)	115 – (289)	116 – (293)	117 – (294)	118 – (294)	7

Lanthanides	6	58 **Ce** 140.1	59 **Pr** 140.9	60 **Nd** 144.2	61 **Pm** (145)	62 **Sm** 150.4	63 **Eu** 152.0	64 **Gd** 157.3	65 **Tb** 158.9	66 **Dy** 162.5	67 **Ho** 164.9	68 **Er** 167.3	69 **Tm** 168.9	70 **Yb** 173.0	71 **Lu** 175.0	6
Actinides	7	90 **Th** 232.0	91 **Pa** 231.0	92 **U** 238.0	93 **Np** (237)	94 **Pu** (244)	95 **Am** (243)	96 **Cm** (247)	97 **Bk** (247)	98 **Cf** (251)	99 **Es** (252)	100 **Fm** (257)	101 **Md** (258)	102 **No** (259)	103 **Lr** (262)	7

☐ Main group elements   ☐ Transition metal elements   ☐ Inner transition metal elements

- Each element of the periodic table is part of a horizontal row and a vertical column.

- The periodic table consists of seven rows, labeled periods 1–7, and 18 columns that are assigned a group number. Two different numbering systems are indicated.

- Elements are divided into three categories: main group elements (groups 1A–8A, shown in light blue), transition metals (groups 1B–8B, shown in tan), and inner transition metals (shown in light green).

SAMPLE PROBLEM 2.9

Give the period and group number for each element: (a) magnesium; (b) manganese.

Analysis

Use the element symbol to locate an element in the periodic table. Count down the rows of elements to determine the period. The group number is located at the top of each column.

Solution

a. Magnesium (Mg) is located in the third row (period 3), and has group number 2A (or 2).

b. Manganese (Mn) is located in the fourth row (period 4), and has group number 7B (or 7).

PROBLEM 2.17
Give the period and group number for each element: (a) oxygen; (b) calcium; (c) phosphorus; (d) platinum; (e) iodine.

2.4B Characteristics of Groups 1A, 2A, 7A, and 8A

Four columns of main group elements illustrate an important fact about the periodic table.

- **Elements that comprise a particular group have similar chemical properties.**

Alkali Metals (Group 1A) and Alkaline Earth Elements (Group 2A)

The alkali metals and the alkaline earth elements are located on the far left side of the periodic table.

Although hydrogen is also located in group 1A, it is *not* an alkali metal.

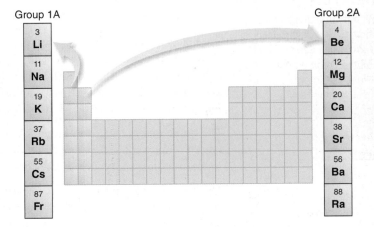

The **alkali metals,** located in group 1A (group 1), include lithium (Li), sodium (Na), potassium (K), rubidium (Rb), cesium (Cs), and francium (Fr). Alkali metals share the following characteristics:

- **They are soft and shiny and have low melting points.**
- **They are good conductors of heat and electricity.**
- **They react readily with water to form basic solutions.**

The **alkaline earth elements,** located in group 2A (group 2), include beryllium (Be), magnesium (Mg), calcium (Ca), strontium (Sr), barium (Ba), and radium (Ra). Alkaline earth metals are also shiny solids but less reactive than the alkali metals.

None of the metals in groups 1A or 2A exist in nature as pure elements; rather, they are always combined with other elements to form compounds. Examples of compounds from group 1A elements include sodium chloride (NaCl), table salt, and potassium iodide (KI), an essential nutrient added to make iodized salt. Examples of compounds from group 2A elements include magnesium sulfate ($MgSO_4$), an anticonvulsant used to prevent seizures in pregnant women, and barium sulfate ($BaSO_4$), which is used to improve the quality of X-ray images of the gastrointestinal tract.

HEALTH NOTE

Chlorpheniramine is an antihistamine that contains the halogen chlorine. Antihistamines are drugs used to treat the symptoms of the common cold and allergies. We will learn more about antihistamines in Chapter 18.

Halogens (Group 7A) and Noble Gases (Group 8A)

The halogens and noble gases are located on the far right side of the periodic table.

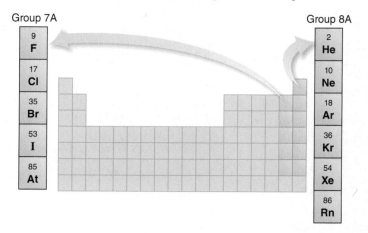

The **halogens,** located in group 7A (group 17), include fluorine (F), chlorine (Cl), bromine (Br), iodine (I), and the rare radioactive element astatine (At). In their elemental form, halogens contain two atoms joined together—F_2, Cl_2, Br_2, and I_2. Fluorine and chlorine are gases at room temperature, bromine is a liquid, and iodine is a solid. Halogens are very reactive and combine with many other elements to form compounds. In Chapter 14, we will learn about carbon compounds that contain halogen atoms.

The **noble gases,** located in group 8A (group 18), include helium (He), neon (Ne), argon (Ar), krypton (Kr), xenon (Xe), and radon (Rn). Unlike other elements, the noble gases are especially stable as atoms, and so they rarely combine with other elements to form compounds.

The noble gas **radon** has received attention in recent years. Radon is a radioactive gas, and generally its concentration in the air is low and therefore its presence harmless. In some types of soil, however, radon levels can be high and radon detectors are recommended for the basement of homes to monitor radon levels. High radon levels are linked to an increased risk of lung cancer.

PROBLEM 2.18

Identify the element fitting each description.

a. an alkali metal in period 4
b. a second-row element in group 7A
c. a noble gas in the third period

d. a main group element in period 5 and group 2A
e. a transition metal in group 12, period 4
f. a transition metal in group 5, period 5

PROBLEM 2.19

Identify each highlighted element in the periodic table and give its [1] element name and symbol; [2] group number; [3] period; [4] classification (main group element, transition metal, or inner transition metal).

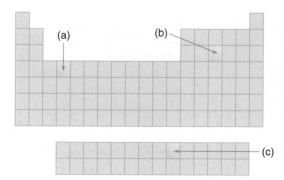

2.4C The Unusual Nature of Carbon

Carbon, a second-row element in group 4A of the periodic table, is different from most other elements in that it has three elemental forms (Figure 2.6). The two most common forms of carbon are diamond and graphite. **Diamond** is hard because it contains a dense three-dimensional network of carbon atoms in six-membered rings. **Graphite,** on the other hand, is a slippery black substance used as a lubricant. It contains parallel sheets of carbon atoms in flat six-membered rings.

Buckminsterfullerene, also referred to as a bucky ball, is a third form that contains 60 carbon atoms joined together in a sphere of 20 hexagons and 12 pentagons in a pattern that resembles a soccer ball. A component of soot, this form of carbon was not discovered until 1985. Its unusual name stems from its shape, which resembles the geodesic dome invented by R. Buckminster Fuller.

Carbon's ability to join with itself and other elements gives it versatility not seen with any other element in the periodic table. In the unscientific but eloquent description by writer Bill Bryson in *A Short History of Nearly Everything,* carbon is described as "the party animal of the atomic world, latching on to many other atoms (including itself) and holding tight, forming molecular conga lines of hearty robustness—the very trick of nature necessary to build proteins and DNA." As a result, millions of compounds that contain the element carbon are known. The chemistry of these compounds is discussed at length in Chapters 11–24.

Figure 2.6   Three Elemental Forms of Carbon

a. Diamond

b. Graphite

c. Buckminsterfullerene

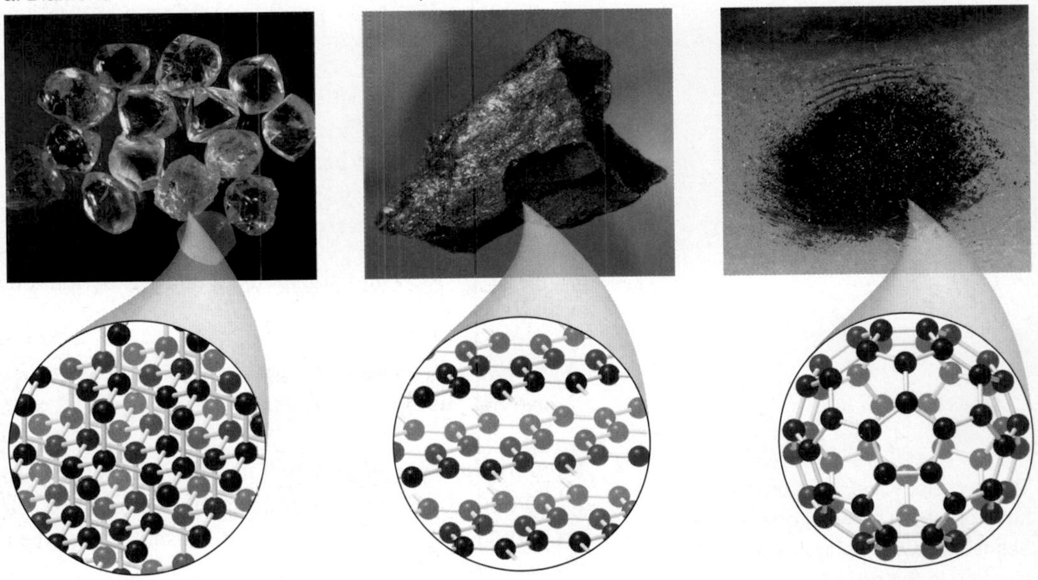

- Diamond consists of an intricate three-dimensional network of carbon atoms.

- Graphite contains parallel sheets of carbon atoms.

- Buckminsterfullerene contains a sphere with 60 carbon atoms.

2.5 Electronic Structure

Why do elements in a group of the periodic table have similar chemical properties? **The chemical properties of an element are determined by the number of *electrons* in an atom.** To understand the properties of an element, therefore, we must learn more about the electrons that surround the nucleus.

The modern description of the electronic structure of an atom is based on the following principles.

- Electrons do not move freely in space; rather, an electron is confined to a specific region, giving it a particular energy.
- Electrons occupy discrete energy levels. The energy of electrons is *quantized;* that is, the energy is restricted to specific values.

The electrons that surround a nucleus are confined to regions called the **principal energy levels** or **shells.**

- The shells are numbered, n = 1, 2, 3, 4, and so forth, beginning closest to the nucleus.
- Electrons closer to the nucleus are held more tightly and are lower in energy.
- Electrons farther from the nucleus are held less tightly and are higher in energy.

The number of electrons that can occupy a given shell is determined by the value of n. **The farther a shell is from the nucleus, the larger its volume becomes, and the more electrons it can hold.** Thus, the first shell can hold only two electrons, the second holds eight, the third 18, and so forth. The maximum number of electrons is given by the formula $2n^2$, where n = the shell number.

Distribution of electrons in the first four shells

Shell		Number of electrons in a shell
4		32
3	Increasing energy	18
2		8
lowest energy → 1		2 (Increasing number of electrons)

Shells are divided into **subshells,** identified by the letters *s, p, d,* and *f.* The subshells consist of **orbitals.**

- An *orbital* is a region of space where the probability of finding an electron is high. Each orbital can hold *two* electrons.

The two electrons in an orbital must have opposite spins. If one electron has a clockwise spin, the second electron in the orbital must have a counterclockwise spin.

A particular type of subshell contains a specific number of orbitals. An *s* subshell contains only **one** *s* orbital. A *p* subshell has **three** *p* orbitals. A *d* subshell has **five** *d* orbitals. An *f* subshell has **seven** *f* orbitals. The number of subshells in a given shell equals the value of n. The energy of orbitals shows the following trend:

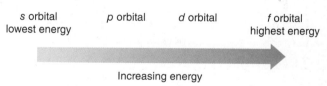

s orbital lowest energy	*p* orbital	*d* orbital	*f* orbital highest energy

Increasing energy

The first shell of electrons around a nucleus (n = 1) has only one *s* orbital. This orbital is called the 1*s* orbital since it is the *s* orbital in the first shell. Since each orbital can hold two electrons and the first shell has only one orbital, the **first shell can hold two electrons.**

shell number
(principal energy level) — 1*s* = the *s* orbital in the first shell

The second shell of electrons ($n = 2$) has two types of orbitals—one s and three p orbitals. These orbitals are called the $2s$ and $2p$ orbitals since they are located in the second shell. Since each orbital can hold two electrons and there are four orbitals, the **second shell can hold eight electrons.**

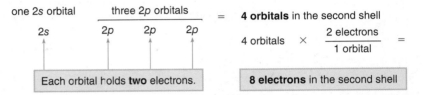

The third shell of electrons ($n = 3$) has three types of orbitals—one s, three p, and five d orbitals. These orbitals are called the $3s$, $3p$, and $3d$ orbitals since they are located in the third shell. Since each orbital can hold two electrons and the third shell has a total of nine orbitals, the **third shell can hold 18 electrons.**

one 3s orbital   three 3p orbitals   five 3d orbitals

3s   3p   3p   3p   3d   3d   3d   3d   3d   =   **9 orbitals** in the third shell

Each orbital holds **two** electrons.

9 orbitals $\times$ $\dfrac{2 \text{ electrons}}{1 \text{ orbital}}$ =

18 electrons in the third shell

The fourth shell of electrons ($n = 4$) has four types of orbitals—one s, three p, five d, and seven f orbitals. These orbitals are called the $4s$, $4p$, $4d$, and $4f$ orbitals since they are located in the fourth shell. Since each orbital can hold two electrons and the fourth shell has a total of sixteen orbitals, the **fourth shell can hold 32 electrons.**

one 4s orbital   three 4p orbitals   five 4d orbitals   seven 4f orbitals

4s   4p   4p   4p   4d   4d   4d   4d   4d   4f   4f   4f   4f   4f   4f   4f   = **16 orbitals** in the fourth shell

16 orbitals $\times$ $\dfrac{2 \text{ electrons}}{1 \text{ orbital}}$ =   **32 electrons** in the fourth shell

Thus, the maximum number of electrons that can occupy a shell is determined by the number of orbitals in the shell. Table 2.4 summarizes the orbitals and electrons in the first four shells.

Table 2.4 Orbitals and Electrons Contained in the Principal Energy Levels ($n = 1$–4)

Shell	Orbitals	Electrons in Each Subshell	Maximum Number of Electrons
1	1s	2	2
2	2s	2	8
	2p 2p 2p	$3 \times 2 = 6$	
3	3s	2	18
	3p 3p 3p	$3 \times 2 = 6$	
	3d 3d 3d 3d 3d	$5 \times 2 = 10$	
4	4s	2	32
	4p 4p 4p	$3 \times 2 = 6$	
	4d 4d 4d 4d 4d	$5 \times 2 = 10$	
	4f 4f 4f 4f 4f 4f 4f	$7 \times 2 = 14$	

Each type of orbital has a particular shape.

> • An *s* orbital has a sphere of electron density. It is lower in energy than other orbitals in the same shell because electrons are kept closer to the positively charged nucleus.
> • A *p* orbital has a dumbbell shape. A *p* orbital is higher in energy than an *s* orbital in the same shell because its electron density is farther from the nucleus.

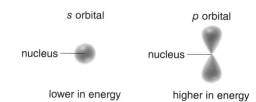

All *s* orbitals are spherical, but the orbital gets larger in size as the shell number increases. Thus, both a 1*s* orbital and a 2*s* orbital are spherical, but the 2*s* orbital is larger. The three *p* orbitals in a shell are perpendicular to each other along the *x, y,* and *z* axes.

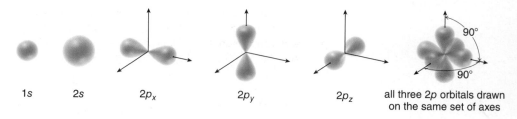

PROBLEM 2.20

How many electrons are present in each shell, subshell, or orbital?

a. a 2*p* orbital   b. the 3*d* subshell   c. a 3*d* orbital   d. the third shell

2.6   Electronic Configurations

We can now examine the **electronic configuration** of an individual atom—that is, how the electrons are arranged in an atom's orbitals. **The lowest energy arrangement of electrons is called the *ground state*.** Three rules are followed.

Rules to Determine the Ground State Electronic Configuration of an Atom

Rule [1]   Electrons are placed in the lowest energy orbitals beginning with the 1*s* orbital.

> • In comparing similar types of orbitals from one shell to another (e.g., 2*s* and 3*s*), an orbital closer to the nucleus is lower in energy. Thus, the energy of a 2*s* orbital is lower than a 3*s* orbital.
> • Within a shell, orbital energies increase in the following order: *s, p, d, f.*
>
> These guidelines result in the following order of energies in the first three periods: 1*s*, 2*s*, 2*p*, 3*s*, 3*p*. Above the 3*p* level, however, all orbitals of one shell do *not* have to be filled before any orbital in the next higher shell gets electrons. For example, a 4*s* orbital is lower in energy than a 3*d* orbital, so it is filled first. Figure 2.7 lists the relative energy of the orbitals used by atoms in the periodic table.

Rule [2]   Each orbital holds a maximum of two electrons.

Rule [3]   When orbitals are equal in energy, one electron is added to each orbital until the orbitals are half-filled, before any orbital is completely filled.

> • For example, one electron is added to each of the three *p* orbitals before filling any *p* orbital with two electrons.
> • Because like charges repel each other (Section 2.2), adding electrons to different *p* orbitals keeps them farther away from each other, which is energetically favorable.

Figure 2.7 Relative Energies of Orbitals

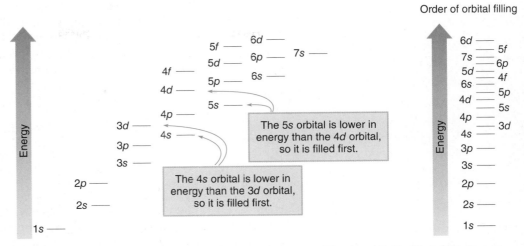

Electrons are added to orbitals in order of increasing energy. The 4s orbital is filled with electrons before the 3d orbital since it is lower in energy. The same is true for filling the 5s orbital with electrons before the 4d orbital. Likewise, the 6s orbital is filled before both the 4f and 5d orbitals, and the 7s orbital is filled before both the 5f and 6d orbitals.

To illustrate how these rules are used, we can write the electronic configuration for several elements using **orbital diagrams.** An orbital diagram uses a box to represent each orbital and arrows to represent electrons. A single electron, called an **unpaired electron,** is shown with a single arrow pointing up ($\uparrow$). Two electrons in an orbital have **paired spins**—that is, the spins are opposite in direction—so up and down arrows ($\uparrow\downarrow$) are used.

Finally, it is not necessary to memorize the order of orbital filling that appears in Figure 2.7. Rather, the periodic table can be used to determine the electronic configuration of an element, as shown in Section 2.6C. This method is especially useful for elements in the fourth row and later, in which an orbital of a higher shell gets electrons before filling a lower shell completely.

2.6A First-Row Elements (Period 1)

The first row of the periodic table contains only two elements—hydrogen and helium. Since the number of protons in the nucleus equals the number of electrons in a neutral atom, the **atomic number tells us how many electrons must be placed in orbitals.**

Hydrogen (H, $Z = 1$) has one electron. In the ground state, this electron is added to the lowest energy orbital, the 1s orbital. To draw an orbital diagram we use one box to represent the 1s orbital, and one up arrow to represent the electron. We can also write out the electron configuration without boxes and arrows, using a superscript with each orbital to show how many electrons it contains.

H $\uparrow$ or $1s^1$ one electron in the 1s orbital

1 electron   1s

Helium (He, $Z = 2$) has two electrons. In the ground state, both electrons are added to the 1s orbital. To draw an orbital diagram we use one box to represent the 1s orbital, and a set of up and down arrows to represent the two electrons with paired spins. The electron configuration can also be written as $1s^2$, meaning the 1s orbital has two electrons. Helium has a filled first shell of electrons.

He $\uparrow\downarrow$ or $1s^2$ two electrons in the 1s orbital

2 electrons   1s

Because the element helium is lighter than air, balloons filled with helium must be secured with ropes or strings so they don't float away.

2.6B Second-Row Elements (Period 2)

To write orbital diagrams for the second-row elements, we must now use the four orbitals in the second shell—the $2s$ orbital and the three $2p$ orbitals. Since electrons are always added to the lowest energy orbitals first, all second-row elements have the $1s$ orbital filled with electrons, and then the remaining electrons are added to the orbitals in the second shell. Since the $2s$ orbital is lower in energy than the $2p$ orbitals, it is completely filled before adding electrons to the $2p$ orbitals.

Lithium (Li, $Z = 3$) has three electrons. In the ground state, two electrons are added to the $1s$ orbital and the remaining electron is an unpaired electron in the $2s$ orbital. Lithium's electronic configuration can also be written as $1s^2 2s^1$ to show the placement of its three electrons.

Li   ⇅   ↑   or $1s^2 2s^1$ two electrons in the $1s$ orbital
3 electrons   1s   2s   one electron in the $2s$ orbital

Carbon (C, $Z = 6$) has six electrons. In the ground state, two electrons are added to both the $1s$ and $2s$ orbitals. The two remaining electrons are added to two different $2p$ orbitals, giving carbon **two unpaired electrons.** These electrons spin in the same direction, so the arrows used to represent them are drawn in the same direction as well (both ↑ in this case). Carbon's electronic configuration is also written as $1s^2 2s^2 2p^2$. This method of writing an electronic configuration indicates that carbon has two electrons in its $2p$ orbitals, but it does not explicitly show that the two $2p$ electrons occupy *different* $2p$ orbitals.

two electrons in two *different* $2p$ orbitals

C   ⇅   ⇅   ↑ ↑   or $1s^2 2s^2 2p^2$
6 electrons   1s   2s   2p

Oxygen (O, $Z = 8$) has eight electrons. In the ground state, two electrons are added to both the $1s$ and $2s$ orbitals. The remaining four electrons must be distributed among the three $2p$ orbitals to give the lowest energy arrangement. This is done by pairing two electrons in one $2p$ orbital, and giving the remaining $2p$ orbitals one electron each. Oxygen has two unpaired electrons.

two electrons in two *different* $2p$ orbitals

O   ⇅   ⇅   ⇅ ↑ ↑   or $1s^2 2s^2 2p^4$
8 electrons   1s   2s   2p

Neon (Ne, $Z = 10$) has 10 electrons. In the ground state, two electrons are added to the $1s$, $2s$, and each of the three $2p$ orbitals, so that the second shell of orbitals is now completely filled with electrons.

Ne   ⇅   ⇅   ⇅ ⇅ ⇅   or $1s^2 2s^2 2p^6$
10 electrons   1s   2s   2p

Sometimes the electronic configuration of an element is shortened by using the name of the noble gas that has a filled shell of electrons from the preceding row, and then adding the electronic configuration of all remaining electrons using orbitals and superscripts. For example, each second-row element has a $1s^2$ configuration like the noble gas helium in the preceding row, so the electronic configuration for carbon can be shortened to $[He]2s^2 2p^2$.

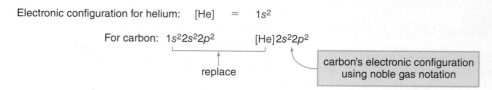

Electronic configuration for helium: [He]   = $1s^2$

For carbon: $1s^2 2s^2 2p^2$ $[He]2s^2 2p^2$

replace   carbon's electronic configuration using noble gas notation

The electronic configurations of all the first- and second-row elements are listed in Table 2.5.

Table 2.5 Electronic Configurations of the First- and Second-Row Elements

Atomic Number	Element	Orbital Diagram 1s	2s	2p	Electronic Configuration	Noble Gas Notation
1	H	↑			$1s^1$	
2	He	↑↓			$1s^2$	
3	Li	↑↓	↑		$1s^2 2s^1$	[He] $2s^1$
4	Be	↑↓	↑↓		$1s^2 2s^2$	[He] $2s^2$
5	B	↑↓	↑↓	↑	$1s^2 2s^2 2p^1$	[He] $2s^2 2p^1$
6	C	↑↓	↑↓	↑ ↑	$1s^2 2s^2 2p^2$	[He] $2s^2 2p^2$
7	N	↑↓	↑↓	↑ ↑ ↑	$1s^2 2s^2 2p^3$	[He] $2s^2 2p^3$
8	O	↑↓	↑↓	↑↓ ↑ ↑	$1s^2 2s^2 2p^4$	[He] $2s^2 2p^4$
9	F	↑↓	↑↓	↑↓ ↑↓ ↑	$1s^2 2s^2 2p^5$	[He] $2s^2 2p^5$
10	Ne	↑↓	↑↓	↑↓ ↑↓ ↑↓	$1s^2 2s^2 2p^6$	[He] $2s^2 2p^6$

PROBLEM 2.21

What element has each electronic configuration?

a. $1s^2 2s^2 2p^6 3s^2 3p^2$
b. [Ne]$3s^2 3p^4$
c. $1s^2 2s^2 2p^6 3s^2 3p^6 4s^2 3d^1$
d. [Ar]$4s^2 3d^{10}$

PROBLEM 2.22

What element(s) in the first and second period fit each description?

a. The element has one electron in the second energy level.

b. There are two electrons in the 2s orbital.

c. The electronic configuration is $1s^2 2s^2 2p^5$.

d. The element contains six electrons in the second energy level.

2.6C Electronic Configurations of Other Elements Using the Periodic Table

Orbital diagrams can be written for every element in the periodic table. We can use the location of an element in the periodic table to determine what orbitals are filled with electrons.

Considering electronic configuration, the periodic table can be divided into four regions called **blocks**, labeled *s*, *p*, *d*, and *f*, and illustrated in Figure 2.8. **The blocks are labeled according to the subshells that are filled with electrons *last*.**

- The *s block* consists of groups 1A and 2A and the element helium. The *s* subshell is filled last in these elements.
- The *p block* consists of groups 3A–8A (except helium). The *p* subshell is filled last in these elements.
- The *d block* consists of the 10 columns of transition metals. The *d* subshell is filled last in these elements.
- The *f block* consists of the two groups of 14 inner transition metals. The *f* subshell is filled last in these elements.

Sample Problems 2.10 and 2.11 illustrate how to use the blocks in Figure 2.8 to write the electronic configuration for two different elements.

Figure 2.8   The Blocks of Elements in the Periodic Table

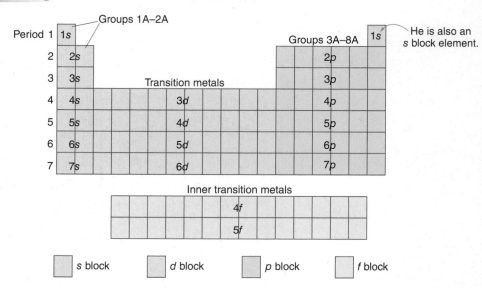

ENVIRONMENTAL NOTE

Coal that is high in **sulfur** content burns to form sulfur oxides, which in turn react with water to form sulfurous and sulfuric acids. Rain that contains these acids has destroyed acres of forests worldwide.

SAMPLE PROBLEM 2.10

Give the orbital diagram for the ground state electronic configuration of the element sulfur.

Analysis

- Use the atomic number to determine the number of electrons.
- Locate the element in the periodic table, and use Figure 2.8 to determine the order of orbitals filled with electrons. Read the table from left-to-right, row-by-row, beginning at the upper left corner and ending at the element in question.
- To fill orbitals of the same energy, place electrons one at a time in the orbitals until they are half-filled.

Solution

Sulfur is located in the p block with an atomic number of 16, so 16 electrons must be placed in orbitals. Reading the periodic table in blocks row-by-row from left-to-right ending at sulfur gives the following order of orbitals to be filled with electrons: $1s$, $2s$, $2p$ (three orbitals), $3s$, and $3p$ (three orbitals).

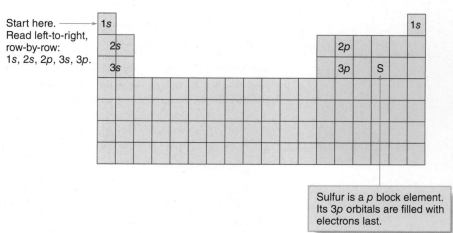

Give each orbital two electrons. In adding the last four electrons to the three 3*p* orbitals, give one orbital two electrons and place one unpaired electron in the remaining two orbitals.

Answer:

two unpaired electrons

S	$\uparrow\downarrow$	$\uparrow\downarrow$	$\uparrow\downarrow$ $\uparrow\downarrow$ $\uparrow\downarrow$	$\uparrow\downarrow$	$\uparrow\downarrow$ $\uparrow$ $\uparrow$

sulfur   1*s*   2*s*   2*p*   3*s*   3*p*
16 electrons

SAMPLE PROBLEM 2.11

Give the ground state electronic configuration of the element calcium. Convert the electronic configuration to noble gas notation.

Analysis

- Use the atomic number to determine the number of electrons.
- Locate the element in the periodic table and use Figure 2.8 to determine the order of orbitals filled with electrons.
- To convert the electronic configuration to noble gas notation, replace the electronic configuration corresponding to the noble gas in the preceding row by the symbol for the noble gas in brackets.

Solution

The atomic number of calcium is 20, so 20 electrons must be placed in orbitals. Figure 2.8 shows the following order of orbitals to be filled: 1*s*, 2*s*, 2*p* (three orbitals), 3*s*, 3*p* (three orbitals), and 4*s*. Give each orbital two electrons. Since calcium is an element in period 4, use the noble gas argon in period 3 to write the noble gas configuration. **Substitute [Ar] for all of the electrons in the first three shells.**

Electronic configuration for Ca $\quad=\quad 1s^22s^22p^63s^23p^64s^2 \quad=\quad [Ar]4s^2$

(20 electrons)   The noble gas argon contains   noble gas notation
these 18 electrons.

Replace with [Ar].

PROBLEM 2.23

Draw an orbital diagram for each element: (a) magnesium; (b) aluminum; (c) bromine.

PROBLEM 2.24

Give the electronic configuration for each element and then convert it to noble gas notation:
(a) sodium; (b) silicon; (c) iodine.

2.7 Valence Electrons

The chemical properties of an element depend on the most loosely held electrons—that is, those electrons in the outermost shell, called the **valence shell.** The period number tells the number of the valence shell.

- **The electrons in the outermost shell are called the *valence electrons.***

2.7A Relating Valence Electrons to Group Number

To identify the electrons in the valence shell, always look for the shell with the *highest* number. Thus, beryllium has two valence electrons that occupy the 2*s* orbital. Chlorine has seven valence electrons since it has a total of seven electrons in the third shell, two in the 3*s* orbital and five in the 3*p* orbitals.

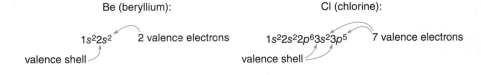

Be (beryllium):   Cl (chlorine):

$1s^22s^2$ 2 valence electrons $1s^22s^22p^63s^23p^5$ 7 valence electrons

valence shell   valence shell

If we examine the electronic configuration of a group in the periodic table, two facts become apparent.

- Elements in the same group have the same number of valence electrons and similar electronic configurations.
- The group number (using the 1A–8A system) equals the number of valence electrons for main group elements (except helium).

As an example, the alkali metals in group 1A all have one valence electron that occupies an s orbital. Thus, a general electronic configuration for the valence electrons of an alkali metal is ns^1, where n = the period in which the element is located.

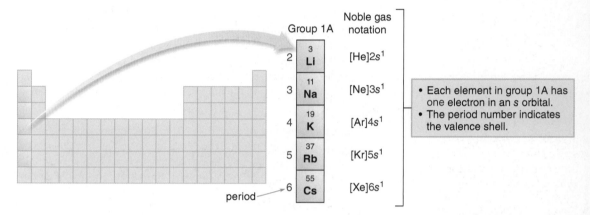

Thus, the periodic table is organized into groups of elements with similar valence electronic configurations in the same column. The valence electronic configurations of the main group elements in the first three rows of the periodic table are given in Table 2.6.

- The chemical properties of a group are similar because these elements contain the same electronic configuration of valence electrons.

Take particular note of the electronic configuration of the noble gases in group 8A. **All of these elements have a completely filled outer shell of valence electrons.** Helium has a filled first shell ($1s^2$ configuration). The remaining elements have a completely filled valence shell of s and p orbitals (s^2p^6). This electronic arrangement is especially stable, and as a result, these elements exist in nature as single atoms. We will learn about the consequences of having a completely filled valence shell in Chapter 3.

Table 2.6 Valence Electronic Configurations for the Main Group Elements in Periods 1–3

Group Number	1A	2A	3A	4A	5A	6A	7A	8A[a]
Period 1	H $1s^1$							He $1s^2$
Period 2	Li $2s^1$	Be $2s^2$	B $2s^2 2p^1$	C $2s^2 2p^2$	N $2s^2 2p^3$	O $2s^2 2p^4$	F $2s^2 2p^5$	Ne $2s^2 2p^6$
Period 3	Na $3s^1$	Mg $3s^2$	Al $3s^2 3p^1$	Si $3s^2 3p^2$	P $3s^2 3p^3$	S $3s^2 3p^4$	Cl $3s^2 3p^5$	Ar $3s^2 3p^6$
General configuration	ns^1	ns^2	$ns^2 np^1$	$ns^2 np^2$	$ns^2 np^3$	$ns^2 np^4$	$ns^2 np^5$	$ns^2 np^6$

[a]The general electronic configuration in group 8A applies to all of the noble gases except helium. Since helium is a first-row element, it has only two electrons, and these occupy the only available orbital in the first shell, the $1s$ orbital.

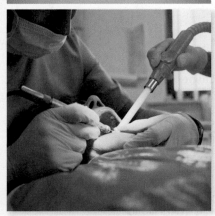

HEALTH NOTE

Mercury (Sample Problem 2.12) is safely used in dental amalgam to fill cavities in teeth. Mercury released into the environment, however, is converted to toxic methylmercury by microorganisms in water, so hazardous levels of this soluble mercury compound can accumulate in fish at the top of the food chain, such as sharks and swordfish.

SAMPLE PROBLEM 2.12

Identify the total number of electrons, the number of valence electrons, and the name of the element with each electronic configuration.

a. $1s^2 2s^2 2p^6 3s^2 3p^2$ b. $1s^2 2s^2 2p^6 3s^2 3p^6 4s^2 3d^{10} 4p^6 5s^2 4d^{10} 5p^6 6s^2 4f^{14} 5d^{10}$

Analysis

To obtain the total number of electrons, add up the superscripts. This gives the atomic number and identifies the element. To determine the number of valence electrons, add up the number of electrons in the shell with the highest number.

Solution

a.   valence shell

$1s^2 2s^2 2p^6 3s^2 3p^2$

4 valence electrons

Total number of electrons =
$2 + 2 + 6 + 2 + 2 = \mathbf{14}$

Answer: Silicon (Si), 14 total electrons and 4 valence electrons

b.   valence shell

$1s^2 2s^2 2p^6 3s^2 3p^6 4s^2 3d^{10} 4p^6 5s^2 4d^{10} 5p^6 6s^2 4f^{14} 5d^{10}$

2 valence electrons

Total number of electrons = **80**

Answer: Mercury (Hg), 80 total electrons and 2 valence electrons

PROBLEM 2.25

Identify the total number of electrons, the number of valence electrons, and the name of the element with each electronic configuration.

a. $1s^2 2s^2 2p^6 3s^2$
b. $1s^2 2s^2 2p^6 3s^2 3p^3$
c. $1s^2 2s^2 2p^6 3s^2 3p^6 4s^2 3d^{10} 4p^6 5s^2 4d^2$
d. $[Ar]4s^2 3d^6$

SAMPLE PROBLEM 2.13

Determine the number of valence electrons and give the electronic configuration of the valence electrons of each element: (a) nitrogen; (b) potassium.

Analysis

The group number of a main group element = the number of valence electrons. Use the general electronic configurations in Table 2.6 to write the configuration of the valence electrons.

Solution

a. Nitrogen is located in group 5A so it has five valence electrons. Since nitrogen is a second-period element, its valence electronic configuration is $2s^2 2p^3$.

b. Potassium is located in group 1A so it has one valence electron. Since potassium is a fourth-period element, its valence electronic configuration is $4s^1$.

PROBLEM 2.26

Determine the number of valence electrons and give the electronic configuration of the valence electrons of each element: (a) fluorine; (b) krypton; (c) magnesium; (d) germanium.

PROBLEM 2.27

Write the valence shell electronic configuration for the elements in periods 4, 5, and 6 of group 6A.

2.7B   Electron-Dot Symbols

The number of valence electrons around an atom is often represented by an **electron-dot symbol.** Representative examples are shown.

	H	C	O	Cl
Number of valence electrons:	1	4	6	7
Electron-dot symbol:	H·	·Ċ·	·Ö·	·Ċl:

- Each dot represents one electron.
- The dots are placed on the four sides of an element symbol.
- For one to four valence electrons, single dots are used. With more than four electrons, the dots are paired.

The location of the dots around the symbol—side, top, or bottom—does not matter. Each of the following representations for the five valence electrons of nitrogen is equivalent.

SAMPLE PROBLEM 2.14

Write an electron-dot symbol for each element: (a) sodium; (b) phosphorus.

Analysis

Write the symbol for each element and use the group number to determine the number of valence electrons for a main group element. Represent each valence electron with a dot.

Solution

a. The symbol for sodium is Na. Na is in group 1A and has one valence electron. Electron-dot symbol:

$$Na\cdot$$

b. The symbol for phosphorus is P. P is in group 5A and has five valence electrons. Electron-dot symbol:

$$\cdot\ddot{P}\cdot$$

PROBLEM 2.28

Give the electron-dot symbol for each element: (a) bromine; (b) lithium; (c) aluminum; (d) sulfur; (e) neon.

2.8   Periodic Trends

Many properties of atoms exhibit **periodic trends;** that is, they change in a regular way across a row or down a column of the periodic table. Two properties that illustrate this phenomenon are **atomic size** and **ionization energy.**

2.8A   Atomic Size

The size of an atom is measured by its atomic radius—that is, the distance from the nucleus to the outer edge of the valence shell. Two periodic trends characterize the size of atoms.

- The size of atoms increases down a column of the periodic table, as the valence electrons are farther from the nucleus.

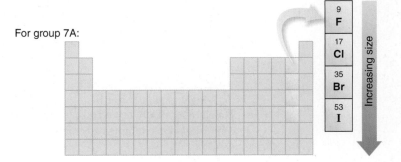

- **The size of atoms decreases across a row of the periodic table as the number of protons in the nucleus increases. An increasing number of protons pulls the electrons closer to the nucleus, so the atom gets smaller.**

For period 2:

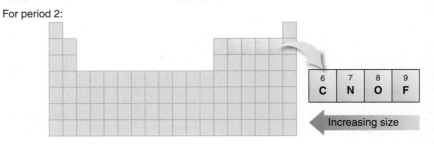

PROBLEM 2.29

Rank the atoms in each group in order of increasing size.

a. boron, carbon, neon
b. calcium, magnesium, beryllium
c. silicon, sulfur, magnesium
d. krypton, neon, xenon
e. sulfur, oxygen, silicon
f. fluorine, sulfur, aluminum

2.8B Ionization Energy

Since a negatively charged electron is attracted to a positively charged nucleus, energy is required to remove an electron from a neutral atom. The more tightly the electron is held, the greater the energy required to remove it. Removing an electron from a neutral atom forms a **cation.**

$$\text{Na} + \text{energy} \longrightarrow \text{Na}^+ + e^-$$

neutral atom | ionization energy | cation

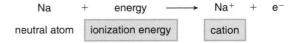

- **The *ionization energy* is the energy needed to remove an electron from a neutral atom.**
- **A *cation* is positively charged, and has fewer electrons than the neutral atom.**

Two periodic trends characterize ionization energy.

- **Ionization energies decrease down a column of the periodic table as the valence electrons get farther from the positively charged nucleus.**

For group 1A:

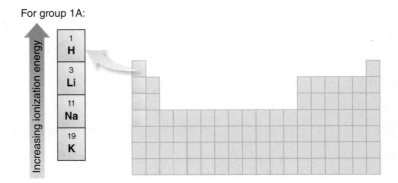

• Ionization energies generally increase across a row of the periodic table as the number of protons in the nucleus increases.

For period 2:

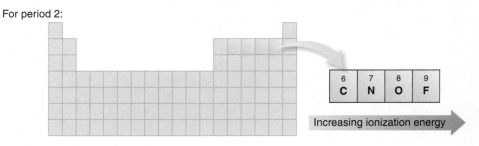

Increasing ionization energy

PROBLEM 2.30

Arrange the elements in each group in order of increasing ionization energy.

a. phosphorus, silicon, sulfur

b. magnesium, calcium, beryllium

c. carbon, fluorine, beryllium

d. neon, krypton, argon

e. tin, silicon, sulfur

f. calcium, aluminum, nitrogen

CHAPTER HIGHLIGHTS

KEY TERMS

Actinide (2.4)

Alkali metal (2.4)

Alkaline earth element (2.4)

Atom (2.2)

Atomic mass unit (2.2)

Atomic number (2.2)

Atomic weight (2.3)

Building-block element (2.1)

Cation (2.8)

Chemical formula (2.1)

Compound (2.1)

d Block (2.6)

Deuterium (2.3)

Electron (2.2)

Electron cloud (2.2)

Electron-dot symbol (2.7)

Electronic configuration (2.6)

Element (2.1)

f Block (2.6)

Ground state (2.6)

Group (2.4)

Group number (2.4)

Halogen (2.4)

Inner transition metal element (2.4)

Ionization energy (2.8)

Isotope (2.3)

Lanthanide (2.4)

Main group element (2.4)

Major mineral (Macronutrient, 2.1)

Mass number (2.2)

Metal (2.1)

Metalloid (2.1)

Neutron (2.2)

Noble gas (2.4)

Nonmetal (2.1)

Nucleus (2.2)

Orbital (2.5)

p Block (2.6)

Period (2.4)

Periodic table (2.1)

p Orbital (2.5)

Proton (2.2)

s Block (2.6)

Shell (2.5)

s Orbital (2.5)

Subshell (2.5)

Trace element (Micronutrient, 2.1)

Transition metal element (2.4)

Tritium (2.3)

Unpaired electron (2.6)

Valence electron (2.7)

KEY CONCEPTS

1 How is the name of an element abbreviated and how does the periodic table help to classify it as a metal, nonmetal, or metalloid? (2.1)

• An element is abbreviated by a one- or two-letter symbol. The periodic table contains a stepped line from boron to astatine. All metals are located to the left of the line. All nonmetals except hydrogen are located to the right of the line. The seven elements located along the line are metalloids.

2 What are the basic components of an atom? (2.2)

• An atom is composed of two parts: a dense nucleus containing positively charged protons and neutral neutrons, and an electron cloud containing negatively charged electrons. Most of the mass of an atom resides in the nucleus, while the electron cloud contains most of its volume.

• The atomic number (Z) of a neutral atom tells the number of protons and the number of electrons. The mass number (A) is the sum of the number of protons (Z) and the number of neutrons.

3 **What are isotopes and how are they related to the atomic weight? (2.3)**
- Isotopes are atoms that have the same number of protons but a different number of neutrons. The atomic weight is the weighted average of the mass of the naturally occurring isotopes of a particular element.

4 **What are the basic features of the periodic table? (2.4)**
- The periodic table is a schematic of all known elements, arranged in rows (periods) and columns (groups), organized so that elements with similar properties are grouped together.
- The vertical columns are assigned group numbers using two different numbering schemes—1–8 plus the letters A or B; or 1–18.
- The periodic table is divided into the main group elements (groups 1A–8A), the transition metals (groups 1B–8B), and the inner transition metals located at the bottom.

5 **How are electrons arranged around an atom? (2.5)**
- Electrons occupy discrete energy levels, organized into shells (numbered 1, 2, 3, and so on), subshells (s, p, d, and f), and orbitals.
- Each orbital can hold two electrons.

6 **What rules determine the electronic configuration of an atom? (2.6)**
- To write the ground state electronic configuration of an atom, electrons are added to the lowest energy orbitals, giving each orbital two electrons. When two orbitals are equal in energy, one electron is added to each orbital until the orbitals are half-filled.
- Orbital diagrams that use boxes for orbitals and arrows for electrons indicate electronic configuration. Electron configuration can also be shown using superscripts to show how many electrons an orbital contains. For example, the electron configuration of the six electrons in a carbon atom is $1s^2 2s^2 2p^2$.

7 **How is the location of an element in the periodic table related to its electronic configuration? (2.6, 2.7)**
- The periodic table is divided into four regions—the s block, p block, d block, and f block—based on the subshells that are filled with electrons last.
- Elements in the same group have the same number of valence electrons and similar electronic configurations.

8 **What is an electron-dot symbol? (2.7)**
- An electron-dot symbol uses a dot to represent each valence electron around the symbol for an element.

9 **How are atomic size and ionization energy related to location in the periodic table? (2.8)**
- The size of an atom decreases across a row and increases down a column.
- Ionization energy—the energy needed to remove an electron from an atom—increases across a row and decreases down a column.

PROBLEMS

Selected in-chapter and odd-numbered end-of-chapter problems have brief answers in Appendix B. The *Student Study Guide and Solutions Manual* contains detailed solutions to all in-chapter and odd-numbered end-of-chapter problems, as well as additional worked examples and a chapter self-test.

Elements

2.31 Identify the elements used in each example of molecular art.

a.   b.

2.32 Write a chemical formula for each example of molecular art.

a.   b.   c.

2.33 Give the name of the elements in each group of three element symbols.
- a. Au, At, Ag
- b. N, Na, Ni
- c. S, Si, Sn
- d. Ca, Cr, Cl
- e. P, Pb, Pt
- f. Ti, Ta, Tl

2.34 What element(s) are designated by each symbol or group of symbols?
- a. CU and Cu
- b. Os and OS
- c. Ni and NI
- d. BIN, BiN, and BIn

2.35 Does each chemical formula represent an element or a compound?
- a. H_2
- b. H_2O_2
- c. S_8
- d. Na_2CO_3
- e. C_{60}

2.36 Identify the elements in each chemical formula and tell how many atoms of each are present.
- a. $K_2Cr_2O_7$
- b. $C_5H_8NNaO_4$ (MSG, flavor enhancer)
- c. $C_{10}H_{16}N_2O_3S$ (vitamin B_7)

2.37 Identify the element that fits each description.
- a. an alkali metal in period 6
- b. a transition metal in period 5, group 8
- c. a main group element in period 3, group 7A
- d. a main group element in period 2, group 2A
- e. a halogen in period 2
- f. an inner transition metal with one 4f electron

2.38 Identify the element that fits each description.

    a. an alkaline earth element in period 3

    b. a noble gas in period 6

    c. a main group element in period 3 that has p orbitals half-filled with electrons

    d. a transition metal in period 4, group 11

    e. an inner transition metal with its $5f$ orbitals completely filled with electrons

    f. a transition metal in period 6, group 10

2.39 Give all of the terms that apply to each element: [1] metal; [2] nonmetal; [3] metalloid; [4] alkali metal; [5] alkaline earth element; [6] halogen; [7] noble gas; [8] main group element; [9] transition metal; [10] inner transition metal.

    a. sodium   c. xenon   e. uranium

    b. silver   d. platinum   f. tellurium

2.40 Give all of the terms that apply to each element: [1] metal; [2] nonmetal; [3] metalloid; [4] alkali metal; [5] alkaline earth element; [6] halogen; [7] noble gas; [8] main group element; [9] transition metal; [10] inner transition metal.

    a. bromine   c. cesium   e. calcium

    b. silicon   d. gold   f. chromium

Atomic Structure

2.41 Give the following information about the atom shown: (a) the number of protons and neutrons in the nucleus; (b) the atomic number; (c) the mass number; (d) the number of electrons in the neutral atom; and (e) the element symbol.

2.42 Give the following information about the atom shown: (a) the number of protons and neutrons in the nucleus; (b) the atomic number; (c) the mass number; (d) the number of electrons in the neutral atom; and (e) the element symbol.

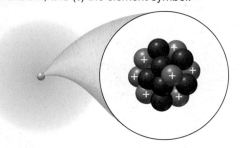

2.43 Complete the following table for neutral elements.

	Element Symbol	Atomic Number	Mass Number	Number of Protons	Number of Neutrons	Number of Electrons
a.	C		12			
b.			31			15
c.					35	30
d.	Mg		24			
e.				53	74	
f.		4			5	
g.		40	91			
h.					16	16

2.44 For the given atomic number (Z) and mass number (A): [1] identify the element; [2] give the element symbol; [3] give the number of protons, neutrons, and electrons.

    a. $Z = 10, A = 20$ d. $Z = 55, A = 133$

    b. $Z = 13, A = 27$ e. $Z = 28, A = 59$

    c. $Z = 38, A = 88$ f. $Z = 79, A = 197$

Periodic Table

2.45 Label each region on the periodic table.

    a. noble gases   e. alkaline earth elements

    b. period 3   f. f block elements

    c. group 4A   g. transition metals

    d. s block elements   h. group 10

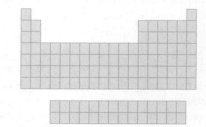

2.46 Identify each highlighted element in the periodic table and give its [1] element name and symbol; [2] group number; [3] period; [4] classification (i.e., main group element, transition metal, or inner transition metal).

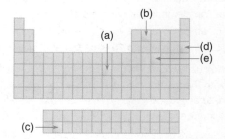

2.47 What element is located in group 1A but is not an alkali metal?

2.48 What s block element is not located in either group 1A or group 2A in the periodic table?

2.49 Classify each element in the fourth row of the periodic table as a metal, nonmetal, or metalloid.

2.50 To which blocks do the elements in the fifth period belong?

2.51 Which group(s) in the periodic table contain only nonmetals?

2.52 Which groups in the periodic table contain metals, nonmetals, and metalloids?

Isotopes and Atomic Weight

2.53 The most common isotope of oxygen has a mass number of 16, but two other isotopes having mass numbers of 17 and 18 are also known. For each isotope, give the following information: (a) the number of protons; (b) the number of neutrons; (c) the number of electrons in the neutral atom; (d) the group number; (e) the element symbols using superscripts and subscripts.

2.54 The three most common isotopes of tin have mass numbers 116, 118, and 120. For each isotope, give the following information: (a) the number of protons; (b) the number of neutrons; (c) the number of electrons in the neutral atom; (d) the group number; (e) the element symbols using superscripts and subscripts.

2.55 How many protons, neutrons, and electrons are contained in each element?

    a. $^{27}_{13}Al$ b. $^{35}_{17}Cl$ c. $^{34}_{16}S$

2.56 Give the number of protons, neutrons, and electrons in each element: (a) silver-115; (b) Au-197; (c) Rn-222; (d) osmium-192.

2.57 Write the element symbol that fits each description, using a superscript for the mass number and a subscript for the atomic number.

    a. an element that contains 53 protons and 74 neutrons

    b. an element with 35 electrons and a mass number of 79

    c. an element with 47 protons and 60 neutrons

2.58 Write the element symbol that fits each description. Use a superscript for the mass number and a subscript for the atomic number.

    a. an element that contains 10 protons and 12 neutrons

    b. an element with atomic number 24 and mass number 52

    c. an element with 10 electrons and 10 neutrons

2.59 Calculate the atomic weight of silver, which has two isotopes with the following properties: Ag-107 (106.91 amu, 51.84% natural occurrence) and Ag-109 (108.90 amu, 48.16% natural occurrence).

2.60 Calculate the atomic weight of antimony, which has two isotopes with the following properties: Sb-121 (120.90 amu, 57.21% natural occurrence) and Sb-123 (122.90 amu, 42.79% natural occurrence).

2.61 Can the neutral atoms of two different elements have the same number of electrons? Explain.

2.62 Can the neutral atoms of two different elements have the same number of neutrons? Explain.

Electronic Configuration

2.63 How many orbitals are contained in each of the following shells of electrons: (a) first shell ($n = 1$); (b) second shell ($n = 2$); (c) third shell ($n = 3$); (d) fourth shell ($n = 4$)?

2.64 What is the maximum number of electrons that can be contained in each shell, subshell, or orbital?

    a. second shell   c. $3p$ subshell   e. fourth shell

    b. $3s$ orbital   d. $4f$ orbital   f. $5p$ orbital

2.65 Write the electronic configuration of each element using an orbital diagram: (a) B; (b) K; (c) Se; (d) Ar; (e) Zn.

2.66 Write the electronic configuration of each element using an orbital diagram: (a) N; (b) I; (c) Ga; (d) Ti; (e) Mn.

2.67 For each element in Problem 2.65: (a) Write out the electronic configuration using a superscript with each orbital; (b) write out the electronic configuration using noble gas notation.

2.68 For each element in Problem 2.66: (a) Write out the electronic configuration using a superscript with each orbital; (b) write out the electronic configuration using noble gas notation.

2.69 How many unpaired electrons are contained in each element: (a) Al; (b) P; (c) Na?

2.70 How many unpaired electrons are contained in each element: (a) Cl; (b) Se; (c) Cs?

2.71 Give the total number of electrons, the number of valence electrons, and the identity of the element with each electronic configuration.

    a. $1s^22s^22p^63s^23p^64s^23d^{10}4p^65s^2$ c. $1s^22s^22p^63s^1$

    b. $1s^22s^22p^63s^23p^4$ d. $[Ne]3s^23p^5$

2.72 Give the total number of electrons, the number of valence electrons, and the identity of the element with each electronic configuration.

    a. $1s^22s^22p^63s^23p^6$ c. $1s^22s^22p^3$

    b. $1s^22s^22p^63s^23p^64s^23d^7$ d. $[Kr]5s^24d^{10}5p^2$

2.73 How do an alkali metal and an alkaline earth element in the same row differ in the electronic configuration of the valence shell electrons?

2.74 How do a halogen and a noble gas in the same row differ in the electronic configuration of the valence shell electrons?

2.75 For each element, give the following information: [1] total number of electrons; [2] group number; [3] number of valence electrons; [4] period; [5] number of the valence shell.

    a. carbon   b. calcium   c. krypton

2.76 For each element, give the following information: [1] total number of electrons; [2] group number; [3] number of valence electrons; [4] period; [5] number of the valence shell.

    a. oxygen   b. sodium   c. phosphorus

2.77 For each element in Problem 2.75, first write the electronic configuration of all the electrons. Then give the electronic configuration of the valence electrons only.

2.78 For each element in Problem 2.76, first write the electronic configuration of all the electrons. Then give the electronic configuration of the valence electrons only.

2.79 How many valence electrons does an element in each group contain: (a) 2A; (b) 4A; (c) 7A?

2.80 In what shell do the valence electrons reside for an element in period: (a) 2; (b) 3; (c) 4; (d) 5?

2.81 Give the number of valence electrons in each element. Write out the electronic configuration for the valence electrons.
   a. sulfur   b. chlorine   c. barium   d. titanium   e. tin

2.82 Give the number of valence electrons in each element. Write out the electronic configuration for the valence electrons.
   a. neon   c. aluminum   e. zirconium
   b. rubidium   d. manganese

2.83 Write an electron-dot symbol for each element: (a) beryllium; (b) silicon; (c) iodine; (d) magnesium; (e) argon.

2.84 Write an electron-dot symbol for each element: (a) K; (b) B; (c) F; (d) Ca; (e) Se.

Periodic Trends

2.85 Which element in each pair is larger?
   a. bromine and iodine   c. silicon and potassium
   b. carbon and nitrogen   d. chlorine and selenium

2.86 Which element in each pair has its valence electrons farther from the nucleus?
   a. sodium and magnesium   c. neon and krypton
   b. carbon and fluorine   d. argon and bromine

2.87 For each pair of elements in Problem 2.85, label the element with the higher ionization energy.

2.88 For each pair of elements in Problem 2.86, label the element from which it is easier to remove an electron.

2.89 Rank the following elements in order of increasing size: sulfur, silicon, oxygen, magnesium, and fluorine.

2.90 Rank the following elements in order of increasing size: aluminum, nitrogen, potassium, oxygen, and phosphorus.

2.91 Rank the following elements in order of increasing ionization energy: nitrogen, fluorine, magnesium, sodium, and phosphorus.

2.92 Rank the following elements in order of decreasing ionization energy: calcium, silicon, oxygen, magnesium, and carbon.

Applications

2.93 Answer the following questions about the macronutrients sodium, potassium, and chlorine.
   a. Is each element classified as a metal, nonmetal, or metalloid?
   b. In which block does each element reside?
   c. Which element has the smallest atomic radius?
   d. Which element has the largest atomic radius?
   e. Which element has the largest ionization energy?
   f. Which element has the smallest ionization energy?
   g. How many valence electrons does each element possess?

2.94 Platinum is a precious metal used in a wide variety of products. Besides fine jewelry, platinum is also the catalyst found in the catalytic converters of automobile exhaust systems, and platinum-containing drugs like cisplatin are used to treat some lung and ovarian cancers. Answer the following questions about the element platinum.
   a. What is its element symbol?
   b. What group number and period are assigned to platinum?
   c. What is its atomic number?
   d. Is platinum classified as a main group element, transition metal, or inner transition metal?
   e. In what block does platinum reside?
   f. What is unusual about the electronic configuration for platinum: $[Xe]6s^14f^{14}5d^9$?

2.95 Carbon-11 is an unnatural isotope used in positron emission tomography (PET) scans. PET scans are used to monitor brain activity and diagnose dementia. How does carbon-11 compare to carbon-12 in terms of the number of protons, neutrons, and electrons? Write the element symbol of carbon-11 using superscripts and subscripts.

2.96 Answer the following questions about the macronutrients calcium, magnesium, and sulfur.
   a. Is each element classified as a metal, nonmetal, or metalloid?
   b. In which block does each element reside?
   c. Which element has the smallest atomic radius?
   d. Which element has the largest atomic radius?
   e. Which element has the largest ionization energy?
   f. Which element has the smallest ionization energy?
   g. How many valence electrons does each element possess?

CHALLENGE PROBLEMS

2.97 Sesame seeds, sunflower seeds, and peanuts are good dietary sources of the trace element copper. Copper is needed for the synthesis of neurotransmitters, compounds that transmit nerve signals from one nerve cell to another. Copper is also needed for the synthesis of collagen, a protein found in bone, tendons, teeth, and blood vessels. What is unusual about the electronic configuration of the trace element copper: $1s^22s^22p^63s^23p^64s^13d^{10}$?

2.98 Strontium-90 is a radioactive element formed in nuclear reactors. When an unusually high level of strontium is released into the air, such as occurred during the Chernobyl nuclear disaster in 1986, the strontium can be incorporated into the bones of exposed individuals. High levels of strontium can cause bone cancer and leukemia. Why does Sr-90 cause this particular health problem?

Zinc oxide is an ionic compound widely used in sunblocks to protect the skin from harmful ultraviolet radiation.

Ionic Compounds

CHAPTER GOALS

In this chapter you will learn how to:

1. Describe the basic features of ionic and covalent bonds
2. Use the periodic table to determine whether an atom forms a cation or an anion, and determine its charge using the group number
3. Describe the octet rule
4. Write the formula for an ionic compound
5. Name ionic compounds
6. Describe the properties of ionic compounds
7. Recognize the structures of common polyatomic ions and name compounds that contain them
8. List useful consumer products and drugs that are composed of ionic compounds

Although much of the discussion in Chapter 2 focused on atoms, individual atoms are rarely encountered in nature. Instead, atoms are far more commonly joined together to form compounds. There are two types of chemical compounds, **ionic** and **covalent. Ionic compounds** are composed of positively and negatively charged ions held together by strong **electrostatic forces**—the electrical attraction between oppositely charged ions. Examples of ionic compounds include the sodium chloride (NaCl) in table salt and the calcium carbonate ($CaCO_3$) in snail shells. **Covalent compounds** are composed of individual molecules, discrete groups of atoms that share electrons. Covalent compounds include water (H_2O) and methane (CH_4), the main component of natural gas. Chapters 3 and 4 focus on the structure and properties of ionic and covalent compounds, respectively.

3.1   Introduction to Bonding

It is rare in nature to encounter individual atoms. Instead, anywhere from two to hundreds or thousands of atoms tend to join together to form compounds. The oxygen we breathe, for instance, consists of two oxygen atoms joined together, whereas the hemoglobin that transports it to our tissues consists of thousands of carbon, hydrogen, oxygen, nitrogen, and sulfur atoms joined together. We say **two atoms are** *bonded* **together.**

- *Bonding* is the joining of two atoms in a stable arrangement.

Bonding is a favorable process because it always forms a compound that is more stable than the atoms from which it is made. Only the noble gases in group 8A of the periodic table are particularly stable as individual atoms; that is, the **noble gases do** *not* **readily react to form bonds,** because the electronic configuration of the noble gases is especially stable to begin with. As a result, one overriding principle explains the process of bonding.

- In bonding, elements gain, lose, or share electrons to attain the electronic configuration of the noble gas closest to them in the periodic table.

Bonding involves only the valence electrons of an atom. There are two different kinds of bonding: **ionic** and **covalent.**

- *Ionic bonds* result from the transfer of electrons from one element to another.
- *Covalent bonds* result from the sharing of electrons between two atoms.

The position of an element in the periodic table determines the type of bonds it makes. **Ionic bonds form between a metal on the left side of the periodic table and a nonmetal on the right side.** As shown in Figure 3.1, when the metal sodium (Na) bonds to the nonmetal chlorine (Cl_2), the ionic compound sodium chloride (NaCl) forms. Since ionic compounds are composed of *ions*—**charged species in which the number of protons and electrons in an atom is** *not* **equal**—we begin our discussion of ionic compounds with how ions are formed in Section 3.2.

Covalent bonds are formed when two nonmetals combine, or when a metalloid bonds to a nonmetal. **A** *molecule* **is a compound containing two or more atoms joined together with covalent bonds.** For example, when two hydrogen atoms bond they form the molecule H_2, and two electrons are shared. Covalent bonds and molecules are discussed in Chapter 4.

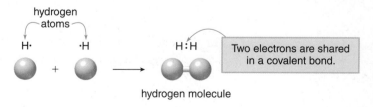

hydrogen molecule

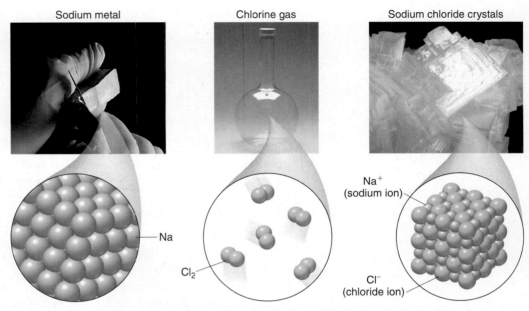

Figure 3.1

Sodium Chloride, an Ionic Compound

Sodium metal and chlorine gas are both elements. Sodium chloride is an ionic compound composed of sodium ions and chloride ions.

SAMPLE PROBLEM 3.1

Predict whether the bonds in the following compounds are ionic or covalent: (a) NaI (sodium iodide); (b) H_2O_2 (hydrogen peroxide).

Analysis

The position of the elements in the periodic table determines the type of bonds they form. When a metal and nonmetal combine, the bond is ionic. When two nonmetals combine, or a metalloid bonds to a nonmetal, the bond is covalent.

Solution

a. Since Na is a metal on the left side and I is a nonmetal on the right side of the periodic table, the bonds in NaI are ionic.

b. Since H_2O_2 contains only the nonmetals hydrogen and oxygen, the bonds must be covalent.

PROBLEM 3.1

Predict whether the bonds in the following species are ionic or covalent.

a. CO   b. CaF_2 c. MgO   d. Cl_2 e. HF   f. C_2H_6

PROBLEM 3.2

Label each of the following as a compound, element, or molecule. In some cases, more than one term applies.

a. CO_2 b. H_2O c. NaF   d. $MgBr_2$ e. F_2 f. CaO

PROBLEM 3.3

Vitamin C has the chemical formula $C_6H_8O_6$. Even if you know nothing about how the atoms in vitamin C are arranged, what type of bonds are likely to be present in vitamin C?

HEALTH NOTE

Vitamin C is important in the formation of collagen, a protein that holds together the connective tissue of skin, muscle, and blood vessels. Oranges and other citrus fruits are an excellent source of vitamin C.

3.2   Ions

Ionic compounds consist of oppositely charged **ions** that have a strong **electrostatic attraction**—electrical attraction between oppositely charged ions—for each other.

3.2A   Cations and Anions

There are two types of ions called **cations** and **anions.**

- *Cations* are positively charged ions. A cation has fewer electrons than protons.
- *Anions* are negatively charged ions. An anion has more electrons than protons.

The nature and magnitude of the charge on an ion depend on the position of an element in the periodic table. In forming an ion, an atom of a main group element loses or gains electrons to obtain the electronic configuration of the noble gas closest to it in the periodic table. This gives the ion an especially stable electronic arrangement with a **completely filled shell of electrons;** that is, the electrons completely fill the shell farthest from the nucleus.

For example, sodium (group 1A) has an atomic number of 11, giving it 11 protons and 11 electrons in the neutral atom. This gives sodium one *more* electron than neon, the noble gas closest to it in the periodic table. In losing one electron, sodium forms a cation with a +1 charge, which still has 11 protons, but now has only 10 electrons in its electron cloud.

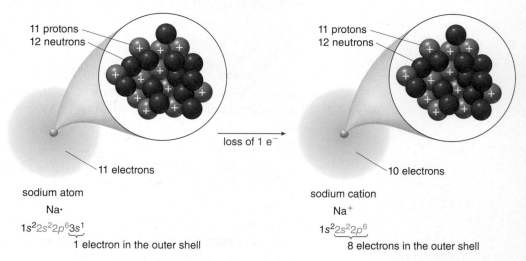

11 protons
12 neutrons

11 electrons

sodium atom

Na·

$1s^2 2s^2 2p^6 3s^1$
1 electron in the outer shell

loss of 1 e⁻

11 protons
12 neutrons

10 electrons

sodium cation

Na⁺

$1s^2 2s^2 2p^6$
8 electrons in the outer shell

What does this mean in terms of valence electrons? A neutral sodium atom, with an electronic configuration of $1s^2 2s^2 2p^6 3s^1$, has a single valence electron. Loss of this valence electron forms a **sodium cation,** symbolized as **Na⁺,** which has the especially stable electronic configuration of the noble gas neon, $1s^2 2s^2 2p^6$. The sodium cation now has **eight electrons** that fill the $2s$ and three $2p$ orbitals.

Magnesium (group 2A) has 12 protons and 12 electrons in the neutral atom. This gives magnesium two *more* electrons than neon, the noble gas closest to it in the periodic table. In losing two electrons, magnesium forms a cation with a +2 charge, which still has 12 protons, but now has only 10 electrons in its electron cloud.

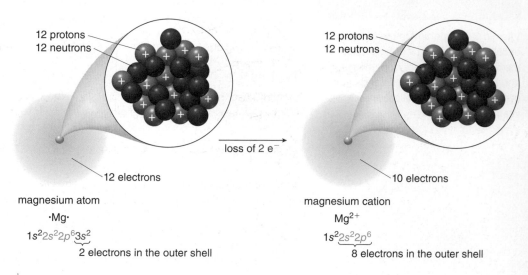

12 protons
12 neutrons

12 electrons

magnesium atom

·Mg·

$1s^2 2s^2 2p^6 3s^2$
2 electrons in the outer shell

loss of 2 e⁻

12 protons
12 neutrons

10 electrons

magnesium cation

Mg²⁺

$1s^2 2s^2 2p^6$
8 electrons in the outer shell

In terms of valence electrons, a neutral magnesium atom, with an electronic configuration of $1s^2 2s^2 2p^6 3s^2$, has two valence electrons. Loss of these valence electrons forms a **magnesium cation,** symbolized as **Mg^{2+},** which has the especially stable electronic configuration of the noble gas neon, $1s^2 2s^2 2p^6$. The magnesium cation now has **eight electrons** that fill the $2s$ and three $2p$ orbitals.

Sodium and magnesium are examples of metals.

Some metals—notably tin and lead—can lose *four* electrons to form cations.

- Metals form *cations.*
- By losing one, two, or three electrons, an atom forms a cation with a completely filled outer shell of electrons.

A neutral chlorine atom (group 7A), on the other hand, has 17 protons and 17 electrons. This gives it one *fewer* electron than argon, the noble gas closest to it in the periodic table. By gaining one electron, chlorine forms an anion with a –1 charge because it still has 17 protons, but now has 18 electrons in its electron cloud.

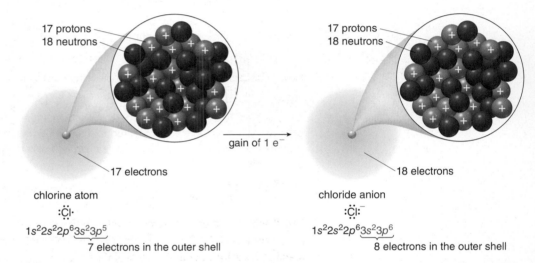

17 protons
18 neutrons

gain of 1 e⁻

17 protons
18 neutrons

17 electrons

18 electrons

chlorine atom
:C̈l·
$1s^2 2s^2 2p^6 \underbrace{3s^2 3p^5}$
7 electrons in the outer shell

chloride anion
:C̈l:⁻
$1s^2 2s^2 2p^6 \underbrace{3s^2 3p^6}$
8 electrons in the outer shell

In terms of valence electrons, a neutral chlorine atom, with an electronic configuration of $1s^2 2s^2 2p^6 3s^2 3p^5$, has seven valence electrons. Gain of one electron forms a **chloride anion,** symbolized as **Cl^-,** which has the especially stable electronic configuration of the noble gas argon, $1s^2 2s^2 2p^6 3s^2 3p^6$. The chloride anion now has **eight valence electrons** that fill the $3s$ and three $3p$ orbitals.

Chlorine is an example of a nonmetal.

- Nonmetals form *anions.*
- By gaining one, two, or sometimes three electrons, an atom forms an anion with a completely filled outer shell of electrons.

Ions are written with the element symbol followed by a superscript to indicate the charge. The number "1" is omitted in ions that have a +1 or –1 charge, as in Na^+ or Cl^-. When the charge is "2" or greater, it is written as 2+ or 2–, as in Mg^{2+} or O^{2-}.

Each of these ions formed from a main group element has the s and three p orbitals filled with **eight electrons.** This illustrates the **octet rule.**

- A main group element is especially stable when it possesses an *octet* of electrons in its outer shell.

SAMPLE PROBLEM 3.2

Write the ion symbol for an atom with: (a) nine protons and 10 electrons; (b) three protons and two electrons.

Analysis

Since the number of protons equals the atomic number (Section 2.2), this quantity identifies the element. The charge is determined by comparing the number of protons and electrons. If the number of electrons is greater than the number of protons, the charge is negative (an anion). If the number of protons is greater than the number of electrons, the charge is positive (a cation).

Solution

a. An element with nine protons has an atomic number of nine, identifying it as fluorine (F). Since there is one more electron than proton (10 vs. 9), the charge is –1.

   Answer: F^-

b. An element with three protons has an atomic number of three, identifying it as lithium (Li). Since there is one more proton than electron (3 vs. 2), the charge is +1.

   Answer: Li^+

PROBLEM 3.4

Write the ion symbol for an atom with the given number of protons and electrons.

a. 19 protons and 18 electrons   c. 35 protons and 36 electrons
b. seven protons and 10 electrons   d. 23 protons and 21 electrons

SAMPLE PROBLEM 3.3

How many protons and electrons are present in each ion: (a) Ca^{2+}; (b) O^{2-}?

Analysis

Use the identity of the element to determine the number of protons. The charge tells how many more or fewer electrons there are compared to the number of protons. A positive charge means more protons than electrons, while a negative charge means more electrons than protons.

Solution

a. Ca^{2+}: The element calcium (Ca) has an atomic number of 20, so it has 20 protons. Since the charge is +2, there are two more protons than electrons, giving the ion 18 electrons.

b. O^{2-}: The element oxygen (O) has an atomic number of eight, so it has eight protons. Since the charge is –2, there are two more electrons than protons, giving the ion 10 electrons.

PROBLEM 3.5

How many protons and electrons are present in each ion?

a. Ni^{2+} b. Se^{2-} c. Zn^{2+} d. Fe^{3+}

3.2B   Relating Group Number to Ionic Charge for Main Group Elements

Since elements with similar electronic configurations are grouped together in the periodic table, **elements in the same group form ions of similar charge.** The group number of a main group element can be used to determine the charge on an ion derived from that element.

- **Metals form cations. For metals in groups 1A, 2A, and 3A, the group number = the charge on the cation.**

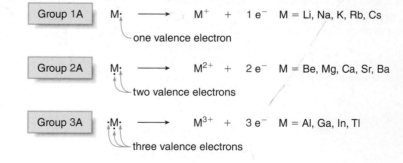

Group **1A** elements (Li, Na, K, Rb, and Cs) have **one** valence electron. Loss of this electron forms a cation with a **+1** charge. Group **2A** elements (Be, Mg, Ca, Sr, and Ba) have **two** valence electrons. Loss of both electrons forms a cation with a **+2** charge. Group **3A** elements (Al, Ga, In, and Tl) form cations, too, but only aluminum is commonly found in ionic compounds. It has **three** valence electrons, so loss of three electrons from aluminum forms a cation with a **+3** charge.

All of the cations derived from group 1A–3A elements have an octet of outer shell electrons except for Li^+ and Be^{2+}. Li^+ and Be^{2+} have a $1s^2$ electronic configuration like helium, the noble gas to which they are closest in the periodic table. Thus, these cations are especially stable because they have a filled outer shell of electrons, although they do *not* have an octet of electrons.

> • Nonmetals form anions. For nonmetals in groups 5A, 6A, and 7A, the anion charge = 8 – (the group number).

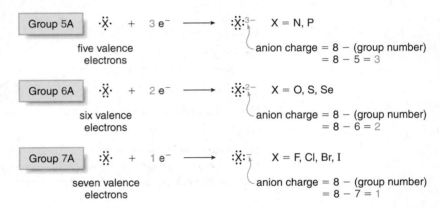

Group **5A** elements have **five** valence electrons. A gain of **three** electrons forms an anion with a −3 charge (anion charge = 8 − 5). Group **6A** elements have **six** valence electrons. A gain of **two** electrons forms an anion with a −2 charge (anion charge = 8 − 6). Group **7A** elements have **seven** valence electrons. A gain of one electron forms an anion with a −1 charge (anion charge = 8 − 7).

Table 3.1 summarizes the ionic charges of the main group elements. The periodic table in Figure 3.2 gives the common ions formed by the main group elements.

Table 3.1 Ionic Charges of the Main Group Elements

Group Number	Number of Valence Electrons	Number of Electrons Gained or Lost	General Structure of the Ion
1A (1)	1	1 e⁻ lost	M^+
2A (2)	2	2 e⁻ lost	M^{2+}
3A (3)	3	3 e⁻ lost	M^{3+}
5A (15)	5	3 e⁻ gained	X^{3-}
6A (16)	6	2 e⁻ gained	X^{2-}
7A (17)	7	1 e⁻ gained	X^-

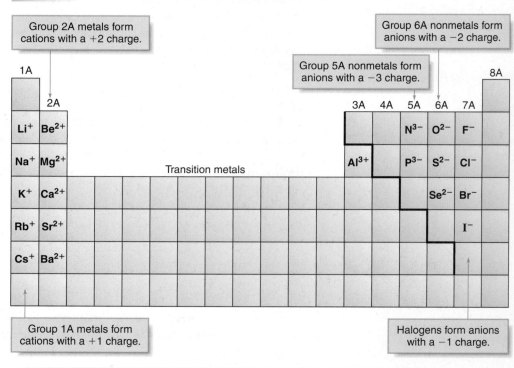

Figure 3.2 Common Ions Formed by Main Group Elements

Group 2A metals form cations with a +2 charge.

Group 6A nonmetals form anions with a −2 charge.

Group 5A nonmetals form anions with a −3 charge.

Transition metals

Group 1A metals form cations with a +1 charge.

Halogens form anions with a −1 charge.

SAMPLE PROBLEM 3.4

Use the group number to determine the charge on an ion derived from each element: (a) barium; (b) sulfur.

Analysis

Locate the element in the periodic table. A metal in groups 1A, 2A, or 3A forms a cation equal in charge to the group number. A nonmetal in groups 5A, 6A, and 7A forms an anion whose charge equals 8 − (the group number).

Solution

a. Barium (Ba) is located in group 2A, so it forms a cation with a +2 charge; Ba^{2+}.

b. Sulfur (S) is located in group 6A, so it forms an anion with a negative charge of 8 − 6 = 2; S^{2-}.

PROBLEM 3.6

Use the group number to determine the charge on an ion derived from each element.

a. magnesium   b. iodine   c. selenium   d. rubidium

PROBLEM 3.7

What noble gas has the same electronic configuration as each ion derived from the elements in Problem 3.6?

3.2C Metals with Variable Charge

The transition metals form cations like other metals, but the magnitude of the charge on the cation is harder to predict. Some transition metals, and a few main group metals as well, form more than one type of cation. For example, iron forms two different cations, Fe^{2+} and Fe^{3+}. Fe^{2+} is formed by losing two valence electrons from the $4s$ orbital. Fe^{3+} is formed by loss of three electrons, two from a $4s$ orbital and one from a $3d$ orbital.

Figure 3.3   Common Cations Derived from Transition Metals and Group 4A Metals

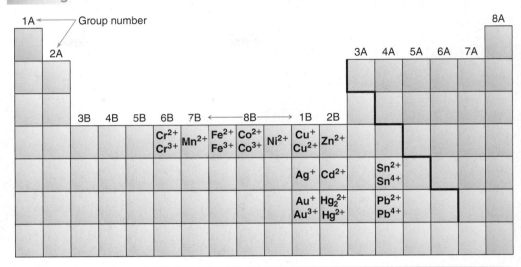

Because transition metal cations generally have additional d electrons that the nearest noble gas does not, the octet rule is not usually followed. Figure 3.3 illustrates the common cations formed from transition metals, as well as some main group elements that form more than one cation.

PROBLEM 3.8

How many electrons and protons are contained in each cation?

a. Au^+ b. Au^{3+} c. Sn^{2+} d. Sn^{4+}

3.2D   FOCUS ON THE HUMAN BODY
Important Ions in the Body

Many different ions are required for proper cellular and organ function (Figure 3.4). The major cations in the body are Na^+, K^+, Ca^{2+}, and Mg^{2+}. K^+ and Mg^{2+} are present in high concentrations inside cells, while Na^+ and Ca^{2+} are present in a higher concentration outside cells, in the extracellular fluids. Na^+ is the major cation present in blood and extracellular bodily fluids and its concentration is carefully regulated through a number of mechanisms to maintain blood volume and blood pressure within acceptable ranges that permit organ function. Ca^{2+} is found mainly in solid body parts such as teeth and bones, but it is also needed for proper nerve conduction and muscle contraction, as is Mg^{2+}.

In addition to these four cations, Fe^{2+} and Cl^- are also important ions. Fe^{2+} is essential for oxygen transport by red blood cells. Cl^- is present in red blood cells, gastric juices, and other body fluids. Along with Na^+, it plays a major role in regulating the fluid balance in the body.

Although Na^+ is an essential mineral needed in the daily diet, the average American consumes three to five times the recommended daily allowance (RDA) of 2,400 mg. Excess sodium intake is linked to high blood pressure and heart disease. Dietary Na^+ comes from salt, NaCl, added during cooking or at the table. Na^+ is also added during the preparation of processed foods and canned products. For example, one 3.5-oz serving of fresh asparagus has only 1 mg of Na^+, but the same serving size of canned asparagus contains 236 mg of Na^+. Potato chips, snack foods, ketchup, processed meats, and many cheeses are particularly high in Na^+. Table 3.2 lists the Na^+ content of some common foods.

HEALTH NOTE

All of these foods are high in sodium.

Figure 3.4   Common Ions in the Human Body

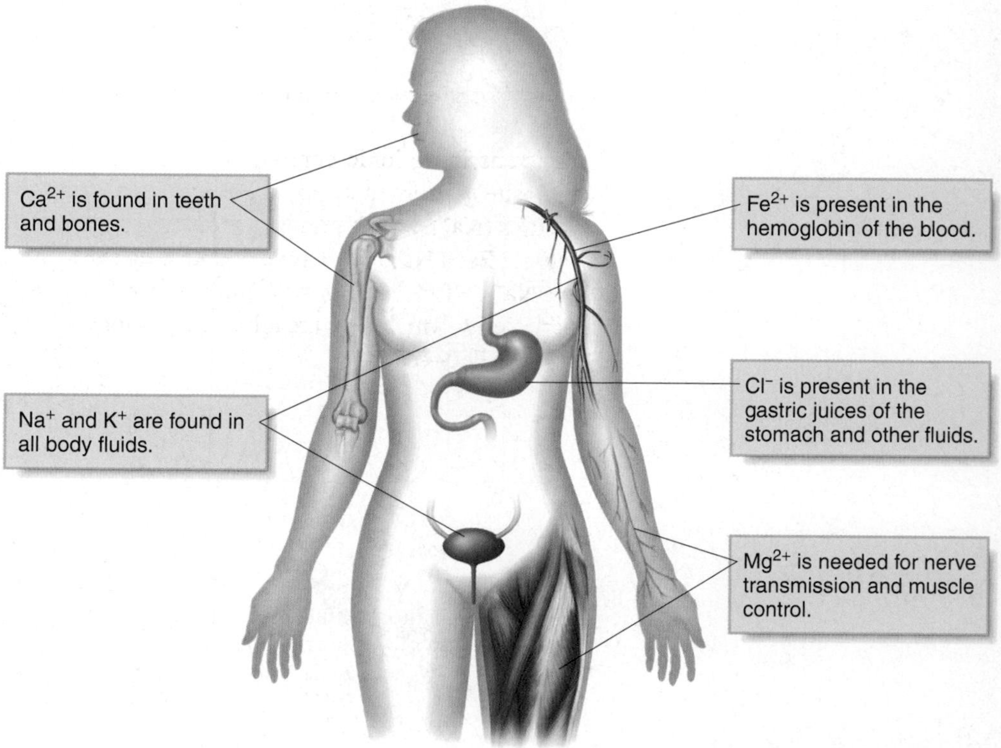

Ca^{2+} is found in teeth and bones.

Fe^{2+} is present in the hemoglobin of the blood.

Na$^+$ and K$^+$ are found in all body fluids.

Cl$^-$ is present in the gastric juices of the stomach and other fluids.

Mg^{2+} is needed for nerve transmission and muscle control.

Na$^+$, K$^+$, Ca^{2+}, Mg^{2+}, Fe^{2+}, and Cl$^-$ are all common ions present throughout the organs of the human body.

Table 3.2 Na$^+$ Content in Common Foods

Foods High in Na$^+$		Foods Low in Na$^+$	
Food	Na$^+$ (mg)	Food	Na$^+$ (mg)
Potato chips (30)	276	Banana (1)	1
Hot dog (1)	504	Orange juice (1 cup)	2
Ham, smoked (3 oz)	908	Oatmeal, cooked (1 cup)	2
Chicken soup, canned (1 cup)	1,106	Cereal, shredded wheat (3.5 oz)	3
Tomato sauce, canned (1 cup)	1,402	Raisins, dried (3.5 oz)	27
Parmesan cheese (1 cup)	1,861	Salmon (3 oz)	55

PROBLEM 3.9

Mn^{2+} is an essential nutrient needed for blood clotting and the formation of the protein collagen. (a) How many protons and electrons are found in a neutral manganese atom? (b) How many electrons and protons are found in the cation Mn^{2+}? (c) Write the electronic configuration of the element manganese and suggest which electrons are lost to form the Mn^{2+} cation.

3.3 Ionic Compounds

When a metal (on the left side of the periodic table) transfers one or more electrons to a nonmetal (on the right side), **ionic bonds** are formed.

- **Ionic compounds are composed of cations and anions.**

The ions in an ionic compound are arranged to maximize the attractive force between the oppositely charged species. For example, sodium chloride, NaCl, is composed of sodium cations (Na^+) and chloride anions (Cl^-), packed together in a regular arrangement in a crystal lattice. Each Na^+ cation is surrounded by six Cl^- anions, and each Cl^- anion is surrounded by six Na^+ cations. In this way, the positively charged cations are located closer to the charged particles to which they are attracted—anions—and farther from the particles from which they are repelled—cations.

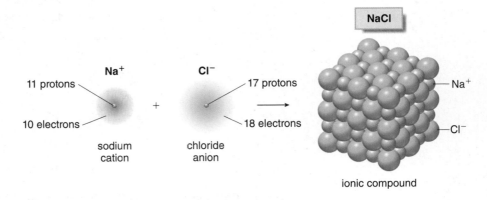

- **The sum of the charges in an ionic compound must always be zero overall.**

The formula for an ionic compound shows the ratio of ions that combine to give zero charge. Since the sodium cation has a +1 charge and the chloride anion has a –1 charge, there must be one Na^+ cation for each Cl^- anion; thus, the formula is **NaCl.**

When cations and anions having charges of different magnitude combine, the number of cations per anion is not equal. Consider an ionic compound formed from calcium (Ca) and fluorine (F). Since calcium is located in group 2A, it loses two valence electrons to form Ca^{2+}. Since fluorine is located in group 7A, it gains one electron to form F^- like other halogens. When Ca^{2+} combines with the fluorine anion F^-, **there must be two F^- anions for each Ca^{2+} cation to have an overall charge of zero.**

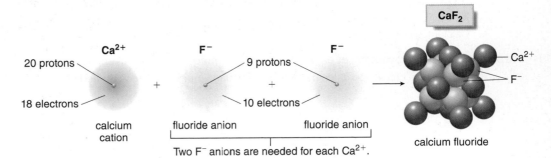

In writing a formula for an ionic compound, we use subscripts when the number of ions needed to achieve zero charge is greater than one. Since two F^- anions are needed for each calcium cation, the formula is **CaF_2.** Figure 3.5 illustrates additional examples of how cations and anions combine to give zero overall charge.

Figure 3.5

Examples of Ionic Compounds
with Zero Overall Charge

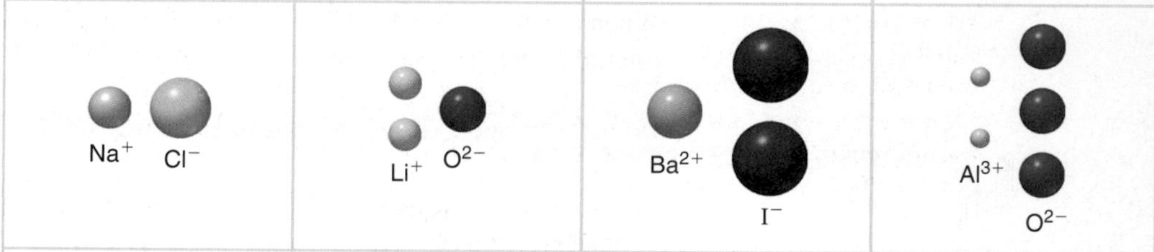

NaCl	Li$_2$O	BaI$_2$	Al$_2$O$_3$
Na$^+$ Cl$^-$	Li$^+$ O^{2-}	Ba^{2+} I$^-$	Al^{3+} O^{2-}
+1 −1	+2 −2	+2 −2	+6 −6

The ratio of oppositely charged ions that combine to form an ionic compound depends on the charge of the ions.

- NaCl: One Na$^+$ cation (+1 charge) combines with one Cl$^-$ anion (−1 charge).
- Li$_2$O: Two Li$^+$ cations (+2 charge total) combine with one O^{2-} anion (−2 charge).
- BaI$_2$: One Ba^{2+} cation (+2 charge) combines with two I$^-$ anions (−2 charge total).
- Al$_2$O$_3$: Two Al^{3+} cations (+6 charge total) combine with three O^{2-} anions (−6 charge total).

PROBLEM 3.10

Which pairs of elements will form ionic compounds?

a. lithium and bromine   c. calcium and magnesium
b. chlorine and oxygen   d. barium and chlorine

3.3A   Formulas for Ionic Compounds

Writing a formula for an ionic compound from two elements is a useful skill that can be practiced by following a series of steps.

How To Write a Formula for an Ionic Compound

Step [1] Identify which element is the cation and which is the anion.
- **Metals form *cations* and nonmetals form *anions.***
- Use the group number of a main group element to determine the charge.

An ionic compound derived from calcium and oxygen has the metal calcium as the cation and the nonmetal oxygen as the anion. Calcium (group 2A) loses two electrons to form Ca^{2+}. Oxygen (group 6A) gains two electrons to form O^{2-}.

Step [2] Determine how many of each ion type are needed for an overall charge of zero.
- When the cation and anion have the *same* charge only *one* of each is needed.

The charges are equal in magnitude,
+2 and −2.

Ca^{2+} + O^{2-} ⟶ CaO

One of each ion is needed
to balance charge.

—Continued

- When the cation and anion have different charges, as is the case with the Ca^{2+} cation and Cl^- anion, use the ion charges to determine the number of ions of each needed. **The charges on the ions tell us how many of the *oppositely* charged ions are needed to balance charge.**
- Write a subscript for the cation that is equal in magnitude to the charge on the anion. Write a subscript for the anion that is equal in magnitude to the charge on the cation.

The charges are not equal in
magnitude, +2 and −1.

Ca^{2+} Cl^{1-} The "1" is written for emphasis.

Ca_1Cl_2 = $\boxed{CaCl_2}$ 2 Cl^- anions for each Ca^{2+}

Step [3] **To write the formula, place the cation first and then the anion, and omit charges.**

- Use subscripts to show the number of each ion needed to have zero overall charge. When no subscript is written it is assumed to be "1."

As shown in step [2], the formula for the ionic compound formed from one calcium cation (Ca^{2+}) and one oxygen anion (O^{2-}) is CaO. The formula for the ionic compound formed from one calcium cation (Ca^{2+}) and two chlorine anions (Cl^-) is $CaCl_2$.

The tarnish on sterling silver is composed of an ionic compound formed from silver and sulfur (Sample Problem 3.5).

SAMPLE PROBLEM 3.5

When sterling silver tarnishes it forms an ionic compound derived from silver and sulfur. Write the formula for this ionic compound.

Analysis

- Identify the cation and the anion, and use the periodic table to determine the charges.
- When ions of equal charge combine, one of each ion is needed. When ions of unequal charge combine, use the ionic charges to determine the relative number of each ion.
- Write the formula with the cation first and then the anion, omitting charges, and using subscripts to indicate the number of each ion.

Solution

Silver is a metal, so it forms the cation. Sulfur is a nonmetal, so it forms the anion. The charge on silver is +1 (Ag^+), as shown in Figure 3.3. Sulfur (group 6A) is a main group element with a −2 charge (S^{2-}). Since the charges are unequal, use their magnitudes to determine the relative number of each ion to give an overall charge of zero.

The "1" is written for emphasis. Ag^{1+} S^{2-}

Ag_2S_1 = $\boxed{Ag_2S}$ 2 Ag^+ cations for each S^{2-}

Answer: Since two Ag^+ cations are needed for each S^{2-} anion, the formula is **Ag_2S.**

PROBLEM 3.11

Write the formula for the ionic compound formed from each pair of elements.

a. sodium and bromine

b. barium and oxygen

c. magnesium and iodine

d. lithium and oxygen

SAMPLE PROBLEM 3.6

Match the given representations of two ionic compounds dissolved in water with the following formulas: (a) KCl; (b) $CaCl_2$.

[1] 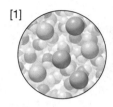   [2]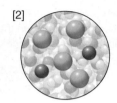

Analysis

Determine the charges on the cation and anion. When the cation and anion have the same charge, an equal number of cations and anions must be present for an overall charge of zero. When the cation and anion have different charges, use the charges on the ions to tell how many of the oppositely charged ions are needed so that the solution has an overall charge of zero.

Solution

a. Since KCl contains a cation (K^+) and anion (Cl^-) with charges of the same magnitude (+1 and −1), an equal number of cations and anions must be present in solution. Representation [1] contains an equal number of yellow and green spheres.

b. Since $CaCl_2$ contains a cation (Ca^{2+}) and anion (Cl^-) with charges of different magnitude (+2 and −1), the solution must contain twice as many anions as cations to have an overall charge of zero. Representation [2] contains twice as many green spheres (Cl^-) as purple spheres (Ca^{2+}).

PROBLEM 3.12

Draw a representation using molecular art for a solution of each of the following ionic compounds dissolved in water: (a) Na_2S; (b) $MgCl_2$.

3.3B   FOCUS ON HEALTH & MEDICINE
Ionic Compounds in Consumer Products

Simple ionic compounds are added to food or consumer products to prevent disease or maintain good health. For example, **potassium iodide** (KI) is an essential nutrient added to table salt. Iodine is needed to synthesize thyroid hormones. A deficiency of iodine in the diet can lead to insufficient thyroid hormone production. In an attempt to compensate, the thyroid gland may become enlarged, producing a swollen thyroid referred to as a goiter. **Sodium fluoride** (NaF) is added to toothpaste to strengthen tooth enamel and help prevent tooth decay.

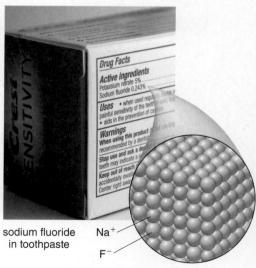

K^+ potassium iodide   sodium fluoride Na^+
I^- in table salt   in toothpaste F^-

HEALTH NOTE

Potassium is a critical cation for normal heart and skeletal muscle function and nerve impulse conduction. Drinking electrolyte replacement beverages like Gatorade or Powerade can replenish K$^+$ lost in sweat.

Potassium chloride (KCl), sold under trade names such as K–Dur, Klor–Con, and Micro–K, is an ionic compound used for patients whose potassium levels are low. Potassium chloride can be given as tablets, an oral suspension, or intravenously. Adequate potassium levels are needed for proper fluid balance and organ function. Although potassium is readily obtained from many different food sources (e.g., potatoes, beans, melon, bananas, and spinach), levels can become low when too much potassium is lost in sweat and urine or through the use of certain medications.

PROBLEM 3.13

Zinc oxide, an ionic compound formed from zinc and oxygen, is a common component of sunblocks, as mentioned in the chapter opener. The zinc oxide crystals reflect sunlight away from the skin, and in this way, protect it from sun exposure. What is the ionic formula for zinc oxide?

3.4 Naming Ionic Compounds

Now that we have learned how to write the formulas of some simple ionic compounds, we must learn how to name them. Assigning an unambiguous name to each compound is called chemical **nomenclature.**

3.4A Naming Cations

Cations of main group metals are given the name of the element from which they are formed.

Na$^+$	K$^+$	Ca^{2+}	Mg^{2+}
sodium	potassium	calcium	magnesium

It is common to add the word "ion" after the name of the metal cation to distinguish it from the neutral metal itself. For example, when the concentration of sodium in a blood sample is determined, what is really measured is the concentration of sodium *ions* (Na$^+$).

When a metal is able to form two different cations, a method is needed to distinguish these cations. Two systems are used, the systematic method and the common method. The systematic method (Method [1]) will largely be followed in this text. Since many ions are still identified by older names, however, the common method (Method [2]) is also given.

- Method [1]: Follow the name of the cation by a Roman numeral in parentheses to indicate its charge.
- Method [2]: Use the suffix *-ous* for the cation with the lower charge, and the suffix *-ic* for the cation with the higher charge. These suffixes are often added to the Latin names of the elements.

For example, the element iron (Fe) forms two cations, Fe^{2+} and Fe^{3+}, which are named in the following way:

	Systematic Name	Common Name
Fe^{2+}	iron(II)	ferr**ous**
Fe^{3+}	iron(III)	ferr**ic**

Table 3.3 lists the systematic and common names for several cations.

3.4B Naming Anions

Anions are named by replacing the ending of the element name by the suffix *-ide*. For example:

Cl	- - - →	Cl$^-$	[Change *-ine* to **-ide.**]
chlorine		chlor**ide**	
O	- - - →	O^{2-}	[Change *-ygen* to **-ide.**]
oxygen		ox**ide**	

Table 3.4 lists the names of common anions derived from nonmetal elements.

Table 3.3 Systematic and Common Names for Some Metal Ions

Element	Ion Symbol	Systematic Name	Common Name
Chromium	Cr^{2+}	Chromium(II)	Chromous
	Cr^{3+}	Chromium(III)	Chromic
Copper	Cu^+	Copper(I)	Cuprous
	Cu^{2+}	Copper(II)	Cupric
Iron	Fe^{2+}	Iron(II)	Ferrous
	Fe^{3+}	Iron(III)	Ferric
Mercury	Hg_2^{2+}	Mercury(I)[a]	Mercurous
	Hg^{2+}	Mercury(II)	Mercuric
Tin	Sn^{2+}	Tin(II)	Stannous
	Sn^{4+}	Tin(IV)	Stannic

[a]Mercury(I) exists as Hg_2^{2+}, containing two atoms of mercury, each with a +1 charge.

Table 3.4 Names of Common Anions

Element	Ion Symbol	Name
Bromine	Br^-	Bromide
Chlorine	Cl^-	Chloride
Fluorine	F^-	Fluoride
Iodine	I^-	Iodide
Nitrogen	N^{3-}	Nitride
Oxygen	O^{2-}	Oxide
Phosphorus	P^{3-}	Phosphide
Sulfur	S^{2-}	Sulfide

PROBLEM 3.14

Give the name of each ion.

a. S^{2-} b. Cu^+ c. Cs^+ d. Al^{3+} e. Sn^{4+}

PROBLEM 3.15

Give the symbol for each ion.

a. stannic   b. iodide   c. manganese ion   d. lead(II)   e. selenide

3.4C Naming Ionic Compounds with Cations from Main Group Metals

To name an ionic compound with a main group metal cation whose charge never varies, **name the cation and then the anion.** Do *not* specify the charge on the cation. Do *not* specify how many ions of each type are needed to balance charge.

$$Na^+ \qquad F^- \qquad \dashrightarrow \qquad NaF$$
sodium   fluoride   sodium fluoride

$$Mg^{2+} \qquad Cl^- \qquad \dashrightarrow \qquad MgCl_2$$
magnesium   chloride   magnesium chloride

Thus, $BaCl_2$ is named barium chloride (*not* barium *di*chloride). The number of ions of each type is inferred in the name because the net charge must be zero.

SAMPLE PROBLEM 3.7

Name each ionic compound: (a) Na_2S; (b) $AlBr_3$.

Analysis

Name the cation and then the anion.

Solution

a. Na_2S: The cation is sodium and the anion is sulfide (derived from sulfur); thus, the name is sodium sulfide.

b. $AlBr_3$: The cation is aluminum and the anion is bromide (derived from bromine); thus, the name is aluminum bromide.

PROBLEM 3.16

Name each ionic compound.

a. NaF   b. MgO   c. SrBr$_2$ d. Li$_2$O   e. TiO$_2$ f. AlCl$_3$

3.4D   Naming Ionic Compounds Containing Metals with Variable Charge

To name an ionic compound that contains a metal with variable charge, we must specify the charge on the cation. The formula of the ionic compound—that is, how many cations there are per anion—allows us to determine the charge on the cation.

How To   Name an Ionic Compound That Contains a Metal with Variable Charge

Example: Give the name for CuCl$_2$.

Step [1]   Determine the charge on the cation.

- Since there are two Cl$^-$ anions, each of which has a −1 charge, the copper cation must have a +2 charge to make the overall charge zero.

$$CuCl_2 \quad 2\ Cl^-\ anions \quad ----\rightarrow \quad \text{The total negative charge is −2.}$$

Cu must have a +2 charge to balance the −2 charge of the anions.

$$\rightarrow Cu^{2+}$$

Step [2]   Name the cation and anion.

- Name the cation using its element name followed by a Roman numeral to indicate its charge. In the common system, use the suffix *-ous* or *-ic* to indicate charge.
- Name the anion by changing the ending of the element name to the suffix *-ide.*

$$Cu^{2+} \quad ---\rightarrow \quad copper(II) \quad or \quad cupric$$
$$Cl^- \quad ---\rightarrow \quad chloride$$

Step [3]   Write the name of the cation first, then the anion.

- **Answer:** Copper(II) chloride or cupric chloride.

HEALTH NOTE

Some toothpastes contain the ionic compounds SnF$_2$ as a source of fluoride and Al$_2$O$_3$ as an abrasive.

Sample Problem 3.8 illustrates the difference in naming ionic compounds derived from metals that have fixed or variable charge.

SAMPLE PROBLEM 3.8

SnF$_2$ and Al$_2$O$_3$ are both ingredients in commercial toothpastes. SnF$_2$ contains fluoride, which strengthens tooth enamel. Al$_2$O$_3$ is an abrasive that helps to scrub the teeth clean when they are brushed. Give names for (a) SnF$_2$; (b) Al$_2$O$_3$.

Analysis

First determine if the cation has a fixed or variable charge. To name an ionic compound that contains a cation that always has the same charge, name the cation and then the anion (using the suffix *-ide*). When the metal has a variable charge, use the overall anion charge to determine the charge on the cation. Then name the cation (using a Roman numeral or the suffix *-ous* or *-ic*), followed by the anion.

Solution

a. SnF$_2$: Sn cations have variable charge so the overall anion charge determines the cation charge.

$$SnF_2 \quad 2\ F^-\ anions \quad ---\rightarrow \quad \text{The total negative charge is −2.}$$

Sn must have a +2 charge to balance the −2 charge of the anions.

$$\rightarrow tin(II)\ or\ stannous \qquad\qquad\qquad \rightarrow fluoride$$

Answer: tin(II) fluoride or stannous fluoride

b. Al_2O_3: Al has a fixed charge of +3. To name the compound, name the cation as the element (aluminum), and the anion by changing the ending of the element name to the suffix -ide (oxygen → oxide).

Al_2O_3 aluminum oxide   **Answer:** aluminum oxide

PROBLEM 3.17

Name each ionic compound.

a. $CrCl_3$ b. PbS c. SnF_4 d. PbO_2 e. $FeBr_2$ f. $AuCl_3$

PROBLEM 3.18

Several copper salts are brightly colored. Give the name for each of the following ionic copper compounds.

a. Cu_2O (brown)   b. CuO (black)   c. $CuCl$ (green)   d. $CuCl_2$ (blue)

PROBLEM 3.19

When iron rusts it forms Fe_2O_3. Name this product of air oxidation.

3.4E Writing a Formula from the Name of an Ionic Compound

Thus far, we have focused on assigning a name to a formula for an ionic compound. Writing a formula from a name is also a useful skill.

How To Derive a Formula from the Name of an Ionic Compound

Example: Write the formula for tin(IV) oxide.

Step [1] Identify the cation and the anion and determine their charges.

- The name of the cation appears first, followed by the anion.
- For metals with variable charge, the Roman numeral gives the charge on the cation.

In this example, tin is the cation. The Roman numeral tells us that its charge is +4, making the cation Sn^{4+}. Oxide is the name of the oxygen anion, O^{2-} (Table 3.4).

Step [2] Balance charges.

- Use the charge on the cation to determine the number of ions of the anion needed to balance charge.

Sn^{4+} O^{2-} Two −2 anions are needed
                                          for each +4 cation.
cation   anion

Step [3] Write the formula with the cation first, and use subscripts to show the number of each ion needed to have zero overall charge.

Answer: SnO_2

PROBLEM 3.20

Write the formula for each ionic compound.

a. calcium bromide   c. ferric bromide   e. chromium(II) chloride
b. copper(I) iodide   d. magnesium sulfide   f. sodium oxide

3.5 Physical Properties of Ionic Compounds

Ionic compounds are crystalline solids composed of ions packed to maximize the interaction of the positive charge of the cations and negative charge of the anions. The relative size and charge of the ions determine the way they are packed in the crystal lattice. Ionic solids are held together by extremely strong interactions of the oppositely charged ions. How is this reflected in the melting point and boiling point of an ionic compound?

When a compound melts to form a liquid, energy is needed to overcome some of the attractive forces of the ordered solid to form the less ordered liquid phase. Since an ionic compound is held together by very strong electrostatic interactions, it takes a great deal of energy to separate the ions from each other. As a result, **ionic compounds have very high melting points.** For example, the melting point of NaCl is 801 °C.

A great deal of energy is needed to overcome the attractive forces present in the liquid phase, too, to form ions that are far apart and very disorganized in the gas phase, so **ionic compounds have extremely high boiling points.** The boiling point of liquid NaCl is 1413 °C.

A great many ionic compounds are soluble in water. When an ionic compound dissolves in water, the ions are separated, and each anion and cation is surrounded by water molecules, as shown in Figure 3.6. The interaction of the water solvent with the ions provides the energy needed to overcome the strong ion–ion attractions of the crystalline lattice. We will learn much more about solubility in Chapter 8.

When an ionic compound dissolves in water, the resulting aqueous solution conducts an electric current. This distinguishes ionic compounds from other compounds discussed in Chapter 4, some of which dissolve in water but do not form ions and therefore do not conduct electricity.

An **aqueous solution** contains a substance dissolved in liquid water.

PROBLEM 3.21
List five physical properties of ionic compounds.

Figure 3.6   Dissolving NaCl in Water

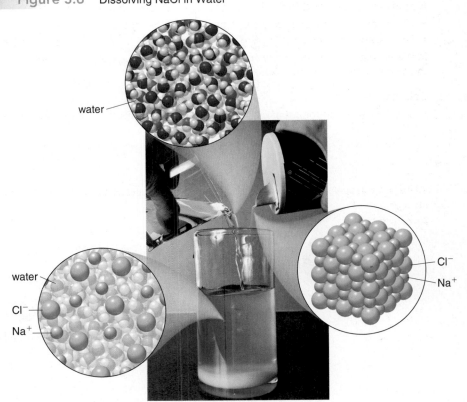

When NaCl dissolves in water, each Na⁺ ion and each Cl⁻ ion are surrounded by water molecules. The interactions of these ions with water molecules provide the energy needed to break apart the ions of the crystal lattice.

3.6 Polyatomic Ions

Sometimes ions are composed of more than one element. The ion bears a charge because the total number of electrons it contains is different from the total number of protons in the nuclei of all of the atoms.

- A *polyatomic ion* is a cation or anion that contains more than one atom.

The atoms in the polyatomic ion are held together by covalent bonds, but since the ion bears a charge, it bonds to other ions by ionic bonding. For example, calcium sulfate, $CaSO_4$, is composed of a calcium cation, Ca^{2+}, and the polyatomic anion sulfate, SO_4^{2-}. $CaSO_4$ is used to make plaster casts for broken bones.

We will encounter only two polyatomic cations: **H_3O^+, the hydronium ion,** which will play a key role in the acid–base chemistry discussed in Chapter 9, and **NH_4^+, the ammonium ion.**

In contrast, there are several common polyatomic anions, most of which contain a nonmetal like carbon, sulfur, or phosphorus, usually bonded to one or more oxygen atoms. Common examples include **carbonate (CO_3^{2-}), sulfate (SO_4^{2-}), and phosphate (PO_4^{3-}).** Table 3.5 lists the most common polyatomic anions.

The names of most polyatomic anions end in the suffix **-ate.** Exceptions to this generalization include hydroxide (OH^-) and cyanide (CN^-). Two other aspects of nomenclature are worthy of note.

- The suffix *-ite* is used for an anion that has one fewer oxygen atom than a similar anion named with the *-ate* ending. Thus, SO_4^{2-} is sulf*ate*, but SO_3^{2-} is sulf*ite*.
- When two anions differ in the presence of a hydrogen, the word *hydrogen* or the prefix *bi-* is added to the name of the anion. Thus, SO_4^{2-} is sulfate, but HSO_4^- is *hydrogen* sulfate or *bi*sulfate.

Table 3.5 Names of Common Polyatomic Anions

Nonmetal	Formula	Name
Carbon	CO_3^{2-}	Carbonate
	HCO_3^-	Hydrogen carbonate or bicarbonate
	$CH_3CO_2^-$	Acetate
	CN^-	Cyanide
Nitrogen	NO_3^-	Nitrate
	NO_2^-	Nitrite
Oxygen	OH^-	Hydroxide
Phosphorus	PO_4^{3-}	Phosphate
	HPO_4^{2-}	Hydrogen phosphate
	$H_2PO_4^-$	Dihydrogen phosphate
Sulfur	SO_4^{2-}	Sulfate
	HSO_4^-	Hydrogen sulfate or bisulfate
	SO_3^{2-}	Sulfite
	HSO_3^-	Hydrogen sulfite or bisulfite

3.6A Writing Formulas for Ionic Compounds with Polyatomic Ions

Writing the formula for an ionic compound with a polyatomic ion is no different than writing a formula for an ion with a single charged atom, so we follow the procedure outlined in Section 3.3A.

HEALTH NOTE

Spam, a canned meat widely consumed in Alaska, Hawaii, and other parts of the United States, contains the preservative sodium nitrite, $NaNO_2$. Sodium nitrite inhibits the growth of *Clostridium botulinum*, a bacterium responsible for a lethal form of food poisoning.

HEALTH NOTE

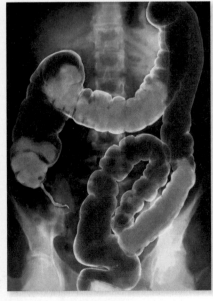

Barium sulfate is used to visualize the digestive system during an X-ray procedure.

When the cation and anion have the *same* charge, only *one* of each ion is needed for an overall charge of zero.

The charges are equal in magnitude +1 and –1.

$$Na^+ + NO_2^- \longrightarrow NaNO_2$$
sodium   nitrite   sodium nitrite

One of each ion is needed to balance charge.

The charges are equal in magnitude, +2 and –2.

$$Ba^{2+} + SO_4^{2-} \longrightarrow BaSO_4$$
barium   sulfate   barium sulfate

One of each ion is needed to balance charge.

In a compound formed from ions of unequal charge, such as magnesium (Mg^{2+}) and hydroxide (OH^-), **the charges on the ions tell us how many of the *oppositely* charged ions are needed to balance the charge.**

The charges are not equal in magnitude, +2 and –1.

$$Mg^{2+} + OH^- \longrightarrow Mg(OH)_2$$

Use a subscript outside the parentheses.

Two OH^- anions are needed to balance charge. Use parentheses around all atoms of the ion.

Parentheses are used around the polyatomic ion, and a subscript indicates how many of each are needed to balance charge. The formula is written as $Mg(OH)_2$ (*not* MgO_2H_2 or $MgOH_2$).

SAMPLE PROBLEM 3.9

A dietary supplement used to prevent and treat calcium deficiencies consists of an ionic compound formed from calcium and phosphate. What is its formula?

Analysis

- Identify the cation and anion and determine the charges.
- When ions of equal charge combine, one of each is needed. When ions of unequal charge combine, use the ionic charges to determine the relative number of each ion.
- Write the formula with the cation first and then the anion, omitting charges. Use parentheses around polyatomic ions when more than one appears in the formula, and use subscripts to indicate the number of each ion.

Solution

The cation (Ca^{2+}) and anion (PO_4^{3-}) have different charges so the magnitude of the ionic charges determines the number of each ion giving an overall charge of zero.

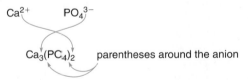

Ca^{2+} PO_4^{3-}

$Ca_3(PO_4)_2$ parentheses around the anion

Answer: Since three Ca^{2+} cations are needed for two PO_4^{3-} anions, the formula is $Ca_3(PO_4)_2$.

PROBLEM 3.22

Write the formula for the compound formed when the sulfate anion (SO_4^{2-}) combines with a cation from each of the following elements: (a) magnesium; (b) sodium; (c) nickel; (d) aluminum; (e) lithium.

PROBLEM 3.23

Write the formula of the ionic compound formed from each pair of cations and anions.

a. sodium and bicarbonate   c. ammonium and sulfate   e. calcium and bisulfate
b. potassium and nitrate   d. magnesium and phosphate   f. barium and hydroxide

PROBLEM 3.24

Write the formula for the compound formed when K^+ combines with each anion.

a. OH^- b. NO_2^- c. SO_4^{2-} d. HSO_3^- e. PO_4^{3-} f. CN^-

3.6B   Naming Ionic Compounds with Polyatomic Ions

Naming ionic compounds derived from polyatomic anions follows the same procedures outlined in Sections 3.4C and 3.4D. There is no easy trick for remembering the names and structures of the anions listed in Table 3.5. The names of the anions in boldface type are especially common and should be committed to memory.

SAMPLE PROBLEM 3.10

Name each ionic compound: (a) $NaHCO_3$, the active ingredient in baking soda; (b) $Al_2(SO_4)_3$, an ingredient once used in antiperspirants, but no longer considered effective.

Analysis

First determine if the cation has a fixed or variable charge. To name an ionic compound that contains a cation that always has the same charge, name the cation and then the anion. When the metal has a variable charge, use the overall anion charge to determine the charge on the cation. Then name the cation (using a Roman numeral or the suffix -ous or -ic), followed by the anion.

Solution

a. $NaHCO_3$: Sodium cations have a fixed charge of +1. The anion HCO_3^- is called bicarbonate or hydrogen carbonate.

   Answer: sodium bicarbonate or sodium hydrogen carbonate

b. $Al_2(SO_4)_3$: Aluminum cations have a fixed charge of +3. The anion SO_4^{2-} is called sulfate.

   Answer: aluminum sulfate

PROBLEM 3.25

Name each compound.

a. Na_2CO_3 b. $Ca(OH)_2$ c. $Mg(NO_3)_2$ d. $Mn(CH_3CO_2)_2$ e. $Fe(HSO_3)_3$ f. $Mg_3(PO_4)_2$

3.6C   FOCUS ON HEALTH & MEDICINE
Useful Ionic Compounds

Ionic compounds are the active ingredients in several over-the-counter drugs. Examples include **calcium carbonate ($CaCO_3$),** the antacid in Tums; **magnesium hydroxide [$Mg(OH)_2$],** one of the active components in the antacids Maalox and milk of magnesia; and **iron(II) sulfate ($FeSO_4$),** an iron supplement used to treat anemia.

The shells of oysters and other mollusks are composed largely of calcium carbonate, $CaCO_3$.

Ca^{2+}

CO_3^{2-}

OH^-

Mg^{2+}

SO_4^{2-}

Fe^{2+}

$CaCO_3$ $Mg(OH)_2$ $FeSO_4$

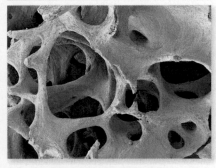

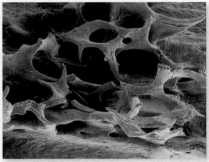

(top) Normal bone; (bottom) brittle bone due to osteoporosis. Osteoporosis results in a decrease in bone density, making bones brittle and easily fractured.

Some ionic compounds are given as intravenous drugs. Bicarbonate (HCO_3^-) is an important polyatomic anion that controls the acid–base balance in the blood. When the blood becomes too acidic, sodium bicarbonate ($NaHCO_3$) is administered intravenously to decrease the acidity. Magnesium sulfate ($MgSO_4$), an over-the-counter laxative, is also given intravenously to prevent seizures caused by extremely high blood pressure associated with some pregnancies.

3.6D FOCUS ON HEALTH & MEDICINE
Treating Osteoporosis

Although much of the body is composed of compounds held together by covalent bonds, about 70% of bone is composed largely of a complex ionic solid with the formula $Ca_{10}(PO_4)_6(OH)_2$ called **hydroxyapatite.** Throughout an individual's life, hydroxyapatite is constantly broken down and rebuilt. In postmenopausal women, however, the rate of bone loss often becomes greater than bone synthesis, and bones get brittle and easily broken. This condition is called **osteoporosis.**

In recent years, some prescription drugs have proven effective in combating osteoporosis. Sodium alendronate, trade name Fosamax, increases bone density by decreasing the rate of bone loss. Fosamax is an ionic compound with the formula $Na(C_4H_{12}NO_7P_2)$. This compound contains a sodium cation, Na^+, and a polyatomic anion, $(C_4H_{12}NO_7P_2)^-$.

PROBLEM 3.26
Using the charges on the ions that compose hydroxyapatite, show that it has zero overall charge.

CHAPTER HIGHLIGHTS

KEY TERMS

Ammonium ion (3.6)

Anion (3.2)

Bonding (3.1)

Carbonate (3.6)

Cation (3.2)

Covalent bond (3.1)

Hydronium ion (3.6)

Hydroxide (3.6)

Ion (3.1)

Ionic bond (3.1)

Molecule (3.1)

Nomenclature (3.4)

Octet rule (3.2)

Phosphate (3.6)

Polyatomic ion (3.6)

Sulfate (3.6)

KEY CONCEPTS

❶ What are the basic features of ionic and covalent bonds? (3.1)

- Both ionic bonding and covalent bonding follow one general rule: Elements gain, lose, or share electrons to attain the electronic configuration of the noble gas closest to them in the periodic table.
- Ionic bonds result from the transfer of electrons from one element to another. Ionic bonds form between a metal and a nonmetal. Ionic compounds consist of oppositely charged ions that feel a strong electrostatic attraction for each other.
- Covalent bonds result from the sharing of electrons between two atoms. Covalent bonds occur between two nonmetals, or when a metalloid combines with a nonmetal. Covalent bonding forms discrete molecules.

❷ How can the periodic table be used to determine whether an atom forms a cation or an anion, and its resulting ionic charge? (3.2)

- Metals form cations and nonmetals form anions.
- By gaining or losing one, two, or three electrons, an atom forms an ion with a completely filled outer shell of electrons.
- The charge on main group ions can be predicted from the position in the periodic table. For metals in groups 1A, 2A, and 3A, the group number = the charge on the cation. For nonmetals in groups 5A, 6A, and 7A, the anion charge = 8 − (the group number).

3 **What is the octet rule? (3.2)**
- Main group elements are especially stable when they possess an octet of electrons. Main group elements gain or lose one, two, or three electrons to form ions with eight outer shell electrons.

4 **What determines the formula of an ionic compound? (3.3)**
- Cations and anions always form ionic compounds that have zero overall charge.
- Ionic compounds are written with the cation first, and then the anion, with subscripts to show how many of each are needed to have zero net charge.

5 **How are ionic compounds named? (3.4)**
- Ionic compounds are always named with the name of the cation first.
- With cations having a fixed charge, the cation has the same name as its neutral element. The name of the anion usually ends in the suffix *-ide* if it is derived from a single atom or *-ate* (or *-ite*) if it is polyatomic.
- When the metal has a variable charge, use the overall anion charge to determine the charge on the cation. Then name the cation using a Roman numeral or the suffix *-ous* (for the ion with the smaller charge) or *-ic* (for the ion with the larger charge).

6 **Describe the properties of ionic compounds. (3.5)**
- Ionic compounds are crystalline solids with the ions arranged to maximize the interactions of the oppositely charged ions.
- Ionic compounds have high melting points and boiling points.
- Most ionic compounds are soluble in water and their aqueous solutions conduct an electric current.

7 **What are polyatomic ions and how are they named? (3.6)**
- Polyatomic ions are charged species that are composed of more than one element.
- The names for polyatomic cations end in the suffix *-onium*.
- Many polyatomic anions have names that end in the suffix *-ate*. The suffix *-ite* is used for an anion that has one fewer oxygen atom than a similar anion named with the *-ate* ending. When two anions differ in the presence of a hydrogen, the word *hydrogen* or the prefix *bi-* is added to the name of the anion.

8 **List useful consumer products and drugs that are composed of ionic compounds.**
- Useful ionic compounds that contain alkali metal cations and halogen anions include KI (iodine supplement), NaF (source of fluoride in toothpaste), and KCl (potassium supplement). (3.3)
- Other products contain SnF_2 (fluoride source in toothpaste), Al_2O_3 (abrasive in toothpaste), and ZnO (sunblock agent). (3.4)
- Useful ionic compounds with polyatomic anions include $CaCO_3$ (antacid and calcium supplement), magnesium hydroxide (antacid), and $FeSO_4$ (iron supplement). (3.6)

PROBLEMS

Selected in-chapter and odd-numbered end-of-chapter problems have brief answers in Appendix B. The *Student Study Guide and Solutions Manual* contains detailed solutions to all in-chapter and odd-numbered end-of-chapter problems, as well as additional worked examples and a chapter self-test.

Ionic and Covalent Bonding

3.27 Which formulas represent ionic compounds and which represent covalent compounds?
a. CO_2 b. H_2SO_4 c. KF   d. CH_5N

3.28 Which formulas represent ionic compounds and which represent covalent compounds?
a. C_3H_8 b. ClBr   c. CuO   d. CH_4O

3.29 Which pairs of elements are likely to form ionic bonds and which pairs are likely to form covalent bonds?
a. potassium and oxygen   c. two bromine atoms
b. sulfur and carbon   d. carbon and oxygen

3.30 Which pairs of elements are likely to form ionic bonds and which pairs are likely to form covalent bonds?
a. carbon and hydrogen   c. hydrogen and oxygen
b. sodium and sulfur   d. magnesium and bromine

3.31 Why do ionic bonds form between a metal and a nonmetal?

3.32 Is it proper to speak of sodium chloride molecules? Explain.

Ions

3.33 Write the ion symbol for an atom with the given number of protons and electrons.
a. four protons and two electrons
b. 22 protons and 20 electrons
c. 16 protons and 18 electrons
d. 13 protons and 10 electrons
e. 17 protons and 18 electrons
f. 20 protons and 18 electrons

3.34 How many protons and electrons are present in each ion?
a. K^+ b. S^{2-} c. Mn^{2+} d. Fe^{2+} e. Cs^+ f. I^-

3.35 What element fits each description?
a. a period 2 element that forms a +2 cation
b. an ion from group 7A with 18 electrons
c. a cation from group 1A with 36 electrons

3.36 What element fits each description?
a. a period 3 element that forms an ion with a −1 charge
b. an ion from group 2A with 36 electrons
c. an ion from group 6A with 18 electrons

3.37 Why do elements in group 6A gain electrons to form anions?

3.38 Why do elements in group 2A lose electrons to form cations?

3.39 Give the ion symbol for each ion.
a. sodium ion   c. manganese ion   e. stannic
b. selenide   d. gold(III)   f. mercurous

3.40 Give the ion symbol for each ion.
   a. barium ion   c. oxide   e. lead(IV)
   b. iron(II)   d. ferrous   f. cobalt(III)

3.41 What noble gas has the same electronic configuration as each ion?
   a. O^{2-} b. Mg^{2+} c. Al^{3+} d. S^{2-} e. F^- f. Be^{2+}

3.42 Give two cations and two anions that have the same electronic configuration as each noble gas: (a) neon; (b) argon.

3.43 How many electrons must be gained or lost by each element to achieve a noble gas configuration of electrons?
   a. lithium   b. iodine   c. sulfur   d. strontium

3.44 How many electrons must be gained or lost by each element to achieve a noble gas configuration of electrons?
   a. cesium   b. barium   c. selenium   d. aluminum

3.45 Which ions are likely to form? For those ions that are not likely to form, explain why this is so.
   a. S^- b. S^{2-} c. S^{3-} d. Na^+ e. Na^{2+} f. Na^-

3.46 Which ions are likely to form? For those ions that are not likely to form, explain why this is so.
   a. Mg^+ b. Mg^{2+} c. Mg^{3+} d. Cl^+ e. Cl^- f. Cl^{2-}

3.47 For each of the general electron-dot formulas for elements, give the following information: [1] the number of valence electrons; [2] the group number of the element; [3] how many electrons would be gained or lost to achieve a noble gas configuration; [4] the charge on the resulting ion; [5] an example of the element.
   a. X·   b. ·Q·   c. ·Z̈·   d. :Ä·

3.48 Label each of the following elements or regions in the periodic table.

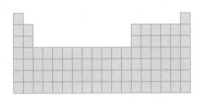

   a. a group that forms cations with a +2 charge
   b. a group that forms anions with a –2 charge
   c. a group that forms cations with a +1 charge
   d. a group that forms anions with a –1 charge
   e. elements that form ions with the same electronic configuration as Ne
   f. elements that form ions with the same electronic configuration as He

3.49 Use the element colors in Figure 2.3 (also shown on the inside back cover) and the information in Table 3.5 to identify each of the following anions. Give the name and proper formula, including the charge.

a.   b.   c.

3.50 Use the element colors in Figure 2.3 (also shown on the inside back cover) and the information in Table 3.5 to identify each of the following anions. Give the name and proper formula, including the charge.

a.   b.   c.

3.51 Give the formula for each polyatomic ion.
   a. sulfate   c. hydrogen carbonate
   b. ammonium   d. cyanide

3.52 Give the formula for each polyatomic ion.
   a. acetate   c. dihydrogen phosphate
   b. bisulfite   d. hydronium

3.53 How many protons and electrons are contained in each polyatomic ion?
   a. OH^- b. H_3O^+ c. PO_4^{3-}

3.54 How many protons and electrons are contained in each polyatomic ion?
   a. NH_4^+ b. CN^- c. CO_3^{2-}

3.55 Why isn't the octet rule followed by transition metals when they form cations?

3.56 Do all isotopes of an element form the same type of ions? Explain.

Ionic Compounds

3.57 How does the compound NaF illustrate the octet rule?

3.58 How does the compound LiF "violate" the octet rule?

3.59 Write the formula for the ionic compound formed from each pair of elements.
   a. calcium and sulfur   d. nickel and chlorine
   b. aluminum and bromine   e. sodium and selenium
   c. lithium and iodine

3.60 Write the formula for the ionic compound formed from each pair of elements.
   a. barium and bromine
   b. aluminum and sulfur
   c. manganese and chlorine
   c. zinc and sulfur
   e. magnesium and fluorine

3.61 Write the formula for the ionic compound formed from each cation and anion.
   a. lithium and nitrite
   b. calcium and acetate
   c. sodium and bisulfite
   d. manganese and phosphate
   e. magnesium and hydrogen sulfite

3.62 Write the formula for the ionic compound formed from each cation and anion.

a. potassium and bicarbonate

b. magnesium and nitrate

c. lithium and carbonate

d. potassium and cyanide

e. ammonium and phosphate

3.63 Considering the indicated charges on the cation **X** and the anion **Y,** fill in the table with the formula of the ionic compound that results in zero overall charge. One entry is filled in.

	Y^-	Y^{2-}	Y^{3-}
X^+			
X^{2+}	XY_2		
X^{3+}			

3.64 What is the charge on the cation **M** in each of the following ionic compounds?

a. MCl_2 b. MO c. M_3O_2 d. M_3N

3.65 Complete the following table by filling in the formula of the ionic compound derived from the cations on the left and each of the anions across the top.

	Br^-	OH^-	HCO_3^-	SO_3^{2-}	PO_4^{3-}
Na^+					
Co^{2+}					
Al^{3+}					

3.66 Complete the following table by filling in the formula of the ionic compound derived from the cations on the left and each of the anions across the top.

	I^-	CN^-	NO_3^-	SO_4^{2-}	HPO_4^{2-}
K^+					
Mg^{2+}					
Cr^{3+}					

3.67 Write the formula for the ionic compound formed from the bisulfate anion (HSO_4^-) and each cation: (a) K^+; (b) Ba^{2+}; (c) Al^{3+}; (d) Zn^{2+}.

3.68 Write the formula for the ionic compound formed from the sulfite anion (SO_3^{2-}) and each cation: (a) K^+; (b) Ba^{2+}; (c) Al^{3+}; (d) Zn^{2+}.

3.69 Write the formula for the ionic compound formed from the barium cation (Ba^{2+}) and each anion: (a) CN^-; (b) PO_4^{3-}; (c) HPO_4^{2-}; (d) $H_2PO_4^-$.

3.70 Write the formula for the ionic compound formed from the iron(III) cation (Fe^{3+}) and each anion: (a) CN^-; (b) PO_4^{3-}; (c) HPO_4^{2-}; (d) $H_2PO_4^-$.

Naming Ionic Compounds

3.71 Name each ionic compound.

a. Na_2O d. $AgCl$ f. $RbBr$

b. BaS e. $CoBr_2$ g. $PbBr_2$

c. PbS_2

3.72 Name each ionic compound.

a. KF d. SnO f. Li_2S

b. $ZnCl_2$ e. $AuBr_3$ g. $SnBr_4$

c. Cu_2S

3.73 Name each ionic compound.

a. $FeCl_2$ b. $FeBr_3$ c. FeS d. Fe_2S_3

3.74 Name each ionic compound.

a. $CrCl_2$ b. $CrBr_3$ c. CrO d. Cr_2O_3

3.75 Why is a Roman numeral needed in the name for $CuBr_2$ but not $CaBr_2$? Name both compounds.

3.76 Why is a Roman numeral needed in the name for PbO but not ZnO? Name both compounds.

3.77 Write formulas to illustrate the difference between each pair of compounds.

a. sodium sulfide and sodium sulfate

b. magnesium oxide and magnesium hydroxide

c. magnesium sulfate and magnesium bisulfate

3.78 Write formulas to illustrate the difference between each pair of compounds.

a. lithium sulfite and lithium sulfide

b. sodium carbonate and sodium hydrogen carbonate

c. calcium phosphate and calcium dihydrogen phosphate

3.79 Name each ionic compound.

a. NH_4Cl c. $Cu(NO_3)_2$ e. $Fe(NO_3)_2$

b. $PbSO_4$ d. $Ca(HCO_3)_2$

3.80 Name each ionic compound.

a. $(NH_4)_2SO_4$ c. $Cr(CH_3CO_2)_3$ e. $Ni_3(PO_4)_2$

b. NaH_2PO_4 d. $Sn(HPO_4)_2$

3.81 Write a formula from each name.

a. magnesium carbonate

b. nickel sulfate

c. copper(II) hydroxide

d. potassium hydrogen phosphate

e. gold(III) nitrate

f. lithium phosphate

g. aluminum bicarbonate

h. chromous cyanide

3.82 Write a formula from each name.

a. copper(I) sulfite

b. aluminum nitrate

c. tin(II) acetate

d. lead(IV) carbonate

e. zinc hydrogen phosphate

f. manganese dihydrogen phosphate

g. ammonium cyanide

h. iron(II) nitrate

3.83 Write the formula for the ionic compound formed from Pb^{4+} and each anion. Then name each compound.

    a. OH^- c. HCO_3^- e. PO_4^{3-}

    b. SO_4^{2-} d. NO_3^- f. $CH_3CO_2^-$

3.84 Write the formula for the ionic compound formed from Fe^{3+} and each anion. Then name each compound.

    a. OH^- c. HPO_4^{2-} e. PO_4^{3-}

    b. CO_3^{2-} d. NO_2^- f. $CH_3CO_2^-$

Properties of Ionic Compounds

3.85 Label each statement as "true" or "false." Correct any false statement to make it true.

    a. Ionic compounds have high melting points.

    b. Ionic compounds can be solid, liquid, or gas at room temperature.

    c. Most ionic compounds are insoluble in water.

    d. An ionic solid like sodium chloride consists of discrete pairs of sodium cations and chloride anions.

3.86 Label each statement as "true" or "false." Correct any false statement to make it true.

    a. Ionic compounds have high boiling points.

    b. The ions in a crystal lattice are arranged randomly and the overall charge is zero.

    c. When an ionic compound dissolves in water, the solution conducts electricity.

    d. In an ionic crystal, ions having like charges are arranged close to each other.

3.87 Which compound has the highest melting point: NaCl, CH_4, or H_2SO_4?

3.88 Which compound or element has the lowest boiling point: Cl_2, KI, or LiF?

Applications

3.89 Zinc is an essential nutrient needed by many enzymes to maintain proper cellular function. Zinc is obtained in many dietary sources, including oysters, beans, nuts, whole grains, and sunflower seeds. (a) How many protons and electrons are found in a neutral zinc atom? (b) How many electrons and

protons are found in the Zn^{2+} cation? (c) Write the electronic configuration of the element zinc, and suggest which electrons are lost to form the Zn^{2+} cation.

3.90 Wilson's disease is an inherited defect in copper metabolism in which copper accumulates in tissues, causing neurological problems and liver disease. The disease can be treated with compounds that bind to copper and thus remove it from the tissues. (a) How many protons and electrons are found in a neutral copper atom? (b) How many electrons and protons are found in the Cu^+ cation? (c) How many electrons and protons are found in the Cu^{2+} cation? (d) Zinc acetate inhibits copper absorption and so it is used to treat Wilson's disease. What is the structure of zinc acetate?

3.91 Na^+, K^+, Ca^{2+}, and Mg^{2+} are the four major cations in the body. For each cation, give the following information: (a) the number of protons; (b) the number of electrons; (c) the noble gas that has the same electronic configuration; (d) its role in the body.

3.92 Unlike many ionic compounds, calcium carbonate is insoluble in water. What information contained in this chapter suggested that calcium carbonate is water insoluble?

3.93 Write the formula for silver nitrate, an antiseptic and germ killing agent.

3.94 Ammonium carbonate is the active ingredient in smelling salts. Write its formula.

3.95 $CaSO_3$ is used to preserve cider and fruit juices. Name this ionic compound.

3.96 Many ionic compounds are used as paint pigments. Name each of the following pigments.

    a. CdS (yellow)   c. Cr_2O_3 (white)

    b. TiO_2 (white)   d. $Mn_3(PO_4)_2$ (purple)

3.97 Ammonium nitrate is the most common source of the element nitrogen in fertilizers. When it is mixed with water, the solution gets cold, so it is used in instant cold packs. When mixed with diesel fuel it forms an explosive mixture that can be used as a bomb. Write the formula of ammonium nitrate.

3.98 Write the formula for sodium phosphate, a key ingredient in many commercial detergents.

CHALLENGE PROBLEMS

3.99 Energy bars contain ionic compounds that serve as a source of the trace elements that the body needs each day for proper cellular function. Answer the following questions about some of the ingredients in one commercial product.

    a. Write the formulas for magnesium oxide and potassium iodide.

    b. The ingredient $CaHPO_4$ is called dicalcium phosphate on the label. What name would you give to this ionic compound?

    c. Give two different names for the ingredient $FePO_4$.

    d. Sodium selenite is one ingredient. Selenite is a polyatomic anion that contains a selenium atom in place of the sulfur atom in sulfite. With this in mind, suggest a formula for sodium selenite.

    e. Another ingredient is listed as chromium chloride. What is wrong with this name?

3.100 Some polyatomic anions contain a metal as part of the anion. For example, the anion dichromate has the formula $Cr_2O_7^{2-}$ and the anion permanganate has the formula MnO_4^-. Write the formula of the ionic compound formed from each of these anions and a potassium cation. Name each compound.

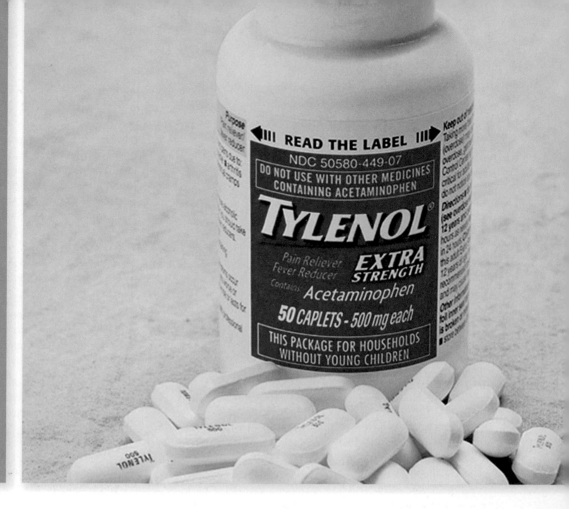

Like many drugs, **acetaminophen**, the active ingredient in the pain reliever Tylenol, is composed of covalent bonds.

Covalent Compounds

CHAPTER GOALS

In this chapter you will learn how to:

1 Recognize the bonding characteristics of covalent compounds

2 Draw Lewis structures for covalent compounds

3 Draw resonance structures for some ions and molecules

4 Name covalent compounds that contain two types of elements

5 Predict the shape around an atom in a molecule

6 Use electronegativity to determine whether a bond is polar or nonpolar

7 Determine whether a molecule is polar or nonpolar

Although all of Chapter 3 was devoted to ionic compounds, in truth, most compounds that we come in contact with in our daily lives are **covalent compounds,** formed by sharing electrons between atoms. The air we breathe is composed largely of the gases nitrogen and oxygen, two covalent molecules. The body is mostly water, which contains two covalent hydrogen–oxygen bonds. Most of the drugs routinely used—aspirin, acetaminophen, ibuprofen, and all antibiotics—are covalent compounds. Virtually all products of the chemical industry—polyethylene, nylon, synthetic dyes, gasoline, and pesticides, to name a few—are covalent compounds. In Chapter 4, we learn about the important features of covalent compounds.

4.1 Introduction to Covalent Bonding

In Section 3.1 we learned that **covalent bonds result from the *sharing* of electrons between two atoms.** For example, when two hydrogen atoms with one electron each (H·) combine, they form a covalent bond that contains two electrons. The two negatively charged electrons are now attracted to both positively charged hydrogen nuclei, forming the hydrogen **molecule, H_2.** This is an especially stable arrangement, since the shared electrons give each hydrogen atom the noble gas configuration of helium.

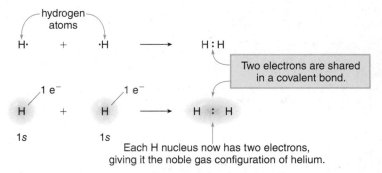

- **A covalent bond is a two-electron bond in which the bonding atoms share valence electrons.**
- **A *molecule* is a discrete group of atoms held together by covalent bonds.**

We use a **solid line between two element symbols to represent a two-electron bond.** Thus, the H_2 molecule can be drawn as:

$$H_2 \; = \; H:H \; = \; H\!-\!H \quad \text{two-electron bond}$$

Hydrogen is called a **diatomic molecule** because it contains just two atoms. In addition to hydrogen, six other elements exist as diatomic molecules: nitrogen (N_2), oxygen (O_2), fluorine (F_2), chlorine (Cl_2), bromine (Br_2), and iodine (I_2).

Hydrogen fluoride, HF, is an example of a diatomic molecule formed between two different atoms, hydrogen and fluorine. Hydrogen has one valence electron and fluorine has seven. H and F each donate one electron to form a single two-electron bond.

$$H\cdot \; + \; \cdot\ddot{\underset{..}{F}}: \; \longrightarrow \; H:\ddot{\underset{..}{F}}: \quad \text{or} \quad H\!-\!\ddot{\underset{..}{F}}: \;\text{—\textbf{three lone pairs}}$$

two electrons around H   **eight electrons** around F

The resulting molecule gives both H and F a filled valence shell: H is surrounded by two electrons, giving it the noble gas configuration of helium, and F is surrounded by eight electrons, giving it the noble gas configuration of neon. The F atom shares two electrons in one covalent bond, and it also contains three pairs of electrons that it does not share with hydrogen. These unshared electron pairs are called **nonbonded electron pairs** or **lone pairs.**

Nonbonded electron pair = lone pair.

- In covalent bonding, atoms share electrons to attain the electronic configuration of the noble gas closest to them in the periodic table.

As a result, hydrogen shares two electrons. Other main group elements are especially stable when they possess an *octet* **of electrons in their outer shell.**

PROBLEM 4.1

Use electron-dot symbols to show how a hydrogen atom and a chlorine atom form the diatomic molecule HCl. Explain how each atom has the electronic configuration of the noble gas closest to it in the periodic table.

PROBLEM 4.2

Use electron-dot symbols to show how two chlorine atoms form the diatomic molecule Cl_2. Explain how each atom has the electronic configuration of the noble gas closest to it in the periodic table.

4.1A   Covalent Bonding and the Periodic Table

When do two atoms form covalent bonds rather than ionic bonds? **Covalent bonds are formed when two nonmetals combine.** Nonmetals do not easily lose electrons, and as a result, one nonmetal does not readily transfer an electron to another nonmetal. **Covalent bonds are also formed when a metalloid bonds to a nonmetal.** Covalent bonding is preferred with elements that would otherwise have to gain or lose several electrons to form an ion with a complete outer shell of electrons.

Methane (CH_4), ammonia (NH_3), and water (H_2O) are three examples of covalent molecules in which each main group element is surrounded by eight electrons. Methane, the main component of natural gas, contains four covalent carbon–hydrogen bonds, each having two electrons. The nitrogen atom in NH_3, an agricultural fertilizer, is surrounded by an octet since it has three bonds and one lone pair. The oxygen atom in H_2O is also surrounded by an octet since it has two bonds and two lone pairs.

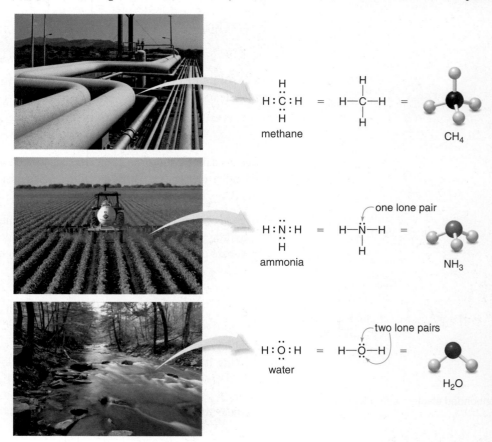

These electron-dot structures for molecules are called Lewis structures. Lewis structures show the location of all valence electrons in a molecule, both the shared electrons in bonds, and the non-bonded electron pairs. In Section 4.2 we will learn a general procedure for drawing Lewis structures.

How many covalent bonds will a particular atom typically form? As you might expect, it depends on the location of the atom in the periodic table. In the first row, hydrogen forms one covalent bond with its one valence electron. Other main group elements generally have no more than eight electrons around them. For neutral molecules, two consequences result.

- Atoms with one, two, or three valence electrons generally form one, two, or three bonds, respectively.
- Atoms with four or more valence electrons form enough bonds to give an octet. Thus, for atoms with four or more valence electrons:

$$\text{Predicted number of bonds} = 8 - \text{number of valence electrons}$$

These guidelines are used in Figure 4.1 to summarize the usual number of covalent bonds formed by some common atoms. Except for hydrogen, these common elements generally follow one rule in bonding:

$$\text{Number of bonds} + \text{Number of lone pairs} = 4$$

SAMPLE PROBLEM 4.1

Without referring to Figure 4.1, how many covalent bonds are predicted for each atom: (a) B; (b) N?

Analysis

Atoms with one, two, or three valence electrons form one, two, or three bonds, respectively. Atoms with four or more valence electrons form enough bonds to give an octet.

Solution

a. B has three valence electrons. Thus, it is expected to form three bonds.
b. N has five valence electrons. Since it contains more than four valence electrons, it is expected to form 8 − 5 = 3 bonds.

PROBLEM 4.3

How many covalent bonds are predicted for each atom: (a) F; (b) Si; (c) Br; (d) O; (e) P; (f) S?

PROBLEM 4.4

Fill in the lone pairs on each atom to give every main group element except hydrogen an octet.

a.
```
      H
      |
 H — C — Cl
      |
      H
```

b.
```
 H — N — O — H
      |
      H
```

c.
```
      H
      |
 H — C — O — H
      |
      H
```

d.
```
      H
      |
 Br — C — Br
      |
      H
```

Figure 4.1

Bonding Patterns for Common Main Group Elements

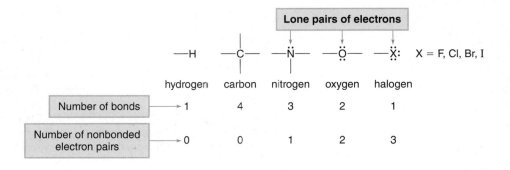

	hydrogen	carbon	nitrogen	oxygen	halogen
Number of bonds	1	4	3	2	1
Number of nonbonded electron pairs	0	0	1	2	3

PROBLEM 4.5

A nonmetal like oxygen forms both ionic and covalent bonds, depending on the identity of the element to which it bonds. What type of bonding is observed in CaO and CO_2? Explain why two different types of bonding are observed.

4.1B FOCUS ON THE HUMAN BODY
Covalent Molecules and the Cardiovascular System

Living organisms are a sea of covalent molecules. The major component in the body, water, is a covalent molecule. In addition, the proteins that compose muscle, the carbohydrates that are metabolized for energy, stored fat, and DNA, the carrier of genetic information, are all covalent molecules. Some of these molecules are very large, and are composed of hundreds or thousands of covalent bonds.

Figure 4.2 contains a schematic of a blood vessel inside the heart, and it illustrates a few covalent molecules—water, hemoglobin, oxygen, glycine, and nitroglycerin—that play a role in the cardiovascular system. Blood is composed of water and red blood cells that contain the protein hemoglobin. Hemoglobin is a large covalent compound that complexes oxygen molecules, and carries oxygen to tissues throughout the body. Heart muscle is composed of complex covalent

Figure 4.2

Covalent Molecules and the Human Heart

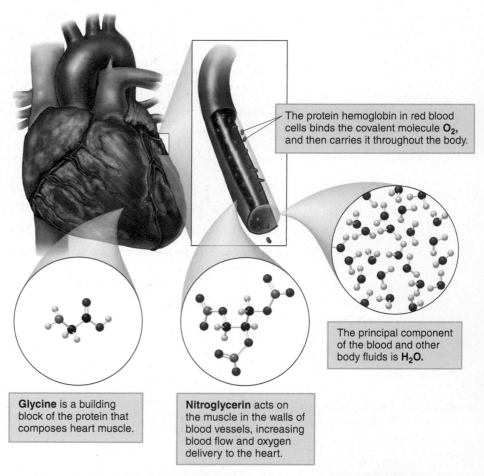

The protein hemoglobin in red blood cells binds the covalent molecule O_2, and then carries it throughout the body.

The principal component of the blood and other body fluids is H_2O.

Glycine is a building block of the protein that composes heart muscle.

Nitroglycerin acts on the muscle in the walls of blood vessels, increasing blood flow and oxygen delivery to the heart.

Some covalent compounds related to the chemistry of the heart include **water,** the most prevalent covalent compound in the body; **oxygen,** which is carried by the protein **hemoglobin** to the tissues; **glycine,** a building block of the proteins that compose heart muscle; and **nitroglycerin,** a drug used to treat some forms of heart disease.

protein molecules, which are synthesized from smaller molecules. The three-dimensional structure of one of those molecules, glycine, is pictured. Finally, covalent compounds are used to treat heart disease. For example, nitroglycerin, a drug used when blood vessels have become narrow, increases blood flow and thereby oxygen delivery to the heart.

4.2 Lewis Structures

A molecular formula shows the number and identity of all of the atoms in a covalent compound, but it does not tell us what atoms are bonded to each other. Thus, the molecular formula NH_3 for ammonia shows that ammonia contains one nitrogen atom and three hydrogen atoms, but it does not tell us that ammonia has three covalent nitrogen–hydrogen bonds and that the N atom has a lone pair. **A Lewis structure, in contrast, shows the connectivity between the atoms, as well as where all the bonding and nonbonding valence electrons reside.**

4.2A Drawing Lewis Structures

There are three general rules for drawing Lewis structures.

1. Draw only the *valence electrons.*
2. Give every main group element (except hydrogen) an *octet* of electrons.
3. Give each hydrogen two electrons.

In Section 4.1, Lewis structures were drawn for several covalent molecules. While drawing a Lewis structure for a diatomic molecule with one bond is straightforward, drawing Lewis structures for compounds with three or more atoms is easier if you follow a general procedure.

How To Draw a Lewis Structure

Step [1] Arrange the atoms next to each other that you think are bonded together.

- **Always place hydrogens and halogens on the periphery** since these atoms form only one bond.

- As a first approximation, **use the common bonding patterns** in Figure 4.1 to arrange the atoms.

In truth, sometimes atom arrangement is not obvious. For this reason, atom arrangement will be specified for you in some problems.

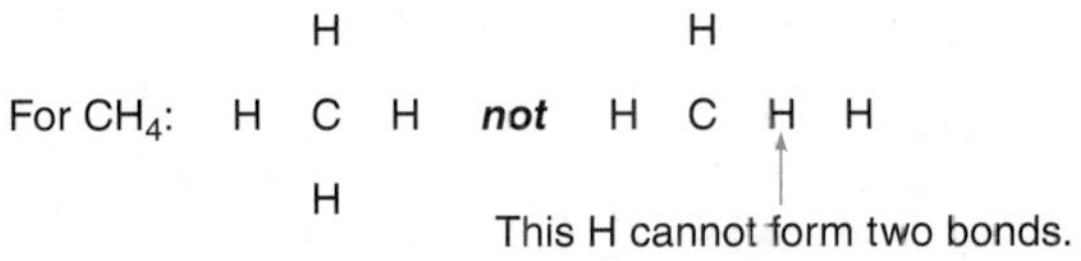

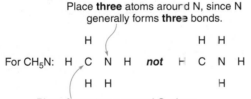

Step [2] Count the valence electrons.

- Use the group number of a main group element to give the number of valence electrons.
- This sum gives the total number of electrons that must be used in drawing the Lewis structure.

—Continued

Step [3] **Arrange the electrons around the atoms.**

- **Place one bond between every two atoms,** giving two electrons to each H and no more than eight to all other main group atoms.
- Use all remaining electrons to **fill octets with lone pairs,** beginning with atoms on the periphery.
- If all valence electrons are used and an atom does not have an octet, proceed to Step [4].

Step [4] **Use multiple bonds to fill octets when needed.**

- **Convert one lone pair to one bonding pair of electrons for each two electrons needed to complete an octet.** This forms double or triple bonds in some molecules, as shown in Section 4.2B. While a single covalent bond contains two electrons, a double bond consists of four electrons and a triple bond consists of six electrons.

Sample Problems 4.2 and 4.3 illustrate how to draw Lewis structures in two molecules that contain only single bonds.

SAMPLE PROBLEM 4.2

Draw a Lewis structure for chloromethane, CH_3Cl, a compound produced by giant kelp and a component of volcanic emissions.

Analysis and Solution

[1] Arrange the atoms.

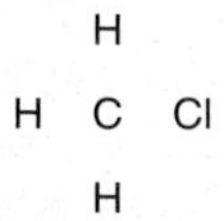

```
    H
H   C   Cl
    H
```

- Place C in the center and 3 H's and 1 Cl on the periphery.
- In this arrangement, C is surrounded by four atoms, its usual number.

[2] Count the electrons.

$$1\,C \times 4\,e^- = 4\,e^-$$
$$3\,H \times 1\,e^- = 3\,e^-$$
$$1\,Cl \times 7\,e^- = 7\,e^-$$
$$\overline{14\,e^-\ \text{total}}$$

The covalent molecule CH_3Cl is one of many gases released into the air from an erupting volcano.

[3] Add the bonds and lone pairs.

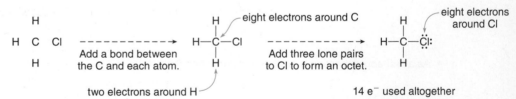

First add four single bonds, three C—H bonds and one C—Cl bond. This uses eight valence electrons, and gives carbon an octet (four two-electron bonds) and each hydrogen two electrons. Next, give Cl an octet by adding three lone pairs. This uses all 14 valence electrons. To check if a Lewis structure is valid, we must answer YES to three questions.

- Have all the electrons been used?
- Is each H surrounded by two electrons?
- Is every other main group element surrounded by eight electrons?

Since the answer to all three questions is YES, we have drawn a valid Lewis structure for CH_3Cl.

SAMPLE PROBLEM 4.3

Draw a Lewis structure for methanol, a compound with molecular formula CH_4O. Methanol is a toxic compound that can cause blindness and even death when ingested in small quantities (Section 14.4).

Analysis and Solution

[1] Arrange the atoms.

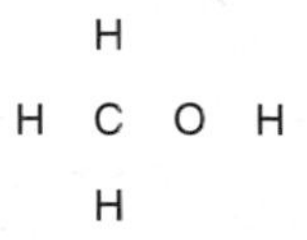

```
     H
                          • four atoms around C
 H   C   O   H            • two atoms around O
     H
```

[2] Count the electrons.

$$1\,C \times 4\,e^- = 4\,e^-$$
$$1\,O \times 6\,e^- = 6\,e^-$$
$$4\,H \times 1\,e^- = 4\,e^-$$

14 e^- total

[3] Add the bonds and lone pairs.

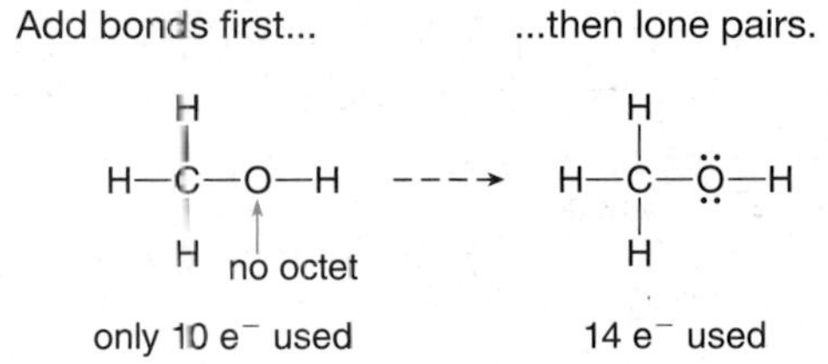

Add bonds first...   ...then lone pairs.

```
       H                                H
       |                                |
  H—C—O—H        - - - →          H—C—Ö—H
       |                                |
       H   no octet                     H

only 10 e⁻ used                      14 e⁻ used
```

In step [3], placing bonds between all atoms uses only 10 electrons, and the O atom, with only four electrons, does not yet have a complete octet. To complete the structure, give the O atom two lone pairs. This uses all 14 electrons, giving every H two electrons and every main group element eight. We have now drawn a valid Lewis structure.

PROBLEM 4.6

Draw a Lewis structure for each covalent molecule.

  a. HBr   b. CH_3F c. H_2O_2 d. N_2H_4 e. C_2H_6 f. CH_2Cl_2

PROBLEM 4.7

Draw a Lewis structure for dimethyl ether (C_2H_6O) with the given arrangement of atoms.

```
        H     H

  H  C  O  C  H

        H     H
```

4.2B Multiple Bonds

Sometimes it is not possible to give every main group element (except hydrogen) an octet of electrons by placing only single bonds in a molecule. For example, in drawing a Lewis structure for N_2, each N has five valence electrons, so there are 10 electrons to place. If there is only one N—N bond, adding lone pairs gives one or both N's fewer than eight electrons.

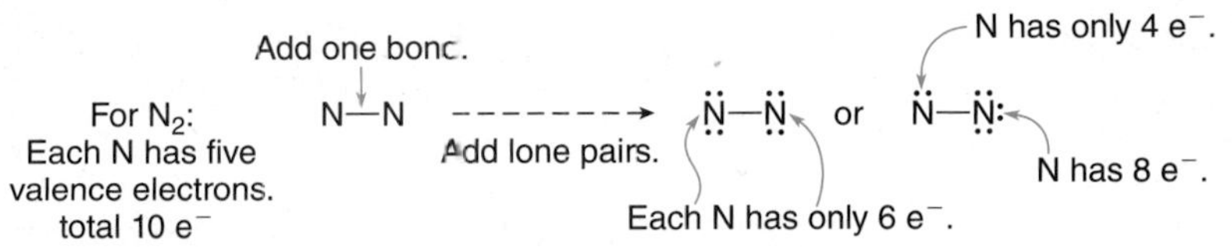

```
                    Add one bond.                              N has only 4 e⁻.
                         |
   For N₂:            N—N    - - - - - →    N̈—N̈   or   N̈—N̈:
   Each N has five            Add lone pairs.                  N has 8 e⁻.
   valence electrons.
   total 10 e⁻                        Each N has only 6 e⁻.
```

In this case, we must convert a lone pair to a bonding pair of electrons to form a multiple bond. Since we have four fewer electrons than needed, **we must convert** *two* **lone pairs to** *two* **bonding pairs of electrons and form a** *triple* **bond.**

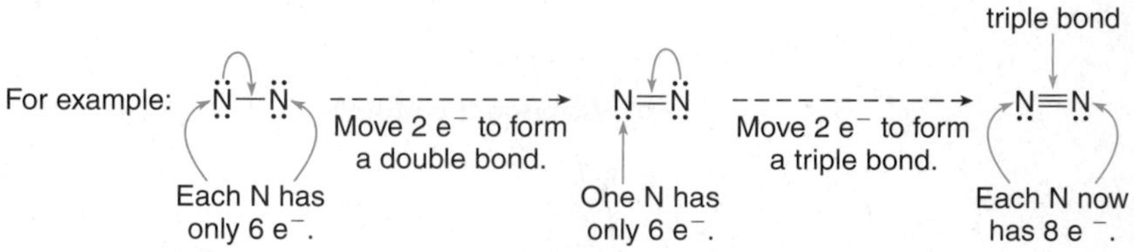

For example:

Move 2 e⁻ to form a double bond. → Move 2 e⁻ to form a triple bond. → triple bond

Each N has only 6 e⁻.   One N has only 6 e⁻.   Each N now has 8 e⁻.

- A triple bond contains six electrons in three two-electron bonds.

Sample Problem 4.4 illustrates another example of a Lewis structure that contains a double bond.

- A double bond contains four electrons in two two-electron bonds.

SAMPLE PROBLEM 4.4

Draw a Lewis structure for ethylene, a compound of molecular formula C_2H_4 in which each carbon is bonded to two hydrogens.

Analysis and Solution

Follow steps [1]–[3] to draw a Lewis structure.

[1] Arrange the atoms.

        H C C H
           H H

- Each C gets 2 H's.

[2] Count the electrons.

$$2\,C \times 4\,e^- = 8\,e^-$$
$$4\,H \times 1\,e^- = 4\,e^-$$
$$\overline{\qquad\qquad\quad 12\,e^-\ \textbf{total}}$$

[3] Add the bonds and lone pairs.

Add bonds first...   ...then lone pairs.

no octet

After placing five bonds between the atoms and adding the two remaining electrons as a lone pair, one C still has no octet.

[4] To give both C's an octet, change *one* **lone pair into** *one* **bonding pair of electrons between the two C atoms, forming a** *double* **bond.**

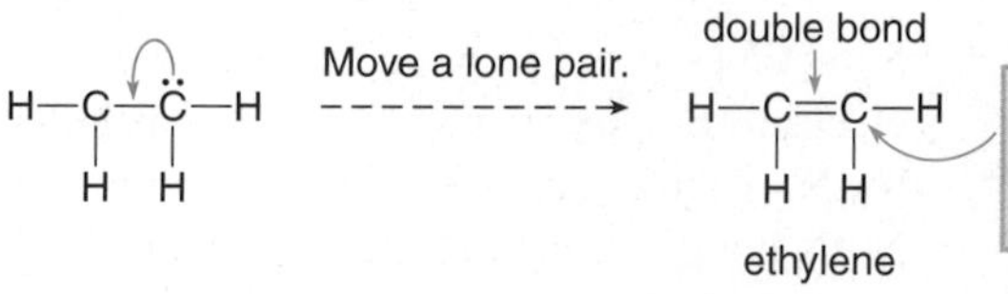

Move a lone pair. →   double bond

ethylene

- Each C now has four bonds.
- Each C is now surrounded by eight electrons.

This uses all 12 electrons, each C has an octet, and each H has two electrons. The Lewis structure is valid. **Ethylene contains a carbon–carbon double bond.**

- After placing all electrons in bonds and lone pairs, use a lone pair to form a multiple bond if an atom does not have an octet.

Formic acid (CH_2O_2, Problem 4.9) is responsible for the sting of some types of ants.

PROBLEM 4.8

Draw a valid Lewis structure for each compound, using the given arrangement of atoms.

a. HCN   H C N   b. CH_2O H C O   c. C_2H_3Cl H C C Cl

   hydrogen cyanide   formaldehyde   H   vinyl chloride   H H

PROBLEM 4.9

Draw a Lewis structure for formic acid with the given arrangement of atoms.

O

H C O H

PROBLEM 4.10

(a) Use the element colors in Figure 2.3 (and shown on the inside back cover) to determine the molecular formula of glycine, depicted as a ball-and-stick model in Figure 4.2. (b) Draw a Lewis structure for glycine and include all nonbonded electron pairs on atoms that contain them.

4.3 Exceptions to the Octet Rule

Most of the common elements in covalent compounds—carbon, nitrogen, oxygen, and the halogens—generally follow the octet rule. **Hydrogen is a notable exception, because it accommodates only two electrons in bonding.** Additional exceptions include elements such as **boron** in group 3A, and elements in the third row and later in the periodic table, particularly **phosphorus** and **sulfur.**

4.3A Elements in Group 3A

Elements in group 3A of the periodic table, such as boron, do not have enough valence electrons to form an octet in a neutral molecule. A Lewis structure for BF_3 illustrates that the boron atom has only six electrons around it. There is nothing we can do about this! There simply aren't enough electrons to form an octet.

$$\overset{\displaystyle :\ddot{F}:}{\underset{\displaystyle :\ddot{F}:}{\overset{|}{:\ddot{F}-B}}} \quad \text{only six electrons around B}$$

4.3B Elements in the Third Row

Another exception to the octet rule occurs with some elements located in the third row and later in the periodic table. These elements have empty *d* orbitals available to accept electrons, and thus they may have *more than eight* **electrons** around them. The two most common elements in this category are phosphorus and sulfur, which can have 10 or even 12 electrons around them.

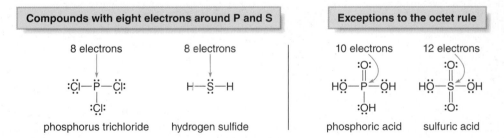

Compounds with eight electrons around P and S		Exceptions to the octet rule	
8 electrons	8 electrons	10 electrons	12 electrons
phosphorus trichloride	hydrogen sulfide	phosphoric acid	sulfuric acid

While PCl_3 and H_2S contain phosphorus and sulfur atoms that follow the octet rule, H_3PO_4 (phosphoric acid) and H_2SO_4 (sulfuric acid) do not. The phosphorus atom in H_3PO_4 is surrounded by 10 electrons, and the sulfur atom in H_2SO_4 is surrounded by 12 electrons.

Glyphosate (Problem 4.12) is an
effective herbicide because it interferes
with the synthesis of key compounds
needed for weed growth.

PROBLEM 4.11

Draw a Lewis structure for BBr_3, and explain why it does not follow the octet rule.

PROBLEM 4.12

Glyphosate is the most widely used weed killer and the active ingredient in Roundup and other
lawn products. (a) Add lone pairs around all N and O atoms to complete octets. (b) How many
electrons surround phosphorus in the given structure? (c) Which atoms in glyphosate do not
follow the octet rule?

$$H-O-\overset{\overset{O}{\|}}{P}-\overset{\overset{H}{|}}{\underset{\underset{H}{|}}{C}}-\overset{\overset{H}{|}}{N}-\overset{\overset{H}{|}}{\underset{\underset{H}{|}}{C}}-\overset{\overset{O}{\|}}{C}-O-H$$

$$H-O$$

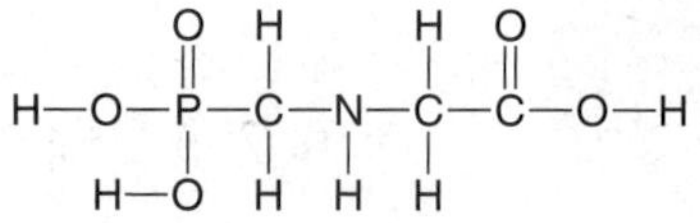

glyphosate

4.4 Resonance

We sometimes must draw Lewis structures for ions that contain covalent bonds—that is, polyatomic ions. In this case, the charge on the ion must be taken into account when counting the
number of valence electrons that must be placed around the atoms. In counting valence electrons:

- Add one electron for each negative charge.
- Subtract one electron for each positive charge.

For example, in drawing a Lewis structure for the cyanide anion, CN^-, there are 10 valence
electrons—four from carbon, five from nitrogen, and one additional electron from the negative
charge. In order to give each atom an octet, the two atoms must be joined by a triple bond, and
both carbon and nitrogen have a lone pair.

Number of valence electrons   Lewis structure

$1\,e^-$ CN^- $[:C\equiv N:]^-$
$4\,e^-$ $5\,e^-$

10 valence electrons   Each atom has an octet.

4.4A Drawing Resonance Structures

Sometimes two or more valid Lewis structures are possible for a given arrangement of atoms. Sample
Problem 4.5 illustrates that two Lewis structures are possible for the bicarbonate anion (HCO_3^-).

SAMPLE PROBLEM 4.5

Draw a Lewis structure for HCO_3^- with the following arrangement of atoms:

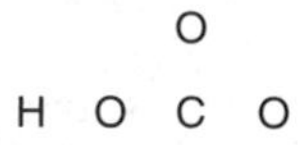

O

H O C O

Analysis and Solution

Follow steps [1]–[3] to draw a Lewis structure.

[1] Arrange the atoms.

O

H O C O

[2] Count the electrons.

$$\begin{array}{lll} 1\,C & \times\ 4\,e^- = & 4\,e^- \\ 3\,O & \times\ 6\,e^- = & 18\,e^- \\ 1\,H & \times\ 1\,e^- = & 1\,e^- \\ 1\,(-) & \times\ 1\,e^- = & 1\,e^- \\ \hline & & \mathbf{24\,e^-\ total} \end{array}$$

[3] Add the bonds and lone pairs.

Add bonds first...   ...then lone pairs.

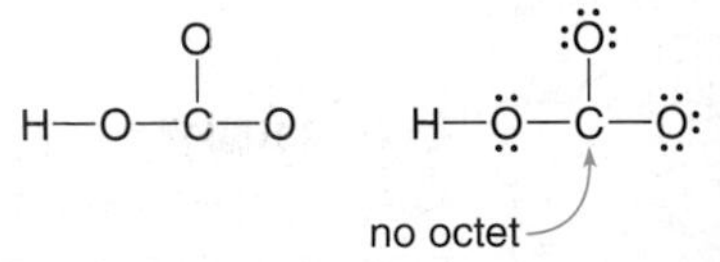

After placing four bonds and adding the remaining 16 electrons as lone pairs, the carbon atom does not have an octet.

[4] Convert one lone pair on O into one bonding pair to form a double bond. There are two ways to do this.

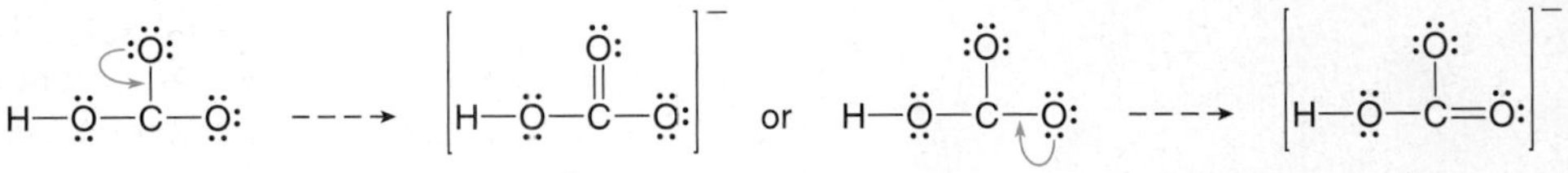

Thus, there are two different Lewis structures, **A** and **B,** for the bicarbonate anion.

The two different Lewis structures (**A** and **B**) for HCO_3^- are called **resonance structures.**

- Resonance structures are two Lewis structures having the same arrangement of atoms but a different arrangement of electrons.

Two resonance structures differ in the location of multiple bonds and the position of lone pairs. In Lewis structures **A** and **B,** the location of one C=O and one lone pair is different. We often use a **double-headed arrow** (⟷) to show that two Lewis structures are resonance structures.

The position of the double bond is different.

The position of a lone pair is different.

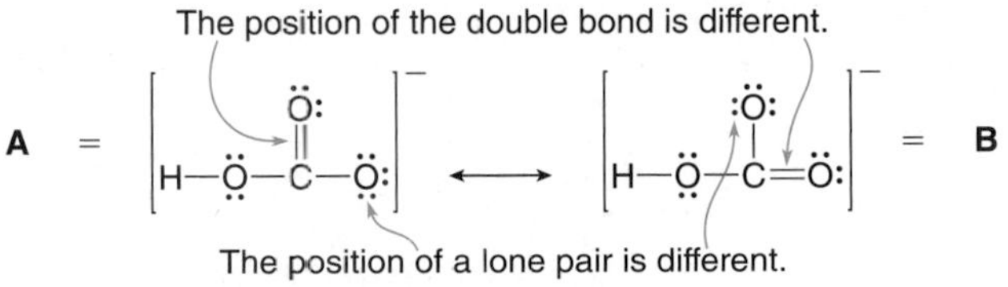

Which structure, **A** or **B,** is an accurate representation for HCO_3^-? The answer is ***neither of them.*** The true structure is a composite of both resonance forms and is called a **hybrid.** Experimentally it is shown that the carbon–oxygen bonds that appear as a double bond in one resonance structure and a single bond in the other, are really somewhere in between a C=O and a C—O. **Resonance stabilizes a molecule** by spreading out lone pairs and electron pairs in multiple bonds over a larger region of space. We say a molecule or ion that has two or more resonance structures is **resonance-stabilized.**

PROBLEM 4.13

Draw a second resonance structure for each ion.

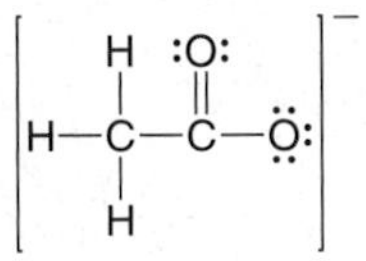

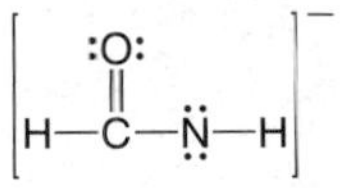

PROBLEM 4.14

Draw resonance structures for each polyatomic anion.

a. NO_2^- (two resonance structures, central N atom)

b. HCO_2^- (two resonance structures, central C atom)

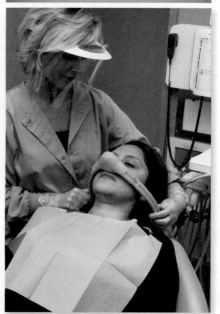

Nitrous oxide (N₂O, Problem 4.16) is a weak general anesthetic used for some dental procedures. Nitrous oxide is sometimes called laughing gas because it induces euphoria and mild hallucinations.

4.4B FOCUS ON THE ENVIRONMENT
Ozone

In addition to polyatomic ions, resonance structures can be drawn for neutral molecules as well. For example, the molecule **ozone, O₃,** can be drawn as two resonance structures that differ in the placement of a double bond and a lone pair.

$$O_3: \quad :\ddot{O}=\ddot{O}-\ddot{O}: \quad \longleftrightarrow \quad :\ddot{O}-\ddot{O}=\ddot{O}:$$

Bonds and lone pairs that differ in the two resonance structures are drawn in red.

Ozone is formed in the upper atmosphere (the stratosphere) by the reaction of oxygen molecules (O₂) with oxygen atoms (O). Stratospheric ozone is vital to life: it acts as a shield, protecting the earth's surface from destructive ultraviolet radiation (Figure 4.3). A decrease in ozone concentration in this protective layer would have some immediate consequences, including an increase in the incidence of skin cancer and eye cataracts. We will learn about the interaction of ozone with covalent molecules that contain carbon–chlorine bonds in Chapter 14.

PROBLEM 4.15

When fossil fuels containing sulfur are burned in power plants to generate electricity, large amounts of sulfur dioxide (SO₂) are formed and released into the atmosphere, where some of it eventually forms the acid in acid rain. If the structure of SO₂ consists of a central sulfur atom surrounded by an octet of electrons and bonded to both oxygen atoms, draw two resonance structures for sulfur dioxide.

PROBLEM 4.16

Nitrous oxide, N₂O, is a sweet-smelling gas sometimes used as an anesthetic in dentistry. Draw two resonance structures for N₂O that contain a central nitrogen atom.

Figure 4.3   Ozone in the Upper Atmosphere

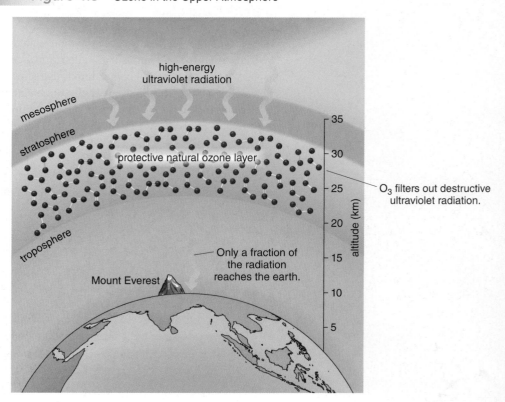

HEALTH NOTE

Cassava is a widely grown root crop, first introduced to Africa by Portuguese traders from Brazil in the sixteenth century. The root must be boiled or roasted to remove linamarin before ingestion. Eating the root without processing affords high levels of HCN, a cellular poison with a characteristic almond odor.

Trigonal = three-sided.

ENVIRONMENTAL NOTE

Over time, some adhesives and insulation made from formaldehyde can decompose back to formaldehyde, a reactive and potentially hazardous substance. Spider plants act as natural air purifiers by removing formaldehyde (H_2CO) from the air.

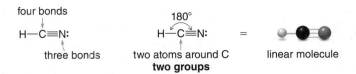

HCN, an extremely toxic gas, is produced by some naturally occurring molecules. For example, cassava, a woody shrub grown as a root crop in South America and Africa, contains the compound linamarin. Linamarin is not toxic itself, but it forms HCN in the presence of water and some enzymes. Cassava is safe to eat when the root has been peeled and boiled, so that the linamarin is removed during processing. If the root is eaten without processing, illness and even death can result from high levels of HCN formed from linamarin.

4.6B   Three Groups Around an Atom

Any atom surrounded by three groups is trigonal planar and has bond angles of 120°. Two examples illustrating this geometry are **BF_3** (boron trifluoride) and **$H_2C{=}O$** (formaldehyde).

three atoms around B
three groups

trigonal planar
molecule

three atoms around C
three groups

trigonal planar
molecule

In BF_3, the boron atom is surrounded by three fluorines and no lone pairs; that is, the boron is surrounded by three groups. A similar situation occurs with the carbon atom in $H_2C{=}O$. The carbon atom is surrounded by three atoms (two H's and one O) and no lone pairs—that is, three groups. To keep the three groups as far from each other as possible, they are arranged in a trigonal planar fashion, with bond angles of 120°.

4.6C   Four Groups Around an Atom

Any atom surrounded by four groups is tetrahedral and has bond angles of (approximately) 109.5°. For example, the simple organic compound methane, **CH_4,** has a central carbon atom with four bonds to hydrogen, each pointing to the corners of a tetrahedron.

tetrahedral carbon

How can we represent the three-dimensional geometry of a tetrahedron on a two-dimensional piece of paper? **Place two of the bonds in the plane of the paper, one bond in front, and one bond behind,** using the following conventions:

- A solid line is used for bonds in the plane.
- A wedge is used for a bond in front of the plane.
- A dashed line is used for a bond behind the plane.

bonds **in the plane**   bond **behind**

bond **in front**

tetrahedral molecule

Up to now, each of the groups around the central atom has been another atom. **A group can also be a lone pair of electrons.** NH_3 and H_2O represent two examples of molecules with atoms surrounded by four groups, some of which are lone pairs.

The Lewis structure for ammonia, **NH_3,** has an N atom surrounded by three hydrogen atoms and one lone pair of electrons—four groups. To keep four groups as far apart as possible, the three H atoms and the one lone pair around N point to the corners of a tetrahedron. The H—N—H bond angle of 107° is close to the tetrahedral bond angle of 109.5°. This shape is referred to as a **trigonal pyramid,** since one of the groups around the N is a nonbonded electron pair, not another atom.

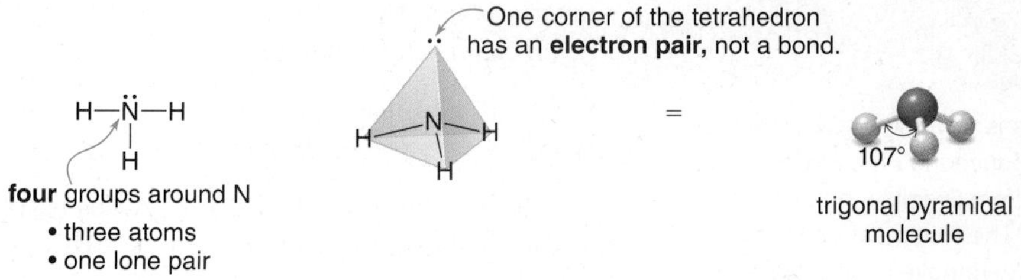

One corner of the tetrahedron has an **electron pair,** not a bond.

H—N̈—H
       |
       H

four groups around N
• three atoms
• one lone pair

=

107°
trigonal pyramidal molecule

The Lewis structure for water, **H_2O,** has an O atom surrounded by two hydrogen atoms and two lone pairs of electrons—four groups. In **H_2O,** the two H atoms and the two lone pairs around O point to the corners of a tetrahedron. The H—O—H bond angle of 105° is close to the tetrahedral bond angle of 109.5°. Water has a *bent* shape, because two of the groups around oxygen are lone pairs of electrons.

Two corners of the tetrahedron have **electron pairs,** not bonds.

H—Ö—H

four groups around O
• two atoms
• two lone pairs

=

105°
bent molecule

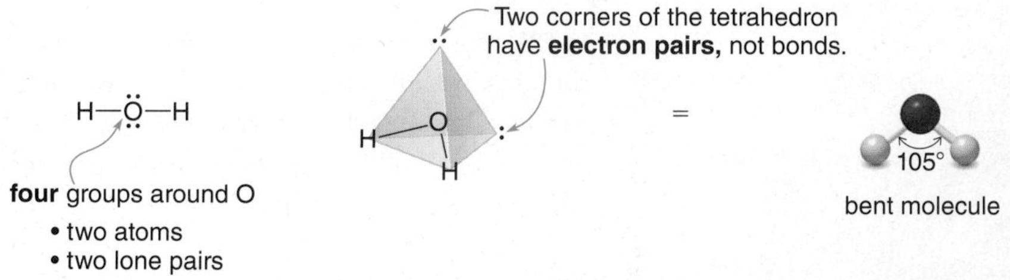

Common molecular shapes are summarized in Table 4.2. The three-dimensional shape determines the polarity of a molecule, which is discussed in Section 4.8. All of Chapter 15 is devoted to the importance of the three-dimensional shapes of molecules.

SAMPLE PROBLEM 4.7

Using the given Lewis structure, determine the shape around the second-row elements in each compound.

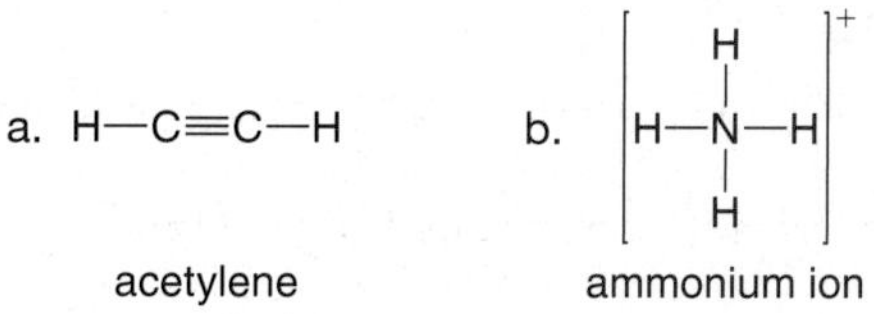

a. H—C≡C—H

acetylene

b. $\left[\begin{array}{c} H \\ | \\ H-N-H \\ | \\ H \end{array} \right]^+$

ammonium ion

Analysis

To predict the shape around an atom, we need a valid Lewis structure, which is given in this problem. Then count groups around the atom to determine molecular shape using the information in Table 4.2.

Solution

a. Each C in H—C≡C—H is surrounded by two atoms (one C and one H) and no lone pairs—that is, two groups. An atom surrounded by two groups is linear with a 180° bond angle.

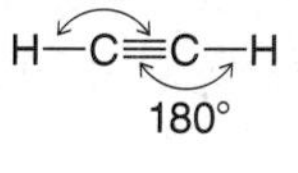

180°
H—C≡C—H
       180°

b. The N atom in NH_4^+ is surrounded by four H atoms—that is, four groups. An atom surrounded by four groups is tetrahedral, with 109.5° bond angles.

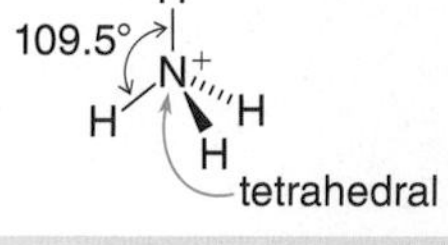

H
|
109.5° N⁺ H
H   H
tetrahedral

Table 4.2 Common Molecular Shapes Around Atoms

Total Number of Groups	Number of Atoms	Number of Lone Pairs	Shape Around an Atom (A)	Approximate Bond Angle (°)	Example
2	2	0	linear	180	CO_2, HCN
3	3	0	trigonal planar	120	BF_3, $H_2C{=}O$
4	4	0	tetrahedral	109.5	CH_4
4	3	1	trigonal pyramidal	~109.5[a]	NH_3
4	2	2	bent	~109.5[a]	H_2O

[a]The symbol "~" means approximately.

PROBLEM 4.19

What is the shape around each carbon atom in ethylene, $H_2C{=}CH_2$?

PROBLEM 4.20

What is the shape around the indicated atom in each molecule? Don't forget to draw in all needed lone pairs before determining molecular shape.

a. H_2S b. CH_2Cl_2 c. NCl_3 d. BBr_3

PROBLEM 4.21

$NaNH_2$, sodium amide, is a salt that contains a sodium cation, Na^+, and the polyatomic anion NH_2^-. Draw a Lewis structure for NH_2^-. Use the Lewis structure to determine which of the following ball-and-stick models represents the geometry of NH_2^-.

a.   b.

4.7   Electronegativity and Bond Polarity

When two atoms share electrons in a covalent bond, are the electrons in the bond attracted to both nuclei to the same extent? That depends on the **electronegativity** of the atoms in the bond.

- *Electronegativity* is a measure of an atom's attraction for electrons in a bond. Electronegativity tells us how much a particular atom "*wants*" electrons.

Figure 4.4 Electronegativity Values for Main Group Elements

Increasing electronegativity →

1A	2A	3A	4A	5A	6A	7A	8A
H 2.1							
Li 1.0	Be 1.5	B 2.0	C 2.5	N 3.0	O 3.5	F 4.0	
Na 0.9	Mg 1.2	Al 1.5	Si 1.8	P 2.1	S 2.5	Cl 3.0	
K 0.8	Ca 1.0	Ga 1.6	Ge 1.8	As 2.0	Se 2.4	Br 2.8	
Rb 0.8	Sr 1.0	In 1.7	Sn 1.8	Sb 1.9	Te 2.1	I 2.5	

Increasing electronegativity ↑

The electronegativity of an atom is assigned a value from 0 to 4; **the *higher* the value, the *more electronegative* an atom is, and the *more it is attracted* to the electrons in a bond.** The electronegativity values for main group elements are shown in Figure 4.4. The noble gases are not assigned values, since they do not typically form bonds.

Electronegativity values exhibit periodic trends.

- **Electronegativity *increases* across a row of the periodic table as the nuclear charge increases (excluding the noble gases).**
- **Electronegativity *decreases* down a column of the periodic table as the atomic radius increases, pushing the valence electrons farther from the nucleus.**

Thus, nonmetals have high electronegativity values compared to metals, because nonmetals have a strong tendency to hold on to and attract electrons. As a result, the most electronegative elements—fluorine and oxygen—are located at the **upper right-hand corner** of the periodic table, and the least electronegative elements are located in the lower left-hand corner.

PROBLEM 4.22

Using the trends in the periodic table, rank the following atoms in order of increasing electronegativity.

a. Li, Na, H b. O, C, Be c. Cl, I, F d. B, O, N

Electronegativity values are used as a guideline to indicate whether the electrons in a bond are *equally* shared or *unequally* shared between two atoms. For example, whenever two *identical* atoms are bonded together, each atom attracts the electrons in the bond to the same extent. The electrons are equally shared, and the bond is said to be **nonpolar.** Thus, a **carbon–carbon bond is nonpolar,** as is the fluorine–fluorine bond in F_2. The same is true whenever two different atoms having *similar* electronegativities are bonded together. **C—H bonds are considered to be nonpolar,** because the electronegativity difference between C (2.5) and H (2.1) is small.

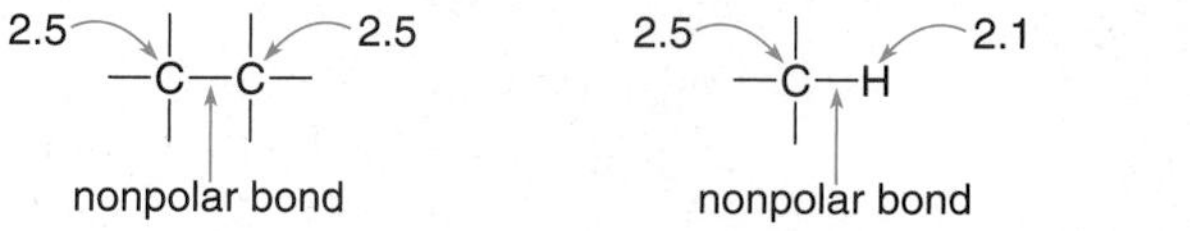

The small electronegativity difference between C and H is ignored.

In contrast, bonding between atoms of *different* electronegativity results in the *unequal* sharing of electrons. For example, in a C—O bond, the electrons are pulled away from C (2.5) towards the element of higher electronegativity, O (3.5). **The bond is *polar,* or *polar covalent.*** The bond is said to have a **dipole**—that is, **a separation of charge.**

$$\overset{\delta^+}{\underset{}{}}\quad\overset{\delta^-}{}$$
$$-\!\!\overset{|}{\underset{|}{C}}\!-\!O\!-$$
a dipole

A C–O bond is a *polar* bond.

The direction of polarity in a bond is often indicated by an arrow, with the head of the arrow pointing towards the more electronegative element. The tail of the arrow, with a perpendicular line drawn through it, is drawn at the less electronegative element. Alternatively, the lower case Greek letter delta (δ) with a positive or negative charge is used, resulting in the symbols δ^+ and δ^- to indicate this unequal sharing of electron density.

- The symbol δ^+ is given to the less electronegative atom.
- The symbol δ^- is given to the more electronegative atom.

Students often wonder how large an electronegativity difference must be to consider a bond polar. That's hard to say. We will set an arbitrary value for this difference and use it as an approximation. **Usually, a polar bond will be one in which the electronegativity difference between two atoms is 0.5 units or greater.**

As the electronegativity difference between the two atoms in a bond increases, the shared electrons are pulled more and more towards the more electronegative element. When the electronegativity difference is larger than 1.9 units, the electrons are essentially transferred from the less electronegative element to the more electronegative element and the bond is considered ionic. Table 4.3 summarizes the relationship between the electronegativity difference of the atoms in a bond and the type of bond formed.

Table 4.3 Electronegativity Difference and Bond Type

Electronegativity Difference	Bond Type	Electron Sharing
Less than 0.5 units	Nonpolar	Electrons are equally shared.
0.5–1.9 units	Polar covalent	Electrons are unequally shared; they are pulled towards the more electronegative element.
Greater than 1.9 units	Ionic	Electrons are transferred from the less electronegative element to the more electronegative element.

SAMPLE PROBLEM 4.8

Use electronegativity values to classify each bond as nonpolar, polar covalent, or ionic: (a) Cl_2; (b) HCl; (c) NaCl.

Analysis

Calculate the electronegativity difference between the two atoms and use the following rules: less than 0.5 (nonpolar); 0.5–1.9 (polar covalent); and greater than 1.9 (ionic).

Solution

	Electronegativity Difference	Bond Type
a. Cl_2	3.0 (Cl) – 3.0 (Cl) = 0	Nonpolar
b. HCl	3.0 (Cl) – 2.1 (H) = 0.9	Polar covalent
c. NaCl	3.0 (Cl) – 0.9 (Na) = 2.1	Ionic

PROBLEM 4.23

Use electronegativity values to classify the bond(s) in each compound as nonpolar, polar covalent, or ionic.

   a. HF   b. MgO   c. F_2 d. ClF   e. H_2O f. NH_3

PROBLEM 4.24

Show the direction of the dipole in each bond. Label the atoms with δ^+ and δ^-.

   a. H—F   b. —B—C—   c. —C—Li   d. —C—Cl

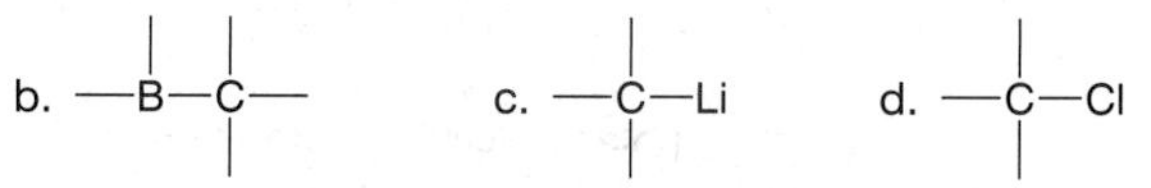

4.8 Polarity of Molecules

Thus far, we have been concerned with the polarity of a single bond. Is an entire covalent molecule polar or nonpolar? That depends on two factors: the polarity of the individual bonds and the overall shape. When a molecule contains zero or one polar bond, the following can be said:

> • A molecule with no polar bonds is a nonpolar molecule.
> • A molecule with one polar bond is a polar molecule.

Thus, CH_4 is a nonpolar molecule because all of the C—H bonds are nonpolar. In contrast, CH_3Cl contains only one polar bond, so it is a polar molecule. The dipole is in the same direction as the dipole of the only polar bond.

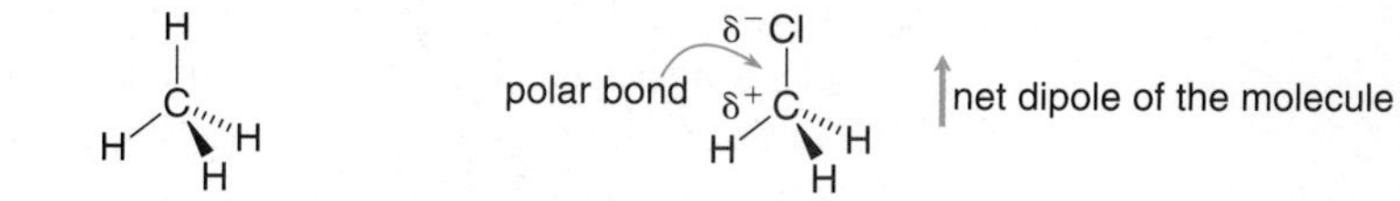

CH₄
no polar bonds
nonpolar molecule

CH₃Cl
one polar bond
polar molecule

With covalent compounds that have more than one polar bond, the shape of the molecule determines the overall polarity.

> • If the individual bond dipoles do not cancel, the molecule is polar.
> • If the individual bond dipoles cancel, the molecule is nonpolar.

To determine the polarity of a molecule that has two or more polar bonds:

> 1. Identify all polar bonds based on electronegativity differences.
> 2. Determine the shape around individual atoms by counting groups.
> 3. Decide if individual dipoles cancel or reinforce.

Figure 4.5 illustrates several examples of polar and nonpolar molecules that contain polar bonds. The net dipole is the sum of all the bond dipoles in a molecule.

Figure 4.5   Examples of Polar and Nonpolar Molecules

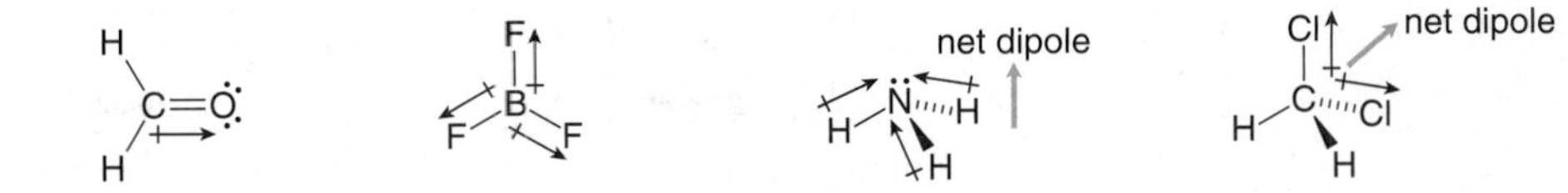

| one polar bond | three polar bonds
All dipoles cancel.
NO net dipole | three polar bonds
All dipoles reinforce. | two polar bonds
Two dipoles reinforce. |

polar molecule   **nonpolar** molecule   **polar** molecule   **polar** molecule

SAMPLE PROBLEM 4.9

Determine whether each molecule is polar or nonpolar: (a) H_2O; (b) CO_2.

Analysis

To determine the overall polarity of a molecule: identify the polar bonds; determine the shape around individual atoms; decide if the individual bond dipoles cancel or reinforce.

Solution

a. **H_2O:** Each O—H bond is polar because the electronegativity difference between O (3.5) and H (2.1) is 1.4. Since the O atom of H_2O has two atoms and two lone pairs around it, H_2O is a bent molecule around the O atom. The two dipoles reinforce (both point *up*), so **H_2O has a net dipole**; that is, **H_2O is a polar molecule.**

The two individual dipoles reinforce.

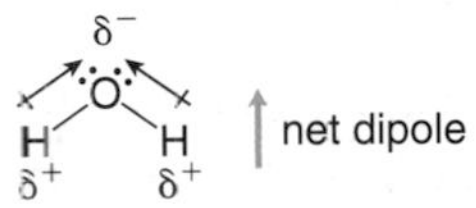

Do NOT draw H_2O as:

The net dipole bisects the H—O—H bond angle.
The bent representation shows that the dipoles reinforce.

Note: **We must know the geometry to determine if two dipoles cancel or reinforce.** For example, do **not** draw H_2O as a linear molecule, because you might think that the two dipoles cancel, when in reality, they reinforce.

b. **CO_2:** Each C—O bond is polar because the electronegativity difference between O (3.5) and C (2.5) is 1.0. The Lewis structure of CO_2 (Section 4.6A) shows that the C atom is surrounded by two groups (two O atoms), making it linear. In this case, the two dipoles are equal and opposite in direction so they cancel. Thus, CO_2 is a **nonpolar molecule** with **no net dipole.**

The two dipoles cancel.

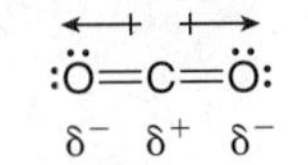

NO net dipole

PROBLEM 4.25

Label the polar bonds in each molecule, and then decide if the molecule is polar or nonpolar.

   a. HCl   b. C_2H_6 c. CH_2F_2 d. HCN   e. CCl_4

4.9 FOCUS ON HEALTH & MEDICINE
Covalent Drugs and Medical Products

Most drugs and products used in medicine are made up of covalent molecules. Some are simple molecules containing only a few atoms, while others are very complex. The principles learned in this chapter apply to all molecules regardless of size. Two examples are shown.

Hydrogen peroxide, H_2O_2, is a simple covalent molecule used to disinfect wounds. We now know a great deal about the structure of H_2O_2. The Lewis structure for H_2O_2 contains an O—O bond and each O atom has two lone pairs to give it an octet of electrons. Since each O atom is surrounded by two atoms and two lone pairs, it has a bent structure. While the O—O bond is nonpolar, both O—H bonds are polar, since the electronegativity difference between oxygen (3.5) and hydrogen (2.1) is large (1.4).

Acetaminophen, a pain-reliever and antipyretic (an agent that reduces fever), is more complex, but we still know much about its structure. Each O atom has two lone pairs and the N atom has one lone pair. Acetaminophen has six polar bonds, labeled in red. The number of groups around each atom determines its shape. One tetrahedral C surrounded by four groups and two trigonal planar C's are labeled.

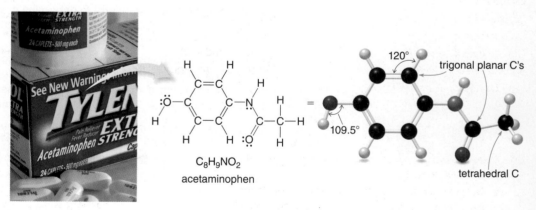

SAMPLE PROBLEM 4.10

Glycolic acid is a starting material used to manufacture dissolving sutures. (a) Place lone pairs where needed in the Lewis structure. (b) Give the shape around each atom in red. (c) Label all polar bonds.

$$H-O-\overset{\overset{\displaystyle H}{|}}{\underset{\underset{\displaystyle H}{|}}{C}}-\overset{\overset{\displaystyle O}{\|}}{C}-O-H$$

glycolic acid

Analysis and Solution

a. Each O atom needs two lone pairs to make an octet.

b. Count groups to determine shape.

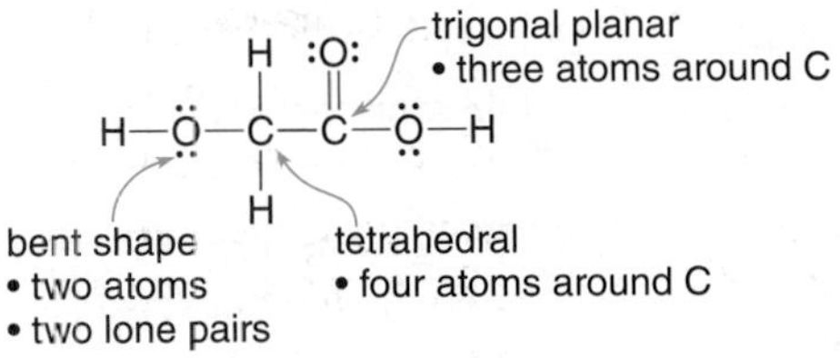

c. Since O is much more electronegative (3.5) than hydrogen (2.1) and carbon (2.5), all C—O and O—H bonds are polar and are labeled in red.

PROBLEM 4.26

In each compound: [1] determine the geometry around each carbon; [2] label each bond as polar or nonpolar.

a. 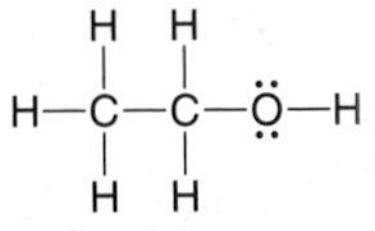 ethanol

b. 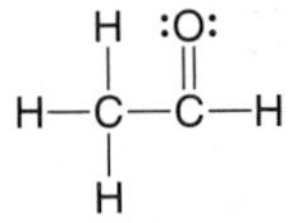 acetaldehyde

Ethanol, the "alcohol" in alcoholic beverages, is the world's most widely abused drug. It is metabolized to acetaldehyde, a toxic compound that produces some of the ill effects of ingesting too much ethanol. Ethanol is discussed in greater detail in Chapter 14.

CHAPTER HIGHLIGHTS

KEY TERMS

Covalent bond (4.1)
Diatomic molecule (4.1)
Dipole (4.7)
Double bond (4.2)
Double-headed arrow (4.4)
Electronegativity (4.7)
Hybrid (4.4)

Lewis structure (4.1)
Lone pair (4.1)
Molecular formula (4.2)
Molecule (4.1)
Multiple bond (4.2)
Nonbonded electron pair (4.1)

Nonpolar bond (4.7)
Polar bond (4.7)
Resonance structure (4.4)
Triple bond (4.2)
Valence shell electron pair repulsion (VSEPR) theory (4.6)

KEY CONCEPTS

❶ **What are the characteristic bonding features of covalent compounds? (4.1)**

- Covalent bonds result from the sharing of electrons between two atoms, forming molecules. Atoms share electrons to attain the electronic configuration of the noble gas nearest them in the periodic table. For many main group elements, this results in an octet of electrons.
- Covalent bonds are formed when two nonmetals combine or when a metalloid bonds to a nonmetal. Covalent bonds are preferred with elements that would have to gain or lose too many electrons to form an ion.
- Except for hydrogen, the common elements—C, N, O, and the halogens—follow one rule: the number of bonds + the number of lone pairs = four.

❷ **What are Lewis structures and how are they drawn? (4.2)**

- Lewis structures are electron-dot representations of molecules. Two-electron bonds are drawn with a solid line and nonbonded electrons are drawn with dots (:).
- Lewis structures contain only valence electrons. Each H gets two electrons and main group elements generally get eight.
- After placing all electrons in bonds and lone pairs in a Lewis structure, it may be necessary to use lone pairs to form double or triple bonds if an atom does not have an octet.

❸ **What are resonance structures? (4.4)**

- Resonance structures are two Lewis structures having the same arrangement of atoms but a different arrangement of electrons.
- The hybrid is a composite of all resonance structures that spreads out electron pairs in multiple bonds and lone pairs.

4 **How are covalent compounds with two elements named? (4.5)**

- Name the first nonmetal by its element name and the second using the suffix *-ide*. Add prefixes to indicate the number of atoms of each element.

5 **How is the molecular shape around an atom determined? (4.6)**

- To determine the shape around an atom, count groups—atoms and lone pairs—and keep the groups as far away from each other as possible.
- Two groups = linear, 180° bond angle; three groups = trigonal planar, 120° bond angle; four groups = tetrahedral, 109.5° bond angle.

6 **How does electronegativity determine bond polarity? (4.7)**

- Electronegativity is a measure of an atom's attraction for electrons in a bond.
- When two atoms have the same electronegativity value, or the difference is less than 0.5 units, the electrons are equally shared and the bond is nonpolar.
- When two atoms have very different electronegativity values—a difference of 0.5–1.9 units—the electrons are unequally shared and the bond is polar.

7 **When is a molecule polar or nonpolar? (4.8)**

- A polar molecule has either one polar bond, or two or more bond dipoles that do not cancel.
- A nonpolar molecule has either all nonpolar bonds, or two or more bond dipoles that cancel.

PROBLEMS

Selected in-chapter and odd-numbered end-of-chapter problems have brief answers in Appendix B. The *Student Study Guide and Solutions Manual* contains detailed solutions to all in-chapter and odd-numbered end-of-chapter problems, as well as additional worked examples and a chapter self-test.

Covalent Bonding

4.27 For each pair of compounds, classify the bonding as ionic or covalent and explain your choice.
   - a. LiCl and HCl
   - b. KBr and HBr

4.28 For each pair of compounds, classify the bonding as ionic or covalent and explain your choice.
   - a. BeH_2 and $BeCl_2$
   - b. Na_3N and NH_3

4.29 How many bonds and lone pairs are typically observed with each element: (a) C; (b) Se; (c) I; (d) P?

4.30 How many bonds and lone pairs are typically observed with each element: (a) O; (b) Si; (c) Ge; (d) B?

4.31 Fill in the lone pairs needed to give the main group elements (except hydrogen) an octet. Acrylonitrile is a starting material used to manufacture synthetic Orlon and Acrilan fibers. Cysteine is an amino acid used to synthesize proteins.

a.
```
    H   H
    |   |
H—C=C—C≡N
```
acrylonitrile

b.
```
        H   H   O
        |   |   ‖
H—S—C—C—C—O—H
        |   |
        H   N—H
            |
            H
```
cysteine

4.32 Fill in the lone pairs needed to give the main group elements (except hydrogen) an octet. Glycerol is a product of the metabolism of fats. Acrylamide is used to make polyacrylamide, which is used in some cosmetics and food packaging.

a.
```
    H   H   H
    |   |   |
H—O—C—C—C—O—H
    |   |   |
    H   O   H
        |
        H
```
glycerol

b.
```
        O
        ‖
H—C=C—C—N—H
    |   |   |
    H   H   H
```
acrylamide

4.33 Convert the 3-D model of oxalic acid into a Lewis structure and include all nonbonded electron pairs on atoms that contain them. Oxalic acid occurs naturally in spinach and rhubarb. Although oxalic acid is toxic, you would have to eat about nine pounds of spinach at one time to ingest a fatal dose.

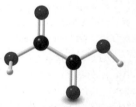

oxalic acid

4.34 Convert the 3-D model of the general anesthetic methoxyflurane into a Lewis structure and include all nonbonded electron pairs on atoms that contain them.

methoxyflurane

Lewis Structures

4.35 Draw a valid Lewis structure for each molecule.

   a. HI   b. CH_2F_2 c. H_2Se d. CO   e. C_2Cl_6

4.36 Draw a valid Lewis structure for each molecule.

   a. CH_3Br b. PH_3 c. HBr   d. SiF_4 e. C_2HCl

4.37 Draw a valid Lewis structure for each compound using the given arrangement of atoms.

   a. CH_5N
   ```
          H
       H  C  N  H
          H  H
   ```

   b. HNO_2 H O N O

   c. C_3H_4
   ```
              H
       H  C  C  C  H
              H
   ```

4.38 Draw a valid Lewis structure for each compound using the given arrangement of atoms.

   a. C_2H_3N
   ```
          H
       H  C  C  N
          H
   ```

   b. HNO_3
   ```
       H  O  N  O
                 O
   ```

   c. C_3H_6
   ```
              H
       H  C  C  C  H
          H  H  H
   ```

4.39 Draw a valid Lewis structure for tetrafluoroethylene, C_2F_4, the industrial starting material used to prepare Teflon. Teflon is most widely used as a nonstick surface on pots and pans, but it has also found application in tape used by plumbers to seal joints, nail polish, and coatings on eye glasses. Assume that each carbon is bonded to two fluorine atoms.

4.40 Draw a valid Lewis structure for phosgene, CCl_2O, which contains a central carbon atom. Phosgene is an extremely toxic gas used as a chemical weapon during World War I. It is now an important industrial starting material for the synthesis of Lexan, a lightweight transparent material used in bike helmets, goggles, and catcher's masks.

4.41 Draw a valid Lewis structure for each ion: (a) OH^-; (b) H_3O^+.

4.42 Draw a valid Lewis structure for each ion: (a) OCl^-; (b) CH_3O^-.

4.43 Keeping in mind that some elements violate the octet rule, draw a Lewis structure for each compound: (a) BCl_3; (b) SO_3.

4.44 Keeping in mind that some elements violate the octet rule, draw a Lewis structure for each compound: (a) BeH_2; (b) PCl_5.

Resonance Structures

4.45 What is the difference between a resonance structure and a resonance hybrid?

4.46 Briefly explain why having two resonance structures for a molecule stabilizes it.

4.47 Draw a second resonance structure for the following anion:

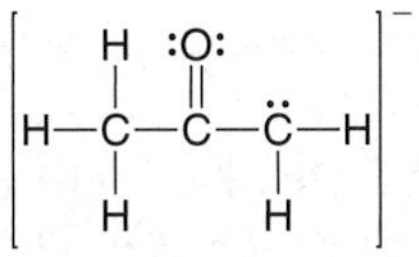

4.48 Draw a second resonance structure for nitromethane, a compound used in drag racing fuels and in the manufacture of pharmaceuticals, pesticides, and fibers.

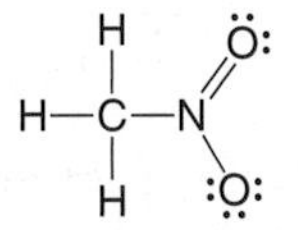

nitromethane

4.49 Label each pair of compounds as resonance structures or not resonance structures.

   a.

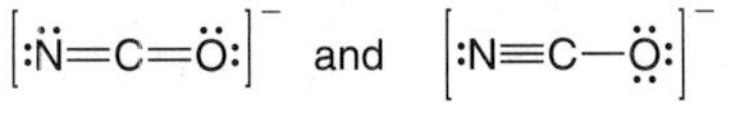

   b.

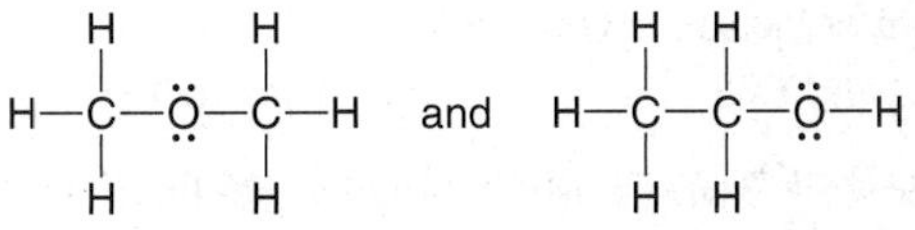

4.50 Label each pair of compounds as resonance structures or not resonance structures.

   a.

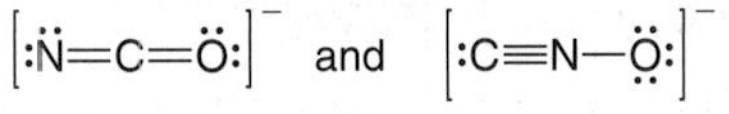

   b.

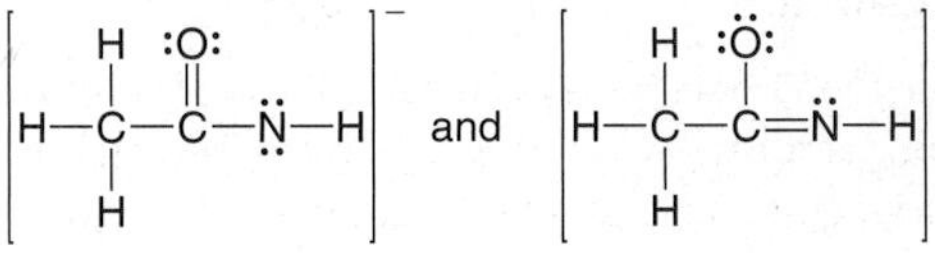

4.51 Draw three resonance structures for the carbonate anion (CO_3^{2-}) that contain a central carbon atom.

4.52 Draw three resonance structures for the nitrate anion (NO_3^-) that contain a central N atom.

Naming Covalent Compounds

4.53 Name each covalent compound.

   a. PBr_3 b. SO_3 c. NCl_3 d. P_2S_5

4.54 Name each covalent compound.

   a. SF_6 b. CBr_4 c. N_2O d. P_4O_{10}

4.55 Write a formula that corresponds to each name.

   a. selenium dioxide

   b. carbon tetrachloride

   c. dinitrogen pentoxide

4.56 Write a formula that corresponds to each name.
  a. silicon tetrafluoride
  b. nitrogen oxide
  c. phosphorus triiodide

4.57 What is the common name for dihydrogen oxide?

4.58 What is the systematic name for H_2S, the compound we commonly call hydrogen sulfide?

Molecular Shape

4.59 Add lone pairs where needed to give octets and then determine the shape around each indicated atom.

a. 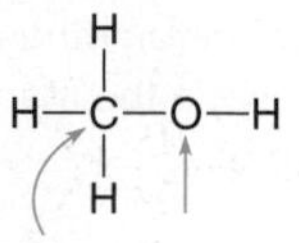 H—C—O—H

c. H—C—C=C—C—H

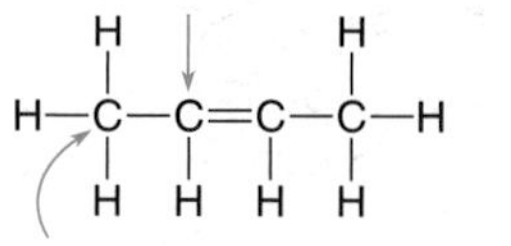

b. NF_3

4.60 Add lone pairs where needed to give octets and then determine the shape around each indicated atom.

a. 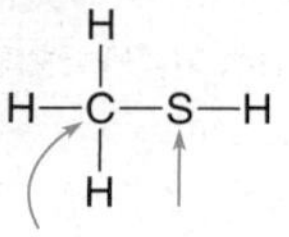 H—C—S—H

c. H—C≡C—C—Cl

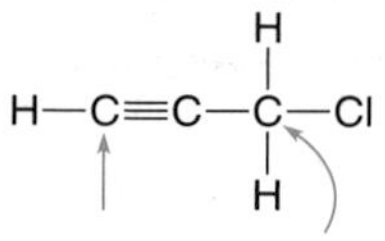

b. PCl_3

4.61 Add lone pairs where needed to give octets and then determine the shape around each indicated atom.

a. 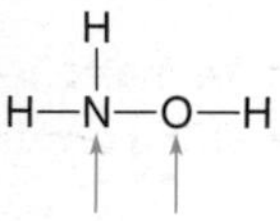 H—N—O—H

c. 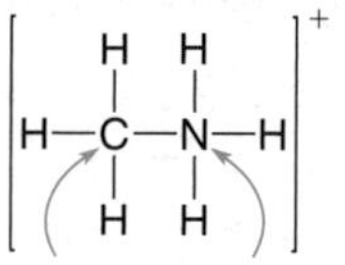 [H—C—N—H]$^+$

b. 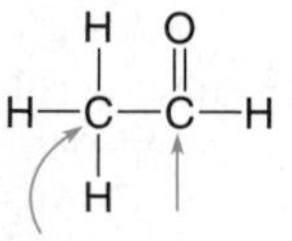 H—C—C—H

4.62 Add lone pairs where needed to give octets and then determine the shape around each indicated atom.

a. 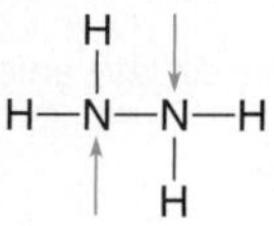 H—N—N—H

c. 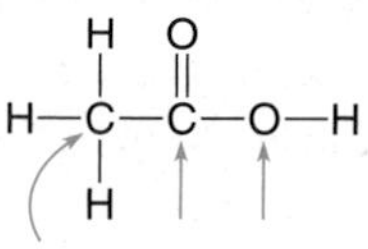 H—C—C—O—H

b. 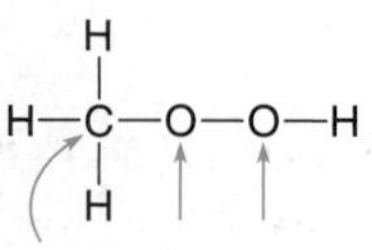 H—C—O—O—H

4.63 Considering each of the given ball-and-stick models: [1] Does the dark red atom have one or more lone pairs of electrons on it? Explain your choice. [2] Give an example of a molecule that has the indicated geometry.

a.   b.

4.64 Considering each of the given ball-and-stick models: [1] Does the dark red atom have one or more lone pairs of electrons on it? Explain your choice. [2] Give an example of a molecule that has the indicated geometry.

a. 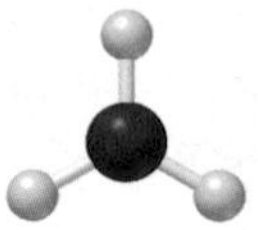   b.

4.65 Give the molecular shape around the boron atom in BCl_3 and the nitrogen atom in NCl_3 and explain why they are different.

4.66 Give the molecular shape for the oxygen atom in H_2O and H_3O^+ and explain why they are different.

4.67 Predict the bond angles around the indicated atoms in each compound. Don't forget to draw in lone pairs where needed to give octets.

a. 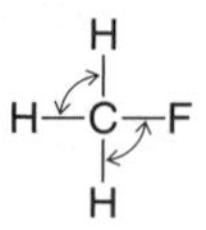 H—C—F

c. H—C≡C=O

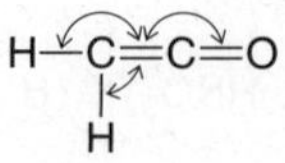

b. 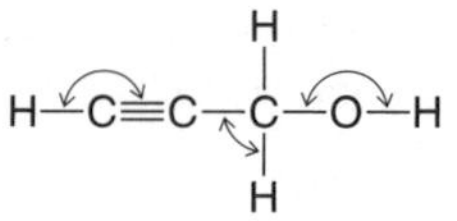 H—C≡C—C—O—H

4.68 Predict the bond angles around the indicated atoms in each compound. Don't forget to draw in lone pairs where needed to give octets.

a. 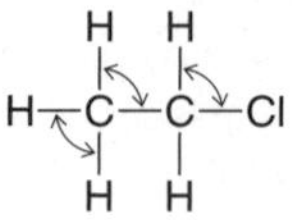 H—C—C—Cl

c. H—C=C—C—H

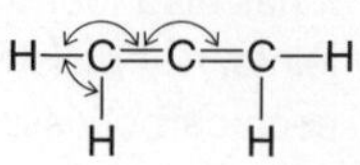

b. 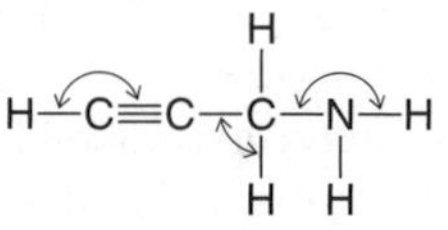 H—C≡C—C—N—H

4.69 Draw Lewis structures for CCl_4 and C_2Cl_4. Give the molecular shape around each carbon atom. Explain why the carbon atoms in the two molecules have different shapes.

4.70 Draw a Lewis structure for N_2H_4 and explain why the shape around each N atom should be described as trigonal pyramidal.

Electronegativity and Polarity

4.71 Rank the atoms in each group in order of increasing electronegativity.

a. Se, O, S   c. Cl, S, F

b. P, Na, Cl   d. O, P, N

4.72 Rank the atoms in each group in order of increasing electronegativity.

a. Si, P, S   c. Se, Cl, Br

b. Be, Mg, Ca   d. Li, Be, Na

4.73 Using electronegativity values, classify the bond formed between each pair of elements as polar covalent or ionic.

a. hydrogen and bromine   c. sodium and sulfur

b. nitrogen and carbon   d. lithium and oxygen

4.74 Using electronegativity values, classify the bond formed between each pair of elements as polar covalent or ionic.

a. nitrogen and oxygen   c. sulfur and chlorine

b. oxygen and hydrogen   d. sodium and chlorine

4.75 Label the bond formed between carbon and each of the following elements as nonpolar, polar, or ionic.

a. carbon   c. lithium   e. hydrogen

b. oxygen   d. chlorine

4.76 Label the bond formed between fluorine and each of the following elements as nonpolar, polar, or ionic.

a. hydrogen   c. carbon   e. sulfur

b. fluorine   d. lithium

4.77 Which bond in each pair is more polar—that is, has the larger electronegativity difference between atoms?

a. C−O or C−N

b. C−F or C−Cl

c. Si−C or P−H

4.78 Which bond in each pair is more polar—that is, has the larger electronegativity difference between atoms?

a. Si−O or Si−S

b. H−F or H−Br

c. C−B or C−Li

4.79 Label each bond in Problem 4.77 with δ^+ and δ^- to show the direction of polarity.

4.80 Label each bond in Problem 4.78 with δ^+ and δ^- to show the direction of polarity.

4.81 Explain why the carbon atom in CH_3NH_2 bears a partial positive charge (δ^+), but the carbon atom in CH_3MgBr bears a partial negative charge (δ^-).

4.82 Explain why the carbon atom in CH_3Cl bears a partial positive charge (δ^+), but the carbon atom in CH_3Li bears a partial negative charge (δ^-).

4.83 Can a compound be nonpolar if it contains one polar bond? Explain.

4.84 Is a compound that contains polar bonds always polar? Explain.

4.85 Label the polar bonds and then decide if each molecule is polar or nonpolar.

4.86 Label the polar bonds and then decide if each molecule is polar or nonpolar.

4.87 Explain why $CHCl_3$ is a polar molecule but CCl_4 is not.

4.88 Explain why H_2O is a polar molecule but H_2S is not.

General Questions

4.89 Answer the following questions about the molecule Cl_2O.

a. How many valence electrons does Cl_2O contain?

b. Draw a valid Lewis structure.

c. Label all polar bonds.

d. What is the shape around the O atom?

e. Is Cl_2O a polar molecule? Explain.

4.90 Answer the following questions about the molecule OCS.

a. How many valence electrons does OCS contain?

b. Draw a valid Lewis structure.

c. Label all polar bonds.

d. What is the shape around the C atom?

e. Is OCS a polar molecule? Explain.

Applications

4.91 Glycine is a building block used to make proteins, such as those in heart muscle (Figure 4.2).

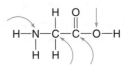

glycine

a. Add lone pairs where needed, and then count the total number of valence electrons in glycine.

b. Determine the shape around the four indicated atoms.

c. Label all of the polar bonds.

d. Is glycine a polar or nonpolar molecule? Explain.

4.92 Lactic acid gives sour milk its distinctive taste. Lactic acid is also an ingredient in several skin care products that purportedly smooth fine lines and improve skin texture.

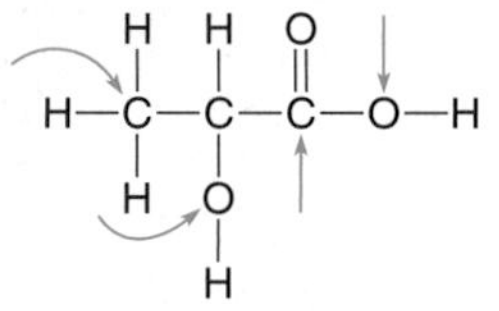

lactic acid

   a. Add lone pairs where needed, and then count the total number of valence electrons in lactic acid.

   b. Determine the shape around the four indicated atoms.

   c. Label all of the polar bonds.

   d. Is lactic acid a polar or nonpolar molecule? Explain.

4.93 Serotonin ($C_{10}H_{12}N_2O$) is a neurotransmitter that is important in mood, sleep, perception, and temperature regulation. Fill in all lone pairs and double bonds to give every atom its usual bonding pattern.

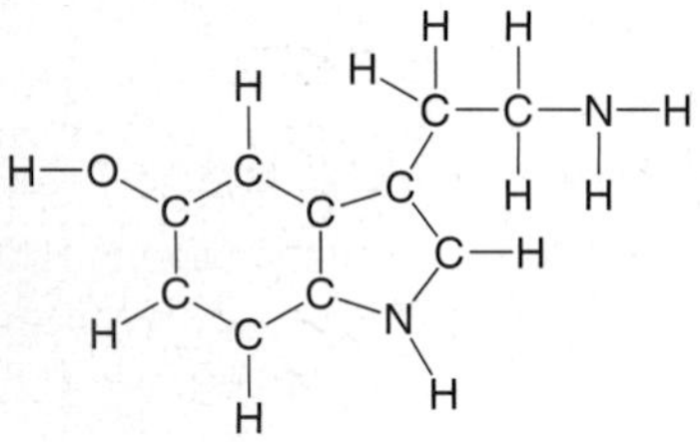

serotonin

4.94 Phenylephrine ($C_9H_{13}NO_2$) is the decongestant in Sudafed PE. Phenylephrine replaced the decongestant pseudoephedrine, which was readily converted to the illegal stimulant methamphetamine. Fill in all lone pairs and double bonds to give every atom its usual bonding pattern.

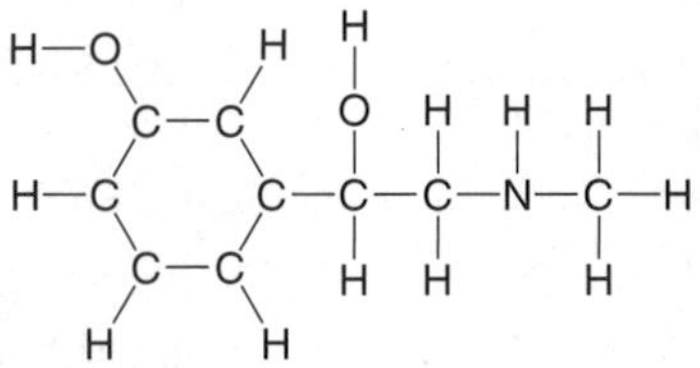

phenylephrine

CHALLENGE PROBLEMS

4.95 Cyclopropane is a stable compound that contains three carbon atoms in a three-membered ring.

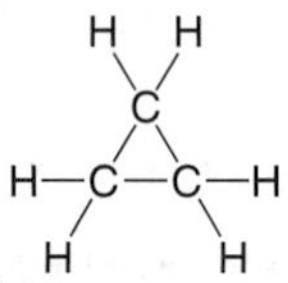

cyclopropane

   a. What is the predicted shape around each carbon atom in the ring, given the number of groups around carbon?

   b. What is the predicted C—C—C bond angle, given the shape and size of the ring?

   c. Explain why cyclopropane is less stable than similar three-carbon compounds that do not contain a ring.

4.96 Although carbon has four bonds in stable molecules, sometimes reactive carbon intermediates that contain carbon atoms without four bonds are formed for very short time periods. Examples of these unstable intermediates include the methyl carbocation $(CH_3)^+$ and the methyl carbanion $(CH_3)^-$. Draw Lewis structures for both unstable ions and predict the shape around carbon.

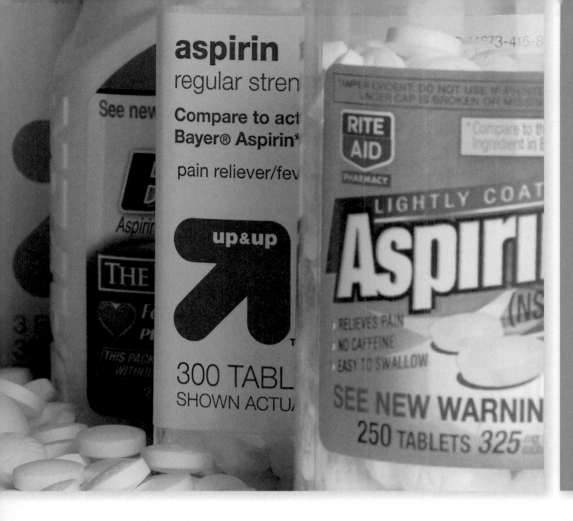

5

Aspirin, a widely used over-the-counter pain reliever, is one of the countless products synthesized by the chemical industry using chemical reactions.

Chemical Reactions

CHAPTER GOALS

In this chapter you will learn how to:

1. Write and balance chemical equations
2. Define a mole and use Avogadro's number in calculations
3. Calculate formula weight and molar mass
4. Relate the mass of a substance to its number of moles
5. Carry out mole and mass calculations in chemical equations
6. Calculate percent yield
7. Determine the limiting reactant in a reaction
8. Define oxidation and reduction and recognize the components of a redox reaction
9. Give examples of common or useful redox reactions

Having learned about atoms, ionic compounds, and covalent molecules in Chapters 2–4, we now turn our attention to chemical reactions. Reactions are at the heart of chemistry. An understanding of chemical processes has made possible the conversion of natural substances into new compounds with different and sometimes superior properties. Aspirin, ibuprofen, and nylon are all products of chemical reactions utilizing substances derived from petroleum. Chemical reactions are not limited to industrial processes. The metabolism of food involves a series of reactions that both forms new compounds and also provides energy for the body's maintenance and growth. Burning gasoline, baking a cake, and photosynthesis involve chemical reactions. In Chapter 5 we learn the basic principles about chemical reactions.

5.1 Introduction to Chemical Reactions

Now that we have learned about compounds and the atoms that compose them, we can better understand the difference between the physical and chemical changes that were first discussed in Section 1.2.

5.1A General Features of Physical and Chemical Changes

- **A physical change alters the physical state of a substance without changing its composition.**

Changes in state—such as melting and boiling—are familiar examples of physical changes. When ice (solid water) melts to form liquid water, the highly organized water molecules in the solid phase become more disorganized in the liquid phase, but no bonds are broken or formed. Each water molecule (H_2O) is composed of two O—H bonds in both the solid and liquid phases.

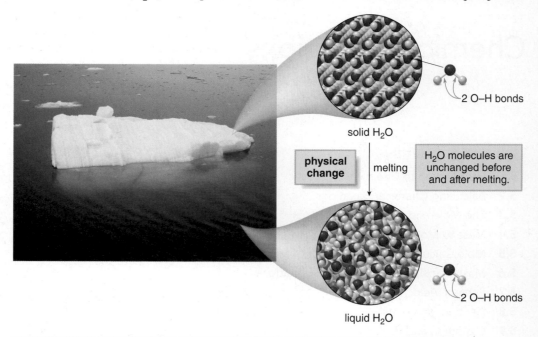

solid H_2O

| physical change | melting |

H_2O molecules are unchanged before and after melting.

2 O—H bonds

2 O—H bonds

liquid H_2O

- **A chemical change—chemical reaction—converts one substance into another.**

Chemical reactions involve breaking bonds in the starting materials, called *reactants,* and forming new bonds in the *products*. The combustion of methane (CH_4), the main constituent of natural gas, in the presence of oxygen (O_2) to form carbon dioxide (CO_2) and water (H_2O) is an example of a chemical reaction. The carbon–hydrogen bonds in methane and the oxygen–oxygen bond in elemental oxygen are broken, and new carbon–oxygen and hydrogen–oxygen bonds are formed in the products.

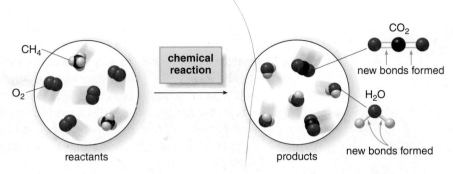

reactants   products

SAMPLE PROBLEM 5.1

Identify each process as a chemical reaction or a physical change.

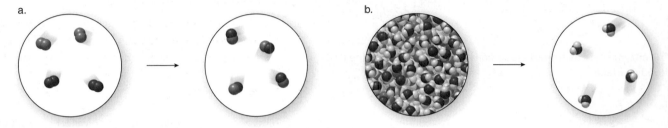

a.

b.

Analysis

A chemical reaction occurs when the bonds in the reactants are broken and new bonds are formed in the products. A physical change occurs when the bonds in the reactants are the same as the bonds in the products.

Solution

Part (a) represents a chemical reaction—the reactants contain two N_2 molecules (with blue spheres joined) and two O_2 molecules (two red spheres joined), while the product contains four NO molecules (a red sphere joined to a blue sphere). Part (b) represents a physical change—boiling—since liquid H_2O molecules are converted to gaseous H_2O molecules and the bonds do not change.

PROBLEM 5.1

Use the molecular art to identify the process as a chemical reaction or a physical change, and explain your choice.

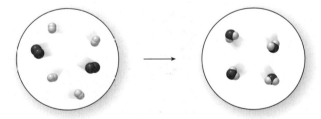

PROBLEM 5.2

Use the molecular art to identify the process as a chemical reaction or a physical change, and explain your choice.

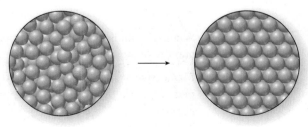

Figure 5.1   Treating Wounds with Hydrogen Peroxide—A Visible Chemical Reaction

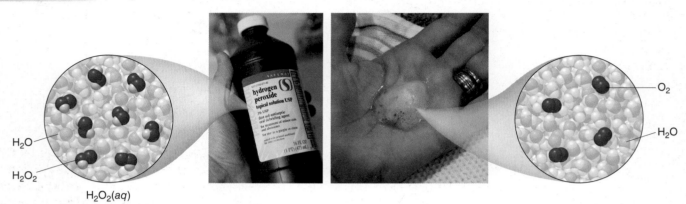

The enzyme catalase in red blood converts hydrogen peroxide (H_2O_2) to water and oxygen gas, which appears as a visible white foam on the bloody surface.

A chemical reaction may be accompanied by a visible change: two colorless reactants can form a colored product; a gas may be given off; two liquid reactants may yield a solid product. Sometimes heat is produced so that a reaction flask feels hot. A reaction having a characteristic visible change occurs when hydrogen peroxide (H_2O_2) is used to clean a bloody wound. An enzyme in the blood called catalase converts the H_2O_2 to water (H_2O) and oxygen (O_2), and bubbles of oxygen appear as a foam, as shown in Figure 5.1.

5.1B   Writing Chemical Equations

- A *chemical equation* is an expression that uses chemical formulas and other symbols to illustrate what reactants constitute the starting materials in a reaction and what products are formed.

Chemical equations are written with the **reactants on the left** and the **products on the right,** separated by a horizontal arrow—a **reaction arrow**—that points from the reactants to the products. In the combustion of methane, methane (CH_4) and oxygen (O_2) are the reactants on the left side of the arrow, and carbon dioxide (CO_2) and water (H_2O) are the products on the right side.

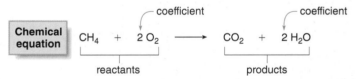

The numbers written in front of any formula are called **coefficients. Coefficients show the number of molecules of a given element or compound that react or are formed.** When no number precedes a formula, the coefficient is assumed to be "1." In the combustion of methane, the coefficients tell us that one molecule of CH_4 reacts with two molecules of O_2 to form one molecule of CO_2 and two molecules of H_2O.

When a formula contains a subscript, **multiply its coefficient by the subscript** to give the total number of atoms of a given type in that formula.

$$2\ O_2 = 4\ O\ atoms$$
$$2\ H_2O = 4\ H\ atoms + 2\ O\ atoms$$

Coefficients are used because all chemical reactions follow a fundamental principle of nature, the **law of conservation of mass,** which states:

- Atoms cannot be created or destroyed in a chemical reaction.

Although bonds are broken and formed in reactions, the number of atoms of each element in the reactants must be the same as the number of atoms of each type in the products. **Coefficients are used to *balance* an equation,** making the number of atoms of each element the same on both sides of the equation.

$$CH_4 \ + \ 2\,O_2 \ \longrightarrow \ CO_2 \ + \ 2\,H_2O$$

Atoms in the reactants:
- 1 C atom
- 4 H atoms
- 4 O atoms

Atoms in the products:
- 1 C atom
- 4 H atoms
- 4 O atoms

Two other important features are worthy of note. If heat is needed for a reaction to occur, the Greek letter delta (Δ) may be written over the arrow. The physical states of the reactants and products are sometimes indicated next to each formula—solid (s), liquid (l), or gas (g). If an aqueous solution is used—that is, if a reactant is dissolved in water—the symbol (aq) is used next to the reactant. When these features are added, the equation for the combustion of methane becomes:

| Combustion of methane | $CH_4(g)$ | $+$ | $2\,O_2(g)$ | $\xrightarrow{\ \Delta\ }$ | $CO_2(g)$ | $+$ | $2\,H_2O(g)$ |

The symbols used for chemical equations are summarized in Table 5.1.

Table 5.1 Symbols Used in Chemical Equations

Symbol	Meaning
$\longrightarrow$	Reaction arrow
Δ	Heat
(s)	Solid
(l)	Liquid
(g)	Gas
(aq)	Aqueous solution

SAMPLE PROBLEM 5.2

Label the reactants and products, and indicate how many atoms of each type of element are present on each side of the equation.

$$C_2H_6O(l) \ + \ 3\,O_2(g) \longrightarrow 2\,CO_2(g) \ + \ 3\,H_2O(g)$$

Analysis

Reactants are on the left side of the arrow and products are on the right side in a chemical equation. When a formula contains a subscript, multiply its coefficient by the subscript to give the total number of atoms of a given type in the formula.

Solution

In this equation, the reactants are C_2H_6O and O_2, while the products are CO_2 and H_2O. If no coefficient is written, it is assumed to be "1." To determine the number of each type of atom when a formula has both a coefficient and a subscript, multiply the coefficient by the subscript.

$1\,C_2H_6O$ = 2 C's + 6 H's + 1 O

$3\,O_2$ = 6 O's   Multiply the coefficient 3 by the subscript 2.

$2\,CO_2$ = 2 C's + 4 O's   Multiply the coefficient 2 by each subscript; 2 × 1 C = 2 C's; 2 × 2 O's = 4 O's.

$3\,H_2O$ = 6 H's + 3 O's   Multiply the coefficient 3 by each subscript; 3 × 2 H's = 6 H's; 3 × 1 O = 3 O's.

Add up the atoms on each side to determine the total number for each type of element.

$$C_2H_6O(l) \ + \ 3\,O_2(g) \longrightarrow 2\,CO_2(g) \ + \ 3\,H_2O(g)$$

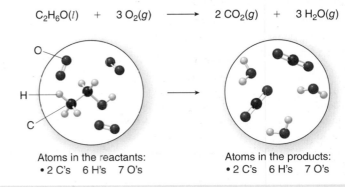

Atoms in the reactants:
- 2 C's   6 H's   7 O's

Atoms in the products:
- 2 C's   6 H's   7 O's

PROBLEM 5.3

Label the reactants and products, and indicate how many atoms of each type of element are present on each side of the following equations.

a. $2\ H_2O_2(aq) \longrightarrow 2\ H_2O(l) + O_2(g)$
b. $2\ C_8H_{18} + 25\ O_2 \longrightarrow 16\ CO_2 + 18\ H_2O$
c. $2\ Na_3PO_4(aq) + 3\ MgCl_2(aq) \longrightarrow Mg_3(PO_4)_2(s) + 6\ NaCl(aq)$

PROBLEM 5.4

One term in a balanced chemical equation contained the coefficient 3 in front of the formula $Al_2(SO_4)_3$. How many atoms of each type of element does this represent?

PROBLEM 5.5

Write a chemical equation from the following description of a reaction: One molecule of gaseous methane (CH_4) is heated with four molecules of gaseous chlorine (Cl_2), forming one molecule of liquid carbon tetrachloride (CCl_4) and four molecules of gaseous hydrogen chloride (HCl).

ENVIRONMENTAL NOTE

The reaction of propane with oxygen forms carbon dioxide, water, and a great deal of energy that can be used for cooking, heating homes and water, drying clothes, and powering generators and vehicles. The combustion of propane and other fossil fuels adds a tremendous amount of CO_2 to the atmosphere each year, with clear environmental consequences (Section 12.8).

5.2 Balancing Chemical Equations

In order to carry out a reaction in the laboratory, we must know how much of each reactant we must combine to give the desired product. For example, if we wanted to synthesize aspirin ($C_9H_8O_4$) from a given amount of salicylic acid ($C_7H_6O_3$), say 100 g, we would have to determine how much acetic acid would be needed to carry out the reaction. A calculation of this sort begins with a **balanced chemical equation.**

| salicylic acid $C_7H_6O_3$ | acetic acid $C_2H_4O_2$ | aspirin $C_9H_8O_4$ |

In this example, the equation is balanced as written and the coefficient in front of each formula is "1." Thus, one molecule of salicylic acid reacts with one molecule of acetic acid to form one molecule of aspirin and one molecule of water. More often, however, an equation must be balanced by adding coefficients in front of some formulas so that the **number of atoms of each element is equal on both sides of the equation.**

How To Balance a Chemical Equation

Example: Write a balanced chemical equation for the reaction of propane (C_3H_8) with oxygen (O_2) to form carbon dioxide (CO_2) and water (H_2O).

Step [1] Write the equation with the correct formulas.

• Write the reactants on the left side and the products on the right side of the reaction arrow, and check if the equation is balanced without adding any coefficients.

$$C_3H_8 + O_2 \longrightarrow CO_2 + H_2O$$

• This equation is not balanced as written since none of the elements—carbon, hydrogen, and oxygen—has the same number of atoms on both sides of the equation. For example, there are 3 C's on the left and only 1 C on the right.

• **The subscripts in a formula can *never* be changed to balance an equation.** Changing a subscript changes the identity of the compound. For example, changing CO_2 to CO would balance oxygen (there would be 2 O's on both sides of the equation), but that would change CO_2 (carbon dioxide) into CO (carbon monoxide).

—Continued

How To, continued . . .

Step [2] **Balance the equation with coefficients one element at a time.**

- Begin with the most complex formula, and start with an element that appears in only one formula on both sides of the equation. In this example, begin with either the C's or H's in C_3H_8. Since there are 3 C's on the left, place the coefficient 3 before CO_2 on the right.

$$C_3H_8 \; + \; O_2 \; \longrightarrow \; 3\,CO_2 \; + \; H_2O$$

3 C's on the left   Place a 3 to balance C's.

- To balance the 8 H's in C_3H_8, place the coefficient 4 before H_2O on the right.

$$C_3H_8 \; + \; O_2 \; \longrightarrow \; 3\,CO_2 \; + \; 4\,H_2O$$

8 H's on the left   Place a 4 to balance H's.
(4×2 H's in H_2O = 8 H's)

- The only element not balanced is oxygen, and at this point there are a total of 10 O's on the right—six from three CO_2 molecules and four from four H_2O molecules. To balance the 10 O's on the right, place the coefficient 5 before O_2 on the left.

$$C_3H_8 \; + \; 5\,O_2 \; \longrightarrow \; 3\,CO_2 \; + \; 4\,H_2O$$

Place a 5 to balance O's.   10 O's on the right

Step [3] **Check to make sure that the smallest set of whole numbers is used.**

$$C_3H_8 \; + \; 5\,O_2 \; \longrightarrow \; 3\,CO_2 \; + \; 4\,H_2O$$

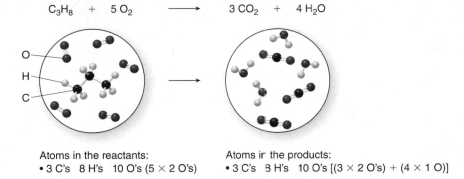

O
H
C

Atoms in the reactants: Atoms in the products:
- 3 C's   8 H's   10 O's (5×2 O's)   • 3 C's   8 H's   10 O's [(3×2 O's) + (4×1 O)]

- This equation is balanced because the same number of C's, O's, and H's is present on both sides of the equation.
- Sometimes an equation is balanced but the lowest set of whole numbers is not used as coefficients. Say, for example, that balancing yielded the following equation:

$$2\,C_3H_8 + 10\,O_2 \longrightarrow 6\,CO_2 + 8\,H_2O$$

- This equation has the same number of C's, O's, and H's on both sides, but *each coefficient must be divided by two* to give the lowest set of whole numbers for the balanced equation, as drawn in the first equation in step [3].

Sample Problems 5.3–5.5 illustrate additional examples of balancing chemical equations. Sample Problem 5.4 shows how to balance an equation when there is an odd–even relationship of atoms in the reactants and products. Sample Problem 5.5 illustrates how to balance an equation that contains several polyatomic anions.

SAMPLE PROBLEM 5.3

Write a balanced equation for the reaction of glucose ($C_6H_{12}O_6$) with oxygen (O_2) to form carbon dioxide (CO_2) and water (H_2O).

Analysis

Balance an equation with coefficients, one element at a time, beginning with the most complex formula and starting with an element that appears in only one formula on both sides of the equation. Continue placing coefficients until the **number of atoms of each element is equal on both sides of the equation.**

Bagels, pasta, bread, and rice are high in starch, which is hydrolyzed to the simple carbohydrate glucose after ingestion. The metabolism of glucose forms CO_2 and H_2O and provides energy for bodily functions.

Solution

[1] Write the equation with correct formulas.

$$C_6H_{12}O_6 + O_2 \longrightarrow CO_2 + H_2O$$
$$\text{glucose}$$

- None of the elements is balanced in this equation. As an example, there are 6 C's on the left side, but only 1 C on the right side.

[2] Balance the equation with coefficients one element at a time.

- Begin with glucose, since its formula is most complex. Balance the 6 C's of glucose by placing the coefficient 6 before CO_2. Balance the 12 H's of glucose by placing the coefficient 6 before H_2O.

$$\overset{\text{Place a 6 to balance C's.}}{C_6H_{12}O_6 \; + \; O_2 \longrightarrow 6\,CO_2 \; + \; 6\,H_2O}$$
$$\text{Place a 6 to balance H's.}$$

- The right side of the equation now has 18 O's. Since glucose already has 6 O's on the left side, 12 additional O's are needed on the left side. The equation will be balanced if the coefficient 6 is placed before O_2.

$$C_6H_{12}O_6 \; + \; 6\,O_2 \longrightarrow 6\,CO_2 \; + \; 6\,H_2O$$
$$\text{Place a 6 to balance O's.}$$

[3] Check.

- The equation is balanced since the number of atoms of each element is the same on both sides.

Answer: $C_6H_{12}O_6 \; + \; 6\,O_2 \longrightarrow 6\,CO_2 \; + \; 6\,H_2O$

Atoms in the reactants:	**Atoms in the products:**
• 6 C's	• 6 C's (6×1 C)
• 12 H's	• 12 H's (6×2 H's)
• 18 O's (1×6 O's) + (6×2 O's)	• 18 O's (6×2 O's) + (6×1 O)

PROBLEM 5.6

Write a balanced equation for each reaction.

a. $H_2 + O_2 \longrightarrow H_2O$ b. $NO + O_2 \longrightarrow NO_2$ c. $CH_4 + Cl_2 \longrightarrow CH_2Cl_2 + HCl$

PROBLEM 5.7

Write a balanced equation for the following reaction, shown with molecular art.

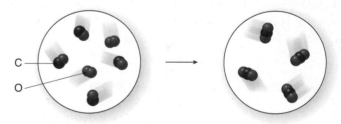

SAMPLE PROBLEM 5.4

The airbag in an automobile inflates when ionic sodium azide (NaN_3), which is composed of Na^+ cations and the polyatomic anion, N_3^- (azide), rapidly decomposes to sodium (Na) and gaseous N_2 (Figure 5.2). Write a balanced equation for this reaction.

Analysis

Balance an equation with coefficients, one element at a time, beginning with the most complex formula and starting with an element that appears in only one formula on both sides of the equation. Continue placing coefficients until the **number of atoms of each element is equal on both sides of the equation.**

Solution

[1] Write the equation with correct formulas.

$$NaN_3 \longrightarrow Na + N_2$$
sodium azide

- The N atoms are not balanced since there are 3 N's on the left side and only 2 N's on the right.

[2] Balance the equation with coefficients.

- To balance the odd number of N atoms (3 N's) on the reactant side with the even number of N atoms on the product side (2 N's) requires the placement of two coefficients. Place the coefficient 2 on the left side (for a total of 6 N's in the reactants). Then place the coefficient 3 before N_2 (for a total of 6 N's in the product). Placing two coefficients is necessary whenever there is an odd–even relationship of atoms in the reactants and products (for any odd number other than one).

Place a 2 to give 6 N's on the left.

$$2\ NaN_3 \longrightarrow Na + 3\ N_2$$

Place a 3 to give 6 N's on the right.

- Note the relationship between the nitrogen-containing species. The subscript of N_2 on the right side is numerically equal to the coefficient (2) before NaN_3 on the left side; similarly, the subscript of NaN_3 on the left side is numerically equal to the coefficient (3) before N_2 on the right side.
- Balance the 2 Na atoms on the left side by placing a 2 before the Na atoms on the right.

$$2\ NaN_3 \longrightarrow 2\ Na + 3\ N_2$$

Place a 2 to balance Na's.

[3] Check and simplify.

- The equation is balanced since the number of atoms of each element is the same on both sides.

$$2\ NaN_3 \longrightarrow 2\ Na + 3\ N_2$$

Atoms in the reactants:	Atoms in the products:
• 2 Na's	• 2 Na's
• 6 N's (2 × 3 N's)	• 6 N's (3 × 2 N's)

Figure 5.2 Chemistry of an Automobile Airbag

a. The chemical reaction that inflates an airbag

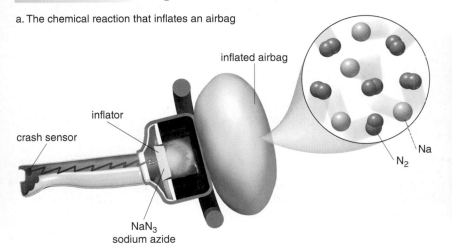

inflated airbag

inflator

crash sensor

NaN_3
sodium azide

Na

N_2

b. An airbag deployed in a head-on collision

A severe car crash triggers an airbag to deploy when an electric sensor causes sodium azide (NaN_3) to ignite, converting it to sodium (Na) and nitrogen gas (N_2). The nitrogen gas causes the bag to inflate fully in 40 milliseconds, helping to protect passengers from serious injury. The sodium atoms formed in this first reaction are hazardous and subsequently converted to a safe sodium salt. It took 30 years to develop a reliable airbag system for automobiles.

PROBLEM 5.8

Write a balanced equation for the reaction of ethane (C_2H_6) with O_2 to form CO_2 and H_2O.

PROBLEM 5.9

The Haber process is an important industrial reaction that converts N_2 and H_2 to ammonia (NH_3), an agricultural fertilizer and starting material for the synthesis of nitrate fertilizers. Write a balanced equation for the Haber process.

SAMPLE PROBLEM 5.5

Balance the following equation.

$$Ca_3(PO_4)_2 \; + \; H_2SO_4 \longrightarrow CaSO_4 \; + \; H_3PO_4$$
calcium phosphate   sulfuric acid   calcium sulfate   phosphoric acid

Analysis

Balance an equation with coefficients, one element at a time, beginning with the most complex formula and starting with an element that appears in only one formula on both sides of the equation. Continue placing coefficients until the **number of atoms of each element is equal on both sides of the equation.**

Solution

[1] Write the equation with correct formulas.

- The correct formula for each compound is given in the problem statement. When the reactants and products contain polyatomic ions, PO_4^{3-} and SO_4^{2-} in this case, **balance each ion as a *unit*,** rather than balancing the individual atoms. Thus, phosphate is not balanced in the equation as written, because the left side has two PO_4^{3-} anions while the right side has only one.

[2] Balance the equation with coefficients.

- Begin with $Ca_3(PO_4)_2$. Balance the 3 Ca's by placing the coefficient 3 before $CaSO_4$. Balance the 2 PO_4^{3-} anions by placing the coefficient 2 before H_3PO_4.

Place a 3 to balance Ca's.

$$Ca_3(PO_4)_2 \; + \; H_2SO_4 \longrightarrow 3\,CaSO_4 \; + \; 2\,H_3PO_4$$
Place a 2 to balance PO_4^{3-}.

- Two components are still not balanced—H atoms and sulfate anions (SO_4^{2-}). Both can be balanced by placing the coefficient 3 before H_2SO_4 on the left.

6 H's   6 H's
$$Ca_3(PO_4)_2 \; + \; 3\,H_2SO_4 \longrightarrow 3\,CaSO_4 \; + \; 2\,H_3PO_4$$
3 SO_4^{2-} in both

Place a 3 to balance H and SO_4^{2-}.

[3] Check.

- The equation is balanced since the number of atoms and polyatomic anions is the same on both sides.

Answer: $Ca_3(PO_4)_2 \; + \; 3\,H_2SO_4 \longrightarrow 3\,CaSO_4 \; + \; 2\,H_3PO_4$

Atoms or ions in the reactants:	Atoms or ions in the products:
• 3 Ca's • 6 H's	• 3 Ca's • 6 H's
• 2 PO_4^{3-} • 3 SO_4^{2-}	• 2 PO_4^{3-} • 3 SO_4^{2-}

Ammonium hydrogen phosphate [$(NH_4)_2HPO_4$], the major phosphorus fertilizer, is formed from phosphoric acid, H_3PO_4, which is synthesized industrially by the chemical reaction in Sample Problem 5.5.

PROBLEM 5.10

Balance each chemical equation.

a. $Al + H_2SO_4 \longrightarrow Al_2(SO_4)_3 + H_2$

b. $Na_2SO_3 + H_3PO_4 \longrightarrow H_2SO_3 + Na_3PO_4$

5.3 The Mole and Avogadro's Number

Although the chemical equations in Section 5.2 were discussed in terms of individual atoms and molecules, atoms are exceedingly small. It is more convenient to talk about larger quantities of atoms, and for this reason, scientists use the **mole.** A mole defines a quantity, much like a dozen items means 12, and a case of soda means 24 cans. The only difference is that a mole is much larger.

• A *mole* is a quantity that contains 6.02×10^{23} items—usually atoms, molecules, or ions.

The definition of a mole is based on the number of atoms contained in exactly 12 g of the carbon-12 isotope. This number is called **Avogadro's number,** after the Italian scientist Amadeo Avogadro, who first proposed the concept of a mole in the nineteenth century. One mole, abbreviated as **mol,** always contains an Avogadro's number of particles.

$$1 \text{ mole of C atoms} = 6.02 \times 10^{23} \text{ C atoms}$$
$$1 \text{ mole of } H_2O \text{ molecules} = 6.02 \times 10^{23} \text{ } H_2O \text{ molecules}$$
$$1 \text{ mole of vitamin C molecules} = 6.02 \times 10^{23} \text{ vitamin C molecules}$$

PROBLEM 5.11

How many items are contained in one mole of (a) baseballs; (b) bicycles; (c) Cheerios; (d) CH_4 molecules?

Each sample contains one mole of the substance—water (H_2O molecules), salt (NaCl, one mole of Na^+ and one mole of Cl^-), and aspirin ($C_9H_8O_4$ molecules). Pictured is a mole of aspirin *molecules,* not a mole of aspirin *tablets,* which is a quantity too large to easily represent. If a mole of aspirin tablets were arranged next to one another to cover a football field and then stacked on top of each other, they would occupy a volume 100 yards long, 53.3 yards wide, and over 20,000,000,000 miles high!

For a number written in scientific notation as $y \times 10^x$, y is the coefficient and x is the exponent in the power of 10 (Section 1.6).

We can use Avogadro's number as a conversion factor to relate the number of moles of a substance to the number of atoms or molecules it contains.

Two possible conversion factors: $\dfrac{1 \text{ mol}}{6.02 \times 10^{23} \text{ atoms}}$ or $\dfrac{6.02 \times 10^{23} \text{ atoms}}{1 \text{ mol}}$

These conversion factors allow us to determine how many atoms or molecules are contained in a given number of moles. To carry out calculations that contain numbers written in scientific notation, we must first learn how to multiply and divide numbers written in this form.

• To multiply two numbers in scientific notation, multiply the coefficients together and add the exponents in the powers of 10.

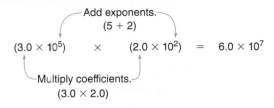

Add exponents.
(5 + 2)
$(3.0 \times 10^5) \times (2.0 \times 10^2) = 6.0 \times 10^7$
Multiply coefficients.
(3.0 × 2.0)

• To divide two numbers in scientific notation, divide the coefficients and subtract the exponents in the powers of 10.

Divide coefficients. $\dfrac{6.0 \times 10^2}{2.0 \times 10^{20}}$ Subtract exponents. $= 3.0 \times 10^{-18}$
(6.0/2.0) (2 − 20)

Sample Problems 5.6 and 5.7 illustrate how to interconvert moles and molecules. In both problems we follow the stepwise procedure for problem solving using conversion factors outlined in Section 1.7B.

SAMPLE PROBLEM 5.6

How many molecules are contained in 5.0 moles of carbon dioxide (CO_2)?

Analysis and Solution

[1] Identify the original quantity and the desired quantity.

$$5.0 \text{ mol of } CO_2 \qquad ? \text{ number of molecules of } CO_2$$

original quantity   desired quantity

[2] Write out the conversion factors.

- Choose the conversion factor that places the unwanted unit, mol, in the denominator so that the units cancel.

$$\frac{1 \text{ mol}}{6.02 \times 10^{23} \text{ molecules}} \quad \text{or} \quad \boxed{\frac{6.02 \times 10^{23} \text{ molecules}}{1 \text{ mol}}}$$

Choose this conversion factor to cancel mol.

[3] Set up and solve the problem.

- Multiply the original quantity by the conversion factor to obtain the desired quantity.

Convert to a number between 1 and 10.

$$5.0 \text{ mol} \quad \times \quad \frac{6.02 \times 10^{23} \text{ molecules}}{1 \text{ mol}} \quad = \quad 30. \times 10^{23} \text{ molecules}$$

Moles cancel.

$$= \quad 3.0 \times 10^{24} \text{ molecules of } CO_2$$

Answer

- Multiplication first gives an answer that is not written in scientific notation since the coefficient (30.) is greater than 10. Moving the decimal point one place to the *left* and *increasing* the exponent by one gives the answer written in the proper form.

PROBLEM 5.12

How many carbon atoms are contained in each of the following number of moles: (a) 2.00 mol; (b) 6.00 mol; (c) 0.500 mol; (d) 25.0 mol?

PROBLEM 5.13

How many molecules are contained in each of the following number of moles?

a. 2.5 mol of penicillin molecules   c. 0.40 mol of sugar molecules
b. 0.25 mol of NH_3 molecules   d. 55.3 mol of acetaminophen molecules

SAMPLE PROBLEM 5.7

How many moles of aspirin contain 8.62×10^{25} molecules?

Analysis and Solution

[1] Identify the original quantity and the desired quantity.

$$8.62 \times 10^{25} \text{ molecules of aspirin} \qquad ? \text{ mole of aspirin}$$

original quantity   desired quantity

[2] Write out the conversion factors.

- Choose the conversion factor that places the unwanted unit, number of molecules, in the denominator so that the units cancel.

$$\frac{6.02 \times 10^{23} \text{ molecules}}{1 \text{ mol}} \quad \text{or} \quad \boxed{\frac{1 \text{ mol}}{6.02 \times 10^{23} \text{ molecules}}}$$

Choose this conversion factor to cancel molecules.

[3] Set up and solve the problem.
- Multiply the original quantity by the conversion factor to obtain the desired quantity.
- To divide numbers using scientific notation, divide the coefficients (8.62/6.02) and subtract the exponents (25 − 23).

$$8.62 \times 10^{25} \text{ molecules} \quad \times \quad \frac{1 \text{ mol}}{6.02 \times 10^{23} \text{ molecules}} \quad = \quad 1.43 \times 10^{2} \text{ mol}$$

Molecules cancel. $= 143$ mol of aspirin

Answer

PROBLEM 5.14

How many moles of water contain each of the following number of molecules?

a. 6.02×10^{25} molecules
b. 3.01×10^{22} molecules
c. 9.0×10^{24} molecules

5.4 Mass to Mole Conversions

In Section 2.3, we learned that the *atomic weight* **is the average mass of an element,** reported in atomic mass units (amu), and that the atomic weight of each element appears just below its chemical symbol in the periodic table. Thus, carbon has an atomic weight of 12.01 amu. We use atomic weights to calculate the mass of a compound.

> - The *formula weight* is the sum of the atomic weights of all the atoms in a compound, reported in atomic mass units (amu).

The term "formula weight" is used for both ionic and covalent compounds. Often the term **"molecular weight"** is used in place of formula weight for covalent compounds, since they are composed of molecules, not ions. The formula weight of ionic sodium chloride (NaCl) is 58.44 amu, which is determined by adding up the atomic weights of Na (22.99 amu) and Cl (35.45 amu). The stepwise procedure for calculating the formula weight of compounds whose chemical formulas contain subscripts is shown in the accompanying *How To*.

Formula weight of NaCl:

Atomic weight of 1 Na = 22.99 amu
Atomic weight of 1 Cl = 35.45 amu
Formula weight of NaCl = 58.44 amu

How To Calculate the Formula Weight of a Compound

Example: Calculate the formula weight for iron(II) sulfate, $FeSO_4$, an iron supplement used to treat anemia.

Step [1] Write the correct formula and determine the number of atoms of each element from the subscripts.
- $FeSO_4$ contains 1 Fe atom, 1 S atom, and 4 O atoms.

Step [2] Multiply the number of atoms of each element by the atomic weight and add the results.

1 Fe atom × 55.85 amu = 55.85 amu
1 S atom × 32.07 amu = 32.07 amu
4 O atoms × 16.00 amu = 64.00 amu
Formula weight of $FeSO_4$ = 151.92 amu

PROBLEM 5.15

Calculate the formula weight of each ionic compound.

a. $CaCO_3$, a common calcium supplement
b. KI, the essential nutrient added to NaCl to make iodized salt

PROBLEM 5.16

Calculate the molecular weight of each covalent compound.

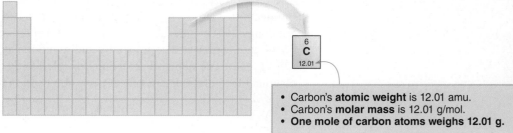

a. ethanol
(alcohol in alcoholic
beverages)

b. phenol
(antiseptic)

c. halothane
(general anesthetic)

5.4A   Molar Mass

When reactions are carried out in the laboratory, single atoms and molecules are much too small to measure out. Instead, substances are weighed on a balance and amounts are typically reported in grams, not atomic mass units. To determine how many atoms or molecules are contained in a given mass, we use its **molar mass.**

• The *molar mass* is the mass of one mole of any substance, reported in grams per mole.

The value of the molar mass of an element in the periodic table (in grams per mole) is the same as the value of its atomic weight (in amu). Thus, the molar mass of carbon is 12.01 g/mol, since its atomic weight is 12.01 amu; that is, one mole of carbon atoms weighs 12.01 g.

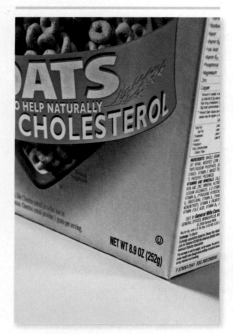

When a consumer product contains a great many lightweight small objects—for example, Cheerios—it is typically sold by weight, not by the number of objects. We buy Cheerios in an 8.9-oz box, not a box that contains 2,554 Cheerios.

| 6 |
| C |
| 12.01 |

• Carbon's **atomic weight** is 12.01 amu.
• Carbon's **molar mass** is 12.01 g/mol.
• **One mole of carbon atoms weighs 12.01 g.**

• The value of the molar mass of a compound in grams equals the value of its formula weight in amu.

Since the formula weight of NaCl is 58.44 amu, its molar mass is 58.44 g/mol. One mole of NaCl weighs 58.44 g. We use a compound's formula weight to calculate its molar mass, as shown in Sample Problem 5.8.

SAMPLE PROBLEM 5.8

What is the molar mass of nicotine ($C_{10}H_{14}N_2$), the toxic and addictive stimulant in tobacco?

Analysis

Determine the number of atoms of each element from the subscripts in the chemical formula, multiply the number of atoms of each element by the atomic weight, and add up the results.

Solution

10 C atoms × 12.01 amu = 120.1 amu
14 H atoms × 1.008 amu =   14.11 amu
2 N atoms × 14.01 amu   =   28.02 amu
Formula weight of nicotine = 162.23 amu rounded to 162.2 amu

Answer: Since the formula weight of nicotine is 162.2 amu, the molar mass of nicotine is 162.2 g/mol.

Ginkgo extracts from the tree *Ginkgo biloba* contain ginkgolide B (Problem 5.17), a complex compound that was synthesized by a series of chemical reactions in the laboratory of Nobel Laureate E. J. Corey at Harvard University in 1988.

PROBLEM 5.17

What is the molar mass of ginkgolide B ($C_{20}H_{24}O_{10}$), a complex compound isolated from the ginkgo tree? Extracts of the roots, bark, and seeds of the ginkgo tree comprise the most widely taken herbal supplements used today.

5.4B Relating Grams to Moles

The molar mass is a very useful quantity because it relates the number of *moles* to the number of *grams* of a substance. In this way, the molar mass can be used as a conversion factor. For example, since the molar mass of H_2O is 18.02 g/mol, two conversion factors can be written.

$$\frac{18.02 \text{ g } H_2O}{1 \text{ mol}} \quad \text{or} \quad \frac{1 \text{ mol}}{18.02 \text{ g } H_2O}$$

Using these conversion factors, we can convert a given number of moles of water to grams, or a specific number of grams of water to moles.

SAMPLE PROBLEM 5.9

Converting moles to mass: What is the mass of 0.25 moles of water?

Analysis and Solution

[1] Identify the original quantity and the desired quantity.

$$\begin{array}{cc} 0.25 \text{ mol of } H_2O & ? \text{ g of } H_2O \\ \text{original quantity} & \text{desired quantity} \end{array}$$

[2] Write out the conversion factors.

- Choose the conversion factor that places the unwanted unit, moles, in the denominator so that the units cancel.

$$\frac{1 \text{ mol}}{18.02 \text{ g } H_2O} \quad \text{or} \quad \boxed{\frac{18.02 \text{ g } H_2O}{1 \text{ mol}}} \quad \begin{array}{l} \text{Choose this conversion} \\ \text{factor to cancel mol.} \end{array}$$

[3] Set up and solve the problem.

- Multiply the original quantity by the conversion factor to obtain the desired quantity.

$$0.25 \text{ mol} \quad \times \quad \frac{18.02 \text{ g } H_2O}{1 \text{ mol}} \quad = \quad 4.5 \text{ g of } H_2O$$

Moles cancel.   **Answer**

PROBLEM 5.18

Calculate the number of grams contained in each of the following number of moles.

a. 0.500 mol of NaCl
b. 2.00 mol of KI
c. 3.60 mol of C_2H_4 (ethylene)
d. 0.820 mol of CH_4O (methanol)

SAMPLE PROBLEM 5.10

Converting mass to moles: How many moles are present in 100. g of aspirin ($C_9H_8O_4$, molar mass 180.2 g/mol)?

Analysis and Solution

[1] Identify the original quantity and the desired quantity.

$$\begin{array}{cc} 100. \text{ g of aspirin} & ? \text{ mol of aspirin} \\ \text{original quantity} & \text{desired quantity} \end{array}$$

[2] Write out the conversion factors.

- Choose the conversion factor that places the unwanted unit, grams, in the denominator so that the units cancel.

$$\frac{180.2 \text{ g aspirin}}{1 \text{ mol}} \quad \text{or} \quad \boxed{\frac{1 \text{ mol}}{180.2 \text{ g aspirin}}} \quad \text{Choose this conversion factor to cancel g.}$$

[3] Set up and solve the problem.

- Multiply the original quantity by the conversion factor to obtain the desired quantity.

$$100. \text{ g} \quad \times \quad \frac{1 \text{ mol}}{180.2 \text{ g aspirin}} \quad = \quad 0.555 \text{ mol of aspirin}$$

Grams cancel.   **Answer**

PROBLEM 5.19

How many moles are contained in each of the following?

a. 100. g of NaCl

b. 25.5 g of CH_4

c. 0.250 g of aspirin ($C_9H_8O_4$)

d. 25.0 g of H_2O

5.4C   Relating Grams to Number of Atoms or Molecules

Since the molar mass of a substance gives the number of grams in a mole and a mole contains 6.02×10^{23} molecules (or atoms), **we can use molar mass to show the relationship between** *grams* **and** *number of molecules* **(or atoms).** For example, since the molar mass of aspirin is 180.2 g/mol, the following relationships exist:

$$\frac{180.2 \text{ g aspirin}}{1 \text{ mol}} \quad = \quad \frac{180.2 \text{ g aspirin}}{6.02 \times 10^{23} \text{ molecules}}$$

1 mol = 6.02×10^{23} molecules

SAMPLE PROBLEM 5.11

Converting mass to number of molecules: How many molecules are contained in a 325-mg tablet of aspirin ($C_9H_8O_4$, molar mass 180.2 g/mol)?

Analysis and Solution

[1] Identify the original quantity and the desired quantity.

325 mg of aspirin   ? molecules of aspirin
original quantity   desired quantity

[2] Write out the conversion factors.

- We have no conversion factor that directly relates milligrams to number of molecules. We do know, however, how to relate milligrams to grams, and grams to number of molecules. In other words, we need two conversion factors to solve this problem.
- Choose the conversion factors that place the unwanted units, grams and milligrams, in the denominator so that the units cancel.

g–mg conversion factors   gram–number of molecules conversion factors

$$\frac{1000 \text{ mg}}{1 \text{ g}} \quad \text{or} \quad \boxed{\frac{1 \text{ g}}{1000 \text{ mg}}} \qquad \frac{180.2 \text{ g aspirin}}{6.02 \times 10^{23} \text{ molecules}} \quad \text{or} \quad \boxed{\frac{6.02 \times 10^{23} \text{ molecules}}{180.2 \text{ g aspirin}}}$$

Choose the conversion factors with the unwanted units—mg and g—in the denominator.

[3] Set up and solve the problem.

- Arrange each term so that the units in the numerator of one term cancel the units in the denominator of the adjacent term. The single desired unit, number of molecules, must be located in the numerator of one term.

$$325 \text{ mg aspirin} \quad \times \quad \frac{1 \text{ g}}{1000 \text{ mg}} \quad \times \quad \frac{6.02 \times 10^{23} \text{ molecules}}{180.2 \text{ g aspirin}} \quad = \quad 1.09 \times 10^{21} \text{ molecules of aspirin}$$

Answer

Milligrams cancel.   Grams cancel.

PROBLEM 5.20

How many molecules are contained in two 500.-mg tablets of penicillin ($C_{16}H_{18}N_2O_4S$, molar mass 334.4 g/mol)?

5.5 Mole Calculations in Chemical Equations

ENVIRONMENTAL NOTE

NO, nitrogen monoxide, is formed from N_2 and O_2 at very high temperature in automobile engines and coal-burning furnaces. NO is a reactive air pollutant that goes on to form other air pollutants, such as ozone (O_3) and nitric acid (HNO_3). HNO_3 is one component of acid rain that can devastate forests and acidify streams, making them unfit for fish and other wildlife.

Having learned about moles and molar mass, we can now return to balanced chemical equations. As we learned in Section 5.2, the coefficients in a balanced chemical equation tell us the number of *molecules* of each compound that react or are formed in a given reaction.

- A balanced chemical equation also tells us the number of *moles* of each reactant that combine and the number of *moles* of each product formed.

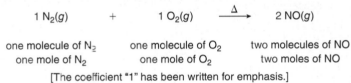

$$1 \text{ N}_2(g) \quad + \quad 1 \text{ O}_2(g) \quad \xrightarrow{\Delta} \quad 2 \text{ NO}(g)$$

one molecule of N_2 one molecule of O_2 two molecules of NO
one mole of N_2 one mole of O_2 two moles of NO

[The coefficient "1" has been written for emphasis.]

For example, the balanced chemical equation for the high temperature reaction of N_2 and O_2 to form nitrogen monoxide, NO, shows that one *molecule* of N_2 combines with one *molecule* of O_2 to form two *molecules* of NO. It also shows that one *mole* of N_2 combines with one *mole* of O_2 to form two *moles* of NO.

Coefficients are used to form mole ratios, which can serve as conversion factors. These ratios tell us the relative number of moles of reactants that combine in a reaction, as well as the relative number of moles of product formed from a given reactant, as shown in Sample Problem 5.12.

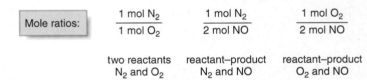

Mole ratios: $\dfrac{1 \text{ mol N}_2}{1 \text{ mol O}_2}$ $\dfrac{1 \text{ mol N}_2}{2 \text{ mol NO}}$ $\dfrac{1 \text{ mol O}_2}{2 \text{ mol NO}}$

two reactants   reactant–product   reactant–product
N_2 and O_2 N_2 and NO O_2 and NO

- Use the mole ratio from the coefficients in the balanced equation to convert the number of moles of one compound (A) into the number of moles of another compound (B).

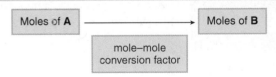

Moles of **A** $\longrightarrow$ Moles of **B**

mole–mole
conversion factor

HEALTH NOTE

Meters that measure CO levels in homes are sold commercially. CO, a colorless, odorless gas, is a minor product formed whenever fossil fuels and wood are burned. In poorly ventilated rooms, such as those found in modern, well-insulated homes, CO levels can reach unhealthy levels.

SAMPLE PROBLEM 5.12

Carbon monoxide (CO) is a poisonous gas that combines with hemoglobin in the blood, thus reducing the amount of oxygen that can be delivered to tissues. Under certain conditions, CO is formed when ethane (C_2H_6) in natural gas is burned in the presence of oxygen. Using the balanced equation, how many moles of CO are produced from 3.5 mol of C_2H_6?

$$2\ C_2H_6(g)\ +\ 5\ O_2(g)\ \xrightarrow{\Delta}\ 4\ CO(g)\ +\ 6\ H_2O(g)$$

Analysis and Solution

[1] Identify the original quantity and the desired quantity.

3.5 mol of C_2H_6	? mol of CO
original quantity	desired quantity

[2] Write out the conversion factors.

- Use the coefficients in the balanced equation to write mole–mole conversion factors for the two compounds, C_2H_6 and CO. Choose the conversion factor that places the unwanted unit, moles of C_2H_6, in the denominator so that the units cancel.

$$\frac{2\ \text{mol}\ C_2H_6}{4\ \text{mol CO}}\quad \text{or}\quad \boxed{\frac{4\ \text{mol CO}}{2\ \text{mol}\ C_2H_6}}\quad \text{Choose this conversion factor to cancel mol}\ C_2H_6.$$

[3] Set up and solve the problem.

- Multiply the original quantity by the conversion factor to obtain the desired quantity.

$$3.5\ \text{mol}\ C_2H_6\ \times\ \frac{4\ \text{mol CO}}{2\ \text{mol}\ C_2H_6}\ =\ 7.0\ \text{mol CO}$$

Moles C_2H_6 cancel. **Answer**

PROBLEM 5.21

Use the balanced equation for the reaction of N_2 and O_2 to form NO at the beginning of Section 5.5 to answer each question.

a. How many moles of NO are formed from 3.3 moles of N_2?
b. How many moles of NO are formed from 0.50 moles of O_2?
c. How many moles of O_2 are needed to completely react with 1.2 moles of N_2?

PROBLEM 5.22

Use the balanced equation in Sample Problem 5.12 to answer each question.

a. How many moles of O_2 are needed to react completely with 3.0 moles of C_2H_6?
b. How many moles of H_2O are formed from 0.50 moles of C_2H_6?
c. How many moles of C_2H_6 are needed to form 3.0 moles of CO?

ENVIRONMENTAL NOTE

Lightning produces O_3 from O_2 during an electrical storm. O_3 at the ground level is an unwanted pollutant. In the stratosphere, however, it protects us from harmful radiation from the sun (Section 4.4B).

5.6 Mass Calculations in Chemical Equations

Since a mole represents an enormously large number of very small molecules, there is no way to directly count the number of moles or molecules used in a chemical reaction. Instead, we utilize a balance to measure the number of grams of a compound used and the number of grams of product formed. The number of grams of a substance and the number of moles it contains are related by the molar mass (Section 5.4).

5.6A Converting Moles of Reactant to Grams of Product

To determine how many grams of product are expected from a given number of moles of reactant, two operations are necessary. First, we must determine how many moles of product to expect using the coefficients of the balanced chemical equation (Section 5.5). Then, we convert the number of moles of product to the number of grams using the molar mass (Section 5.4). Each step needs a conversion factor. The stepwise procedure is outlined in the accompanying *How To*, and then illustrated with an example in Sample Problem 5.13.

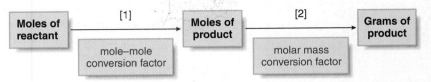

How To Convert Moles of Reactant to Grams of Product

Example: In the upper atmosphere, high-energy radiation from the sun converts oxygen (O_2) to ozone (O_3). Using the balanced equation, how many grams of O_3 are formed from 9.0 mol of O_2?

$$3\ O_2(g) \xrightarrow{\text{sunlight}} 2\ O_3(g)$$

Step [1] **Convert the number of moles of reactant to the number of moles of product using a mole–mole conversion factor.**

- Use the coefficients in the balanced chemical equation to write mole–mole conversion factors.

$$\frac{3\ \text{mol } O_2}{2\ \text{mol } O_3} \quad \text{or} \quad \boxed{\frac{2\ \text{mol } O_3}{3\ \text{mol } O_2}} \quad \text{Choose this conversion factor to cancel mol } O_2.$$

- Multiply the number of moles of starting material (9.0 mol) by the conversion factor to give the number of moles of product. In this example, 6.0 mol of O_3 are formed.

Moles of reactant   Moles of product

$$9.0\ \text{mol } O_2 \quad \times \quad \frac{2\ \text{mol } O_3}{3\ \text{mol } O_2} \quad = \quad 6.0\ \text{mol } O_3$$

Moles O_2 cancel.

Step [2] **Convert the number of moles of product to the number of grams of product using the product's molar mass.**

- Use the molar mass of the product (O_3) to write a conversion factor. The molar mass of O_3 is 48.00 g/mol (3 O atoms × 16.00 g/mol for each O atom = 48.00 g/mol).

$$\frac{1\ \text{mol } O_3}{48.00\ \text{g } O_3} \quad \text{or} \quad \boxed{\frac{48.00\ \text{g } O_3}{1\ \text{mol } O_3}} \quad \text{Choose this conversion factor to cancel mol.}$$

- Multiply the number of moles of product (from step [1]) by the conversion factor to give the number of grams of product.

Moles of product   Grams of product

$$6.0\ \text{mol } O_3 \quad \times \quad \frac{48.00\ \text{g } O_3}{1\ \text{mol } O_3} \quad = \quad 288\ \text{g, rounded to 290 g of } O_3$$

Moles cancel.   **Answer**

It is also possible to combine the multiplication operations from steps [1] and [2] into a single operation using both conversion factors. This converts the moles of starting material to grams of product all at once. Both the one-step and stepwise approaches give the same overall result.

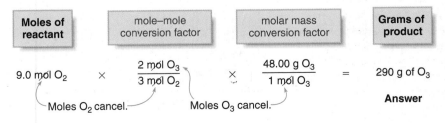

HEALTH NOTE

Ethanol (C_2H_6O) is the alcohol in red wine, formed by the fermentation of grapes. Ethanol depresses the central nervous system, increases the production of stomach acid, and dilates blood vessels. Excessive alcohol consumption is a major health problem in the United States.

SAMPLE PROBLEM 5.13

Wine is produced by the fermentation of grapes. In fermentation, the carbohydrate glucose ($C_6H_{12}O_6$) is converted to ethanol and carbon dioxide according to the given balanced equation. How many grams of ethanol (C_2H_6O, molar mass 46.07 g/mol) are produced from 5.00 mol of glucose?

$$C_6H_{12}O_6(aq) \longrightarrow 2\ C_2H_6O(aq)\ +\ 2\ CO_2(g)$$
$$\text{glucose} \qquad\qquad \text{ethanol}$$

Analysis and Solution

[1] Convert the number of moles of reactant to the number of moles of product using a mole-mole conversion factor.

- Use the coefficients in the balanced chemical equation to write mole–mole conversion factors for the two compounds—one mole of glucose ($C_6H_{12}O_6$) forms two moles of ethanol (C_2H_6O).
- Multiply the number of moles of reactant (glucose) by the conversion factor to give the number of moles of product (ethanol).

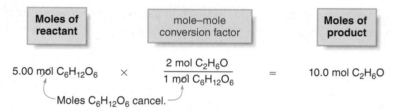

$$5.00\ \text{mol}\ C_6H_{12}O_6 \quad \times \quad \frac{2\ \text{mol}\ C_2H_6O}{1\ \text{mol}\ C_6H_{12}O_6} \quad = \quad 10.0\ \text{mol}\ C_2H_6O$$

Moles $C_6H_{12}O_6$ cancel.

[2] Convert the number of moles of product to the number of grams of product using the product's molar mass.

- Use the molar mass of the product (C_2H_6O, molar mass 46.07 g/mol) to write a conversion factor.
- Multiply the number of moles of product (from step [1]) by the conversion factor to give the number of grams of product.

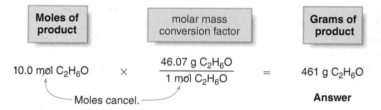

$$10.0\ \text{mol}\ C_2H_6O \quad \times \quad \frac{46.07\ \text{g}\ C_2H_6O}{1\ \text{mol}\ C_2H_6O} \quad = \quad 461\ \text{g}\ C_2H_6O$$

Moles cancel.

Answer

PROBLEM 5.23

Using the balanced equation for fermentation written in Sample Problem 5.13, answer the following questions.

a. How many grams of ethanol are formed from 0.55 mol of glucose?
b. How many grams of CO_2 are formed from 0.25 mol of glucose?
c. How many grams of glucose are needed to form 1.0 mol of ethanol?

PROBLEM 5.24

Using the balanced equation for the combustion of ethanol, answer the following questions.

$$C_2H_6O(l)\ +\ 3\ O_2(g) \longrightarrow 2\ CO_2(g)\ +\ 3\ H_2O(g)$$
$$\text{ethanol}$$

a. How many grams of CO_2 are formed from 0.50 mol of ethanol?
b. How many grams of H_2O are formed from 2.4 mol of ethanol?
c. How many grams of O_2 are needed to react with 0.25 mol of ethanol?

5.6B Converting Grams of Reactant to Grams of Product

The coefficients in chemical equations tell us the ratio of the number of *molecules* or *moles* that are involved in a chemical reaction. The coefficients do *not*, however, tell us directly about the number of grams. That's because the molar mass—the number of grams in one mole—of a substance depends on the identity of the elements that compose it. One mole of H_2O molecules weighs 18.02 g, one mole of NaCl weighs 58.44 g, and one mole of sugar molecules weighs 342.3 g (Figure 5.3).

In the laboratory, we measure out the number of grams of a reactant on a balance. This does not tell us directly the number of grams of a particular product that will form, because in all likelihood, the molar masses of the reactant and product are different. To carry out this type of calculation—grams of one compound (reactant) to grams of another compound (product)—three operations are necessary.

First, we must determine how many moles of reactant are contained in the given number of grams using the molar mass. Then, we can determine the number of moles of product expected using the coefficients of the balanced chemical equation. Finally, we convert the number of moles of product to the number of grams of product using its molar mass. Now there are three steps and three conversion factors. The stepwise procedure is outlined in the accompanying *How To,* and then illustrated with an example in Sample Problem 5.14.

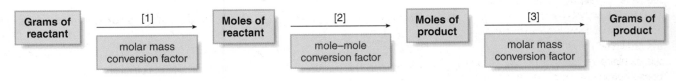

Figure 5.3   One Mole of Water, Table Salt, and Table Sugar

one mole of table sugar
$C_{12}H_{22}O_{11}$
342.3 g/mol

one mole of table salt
NaCl
58.44 g/mol

one mole of water molecules
H_2O
18.02 g/mol

One mole of each substance has the same number of units—6.02×10^{23} H_2O molecules, 6.02×10^{23} Na^+ and Cl^- ions, and 6.02×10^{23} sugar molecules. The molar mass of each substance is *different,* however, because they are each composed of *different* elements.

How To Convert Grams of Reactant to Grams of Product

Example: Ethanol (C_2H_6O, molar mass 46.07 g/mol) is synthesized by reacting ethylene (C_2H_4, molar mass 28.05 g/mol) with water. How many grams of ethanol are formed from 14 g of ethylene?

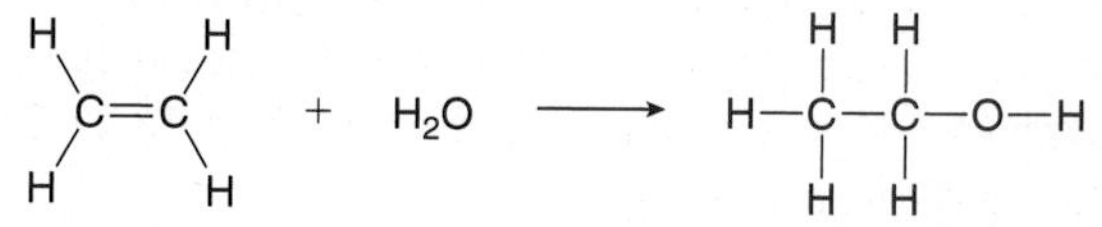

ethylene   ethanol

Step [1] **Convert the number of grams of reactant to the number of moles of reactant using the reactant's molar mass.**

• Use the molar mass of the reactant (C_2H_4) to write a conversion factor.

$$\frac{28.05\ \text{g } C_2H_4}{1\ \text{mol } C_2H_4} \quad \text{or} \quad \boxed{\frac{1\ \text{mol } C_2H_4}{28.05\ \text{g } C_2H_4}}$$

Choose this conversion factor to cancel g.

• Multiply the number of grams of reactant by the conversion factor to give the number of moles of reactant.

Grams of reactant		Moles of reactant

$$14\ \cancel{\text{g }} C_2H_4 \quad \times \quad \frac{1\ \text{mol } C_2H_4}{28.05\ \cancel{\text{g }} C_2H_4} \quad = \quad 0.50\ \text{mol } C_2H_4$$

Grams cancel.

Step [2] **Convert the number of moles of reactant to the number of moles of product using a mole–mole conversion factor.**

• Use the coefficients in the balanced chemical equation to write mole–mole conversion factors.

$$\frac{1\ \text{mol } C_2H_4}{1\ \text{mol } C_2H_6O} \quad \text{or} \quad \boxed{\frac{1\ \text{mol } C_2H_6O}{1\ \text{mol } C_2H_4}}$$

Choose this conversion factor to cancel mol C_2H_4.

• Multiply the number of moles of reactant by the conversion factor to give the number of moles of product. In this example, 0.50 mol of C_2H_6O is formed.

Moles of reactant		Moles of product

$$0.50\ \cancel{\text{mol }} C_2H_4 \quad \times \quad \frac{1\ \text{mol } C_2H_6O}{1\ \cancel{\text{mol }} C_2H_4} \quad = \quad 0.50\ \text{mol } C_2H_6O$$

Moles C_2H_4 cancel.

Step [3] **Convert the number of moles of product to the number of grams of product using the product's molar mass.**

• Use the molar mass of the product (C_2H_6O) to write a conversion factor.

$$\frac{1\ \text{mol } C_2H_6O}{46.07\ \text{g } C_2H_6O} \quad \text{or} \quad \boxed{\frac{46.07\ \text{g } C_2H_6O}{1\ \text{mol } C_2H_6O}}$$

Choose this conversion factor to cancel mol C_2H_6O.

• Multiply the number of moles of product (from step [2]) by the conversion factor to give the number of grams of product.

Moles of product		Grams of product

$$0.50\ \cancel{\text{mol }} C_2H_6O \quad \times \quad \frac{46.07\ \text{g } C_2H_6O}{1\ \cancel{\text{mol }} C_2H_6O} \quad = \quad 23\ \text{g } C_2H_6O$$

Moles C_2H_6O cancel.   **Answer**

It is also possible to combine the multiplication operations from steps [1], [2], and [3] into a single operation using all three conversion factors. This converts grams of starting material to grams of product all at once. Both the one-step and stepwise approaches give the same overall result.

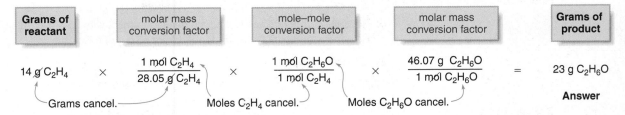

Grams of reactant		molar mass conversion factor		mole–mole conversion factor		molar mass conversion factor		Grams of product
$14\ g\ C_2H_4$	$\times$	$\dfrac{1\ mol\ C_2H_4}{28.05\ g\ C_2H_4}$	$\times$	$\dfrac{1\ mol\ C_2H_6O}{1\ mol\ C_2H_4}$	$\times$	$\dfrac{46.07\ g\ C_2H_6O}{1\ mol\ C_2H_6O}$	$=$	$23\ g\ C_2H_6O$

Grams cancel.   Moles C_2H_4 cancel.   Moles C_2H_6O cancel.

Answer

ENVIRONMENTAL NOTE

Ethanol is used as a gasoline additive. Although some of the ethanol used for this purpose comes from corn and other grains, much of it is still produced by the reaction of ethylene with water. Ethanol produced from grains is a renewable resource, whereas ethanol produced from ethylene is not, because ethylene is made from crude oil. Thus, running your car on gasohol (gasoline mixed with ethanol) reduces our reliance on fossil fuels only if the ethanol is produced from renewable sources such as grains or sugarcane.

SAMPLE PROBLEM 5.14

How many grams of aspirin are formed from 10.0 g of salicylic acid using the given balanced equation?

$$C_7H_6O_3(s)\ +\ C_2H_4O_2(l)\ \longrightarrow\ C_9H_8O_4(s)\ +\ H_2O(l)$$

salicylic acid   acetic acid   aspirin

Analysis and Solution

[1] Convert the number of grams of reactant to the number of moles of reactant using the reactant's molar mass.

- Use the molar mass of the reactant ($C_7H_6O_3$, molar mass 138.1 g/mol) to write a conversion factor. Multiply the number of grams of reactant by the conversion factor to give the number of moles of reactant.

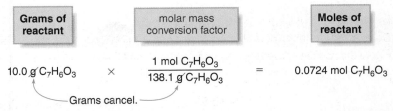

Grams of reactant		molar mass conversion factor		Moles of reactant
$10.0\ g\ C_7H_6O_3$	$\times$	$\dfrac{1\ mol\ C_7H_6O_3}{138.1\ g\ C_7H_6O_3}$	$=$	$0.0724\ mol\ C_7H_6O_3$

Grams cancel.

[2] Convert the number of moles of reactant to the number of moles of product using a mole–mole conversion factor.

- Use the coefficients in the balanced chemical equation to write mole–mole conversion factors for the two compounds—one mole of salicylic acid ($C_7H_6O_3$) forms one mole of aspirin ($C_9H_8O_4$).
- Multiply the number of moles of reactant (salicylic acid) by the conversion factor to give the number of moles of product (aspirin).

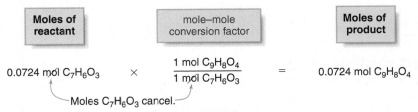

Moles of reactant		mole–mole conversion factor		Moles of product
$0.0724\ mol\ C_7H_6O_3$	$\times$	$\dfrac{1\ mol\ C_9H_8O_4}{1\ mol\ C_7H_6O_3}$	$=$	$0.0724\ mol\ C_9H_8O_4$

Moles $C_7H_6O_3$ cancel.

[3] Convert the number of moles of product to the number of grams of product using the product's molar mass.

- Use the molar mass of the product ($C_9H_8O_4$, molar mass 180.2 g/mol) to write a conversion factor. Multiply the number of moles of product (from step [2]) by the conversion factor to give the number of grams of product.

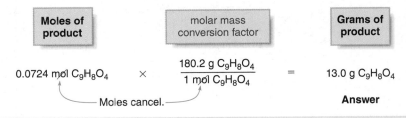

Moles of product		molar mass conversion factor		Grams of product
$0.0724\ mol\ C_9H_8O_4$	$\times$	$\dfrac{180.2\ g\ C_9H_8O_4}{1\ mol\ C_9H_8O_4}$	$=$	$13.0\ g\ C_9H_8O_4$

Moles cancel.

Answer

PROBLEM 5.25

Use the balanced equation in Sample Problem 5.14 for the conversion of salicylic acid and acetic acid to aspirin to answer the following questions.

   a. How many grams of aspirin are formed from 55.5 g of salicylic acid?
   b. How many grams of acetic acid are needed to react with 55.5 g of salicylic acid?
   c. How many grams of water are formed from 55.5 g of salicylic acid?

PROBLEM 5.26

Use the balanced equation, $N_2 + O_2 \longrightarrow 2\ NO$, to answer the following questions.

   a. How many grams of NO are formed from 10.0 g of N_2?
   b. How many grams of NO are formed from 10.0 g of O_2?
   c. How many grams of O_2 are needed to react completely with 10.0 g of N_2?

5.7 Percent Yield

In determining the number of moles or grams of product in Sections 5.5 and 5.6, we assumed that each reaction gives the maximum amount of product from a given amount of reactant. This value is called the **theoretical yield** of a reaction.

> • The *theoretical yield* is the amount of product expected from a given amount of reactant based on the coefficients in the balanced chemical equation.

Usually, however, the amount of product formed is *less* than the maximum amount predicted. Sometimes other undesired reactions, called **side reactions,** occur between the reactants. At other times the desired product is formed, but it goes on to react further to form another product. Moreover, each time material is weighed and transferred to a reaction vessel, or anytime a separation or purification step is carried out, material is inadvertently lost.

> • The *actual yield* is the amount of product isolated from a reaction.

The actual yield is an experimental value determined by weighing the product obtained on a balance. The theoretical yield, on the other hand, is calculated from the coefficients of the balanced equation.

5.7A Calculating Percent Yield

The theoretical and actual yields are typically reported in grams. The amount of product actually formed in a particular reaction is reported as a **percent yield.**

$$\boxed{\text{Percent yield}} \quad = \quad \frac{\text{actual yield (g)}}{\text{theoretical yield (g)}} \quad \times \quad 100\%$$

For example, if a reaction forms 25.0 g of product and the theoretical yield is 40.0 g, the percent yield is calculated as follows.

$$\text{Percent yield} = \frac{25.0\ \text{g}}{40.0\ \text{g}} \times 100\% = 62.5\%$$

SAMPLE PROBLEM 5.15

Consider the reaction of ethylene (C_2H_4) and water to form ethanol (C_2H_6O), which was mentioned in Section 5.6B. If the theoretical yield of ethanol is 23 g in a reaction, what is the percent yield of ethanol if only 15 g of ethanol are actually formed?

Analysis

Use the formula, percent yield = (actual yield/theoretical yield) × 100% to calculate the percent yield.

Solution

$$\text{Percent yield} = \frac{\text{actual yield (g)}}{\text{theoretical yield (g)}} \times 100\%$$

$$= \frac{15\ \text{g}}{23\ \text{g}} \times 100\% = 65\%$$

Answer

Charcoal is composed of a network of covalently bonded carbon atoms. When charcoal is burned in a grill or coal is burned in a furnace, carbon atoms combine with O_2 from the air to form carbon dioxide (CO_2).

SAMPLE PROBLEM 5.16

When charcoal is burned, the carbon (C) it contains reacts with oxygen (O_2) to form carbon dioxide (CO_2). (a) What is the theoretical yield of CO_2 in grams from 0.50 mol of C? (b) What is the percent yield if 10.0 g of CO_2 are formed?

$$C(s) + O_2(g) \longrightarrow CO_2(g)$$

Analysis

To answer part (a), convert the number of moles of reactant to the number of moles of product, as in Section 5.6A. Then, convert the number of moles of product to the number of grams of product using the product's molar mass. This is the theoretical yield. To answer part (b), use the formula, percent yield = (actual yield/theoretical yield) × 100%.

Solution

a. Calculate the theoretical yield using the procedure outlined in Sample Problem 5.13.

[1] Convert the number of moles of reactant to the number of moles of product using a mole-mole conversion factor.

- Use the coefficients in the balanced equation to write a mole–mole conversion factor for the two compounds—one mole of carbon forms one mole of CO_2. Multiply the number of moles of reactant (carbon) by the conversion factor to give the number of moles of product (CO_2).

Moles of reactant	mole–mole conversion factor	Moles of product

$$0.50 \text{ mol C} \quad \times \quad \frac{1 \text{ mol } CO_2}{1 \text{ mol C}} \quad = \quad 0.50 \text{ mol } CO_2$$

[2] Convert the number of moles of product to the number of grams of product—the theoretical yield—using the product's molar mass.

- Use the molar mass of the product (CO_2, molar mass 44.01 g/mol) to write a conversion factor. Multiply the number of moles of product (from step [1]) by the conversion factor to give the number of grams of product.

Moles of product	molar mass conversion factor	Grams of product

$$0.50 \text{ mol } CO_2 \quad \times \quad \frac{44.01 \text{ g } CO_2}{1 \text{ mol } CO_2} \quad = \quad 22 \text{ g } CO_2$$

Theoretical yield
Answer: part (a)

b. Use the theoretical yield from part (a) and the given actual yield to calculate the percent yield.

$$\text{Percent yield} = \frac{\text{actual yield (g)}}{\text{theoretical yield (g)}} \times 100\%$$

$$= \frac{10.0 \text{ g}}{22 \text{ g}} \times 100\% = 45\%$$

Answer: part (b)

PROBLEM 5.27

Using the chemical equation in Sample Problem 5.16, answer each question. (a) What is the theoretical yield of CO_2 from 3.50 mol of charcoal? (b) What is the percent yield if the reaction gives 53.5 g of CO_2?

PROBLEM 5.28

Consider the conversion of oxygen (O_2) to ozone (O_3) described in Section 5.6A; that is, $3 O_2 \longrightarrow 2 O_3$. (a) What is the theoretical yield of O_3 in grams from 8.0 mol of O_2? (b) What is the percent yield if the reaction actually gives 155 g of O_3?

5.7B Calculating Percent Yield from Grams of Reactant

Since we weigh the amount of reactants and products on a balance, we must be able to calculate a percent yield from the number of grams of reactant used and the number of grams of product formed. This latter quantity is the **actual yield**, and it is always experimentally determined; that is, it is *not* a calculated value. We can carry out this lengthy calculation by putting together the steps in Sample Problems 5.14 and 5.15. Sample Problem 5.17 illustrates the steps used to calculate a percent yield when the number of grams of reactant used and the actual yield of product formed are both known.

SAMPLE PROBLEM 5.17

Acetaminophen, the active ingredient in Tylenol, can be prepared by the chemical reaction given below. What is the percent yield when 60.0 g of 4-aminophenol reacts with acetyl chloride to form 70.0 g of acetaminophen?

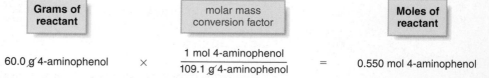

| 4-aminophenol | acetyl | acetaminophen |
| molar mass 109.1 g/mol | chloride | molar mass 151.2 g/mol |

Analysis

To find the theoretical yield, convert grams of reactant to grams of product, following the three steps in Sample Problem 5.14. Then, use the formula, percent yield = (actual yield/theoretical yield) × 100%.

Solution

[1] Convert the number of grams of reactant to the number of moles of reactant using the reactant's molar mass.

- Use the molar mass of the reactant, 4-aminophenol, to write a conversion factor. Multiply the number of grams of reactant by the conversion factor to give the number of moles of reactant.

Grams of reactant		**Moles of reactant**
	molar mass conversion factor	
60.0 g 4-aminophenol	× $\dfrac{\text{1 mol 4-aminophenol}}{\text{109.1 g 4-aminophenol}}$ =	0.550 mol 4-aminophenol

[2] Convert the number of moles of reactant to the number of moles of product using a mole–mole conversion factor.

- Use the coefficients in the balanced chemical equation to write a mole–mole conversion factor—one mole of 4-aminophenol forms one mole of acetaminophen. Multiply the number of moles of reactant by the conversion factor to give the number of moles of product.

Moles of reactant		**Moles of product**
	mole–mole conversion factor	
0.550 mol 4-aminophenol	× $\dfrac{\text{1 mol acetaminophen}}{\text{1 mol 4-aminophenol}}$ =	0.550 mol acetaminophen

[3] Convert the number of moles of product to the number of grams of product using the product's molar mass.

- Use the molar mass of the product to write a conversion factor. Multiply the number of moles of product (from step [2]) by the conversion factor to give the number of grams of product.

Moles of product	molar mass conversion factor	Grams of product

$$0.550 \text{ mol acetaminophen} \quad \times \quad \frac{151.2 \text{ g acetaminophen}}{1 \text{ mol acetaminophen}} \quad = \quad 83.2 \text{ g acetaminophen}$$

Theoretical yield

[4] Use the theoretical yield and the given actual yield to calculate the percent yield.

$$\text{Percent yield} = \frac{\text{actual yield (g)}}{\text{theoretical yield (g)}} \times 100\%$$

$$= \frac{70.0 \text{ g}}{83.2 \text{ g}} \times 100\% = 84.1\%$$

Answer

PROBLEM 5.29

Using the equation in Sample Problem 5.17, answer each question. (a) What is the theoretical yield of acetaminophen from 80.0 g of 4-aminophenol? (b) What is the percent yield if the reaction gives 65.5 g of acetaminophen?

PROBLEM 5.30

Consider the conversion of oxygen (O_2) to ozone (O_3) described in Section 5.6A; that is, $3 O_2 \longrightarrow 2 O_3$. (a) What is the theoretical yield of O_3 in grams from 324 g of O_2? (b) What is the percent yield if the reaction actually gives 122 g of O_3?

5.7C FOCUS ON HEALTH & MEDICINE
The Importance of Percent Yield in the Pharmaceutical Industry

Although some drugs, like the cardiac drug digoxin (used to treat congestive heart failure, Section 1.1), are isolated directly from a natural source, most widely used drugs are synthesized in the laboratory. All common pain relievers—aspirin, acetaminophen, and ibuprofen—are synthetic. The same is true for the bronchodilator albuterol (trade name Proventil or Ventolin), the antidepressant fluoxetine (trade name Prozac), and the cholesterol-lowering medication atorvastatin (trade name Lipitor), whose three-dimensional structures are shown in Figure 5.4.

Once it has been determined that a drug is safe and effective, a pharmaceutical company must be able to prepare large quantities of the material cost-efficiently. This means that cheap and readily available starting materials must be used. It also means that the reactions used to synthesize a drug must proceed in high yield. Rarely is a drug prepared in a single step, and typically, five or more steps may be required in a synthesis.

- To determine the overall percent yield in a synthesis that has more than one step, multiply the percent yield for each step.

For example, if a synthesis has five steps and each step has a 90.% yield (0.90 written as a decimal), the overall yield is

$$0.90 \times 0.90 \times 0.90 \times 0.90 \times 0.90 = 0.59 = 59\%$$

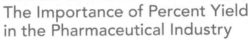

yield for each step, written as a decimal

overall yield for five steps

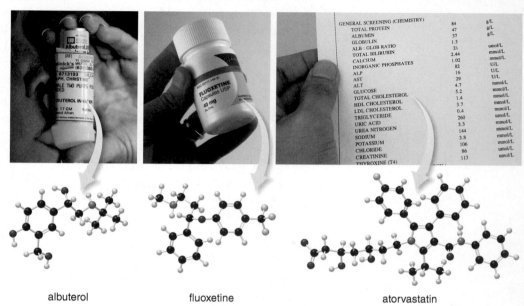

Figure 5.4   Three Widely Used Synthetic Drugs—Albuterol, Fluoxetine, and Atorvastatin

albuterol   fluoxetine   atorvastatin

Most commonly prescribed drugs are synthesized in the laboratory. Albuterol (Proventil, Ventolin) is a bronchodilator—that is, it widens airways—and so it is used to treat asthma. Fluoxetine (Prozac) is one of the most common antidepressants currently on the market, used by over 40 million individuals since 1986. Atorvastatin (Lipitor) lowers cholesterol levels, and in this way decreases the risk of heart attack and stroke.

Thus, even if all steps proceed in high yield, the overall yield is considerably lower—59% in this example. If only one step has a lower yield, say 50.%, the overall yield drops even more, from 59% to 33%.

$$0.50 \times 0.90 \times 0.90 \times 0.90 \times 0.90 = 0.33 = 33\%$$

one low-yield reaction   **overall yield
for five steps**

Moreover, many drugs are synthesized by routes that require 10 or more steps, resulting in a low overall yield. Thus, pharmaceutical companies are faced with the task of developing drugs that have the desired physiological effects, which are prepared by reactions that give high yields of the desired compounds.

PROBLEM 5.31

The synthetic antiviral drug Tamiflu, currently the most effective agent against avian influenza, is prepared by a 10-step synthesis. What is the overall yield of Tamiflu in each of the following 10-step syntheses?

a. Each step proceeds in 90.% yield.
b. Each step proceeds in 80.% yield.
c. One step proceeds in 50.% yield, while the rest occur in 90.% yield.
d. The following yields are recorded: 20.% (one reaction), 50.% (two reactions), 80.% (all remaining reactions).

5.8   Limiting Reactants

Up to now we have assumed that we have the exact ratio of the reactants needed to carry out a reaction. In the following reaction, the mole ratio of **A** to **B** is 1:1, so one molecule of **A** is needed to react with one molecule of **B** to form one molecule of the product, **AB.**

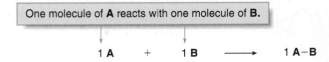

One mole of each reactant is needed.

Suppose, instead, that the reaction contains an *excess* of **B**, as shown in the molecular art, where the reaction mixture contains six molecules of **A** and eight molecules of **B**. In this case, all six **A** molecules react with six **B** molecules, and two **B** molecules are left over. Reactant **A** is all used up, so the amount of **A** *limits* how much product **AB** can be formed.

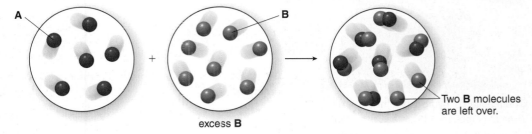

- The *limiting reactant* is the reactant that is completely used up in a reaction.

In this example, **A** is the limiting reactant since **B** is present in excess.

5.8A   Determining the Limiting Reactant

We deal with the concept of limiting reactants often in everyday life. To make turkey sandwiches, we may use two pieces of bread for each slice of turkey. If we had eight slices of bread and three slices of turkey, we could make three sandwiches using six slices of bread and three pieces of turkey, leaving two pieces of bread left over. In this case, the turkey is the limiting reactant and the bread is present in excess.

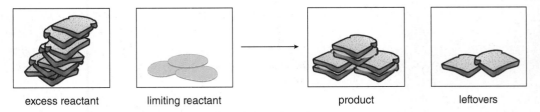

excess reactant   limiting reactant   product   leftovers

Sample Problem 5.18 illustrates how to determine which reactant is limiting using the mole ratios in a balanced equation.

SAMPLE PROBLEM 5.18

Consider the reaction of hydrogen and oxygen to form water, according to the balanced equation: $2 H_2(g) + O_2(g) \longrightarrow 2 H_2O(l)$. Identify the limiting reactant in the molecular art, and draw a representation showing how much product is formed and what reactant molecules are left over.

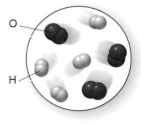

ENVIRONMENTAL NOTE

The reaction of hydrogen with oxygen (Sample Problem 5.18) releases a great deal of energy and offers an alternative to burning fossil fuels for powering vehicles. Current research efforts are underway to make this process economical and feasible for widespread use.

Analysis

Use the amount of each reactant and the mole ratio from the balanced equation to determine the limiting reactant. Use the amount of limiting reactant to determine the amount of product formed.

Solution

[1] **To determine how much of one reactant is needed to react with a second reactant, label one reactant as the original quantity and the second reactant as the unknown quantity.**

- These labels are completely arbitrary. In this example we identify the number of molecules of H_2 as the original quantity.

4 molecules of H_2 ? molecules of O_2

original quantity   unknown quantity

[2] **Write out the conversion factors that relate the number of moles (or molecules) of reactants.**

- Use the coefficients in the balanced equation to write a mole–mole (or molecule–molecule) conversion factor for H_2 and O_2.

$$\dfrac{2 \text{ molecules } H_2}{1 \text{ molecule } O_2} \quad \text{or} \quad \boxed{\dfrac{1 \text{ molecule } O_2}{2 \text{ molecules } H_2}}$$

Choose this conversion factor to cancel molecules of H_2.

[3] **Calculate the number of moles (or molecules) of the second reactant needed for complete reaction.**

$$4 \text{ molecules } H_2 \times \frac{1 \text{ molecule } O_2}{2 \text{ molecules } H_2} = 2 \text{ molecules of } O_2 \text{ needed}$$

[4] **Analyze the two possible outcomes.**

- If the amount present of the second reactant is *less than* what is needed, the *second reactant is the limiting reactant.*
- If the amount present of the second reactant is *greater than* what is needed, the *second reactant is in excess.*

In this reaction only two molecules of O_2 are needed but three molecules of O_2 are present, so O_2 is present in excess and **H_2 is the limiting reactant.** To draw the molecular art representing the product, we must know what happens to each reactant and how much product is formed.

4 molecules of H_2O

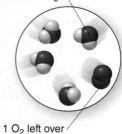

1 O_2 left over

- Since H_2 is the limiting reactant, all of the H_2 is consumed and none is left.
- Since two molecules of O_2 react and three were present at the outset, one molecule of O_2 is left over.
- Using the balanced equation, the number of molecules of product formed equals the number of molecules of the limiting reactant consumed. Thus, four molecules of H_2 yield four molecules of H_2O.

Summary	Reactants		Product
Equation	2 H_2 +	O_2 ⟶	2 H_2O
Initial quantities	4 molecules	3 molecules	0 molecules
Used or formed	−4 molecules	−2 molecules	+4 molecules
Molecules remaining	0 molecules	1 molecule	4 molecules
	Limiting reactant	Excess reactant	

PROBLEM 5.32

Consider the reaction of hydrogen and nitrogen to form ammonia, according to the balanced equation: $3 H_2(g) + N_2(g) \longrightarrow 2 NH_3(g)$. Identify the limiting reactant in the molecular art, and draw a representation showing how much product is formed and what reactant molecules are left over.

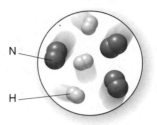

PROBLEM 5.33

Using the balanced equation for the reaction of H_2 with O_2 to form H_2O in Sample Problem 5.18, determine the limiting reactant under each of the following conditions.

a. 5.0 mol H_2 and 5.0 mol O_2

b. 5.0 mol H_2 and 8.0 mol O_2

c. 8.0 mol H_2 and 2.0 mol O_2

d. 2.0 mol H_2 and 5.0 mol O_2

5.8B Using the Limiting Reactant to Determine How Much Product Is Formed

When a reaction has a limiting reactant,

> • The number of moles of limiting reactant determines the number of moles of product that can form.

For example, the molecular art shows the reaction of A_2 with B_2 to form **AB**, with B_2 present in excess. The amount of A_2, the limiting reactant, determines how much **AB** can form. Since the balanced equation shows that each A_2 molecule forms two **AB** molecules, three A_2 molecules form six **AB** molecules.

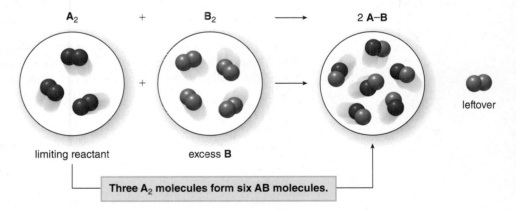

Sample Problem 5.19 illustrates how to determine the amount of product formed from a limiting reactant using mole ratios in a balanced equation. **Keep in mind that the number of moles (*not* grams) of the limiting reactant determines the number of moles (*not* grams) of product.**

SAMPLE PROBLEM 5.19

Using the balanced equation, $3 H_2(g) + N_2(g) \longrightarrow 2 NH_3(g)$, calculate the number of moles of product formed from 5.0 moles of H_2 and 3.0 moles of N_2.

Analysis and Solution

[1] Determine the limiting reactant as in Sample Problem 5.18.

- Identify H_2 as the original quantity and use the mole ratio from the balanced equation as a conversion factor to calculate how much N_2 is needed for complete reaction.

$$\boxed{\substack{\text{mole–mole} \\ \text{conversion factor}}}$$

$$5.0 \text{ mol } H_2 \quad \times \quad \frac{1 \text{ mol } N_2}{3 \text{ mol } H_2} \quad = \quad 1.7 \text{ mol } N_2 \text{ needed}$$

- Since the amount of N_2 present is greater than what is needed, N_2 is present in excess and **H_2 is the limiting reactant.**

[2] Convert the number of moles of limiting reactant to the number of moles of product using a mole–mole conversion factor.

$$\boxed{\substack{\text{mole–mole} \\ \text{conversion factor}}}$$

$$5.0 \text{ mol } H_2 \quad \times \quad \frac{2 \text{ mol } NH_3}{3 \text{ mol } H_2} \quad = \quad 3.3 \text{ mol } NH_3 \text{ formed}$$

Answer

PROBLEM 5.34

Using the balanced equation, $3 H_2(g) + N_2(g) \longrightarrow 2 NH_3(g)$, calculate the number of moles of product formed under each of the following reaction conditions.

a. 1.5 mol H_2 and 1.0 mol N_2 c. 2.0 mol H_2 and 3.0 mol N_2
b. 1.0 mol H_2 and 2.0 mol N_2 d. 7.5 mol H_2 and 2.0 mol N_2

5.8C   Determining the Limiting Reactant Using the Number of Grams

In the laboratory, we measure out the number of grams (not the number of moles) of each reactant on a balance. To determine the limiting reactant from the number of grams, we must first determine the number of moles of each reactant using the molar mass, as shown in Sample Problem 5.20.

SAMPLE PROBLEM 5.20

Using the balanced equation, $N_2(g) + O_2(g) \longrightarrow 2 NO(g)$, determine the limiting reactant when 10.0 g of N_2 (molar mass 28.02 g/mol) react with 10.0 g of O_2 (molar mass 32.00 g/mol).

Analysis

Convert the number of grams to the number of moles for each reactant, and then use the steps in Sample Problem 5.18 to determine the limiting reactant.

Solution

[1] Convert the number of grams of each reactant to the number of moles using the molar masses.

$$\boxed{\text{Moles of } N_2:} \quad 10.0 \text{ g } N_2 \quad \times \quad \frac{1 \text{ mol } N_2}{28.02 \text{ g } N_2} \quad = \quad 0.357 \text{ mol } N_2$$

$$\boxed{\text{Moles of } O_2:} \quad 10.0 \text{ g } O_2 \quad \times \quad \frac{1 \text{ mol } O_2}{32.00 \text{ g } O_2} \quad = \quad 0.313 \text{ mol } O_2$$

[2] Determine the limiting reactant as in Sample Problem 5.18.

- Identify N_2 as the original quantity and use the mole ratio from the balanced equation as a conversion factor to calculate how much O_2 is needed for complete reaction.

$$\text{0.357 mol } N_2 \quad \times \quad \boxed{\begin{array}{c}\text{mole–mole}\\\text{conversion factor}\end{array}} \quad \frac{1 \text{ mol } O_2}{1 \text{ mol } N_2} \quad = \quad \text{0.357 mol } O_2 \text{ needed}$$

- Since the amount of O_2 present is less than what is needed, **O_2 is the limiting reactant.**

PROBLEM 5.35

Using the balanced equation, $N_2(g) + O_2(g) \longrightarrow 2\ NO(g)$, determine the limiting reactant under the following conditions (N_2, molar mass 28.02 g/mol; O_2, molar mass 32.00 g/mol).

a. 12.5 g N_2 and 15.0 g O_2 b. 14.0 g N_2 and 13.0 g O_2

SAMPLE PROBLEM 5.21

Using the balanced equation, $N_2(g) + O_2(g) \longrightarrow 2\ NO(g)$, calculate the number of grams of NO (molar mass 30.01 g/mol) formed when 10.0 g of N_2 (molar mass 28.02 g/mol) react with 10.0 g of O_2 (molar mass 32.00 g/mol).

Analysis

Three steps are required:

- Determine the limiting reactant.
- Use the mole ratio from the balanced equation to calculate the number of moles of product formed.
- Convert the moles of product to grams using the molar mass.

Solution

[1] Determine the limiting reactant.

- Convert the number of grams of each reactant to the number of moles using the molar masses.
- Use a mole–mole conversion factor to determine which reactant is present in excess.
- As shown in Sample Problem 5.20, when 10.0 g of N_2 (0.357 mol) react with 10.0 g (0.313 mol) of O_2, O_2 is the limiting reactant.

[2] Convert the number of moles of limiting reactant to the number of moles of product using a mole–mole conversion factor.

$$\text{0.313 mol } O_2 \quad \times \quad \boxed{\begin{array}{c}\text{mole–mole}\\\text{conversion factor}\end{array}} \quad \frac{2 \text{ mol NO}}{1 \text{ mol } O_2} \quad = \quad \text{0.626 mol NO formed}$$

[3] Convert the number of moles of product to the number of grams using the molar mass.

$$\text{0.626 mol NO} \times \frac{30.01 \text{ g NO}}{1 \text{ mol NO}} = 18.8 \text{ g NO formed}$$
Answer

PROBLEM 5.36

For each set of reaction conditions in Problem 5.35, calculate the number of grams of product formed.

PROBLEM 5.37

Using the balanced equation, $2\ H_2(g) + O_2(g) \longrightarrow 2\ H_2O(l)$, calculate the number of grams of H_2O (molar mass 18.02 g/mol) formed when 5.00 g of H_2 (molar mass 2.016 g/mol) react with 10.0 g of O_2 (molar mass 32.00 g/mol).

5.9 Oxidation and Reduction

Thus far we have examined features that are common to all types of chemical reactions. We conclude with an examination of one class of reactions that involves electron transfer—oxidation–reduction reactions.

Another group of reactions—acid–base reactions—is discussed in Chapter 9.

5.9A General Features of Oxidation–Reduction Reactions

A common type of chemical reaction involves the transfer of electrons from one element to another. When iron rusts, methane and wood burn, and a battery generates electricity, one element gains electrons and another loses them. These reactions involve **oxidation** and **reduction.**

- Oxidation is the loss of electrons from an atom.
- Reduction is the gain of electrons by an atom.

Oxidation and reduction are opposite processes, and both occur together in a single reaction called an **oxidation–reduction** or **redox reaction.** A redox reaction always has two components—one that is oxidized and one that is reduced.

- A redox reaction involves the transfer of electrons from one element to another.

An example of an oxidation–reduction reaction occurs when Zn metal reacts with Cu^{2+} cations, as shown in Figure 5.5.

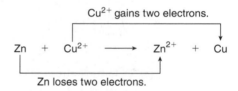

$$\text{Zn} \quad + \quad \text{Cu}^{2+} \quad \longrightarrow \quad \text{Zn}^{2+} \quad + \quad \text{Cu}$$

Cu²⁺ gains two electrons.

Zn loses two electrons.

- Zn loses two electrons to form Zn^{2+}, so Zn is oxidized.
- Cu^{2+} gains two electrons to form Cu metal, so Cu^{2+} is reduced.

CONSUMER NOTE

Benzoyl peroxide ($C_{14}H_{10}O_4$) is the active ingredient in several acne medications. Benzoyl peroxide kills bacteria by oxidation reactions.

Figure 5.5 A Redox Reaction—The Transfer of Electrons from Zn to Cu^{2+}

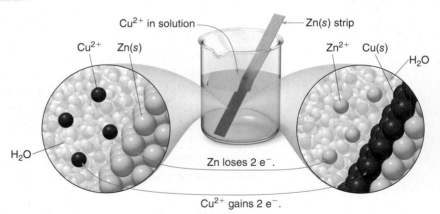

A redox reaction occurs when a strip of Zn metal is placed in a solution of Cu^{2+} ions. In this reaction, Zn loses two electrons to form Zn^{2+}, which goes into solution. Cu^{2+} gains two electrons to form Cu metal, which precipitates out of solution, forming a coating on the zinc strip.

Figure 5.6   Examples of Oxidation and Reduction Reactions

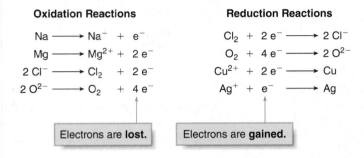

Each of these processes can be written as individual reactions, called **half reactions,** to emphasize which electrons are gained and lost.

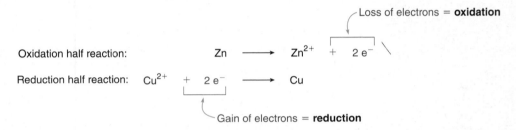

- A compound that gains electrons (is reduced) while causing another compound to be oxidized is called an *oxidizing agent.*
- A compound that loses electrons (is oxidized) while causing another compound to be reduced is called a *reducing agent.*

In this example, Zn loses electrons to Cu^{2+}. We can think of Zn as a **reducing agent** since it causes Cu^{2+} to gain electrons and become reduced. We can think of Cu^{2+} as an **oxidizing agent** since it causes Zn to lose electrons and become oxidized.

To draw the products of an oxidation–reduction reaction, we must decide which element or ion gains electrons and which element or ion loses electrons. Use the following guidelines.

- When considering neutral atoms, metals lose electrons and nonmetals gain electrons.
- When considering ions, cations tend to gain electrons and anions tend to lose electrons.

Thus, the metals sodium (Na) and magnesium (Mg) readily lose electrons to form the cations Na^+ and Mg^{2+}, respectively; that is, they are oxidized. The nonmetals O_2 and Cl_2 readily gain electrons to form $2\,O^{2-}$ and $2\,Cl^-$, respectively; that is, they are reduced. A positively charged ion like Cu^{2+} is reduced to Cu by gaining two electrons, while two negatively charged Cl^- anions are oxidized to Cl_2 by losing two electrons. These reactions and additional examples are shown in Figure 5.6.

SAMPLE PROBLEM 5.22

Identify the species that is oxidized and the species that is reduced in the following reaction. Write out half reactions to show how many electrons are gained or lost by each species.

$$Mg(s) + 2\,H^+(aq) \longrightarrow Mg^{2+}(aq) + H_2(g)$$

Analysis

Metals and anions tend to lose electrons and thus undergo oxidation. Nonmetals and cations tend to gain electrons and thus undergo reduction.

Solution

The metal Mg is oxidized to Mg^{2+}, thus losing two electrons. Two H^+ cations gain a total of two electrons, and so are reduced to the nonmetal H_2.

$$Mg(s) \longrightarrow Mg^{2+}(aq) + 2\,e^- \qquad\qquad 2\,H^+(aq) + 2\,e^- \longrightarrow H_2(g)$$

       Mg is oxidized. H^+ is reduced.   Two electrons are needed
                                                                        to balance charge.

We need enough electrons so that **the total charge is the same on both sides of the equation.** Since 2 H^+ cations have a +2 overall charge, this means that 2 e^- must be gained so that the total charge on both sides of the equation is zero.

PROBLEM 5.38

Identify the species that is oxidized and the species that is reduced in each reaction. Write out half reactions to show how many electrons are gained or lost by each species.

a. $Zn(s) + 2\,H^+(aq) \longrightarrow Zn^{2+}(aq) + H_2(g)$ c. $2\,I^- + Br_2 \longrightarrow I_2 + 2\,Br^-$
b. $Fe^{3+}(aq) + Al(s) \longrightarrow Al^{3+}(aq) + Fe(s)$ d. $2\,AgBr \longrightarrow 2\,Ag + Br_2$

PROBLEM 5.39

Classify each reactant in Problem 5.38 as an oxidizing agent or a reducing agent.

5.9B Examples of Oxidation–Reduction Reactions

Many common processes involve oxidation and reduction. For example, common antiseptics like iodine (I_2) and hydrogen peroxide (H_2O_2) are oxidizing agents that clean wounds by oxidizing, thereby killing bacteria that might cause infection.

When iron (Fe) rusts, it is oxidized by the oxygen in air to form iron(III) oxide, Fe_2O_3. In this redox reaction, neutral iron atoms are oxidized to Fe^{3+} cations, and elemental O_2 is reduced to O^{2-} anions.

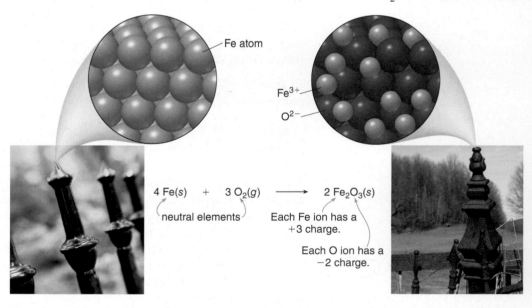

$$4\,Fe(s) + 3\,O_2(g) \longrightarrow 2\,Fe_2O_3(s)$$

           neutral elements   Each Fe ion has a
                                      +3 charge.

                                      Each O ion has a
                                      −2 charge.

Batteries consist of a metal and a cation that undergo a redox reaction. When the electrons are transferred from the metal to the cation, an electric current results, which can supply power for a lightbulb, radio, computer, or watch. For example, an alkaline battery usually contains zinc powder and Mn^{4+} cations, together with sodium or potassium hydroxide (NaOH or KOH), as shown in Figure 5.7.

$$Zn + 2\,MnO_2 \longrightarrow ZnO + Mn_2O_3$$

                     Mn^{4+} Zn^{2+} Mn^{3+}

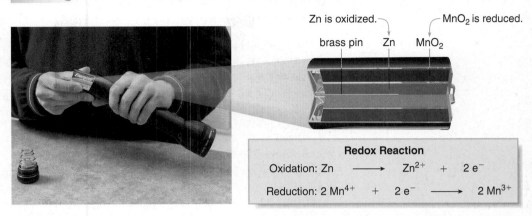

Figure 5.7   A Flashlight Battery—An Example of a Redox Reaction

Alkaline batteries consist of zinc powder (Zn) and manganese dioxide (MnO_2), along with a paste of sodium hydroxide (NaOH) or potassium hydroxide (KOH). When electrical contact is made, Zn atoms lose electrons, which flow towards the Mn^{4+} cations in MnO_2. The resulting electric current can be used to power a lightbulb, radio, or other electrical device.

In this redox reaction, neutral Zn atoms are oxidized to Zn^{2+} cations. Mn^{4+} cations are reduced to Mn^{3+} cations. The oxygen anions (O^{2-}) just balance the charge of the metal cations and are neither oxidized nor reduced.

In some reactions it is much less apparent which reactant is oxidized and which is reduced. For example, in the combustion of methane (CH_4) with oxygen to form CO_2 and H_2O, there are no metals or cations that obviously lose or gain electrons, yet this is a redox reaction. In these instances, it is often best to count oxygen and hydrogen atoms.

- Oxidation results in the gain of oxygen atoms or the loss of hydrogen atoms.
- Reduction results in the loss of oxygen atoms or the gain of hydrogen atoms.

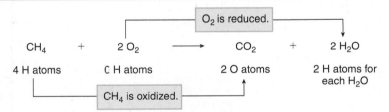

CH_4 is oxidized since it gains two oxygen atoms to form CO_2. O_2 is reduced since it gains two hydrogen atoms to form H_2O.

PROBLEM 5.40

The following redox reaction occurs in mercury batteries for watches. Identify the species that is oxidized and the species that is reduced, and write out two half reactions to show how many electrons are gained or lost.

$$Zn + HgO \longrightarrow ZnO + Hg$$

PROBLEM 5.41

Identify the species that is oxidized and the species that is reduced in the following redox reaction. Explain your choices.

$$C_2H_4O_2 + 2 H_2 \longrightarrow C_2H_6O + H_2O$$

5.10 FOCUS ON HEALTH & MEDICINE
Pacemakers

A pacemaker is a small electrical device implanted in an individual's chest and used to maintain an adequate heart rate (Figure 5.8). When a pacemaker detects that the heart is beating too slowly, it sends an electrical signal to the heart so that the heart muscle beats faster. A pacemaker contains a small, long-lasting battery that generates an electrical impulse by a redox reaction.

Most pacemakers used today contain a lithium–iodine battery. Each neutral lithium atom is oxidized to Li^+ by losing one electron. Each I_2 molecule is reduced by gaining two electrons and forming $2\ I^-$. Since the balanced equation contains two Li atoms for each I_2 molecule, the number of electrons lost by Li atoms equals the number of electrons gained by I_2.

- I_2 gains $2\ e^-$, forming $2\ I^-$.
- I_2 is **reduced.**

$$2\ Li\quad +\quad I_2\quad \longrightarrow\quad 2\ LiI$$

- Each Li atom loses $1\ e^-$, forming Li^+.
- Li metal is **oxidized.**

The lithium–iodine battery has a much longer battery life (over 10 years) than earlier batteries, greatly improving the quality of life for the many individuals with pacemakers.

PROBLEM 5.42

Early pacemakers generated an electrical impulse by the following reaction. What species is the oxidizing agent and what species is the reducing agent in this reaction?

$$Zn + Hg^{2+} \longrightarrow Zn^{2+} + Hg$$

Figure 5.8 The Lithium–Iodine Battery in a Pacemaker

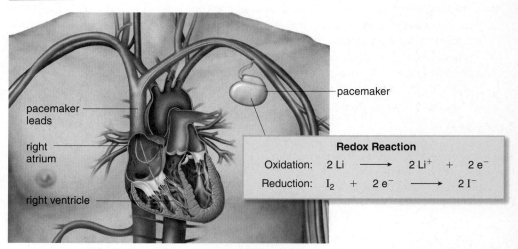

A pacemaker generates a small electrical impulse that triggers the heart to beat. Today's pacemakers sense when the heart beats normally and provide an electrical signal only when the heart rate slows. Such devices are called "demand" pacemakers, and they quickly replaced earlier "fixed" rate models that continuously produced impulses to set the heart rate at a fixed value.

CHAPTER HIGHLIGHTS

KEY TERMS

Actual yield (5.7)
Avogadro's number (5.3)
Balanced chemical equation (5.2)
Chemical equation (5.1)
Formula weight (5.4)
Half reaction (5.9)
Law of conservation of mass (5.1)

Limiting reactant (5.8)
Molar mass (5.4)
Mole (5.3)
Molecular weight (5.4)
Oxidation (5.9)
Oxidizing agent (5.9)
Percent yield (5.7)

Product (5.1)
Reactant (5.1)
Redox reaction (5.9)
Reducing agent (5.9)
Reduction (5.9)
Theoretical yield (5.7)

KEY CONCEPTS

1 **What do the terms in a chemical equation mean and how is an equation balanced? (5.1, 5.2)**

- A chemical equation contains the reactants on the left side of an arrow and the products on the right. The coefficients tell how many molecules or moles of a substance react or are formed.
- A chemical equation is balanced by placing coefficients in front of chemical formulas one at a time, beginning with the most complex formula, so that the number of atoms of each element is the same on both sides. You must *not* balance the chemical equation by changing the subscripts in the chemical formulas of the reactants or products.

2 **Define the terms mole and Avogadro's number. (5.3)**

- A mole is a quantity that contains 6.02×10^{23} atoms, molecules, or ions.
- Avogadro's number is the number of particles in a mole—6.02×10^{23}.
- The number of molecules in a given number of moles is calculated using Avogadro's number.

3 **How are formula weight and molar mass calculated? (5.4)**

- The formula weight is the sum of the atomic weights of all the atoms in a compound, reported in atomic mass units.
- The molar mass is the mass of one mole of a substance, reported in grams. The molar mass is numerically equal to the formula weight but the units are different (g/mol not amu).

4 **How are the mass of a substance and its number of moles related? (5.4)**

- The molar mass is used as a conversion factor to determine how many grams are contained in a given number of moles of a substance. Similarly, the molar mass is used to determine how many moles of a substance are contained in a given number of grams.

5 **How can a balanced equation and molar mass be used to calculate the number of moles and mass of a reaction product? (5.5, 5.6)**

- The coefficients in a balanced chemical equation tell us the number of moles of each reactant that combine and the number of moles of each product formed. Coefficients are used to form mole ratios that serve as conversion factors relating the number of moles of reactants and products.
- When the mass of a substance in a reaction must be calculated, first its number of moles is determined using mole ratios, and then the molar mass is used to convert moles to grams.

6 **What is percent yield? (5.7)**

- Percent yield = (actual yield/theoretical yield) $\times$ 100%.
- The actual yield is the amount of product formed in a reaction, determined by weighing a product on a balance. The theoretical yield is a quantity calculated from a balanced chemical equation, using mole ratios and molar masses. The theoretical yield is the maximum amount of product that can form in a chemical reaction from the amount of reactants used.

7 **What is the limiting reactant in a reaction? (5.8)**

- The limiting reactant is the reactant that is completely used up in a reaction. The number of moles of limiting reactant determines the number of moles of product formed using mole ratios in the balanced equation.

8 **What are oxidation and reduction reactions? (5.9)**

- Oxidation–reduction or redox reactions are electron transfer reactions.
- Oxidation results in the loss of electrons. Metals and anions tend to undergo oxidation. In some reactions, oxidation results in the gain of O atoms or the loss of H atoms.
- Reduction results in the gain of electrons. Nonmetals and cations tend to undergo reduction. In some reactions, reduction results in the loss of O atoms or the gain of H atoms.

9 **Give some examples of common or useful redox reactions. (5.9, 5.10)**

- Common examples of redox reactions include the rusting of iron and the combustion of methane. The electric current generated in batteries used for flashlights and pacemakers results from redox reactions.

PROBLEMS

Selected in-chapter and odd-numbered end-of-chapter problems have brief answers in Appendix B. The *Student Study Guide and Solutions Manual* contains detailed solutions to all in-chapter and odd-numbered end-of-chapter problems, as well as additional worked examples and a chapter self-test.

Chemical Reactions and Chemical Equations

5.43 Use the molecular art to identify the process as a chemical reaction or a physical change. If a chemical reaction occurs, write the equation from the molecular art. If a physical change occurs, identify the phase change.

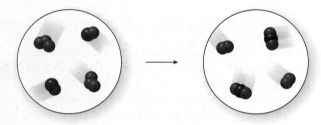

5.44 Diagram [1] represents the compound **AB,** which contains two elements, **A** shown with red spheres, and **B** shown with blue spheres. Label each transformation as a physical change or a chemical reaction: (a) [1] ⟶ [2]; (b) [1] ⟶ [3].

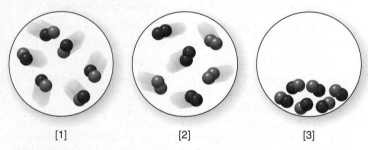

[1]   [2]   [3]

5.45 What is the difference between a coefficient in a chemical equation and a subscript in a chemical formula?

5.46 Why is it not possible to change the subscripts of a chemical formula to balance an equation?

5.47 How many atoms of each element are drawn on each side of the following equations? Label the equations as balanced or not balanced.
a. $2\ HCl(aq) + Ca(s) \longrightarrow CaCl_2(aq) + H_2(g)$
b. $TiCl_4 + 2\ H_2O \longrightarrow TiO_2 + HCl$
c. $Al(OH)_3 + H_3PO_4 \longrightarrow AlPO_4 + 3\ H_2O$

5.48 How many atoms of each element are drawn on each side of the following equations? Label the equations as balanced or not balanced.
a. $3\ NO_2 + H_2O \longrightarrow HNO_3 + 2\ NO$
b. $2\ H_2S + 3\ O_2 \longrightarrow H_2O + 2\ SO_2$
c. $Ca(OH)_2 + 2\ HNO_3 \longrightarrow 2\ H_2O + Ca(NO_3)_2$

5.49 Use the molecular art to write a balanced equation for the given reaction.

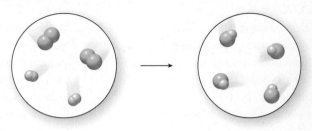

5.50 Use the molecular art to write a balanced equation for the given reaction.

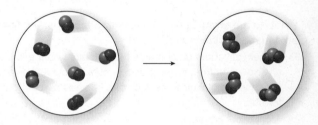

5.51 Balance each equation.
a. $Ni(s) + HCl(aq) \longrightarrow NiCl_2(aq) + H_2(g)$
b. $CH_4(g) + Cl_2(g) \longrightarrow CCl_4(g) + HCl(g)$
c. $KClO_3 \longrightarrow KCl + O_2$
d. $Al_2O_3 + HCl \longrightarrow AlCl_3 + H_2O$
e. $Al(OH)_3 + H_2SO_4 \longrightarrow Al_2(SO_4)_3 + H_2O$

5.52 Balance each equation.
a. $Mg(s) + HBr(aq) \longrightarrow MgBr_2(s) + H_2(g)$
b. $CO(g) + O_2(g) \longrightarrow CO_2(g)$
c. $PbS(s) + O_2(g) \longrightarrow PbO(s) + SO_2(g)$
d. $H_2SO_4 + NaOH \longrightarrow Na_2SO_4 + H_2O$
e. $H_3PO_4 + Ca(OH)_2 \longrightarrow Ca_3(PO_4)_2 + H_2O$

5.53 Hydrocarbons are compounds that contain only C and H atoms. When a hydrocarbon reacts with O_2, CO_2 and H_2O are formed. Write a balanced equation for the combustion of each of the following hydrocarbons, all of which are high-octane components of gasoline.
a. C_6H_6 (benzene)
b. C_7H_8 (toluene)
c. C_8H_{18} (isooctane)

5.54 MTBE ($C_5H_{12}O$) is a high-octane gasoline additive with a sweet, nauseating odor. Because small amounts of MTBE have contaminated the drinking water in some towns, it is now banned as a fuel additive in many areas. MTBE reacts with O_2 to form CO_2 and H_2O. Write a balanced equation for the combustion of MTBE.

5.55 Some coal is high in sulfur (S) content, and when it burns, it forms sulfuric acid (H_2SO_4), a major component of acid rain, by a series of reactions. Balance the equation for the overall conversion drawn below.

$$S(s) + O_2(g) + H_2O(l) \longrightarrow H_2SO_4(l)$$

5.56 Balance the equation for the formation of magnesium hydroxide [Mg(OH)$_2$], one of the active ingredients in milk of magnesia.

$$MgCl_2 + NaOH \longrightarrow Mg(OH)_2 + NaCl$$

5.57 Consider the reaction, $O_3 + CO \longrightarrow O_2 + CO_2$. Molecular art is used to show the starting materials for this reaction. Fill in the molecules of the products using the balanced equation and following the law of conservation of mass.

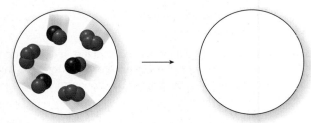

5.58 Consider the reaction, $2\,NO + 2\,CO \longrightarrow N_2 + 2\,CO_2$. Molecular art is used to show the starting materials for this reaction. Fill in the molecules of the products using the balanced equation and following the law of conservation of mass.

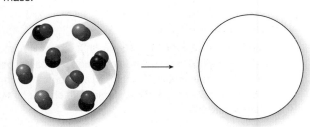

Formula Weight and Molar Mass

5.59 Calculate the formula weight and molar mass of each compound.
   a. NaNO$_2$ (sodium nitrite), a preservative in hot dogs, ham, and other cured meats
   b. Al$_2$(SO$_4$)$_3$ (aluminum sulfate), once used as a common antiperspirant
   c. C$_6$H$_8$O$_6$ (vitamin C)

5.60 Calculate the formula weight and molar mass of each compound.
   a. MgSO$_4$ (magnesium sulfate), a laxative
   b. Ca$_3$(PO$_4$)$_2$ (calcium phosphate), a calcium supplement
   c. C$_16$H$_16$ClNO$_2$S (Plavix), a drug used to treat coronary artery disease

5.61 L-Dopa is a drug used to treat Parkinson's disease.

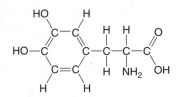

L-dopa

   a. What is the molecular formula of L-dopa?
   b. What is the formula weight of L-dopa?
   c. What is the molar mass of L-dopa?

5.62 Niacin, vitamin B$_3$, is found in soybeans, which contain it naturally, and cereals, which are fortified with it.

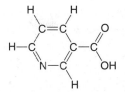

niacin

   a. What is the molecular formula of niacin?
   b. What is the formula weight of niacin?
   c. What is the molar mass of niacin?

Moles, Mass, and Avogadro's Number

5.63 Which quantity has the greater mass?
   a. 1 mol of Fe atoms or 1 mol of Sn atoms
   b. 1 mol of C atoms or 6.02×10^{23} N atoms
   c. 1 mol of N atoms or 1 mol of N$_2$ molecules
   d. 1 mol of CO$_2$ molecules or 3.01×10^{23} N$_2$O molecules

5.64 Which quantity has the greater mass?
   a. 1 mol of Si atoms or 1 mol of Ar atoms
   b. 1 mol of He atoms or 6.02×10^{23} H atoms
   c. 1 mol of Cl atoms or 1 mol of Cl$_2$ molecules
   d. 1 mol of C$_2$H$_4$ molecules or 3.01×10^{23} C$_2$H$_4$ molecules

5.65 How many grams are contained in 5.00 mol of each compound?
   a. HCl   b. Na$_2$SO$_4$ c. C$_2$H$_2$ d. Al(OH)$_3$

5.66 How many grams are contained in 0.50 mol of each compound?
   a. NaOH   b. CaSO$_4$ c. C$_3$H$_6$ d. Mg(OH)$_2$

5.67 How many moles are contained in each number of grams of table sugar (C$_12$H$_22$O$_11$, molar mass 342.3 g/mol)?
   a. 0.500 g   b. 5.00 g   c. 25.0 g   d. 0.0250 g

5.68 How many moles are contained in each number of grams of fructose (C$_6$H$_12$O$_6$, molar mass 180.2 g/mol), a carbohydrate that is about twice as sweet as table sugar? "Lite" food products use half as much fructose as table sugar to achieve the same sweet taste, but with fewer calories.
   a. 0.500 g   b. 5.00 g   c. 25.0 g   d. 0.0250 g

5.69 How many molecules of butane (C$_4$H$_10$) are contained in the following number of moles: (a) 2.00 mol; (b) 0.250 mol; (c) 26.5 mol; (d) 222 mol; (e) 5.00×10^5 mol?

5.70 How many moles of pentane (C$_5$H$_12$) are contained in the following number of molecules?
   a. 5.00×10^{19} molecules   c. 8.32×10^{21} molecules
   b. 6.51×10^{28} molecules   d. 3.10×10^{20} molecules

5.71 What is the mass in grams of each quantity of lactic acid (C$_3$H$_6$O$_3$, molar mass 90.08 g/mol), the compound responsible for the aching feeling of tired muscles during vigorous exercise?
   a. 3.60 mol   c. 7.3×10^{24} molecules
   b. 0.580 mol   d. 6.56×10^{22} molecules

5.72 What is the mass in grams of each quantity of vitamin D (molar mass 384.7 g/mol), which is needed for forming and maintaining healthy bones?

    a. 3.6 mol   c. 7.3×10^{24} molecules

    b. 0.58 mol   d. 6.56×10^{22} molecules

Mass and Mole Calculations in Chemical Equations

5.73 Using the balanced equation for the combustion of acetylene, answer the following questions.

$$2\ H\!-\!C\!\equiv\!C\!-\!H + 5\ O_2 \longrightarrow 4\ CO_2 + 2\ H_2O$$
$$\text{acetylene}$$

    a. How many moles of O_2 are needed to react completely with 5.00 mol of C_2H_2?

    b. How many moles of CO_2 are formed from 6.0 mol of C_2H_2?

    c. How many moles of H_2O are formed from 0.50 mol of C_2H_2?

    d. How many moles of C_2H_2 are needed to form 0.80 mol of CO_2?

5.74 Sodium metal (Na) reacts violently when added to water according to the following balanced equation.

$$2\ Na(s) + 2\ H_2O(l) \longrightarrow 2\ NaOH(aq) + H_2(g)$$

    a. How many moles of H_2O are needed to react completely with 3.0 mol of Na?

    b. How many moles of H_2 are formed from 0.38 mol of Na?

    c. How many moles of H_2 are formed from 3.64 mol of H_2O?

5.75 Using the balanced equation for the combustion of acetylene in Problem 5.73, answer the following questions.

    a. How many grams of CO_2 are formed from 2.5 mol of C_2H_2?

    b. How many grams of CO_2 are formed from 0.50 mol of C_2H_2?

    c. How many grams of H_2O are formed from 0.25 mol of C_2H_2?

    d. How many grams of O_2 are needed to react with 3.0 mol of C_2H_2?

5.76 Using the balanced equation for the reaction of Na with H_2O in Problem 5.74, answer the following questions.

    a. How many grams of NaOH are formed from 3.0 mol of Na?

    b. How many grams of H_2 are formed from 0.30 mol of Na?

    c. How many grams of H_2O are needed to react completely with 0.20 mol of Na?

Theoretical Yield and Percent Yield

5.77 What is the percent yield of **B** in a reaction that uses 10.0 g of starting material **A**, has a theoretical yield of 12.0 g of **B**, and an actual yield of 9.0 g of **B?**

5.78 What is the percent yield of **B** in a reaction that uses 25.0 g of starting material **A**, has a theoretical yield of 20.0 g of **B**, and an actual yield of 17.0 g of **B?**

5.79 The reaction of methane (CH_4) with Cl_2 forms chloroform ($CHCl_3$) and HCl. Although $CHCl_3$ is a general anesthetic, it is no longer used for this purpose since it is also carcinogenic. The molar masses for all substances are given under the balanced equation.

$$CH_4(g) + 3\ Cl_2(g) \longrightarrow CHCl_3(l) + 3\ HCl(g)$$
$$16.04\ \text{g/mol} \quad 70.90\ \text{g/mol} \qquad 119.4\ \text{g/mol} \quad 36.46\ \text{g/mol}$$

    a. What is the theoretical yield of $CHCl_3$ in grams from 3.20 g of CH_4?

    b. What is the percent yield if 15.0 g of $CHCl_3$ are actually formed in this reaction?

5.80 Methanol (CH_4O), which is used as a fuel in high-performance racing cars, burns in the presence of O_2 to form CO_2 and H_2O. The molar masses for all substances are given under the balanced equation.

$$2\ CH_4O(l) + 3\ O_2(g) \longrightarrow 2\ CO_2(g) + 4\ H_2O(g)$$
$$32.04\ \text{g/mol} \quad 32.00\ \text{g/mol} \qquad 44.01\ \text{g/mol} \quad 18.02\ \text{g/mol}$$

    a. What is the theoretical yield of CO_2 from 48.0 g of methanol?

    b. What is the percent yield of CO_2 if 48.0 g of CO_2 are formed?

Limiting Reactants

5.81 Consider the given reaction mixture that contains **A** and **B** molecules, represented by red and blue spheres, respectively. Given each of the following chemical equations, which reactant, **A** or **B,** is present in excess? Which reactant is the limiting reactant?

    a. **A** + **B** $\longrightarrow$ **C**

    b. 2 **A** + **B** $\longrightarrow$ **C**

    c. **A** + 2 **B** $\longrightarrow$ **C**

5.82 Consider the reaction of **A**₂ and **B**₂ to form **A**₂**B**, according to the balanced equation: 2 **A**₂ + **B**₂ $\longrightarrow$ 2 **A**₂**B**. Identify the limiting reactant in the molecular art, and draw a representation showing how much product is formed and what reactant molecules are left over.

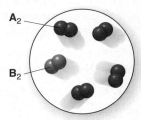

5.83 Using the balanced equation, 2 NO + O_2 $\longrightarrow$ 2 NO_2, determine the limiting reactant under each of the following conditions.

a. 1.0 mol NO and 1.0 mol O_2
b. 2.0 mol NO and 0.50 mol O_2
c. 10.0 g NO and 10.0 g O_2
d. 28.0 g NO and 16.0 g O_2

5.84 Use the balanced equation in Problem 5.83 to determine the limiting reactant under each of the following conditions.

a. 2.0 mol NO and 1.1 mol O_2
b. 4.2 mol NO and 2.0 mol O_2
c. 15.0 g NO and 10.0 g O_2
d. 10.0 g NO and 4.00 g O_2

5.85 For each set of reaction conditions in Problem 5.83, calculate how many moles of the product NO_2 forms. Then, calculate the number of grams of product that forms.

5.86 For each set of reaction conditions in Problem 5.84, calculate how many moles of the product NO_2 forms. Then, calculate the number of grams of product that forms.

5.87 The local anesthetic ethyl chloride (C_2H_5Cl, molar mass 64.51 g/mol) can be prepared by reaction of ethylene (C_2H_4, molar mass 28.05 g/mol) with HCl (molar mass 36.46 g/mol), according to the balanced equation, C_2H_4 + HCl $\longrightarrow$ C_2H_5Cl.

a. If 8.00 g of ethylene and 12.0 g of HCl are used, how many moles of each reactant are used?
b. What is the limiting reactant?
c. How many moles of product are formed?
d. How many grams of product are formed?
e. If 10.6 g of product are formed, what is the percent yield of the reaction?

5.88 The solvent dichloromethane (CH_2Cl_2, molar mass 84.93 g/mol) can be prepared by reaction of methane (CH_4, molar mass 16.04 g/mol) with Cl_2 (molar mass 70.90 g/mol), according to the balanced equation, CH_4 + 2 Cl_2 $\longrightarrow$ CH_2Cl_2 + 2 HCl.

a. If 5.00 g of methane and 15.0 g of Cl_2 are used, how many moles of each reactant are used?
b. What is the limiting reactant?
c. How many moles of product are formed?
d. How many grams of product are formed?
e. If 15.6 g of product are formed, what is the percent yield of the reaction?

Oxidation–Reduction Reactions

5.89 What is the difference between a substance that is oxidized and an oxidizing agent?

5.90 What is the difference between a substance that is reduced and a reducing agent?

5.91 Identify the species that is oxidized and the species that is reduced in each reaction. Write out two half reactions to show how many electrons are gained or lost by each species.

a. Fe + Cu^{2+} $\longrightarrow$ Fe^{2+} + Cu
b. Cl_2 + 2 I^- $\longrightarrow$ I_2 + 2 Cl^-
c. 2 Na + Cl_2 $\longrightarrow$ 2 NaCl

5.92 Identify the species that is oxidized and the species that is reduced in each reaction. Write out two half reactions to show how many electrons are gained or lost by each species.

a. Mg + Fe^{2+} $\longrightarrow$ Mg^{2+} + Fe
b. Cu^{2+} + Sn $\longrightarrow$ Sn^{2+} + Cu
c. 4 Na + O_2 $\longrightarrow$ 2 Na_2O

5.93 Zinc–silver oxide batteries are used in cameras and hearing aids. Identify the species that is oxidized and the species that is reduced in the following redox reaction. Identify the oxidizing agent and the reducing agent.

$$Zn + Ag_2O \longrightarrow ZnO + 2 Ag$$

5.94 Rechargeable nickel–cadmium batteries are used in appliances and power tools. Identify the species that is oxidized and the species that is reduced in the following redox reaction. Identify the oxidizing agent and the reducing agent.

$$Cd + Ni^{4+} \longrightarrow Cd^{2+} + Ni^{2+}$$

5.95 The reaction of hydrogen (H_2) with acetylene (C_2H_2) forms ethane (C_2H_6). Is acetylene oxidized or reduced in this reaction? Explain your choice.

5.96 When Cl_2 is used to disinfect drinking water, Cl^- is formed. Is Cl_2 oxidized or reduced in this process?

5.97 The reaction of magnesium metal (Mg) with oxygen (O_2) forms MgO. Write a balanced equation for this redox reaction. Write two half reactions to show how many electrons are gained or lost by each species.

5.98 The reaction of aluminum metal (Al) with oxygen (O_2) forms Al_2O_3. Write a balanced equation for this redox reaction. Write two half reactions to show how many electrons are gained or lost by each species.

General Questions

5.99 Answer the following questions about the conversion of the sucrose ($C_{12}H_{22}O_{11}$) in sugarcane to ethanol (C_2H_6O) and CO_2 according to the following unbalanced equation. In this way sugarcane is used as a renewable source of ethanol, which is used as a fuel additive in gasoline.

$$C_{12}H_{22}O_{11}(s) + H_2O(l) \longrightarrow C_2H_6O(l) + CO_2(g)$$
$$\text{sucrose} \qquad\qquad\qquad \text{ethanol}$$

a. What is the molar mass of sucrose?
b. Balance the given equation.
c. How many moles of ethanol are formed from 2 mol of sucrose?
d. How many moles of water are needed to react with 10 mol of sucrose?
e. How many grams of ethanol are formed from 0.550 mol of sucrose?
f. How many grams of ethanol are formed from 34.2 g of sucrose?
g. What is the theoretical yield of ethanol in grams from 17.1 g of sucrose?
h. If 1.25 g of ethanol are formed in the reaction in part (g), what is the percent yield of ethanol?

5.100 Answer the following questions about diethyl ether ($C_4H_{10}O$), the first widely used general anesthetic. Diethyl ether can be prepared from ethanol according to the following unbalanced equation.

$$C_2H_6O(l) \longrightarrow C_4H_{10}O(l) + H_2O(l)$$
$$\text{ethanol} \qquad\qquad \text{diethyl ether}$$

a. What is the molar mass of diethyl ether?

b. Balance the given equation.

c. How many moles of diethyl ether are formed from 2 mol of ethanol?

d. How many moles of water are formed from 10 mol of ethanol?

e. How many grams of diethyl ether are formed from 0.55 mol of ethanol?

f. How many grams of diethyl ether are formed from 4.60 g of ethanol?

g. What is the theoretical yield of diethyl ether in grams from 2.30 g of ethanol?

h. If 1.80 g of diethyl ether are formed in the reaction in part (g), what is the percent yield of diethyl ether?

Applications

5.101 A bottle of the pain reliever ibuprofen ($C_{13}H_{18}O_2$, molar mass 206.3 g/mol) contains 500 200.-mg tablets. (a) How many moles of ibuprofen does the bottle contain? (b) How many molecules of ibuprofen does the bottle contain?

5.102 One dose of Maalox contains 500. mg each of $Mg(OH)_2$ and $Al(OH)_3$. How many moles of each compound are contained in a single dose?

5.103 The average nicotine ($C_{10}H_{14}N_2$, molar mass 162.3 g/mol) content of a Camel cigarette is 1.93 mg. Suppose an individual smokes one pack of 20 cigarettes a day.

a. How many moles of nicotine are smoked in a day?

b. How many molecules of nicotine are smoked in a day?

5.104 How many moles of sucrose (table sugar, $C_{12}H_{22}O_{11}$, molar mass 342.3 g/mol) are contained in a 5-lb bag of sugar?

5.105 If the daily recommended intake of sodium ions is 2,400 mg, how many Na^+ ions does this correspond to?

5.106 How many molecules are contained in a glass that holds 250 g of water? How many moles does that correspond to?

5.107 DDT, a pesticide that kills disease-carrying mosquitoes, is synthesized by the given equation. DDT is now banned in the United States because it is a persistent environmental pollutant that only slowly degrades.

chlorobenzene
112.6 g/mol

DDT
$C_{14}H_9Cl_5$

a. What is the molar mass of DDT?

b. How many grams of DDT would be formed from 0.10 mol of chlorobenzene?

c. What is the theoretical yield of DDT in grams from 11.3 g of chlorobenzene?

d. If 15.0 g of DDT are formed in the reaction in part (c), what is the percent yield of DDT?

5.108 Fats, such as butter, and oils, such as corn oil, are formed from compounds called fatty acids, one of which is linolenic acid ($C_{18}H_{30}O_2$). Linolenic acid undergoes reactions with hydrogen and oxygen to form the products shown in each equation.

[1] $C_{18}H_{30}O_2 + H_2 \longrightarrow C_{18}H_{36}O_2$
linolenic acid

[2] $C_{18}H_{30}O_2 + O_2 \longrightarrow CO_2 + H_2O$
linolenic acid

a. Calculate the molar mass of linolenic acid.

b. Balance Equation [1], which shows the reaction with hydrogen.

c. Balance Equation [2], which shows the reaction with oxygen.

d. How many grams of product are formed from 10.0 g of linolenic acid in Equation [1]?

CHALLENGE PROBLEMS

5.109 TCDD, also called dioxin ($C_{12}H_4Cl_4O_2$, molar mass 322.0 g/mol), is a potent poison. The average lethal dose in humans is estimated to be 3.0×10^{-2} mg per kg of body weight. (a) How many grams constitute a lethal dose for a 70.-kg individual? (b) How many molecules of TCDD does this correspond to?

5.110 The lead–acid battery in a car consists of lead (Pb), lead(IV) oxide (PbO_2), and sulfuric acid (H_2SO_4), which undergo a redox reaction according to the given equation. Explain the oxidation and reduction reactions that occur with the lead atoms and ions in this battery.

$$Pb + PbO_2 + 2\ H_2SO_4 \longrightarrow 2\ PbSO_4 + 2\ H_2O$$

The combustion of gasoline and the metabolism of carbohydrates during exercise are examples of oxidation reactions that release a great deal of useful energy.

6

Energy Changes, Reaction Rates, and Equilibrium

CHAPTER GOALS

In this chapter you will learn how to:

1. Define energy and become familiar with the units of energy
2. Use bond dissociation energies to predict bond strength
3. Describe energy changes in a reaction, and classify reactions as endothermic or exothermic
4. Draw energy diagrams
5. Predict the effect of concentration, temperature, and the presence of a catalyst on the rate of a reaction
6. Describe the basic features of chemical equilibrium and write an expression for an equilibrium constant
7. Use Le Châtelier's principle to predict what happens when equilibrium is disturbed
8. Use Le Châtelier's principle and reaction rates to explain the regulation of body temperature

In Chapter 6 we turn our attention to two facets of chemical reactions: energy changes and reaction rates. Why do some reactions—like the combustion of fossil fuels or the metabolism of carbohydrates—release a great deal of energy that can be used for powering a car or running a marathon, while other reactions absorb energy from the environment? What factors affect how fast a reaction proceeds? To answer these and related questions, we must learn about what happens when molecules come together in a reaction, as well as what energy changes are observed when bonds are broken and formed.

6.1 Energy

Energy **is the capacity to do work.** Whenever you throw a ball, ride a bike, or read a newspaper, you use energy to do work. There are two types of energy.

> • Potential energy is stored energy.
> • Kinetic energy is the energy of motion.

A ball at the top of a hill or the water in a reservoir behind a dam are examples of potential energy. When the ball rolls down the hill or the water flows over the dam, the stored potential energy is converted to the kinetic energy of motion. Although energy can be converted from one form to another, one rule, the **law of conservation of energy,** governs the process.

> • The total energy in the universe does not change. Energy cannot be created or destroyed.

The energy stored in chemical bonds—both ionic and covalent—is a form of potential energy. In chemical reactions, potential energy may be released and converted to heat, the kinetic energy of the moving particles of the product. **Reactions that form products having *lower* potential energy than the reactants are favored.**

> • A compound with lower potential energy is more stable than a compound with higher potential energy.

6.1A The Units of Energy

Energy can be measured using two different units, **calories (cal)** and **joules (J). A calorie** is the amount of energy needed to raise the temperature of 1 g of water 1 °C. Joules and calories are related in the following way.

$$1 \text{ cal} = 4.184 \text{ J}$$

Since both the calorie and the joule are small units of measurement, more often energies in reactions are reported with kilocalories (kcal) and kilojoules (kJ). Recall from Table 1.2 that the prefix *kilo* means 1,000.

$$1 \text{ kcal} = 1,000 \text{ cal}$$
$$1 \text{ kJ} = 1,000 \text{ J}$$
$$1 \text{ kcal} = 4.184 \text{ kJ}$$

To convert a quantity from one unit of measurement to another, set up conversion factors and use the method first shown in Section 1.7B and illustrated in Sample Problem 6.1.

The water at the top of a waterfall has potential energy because of its position. This potential energy becomes kinetic energy as the water falls.

The joule, named after the nineteenth-century English physicist James Prescott Joule, is pronounced *jewel*.

SAMPLE PROBLEM 6.1

A reaction releases 421 kJ of energy. How many kilocalories does this correspond to?

Analysis and Solution

[1] Identify the original quantity and the desired quantity.

421 kJ   ? kcal

original quantity   desired quantity

[2] Write out the conversion factors.

- Choose the conversion factor that places the unwanted unit, kilojoules, in the denominator so that the units cancel.

kJ–kcal conversion factors

$$\frac{4.184 \text{ kJ}}{1 \text{ kcal}} \quad \text{or} \quad \boxed{\frac{1 \text{ kcal}}{4.184 \text{ kJ}}} \quad \text{Choose this conversion factor to cancel kJ.}$$

[3] Set up and solve the problem.

- Multiply the original quantity by the conversion factor to obtain the desired quantity.

$$421 \text{ kJ} \quad \times \quad \frac{1 \text{ kcal}}{4.184 \text{ kJ}} \quad = \quad 100.6 \text{ kcal, rounded to 101 kcal}$$

Kilojoules cancel.   **Answer**

PROBLEM 6.1

Carry out each of the following conversions.

a. 42 J to cal   b. 55.6 kcal to cal   c. 326 kcal to kJ   d. 25.6 kcal to J

PROBLEM 6.2

Combustion of 1 g of gasoline releases 11.5 kcal of energy. How many kilojoules of energy is released? How many joules does this correspond to?

6.1B FOCUS ON THE HUMAN BODY
Energy and Nutrition

When we eat food, the protein, carbohydrates, and fat (lipid) in the food are metabolized to form simpler molecules that in turn are used to prepare new molecules that cells need for maintenance and growth. This process also generates the energy needed for the organs to function, allowing the heart to beat, the lungs to breathe, and the brain to think.

The amount of stored energy in food is measured using nutritional Calories (upper case C), where 1 Cal = 1,000 cal. Since 1,000 cal = 1 kcal, the following relationships exist.

Nutritional Calorie	1 Cal	=	1 kcal
	1 Cal	=	1,000 cal

Upon metabolism, proteins, carbohydrates, and fat each release a predictable amount of energy, the **caloric value** of the substance. For example, one gram of protein or one gram of carbohydrate typically releases about 4 Cal/g, while fat releases 9 Cal/g (Table 6.1). If we know the amount of each of these substances contained in a food product, we can make a first approximation of the number of Calories it contains by using caloric values as conversion factors, as illustrated in Sample Problem 6.2.

Table 6.1 Caloric Value for Three Classes of Compounds

	Cal/g	cal/g
Protein	4	4,000
Carbohydrate	4	4,000
Fat	9	9,000

One nutritional Calorie (1 Cal) = 1,000 cal = 1 kcal.

When an individual eats more Calories than are needed for normal bodily maintenance, the body stores the excess as fat. The average body fat content for men and women is about 20% and 25%, respectively. This stored fat can fill the body's energy needs for two or three months. Frequent ingestion of a large excess of Calories results in a great deal of stored fat, causing an individual to be overweight.

SAMPLE PROBLEM 6.2

If a baked potato contains 3 g of protein, a trace of fat, and 23 g of carbohydrates, estimate its number of Calories.

Analysis

Use the caloric value (Cal/g) of each class of molecule to form a conversion factor to convert the number of grams to Calories and add up the results.

Solution

[1] Identify the original quantity and the desired quantity.

3 g protein

23 g carbohydrates   ? Cal

original quantities   desired quantity

[2] Write out the conversion factors.

- Write out conversion factors that relate the number of grams to the number of Calories for each substance. Each conversion factor must place the unwanted unit, grams, in the denominator so that the units cancel.

Cal–g conversion factor for protein   Cal–g conversion factor for carbohydrates

$$\frac{4 \text{ Cal}}{1 \text{ g protein}} \qquad\qquad \frac{4 \text{ Cal}}{1 \text{ g carbohydrate}}$$

[3] Set up and solve the problem.

- Multiply the original quantity by the conversion factor for both protein and carbohydrates and add up the results to obtain the desired quantity.

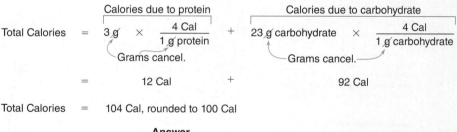

Total Calories $= 3 \text{ g} \times \dfrac{4 \text{ Cal}}{1 \text{ g protein}} + 23 \text{ g carbohydrate} \times \dfrac{4 \text{ Cal}}{1 \text{ g carbohydrate}}$

Grams cancel.   Grams cancel.

$= \qquad 12 \text{ Cal} \qquad + \qquad 92 \text{ Cal}$

Total Calories $= \quad$ 104 Cal, rounded to 100 Cal

Answer

PROBLEM 6.3

How many Calories are contained in one tablespoon of olive oil, which has 14 g of fat?

PROBLEM 6.4

One serving (36 crackers) of wheat crackers contains 6 g of fat, 20 g of carbohydrates, and 2 g of protein. Estimate the number of Calories.

6.2 Energy Changes in Reactions

When molecules come together and react, bonds are broken in the reactants and new bonds are formed in the products. **Breaking a bond requires energy.** For example, 58 kcal of energy is needed to break the chlorine–chlorine bond in a mole of chlorine molecules (Cl_2).

CONSUMER NOTE

Knowing the number of grams of protein, carbohydrates, and fat allows you to estimate how many Calories a food product contains. A quarter-pound burger with cheese with 29 g of protein, 40 g of carbohydrates, and 26 g of fat contains 510 Calories.

To cleave this bond...

$$:\overset{..}{\underset{..}{Cl}}-\overset{..}{\underset{..}{Cl}}: \longrightarrow :\overset{..}{\underset{..}{Cl}}\cdot \;+\; \cdot\overset{..}{\underset{..}{Cl}}:$$

...58 kcal/mol of energy must be added.

In contrast, when the chlorine–chlorine bond is formed, 58 kcal of energy is *released.* The amount of energy needed to break a bond is the same amount that is released when that bond is formed.

When this bond is formed...

$$:\overset{..}{\underset{..}{Cl}}\cdot \;+\; \cdot\overset{..}{\underset{..}{Cl}}: \longrightarrow :\overset{..}{\underset{..}{Cl}}-\overset{..}{\underset{..}{Cl}}:$$

...58 kcal/mol of energy is released.

- **Bond breaking always requires an input of energy and bond formation always releases energy.**

The energy absorbed or released in any reaction is called the **heat of reaction** or the **enthalpy change,** symbolized by ΔH. The heat of reaction is given a positive (+) or negative (–) sign depending on whether energy is absorbed or released.

- **When energy is absorbed, the reaction is said to be *endothermic* and ΔH is positive (+).**
- **When energy is released, the reaction is said to be *exothermic* and ΔH is negative (–).**

Thus, $\Delta H = +58$ kcal/mol for cleaving the Cl—Cl bond and the reaction is endothermic; on the other hand, $\Delta H = -58$ kcal/mol for forming the Cl—Cl bond and that reaction is exothermic. The heat of reaction is reported as the number of kilocalories *per mole*. The cleavage of two moles of chlorine–chlorine bonds requires twice as much energy; that is, (2 mol)(+58 kcal/mol) = +116 kcal.

6.2A   Bond Dissociation Energy

The heat of reaction (ΔH) for breaking a covalent bond by equally dividing the electrons between the two atoms in the bond is called the **bond dissociation energy.** Because bond breaking requires energy, **bond dissociation energies are always *positive* numbers,** and breaking a covalent bond into the atoms that compose it is always **endothermic.** Since **bond formation always *releases* energy,** forming a bond is **exothermic and ΔH is a *negative* number.** The H—H bond requires +104 kcal/mol to cleave and releases –104 kcal/mol when formed. Table 6.2 lists bond dissociation energies for some simple molecules.

Bond breaking is **endothermic.**
Energy must be added.

$$H-H \longrightarrow H\cdot \;+\; \cdot H \qquad \Delta H = +104 \text{ kcal/mol}$$

$$H\cdot \;+\; \cdot H \longrightarrow H-H \qquad \Delta H = -104 \text{ kcal/mol}$$

Bond making is **exothermic.**
Energy is released.

Table 6.2 Bond Dissociation Energies (ΔH) for Some Common Bonds ($A—B \rightarrow A\cdot + \cdot B$)

Bond	ΔH (kcal/mol)
H—H	+104
F—F	+38
Cl—Cl	+58
Br—Br	+46
I—I	+36
H—OH	+119
H—F	+136
H—Cl	+103
H—Br	+88
H—I	+71

SAMPLE PROBLEM 6.3

Write the equation for the formation of HCl from H and Cl atoms. Classify the reaction as endothermic or exothermic, and give the ΔH using the values in Table 6.2.

Analysis

Bond formation is exothermic and ΔH is (–). The energy released in forming a bond is (–) the bond dissociation energy.

Solution

Energy is released.

$$H\cdot \;+\; \cdot\overset{..}{\underset{..}{Cl}}: \longrightarrow H-\overset{..}{\underset{..}{Cl}}: \qquad \Delta H = -103 \text{ kcal/mol}$$

Bond formation is **exothermic.**

PROBLEM 6.5

Using the values in Table 6.2, give ΔH for each reaction, and classify the reaction as endothermic or exothermic.

a. H—B̈r̈: $\longrightarrow$ H· + ·B̈r̈:   c. H—Ö̈H $\longrightarrow$ H· + ·Ö̈H

b. H· + ·F̈: $\longrightarrow$ H—F̈:

Bond dissociation energies tell us about bond strength.

- **The *stronger* the bond, the *higher* its bond dissociation energy.**

For example, since the bond dissociation energy for the H—H bond (+104 kcal/mol) is higher than the bond dissociation energy for the Cl—Cl bond (+58 kcal/mol), the H—H bond is stronger.

Bond dissociation energies exhibit periodic trends, much like atomic radius (Section 2.8A) and electronegativity (Section 4.7). In the series, HF, HCl, HBr, and HI, hydrogen is bonded to the first four elements of group 7A (the halogens). According to Table 6.2, the bond dissociation energies of these compounds *decrease* down the column from HF → HCl → HBr → HI. HI has the *weakest* of these four bonds because the valence electrons used by I to form the H—I bond are farther from the nucleus than the valence electrons in Br, Cl, or F. Similarly, HF has the *strongest* of these four bonds because the valence electrons in F are closer to the nucleus than those in Cl, Br, or I. This is a specific example of a general periodic trend.

highest bond dissociation energy strongest bond		lowest bond dissociation energy weakest bond	
H—F̈:	H—C̈l:	H—B̈r̈:	H—Ï:
ΔH = +136 kcal/mol	+103 kcal/mol	+88 kcal/mol	+71 kcal/mol

- **In comparing bonds formed from elements in the same group of the periodic table, bond dissociation energies generally *decrease* going down the column.**

SAMPLE PROBLEM 6.4

Considering the indicated carbon–halogen bonds, which bond is predicted to have the higher bond dissociation energy? Which bond is stronger?

$$
\underset{\overset{|}{H}}{\overset{\overset{H}{|}}{H-C}}-\ddot{F}: \qquad \underset{\overset{|}{H}}{\overset{\overset{H}{|}}{H-C}}-\ddot{C}l:
$$

Analysis

The higher the bond dissociation energy, the stronger the bond. In comparing bonds to atoms in the same group of the periodic table, bond dissociation energies and bond strength decrease down a column.

Solution

Since Cl is below F in the same group of the periodic table, the C—Cl bond is predicted to have the lower bond dissociation energy, thus making it weaker. The actual values for the bond dissociation energies are given and illustrate that the prediction is indeed true.

lower bond dissociation energy
weaker bond

$$
\underset{\overset{|}{H}}{\overset{\overset{H}{|}}{H-C}}-\ddot{F}: \quad \Delta H = +109\ \text{kcal/mol} \qquad \underset{\overset{|}{H}}{\overset{\overset{H}{|}}{H-C}}-\ddot{C}l: \quad \Delta H = +84\ \text{kcal/mol}
$$

PROBLEM 6.6

Which indicated bond in each pair of compounds has the higher bond dissociation energy? Which is the stronger bond?

a.
$$H-\overset{\overset{H}{|}}{\underset{\underset{H}{|}}{C}}-\ddot{I}:$$
  or
$$H-\overset{\overset{H}{|}}{\underset{\underset{H}{|}}{C}}-\ddot{B}r:$$
   b. $H-OH$ or $H-SH$

6.2B Calculations Involving ΔH Values

ENVIRONMENTAL NOTE

The methane produced by decomposing waste material in large landfills is burned to produce energy for heating and generating electricity.

Most reactions involve breaking and forming more than one bond. In these instances, the heat of reaction measures the difference between the energy needed to break bonds in the reactants and the energy released from the bonds formed in the products. In other words, **ΔH indicates the relative strength of bonds broken and formed in a reaction.**

- When ΔH is negative, more energy is released in forming bonds than is needed to break bonds. The bonds formed in the products are *stronger* than the bonds broken in the reactants. The reaction is exothermic.

For example, when methane (CH_4) burns in the presence of oxygen (O_2) to form CO_2 and H_2O, 213 kcal/mol of energy is released in the form of heat.

Heat is released.

$$CH_4(g) \; + \; 2\,O_2(g) \; \longrightarrow \; CO_2(g) \; + \; 2\,H_2O(l) \quad \Delta H = -213\ \text{kcal/mol}$$

In this reaction energy is released, ΔH is negative (–), and the reaction is exothermic. The bonds formed are stronger than the bonds broken, since more energy is released in forming the bonds in CO_2 and H_2O than is absorbed in breaking the bonds in CH_4 and O_2. **Since energy is released, the products are *lower* in energy than the reactants.**

The values for ΔH are reported in kilocalories per mole (kcal/mol). This means that the given amount of energy is released (or absorbed) for the molar quantities shown by the coefficients in the balanced chemical equation. Thus, 213 kcal of energy is released when 1 mol of CH_4 reacts with 2 mol of O_2 to form 1 mol of CO_2 and 2 mol of H_2O.

- When ΔH is positive, more energy is needed to break bonds than is released in forming bonds. The bonds broken in the reactants are *stronger* than the bonds formed in the product. The reaction is endothermic.

For example, in the process of photosynthesis, green plants use chlorophyll to convert CO_2 and H_2O to glucose ($C_6H_{12}O_6$, a simple carbohydrate) and O_2 and 678 kcal of energy is absorbed.

$$6\,CO_2(g) + 6\,H_2O(l) \longrightarrow C_6H_{12}O_6(aq) + 6\,O_2(g) \quad \Delta H = +678\ \text{kcal/mol}$$

In this reaction energy is absorbed, ΔH is positive (+), and the reaction is endothermic. The bonds broken are stronger than the bonds formed, since more energy is needed to break the bonds in CO_2 and H_2O than is released in forming the bonds in $C_6H_{12}O_6$ and O_2. **Since energy is absorbed, the products are *higher* in energy than the reactants.**

Table 6.3 summarizes the characteristics of energy changes in reactions.

Photosynthesis is an endothermic reaction. Energy from sunlight is absorbed in the reaction and stored in the bonds of the products.

PROBLEM 6.7

Answer the following questions using the given equation and ΔH. (a) Is heat absorbed or released? (b) Which bonds are stronger, those in the reactants or those in the products? (c) Are the reactants or products lower in energy? (d) Is the reaction endothermic or exothermic?

$$2\,NH_3(g) \longrightarrow 3\,H_2(g) + N_2(g) \quad \Delta H = +22.0\ \text{kcal/mol}$$

Table 6.3 Endothermic and Exothermic Reactions

Endothermic Reaction	Exothermic Reaction
• Heat is absorbed.	• Heat is released.
• ΔH is positive.	• ΔH is negative.
• The bonds broken in the reactants are *stronger* than the bonds formed in the products.	• The bonds formed in the products are *stronger* than the bonds broken in the reactants.
• The products are higher in energy than the reactants.	• The products are lower in energy than the reactants.

Once we know the ΔH for a balanced chemical reaction, we can use this information to calculate how much energy is absorbed or released for any given amount of reactant or product. A value for ΔH and the coefficients of the balanced equation are used to set up conversion factors, as shown in Sample Problem 6.5. To convert the number of grams of a reactant to the number of kilocalories released, we must use the molar mass, as shown in Sample Problem 6.6.

SAMPLE PROBLEM 6.5

The combustion of propane (C_3H_8) with O_2 according to the given balanced chemical equation releases 531 kcal/mol. How many kilocalories of energy are released when 0.750 mol of propane is burned?

$$C_3H_8(g) + 5\,O_2(g) \longrightarrow 3\,CO_2(g) + 4\,H_2O(l) \qquad \Delta H = -531 \text{ kcal/mol}$$
propane

Analysis

Use the given value of ΔH to set up a conversion factor that relates the kcal of energy released to the number of moles of C_3H_8.

Solution

The given ΔH value is the amount of energy released when 1 mol of C_3H_8 reacts with 5 mol of O_2. Set up a conversion factor that relates kilocalories to moles of C_3H_8, with moles in the denominator to cancel this unwanted unit.

kcal–mol conversion factor

$$0.750 \text{ mol } C_3H_8 \times \frac{531 \text{ kcal}}{1 \text{ mol } C_3H_8} = 398 \text{ kcal of energy released}$$

Moles cancel.

Answer

PROBLEM 6.8

Given the ΔH and balanced equation in Sample Problem 6.5, how many kilocalories of energy are released when 1.00 mol of O_2 reacts with propane?

SAMPLE PROBLEM 6.6

Using the ΔH and balanced equation for the combustion of propane (C_3H_8) with O_2 shown in Sample Problem 6.5, how many kilocalories of energy are released when 20.0 g of propane is burned?

Analysis

To relate the number of grams of propane to the number of kilocalories of energy released on combustion, two operations are needed: [1] Convert the number of grams to the number of moles using the molar mass. [2] Convert the number of moles to the number of kilocalories using ΔH (kcal/mol) and the coefficients of the balanced chemical equation.

Solution

[1] Convert the number of grams of propane to the number of moles of propane.

- Use the molar mass of the reactant (C_3H_8, molar mass 44.09 g/mol) to write a conversion factor. Multiply the number of grams of propane by the conversion factor to give the number of moles of propane.

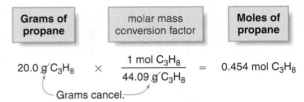

Grams of propane		molar mass conversion factor		Moles of propane

$$20.0 \text{ g } C_3H_8 \quad \times \quad \frac{1 \text{ mol } C_3H_8}{44.09 \text{ g } C_3H_8} \quad = \quad 0.454 \text{ mol } C_3H_8$$

Grams cancel.

[2] Convert the number of moles of propane to the number of kilocalories using a kcal–mole conversion factor.

- Use the ΔH and the number of moles of propane in the balanced chemical equation to write a kcal–mole conversion factor—one mole of propane (C_3H_8) releases 531 kcal of energy. Multiply the number of moles of propane by the conversion factor to give the number of kilocalories of energy released. This process was illustrated in Sample Problem 6.5.

kcal–mol conversion factor

$$0.454 \text{ mol } C_3H_8 \quad \times \quad \frac{531 \text{ kcal}}{1 \text{ mol } C_3H_8} \quad = \quad 241 \text{ kcal of energy released}$$

Moles cancel.

Answer

PROBLEM 6.9

Answer the following questions about the fermentation of glucose ($C_6H_{12}O_6$, molar mass 180.2 g/mol) to ethanol (C_2H_6O) and CO_2.

$$C_6H_{12}O_6(s) \longrightarrow 2 \, C_2H_6O(l) + 2 \, CO_2(g) \qquad \Delta H = -16 \text{ kcal/mol}$$

glucose   ethanol

a. How many kilocalories of energy are released from 6.0 mol of glucose?
b. How many kilocalories of energy are released when 1.0 mol of ethanol is formed?
c. How many kilocalories of energy are released from 20.0 g of glucose?

6.3 Energy Diagrams

On a molecular level, what happens when a reaction occurs? In order for two molecules to react, they must collide, and in the collision, the kinetic energy they possess is used to break bonds. Not every collision between two molecules, however, leads to a reaction. Collisions must have the proper orientation and enough energy for the reaction to occur.

How does the orientation of a collision affect a reaction? Consider a general reaction between two starting materials, A—B and C in which the A—B bond is broken and a new B—C bond is formed.

This bond breaks.   This bond forms.

Since **C** forms a new bond with **B**, a reaction occurs only when **C** collides with **B**. If **C** collides with **A**, no bond breaking or bond making can occur, and a reaction does not take place. Since molecular collisions are random events, many collisions are ineffective because they do not place the reacting atoms close to each other.

proper orientation	improper orientation
C collides with **B**, so a new **B—C** bond can form.	**C** collides with **A**, so a new **B—C** bond cannot form.

The energy of the reacting molecules also determines whether a particular collision will lead to a reaction. In any given sample, molecules possess a wide range of kinetic energies. Some are fast moving and thus possess more kinetic energy than others that are slow moving. Since the kinetic energy of the reacting molecules **A—B** and **C** provides the energy to break the **A—B** bond, reaction occurs only when the reactants possess sufficient energy.

- **Thus, only collisions that have sufficient energy and proper orientation lead to a reaction.**

The energy changes in a reaction are often illustrated on an **energy diagram,** which plots energy on the vertical axis, and the progress of the reaction—the **reaction coordinate**—on the horizontal axis. The reactants are written on the left side and the products on the right side, and a smooth curve that illustrates how energy changes with time connects them. Let's assume that the products, **A** and **B—C,** are lower in energy than the reactants, **A—B** and **C.**

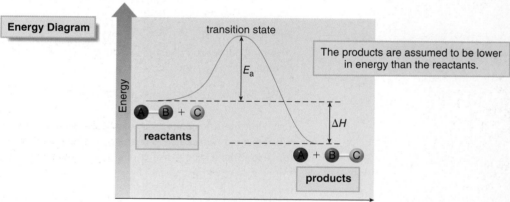

When the reactants **A—B** and **C** approach each other, their electron clouds feel some repulsion, causing an increase in energy until a maximum value is reached. This point is called the **transition state.** In the transition state, the bond between **A** and **B** is partially broken and the bond between **B** and **C** is partially formed. The transition state is located at the top of the energy hill that separates reactants from products. To draw a transition state, we use dashed lines for any bond that is broken or formed.

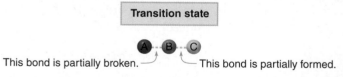

At the transition state, the bond between **A** and **B** can re-form to regenerate reactants, or the bond between **B** and **C** can form to generate products. As the bond forms between **B** and **C,** the energy decreases until some stable energy minimum is reached. The products are drawn lower in energy than the reactants to reflect the initial assumption about their relative energies.

- **The difference in energy between the reactants and the transition state is called the *energy of activation,* symbolized by E_a.**

Figure 6.1

Energy Diagram for an
Endothermic Reaction

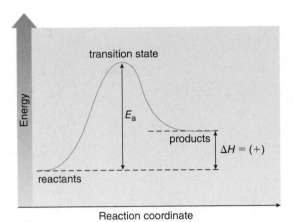

E_a is the energy difference between the reactants and the transition state. ΔH is the difference in energy between the reactants and products. Since the products are higher in energy than the reactants, ΔH is positive (+) and the reaction is endothermic.

The energy of activation is the minimum amount of energy needed for a reaction to occur. It represents the amount of energy that the reactants must possess for the reaction to take place. The energy of activation is often called the **energy barrier** that must be crossed. The height of the energy barrier—the magnitude of the energy of activation—determines the **reaction rate, how fast the reaction occurs.**

- When the energy of activation is *high,* few molecules have enough energy to cross the energy barrier and the reaction is *slow.*
- When the energy of activation is *low,* many molecules have enough energy to cross the energy barrier and the reaction is *fast.*

The difference in energy between the reactants and products is the ΔH, which is also labeled on the energy diagram. When the products are lower in energy than the reactants, as is the case here, the bonds in the product are stronger than the bonds in the reactants. ΔH is negative (−), and the reaction is exothermic.

Energy diagrams can be drawn for any reaction. In the endothermic reaction shown in Figure 6.1, the products are higher in energy than the reactants.

An energy diagram is a visual tool that helps to illustrate both the rate of a reaction (by the height of the energy barrier), and the energy difference between the reactants and the products. Keep in mind that these two quantities are independent. A large E_a does not tell us anything about the relative energies of the reactants and products.

- The size of E_a determines the rate of a reaction.
- The sign of ΔH determines whether the products or reactants are lower in energy. Reactions are favored in which ΔH is negative and the products are lower in energy, making them more stable than the reactants.

SAMPLE PROBLEM 6.7

Draw an energy diagram for a reaction with a low energy of activation and a ΔH of −10 kcal/mol. Label the axes, reactants, products, transition state, E_a, and ΔH.

Analysis

A low energy of activation means a low energy barrier and a small hill that separates reactants and products. When ΔH is (−), the products are lower in energy than the reactants.

Solution

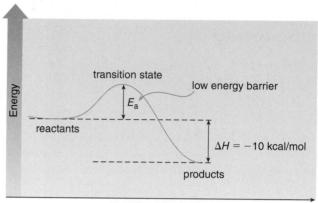

PROBLEM 6.10

Draw an energy diagram for a reaction with a high E_a and a $\Delta H = +20$ kcal/mol.

PROBLEM 6.11

Draw an energy diagram for the following reaction: $H_2O + HCl \longrightarrow H_3O^+ + Cl^-$. Assume the energy of activation is low and the products are lower in energy than the reactants. Clearly label the reactants and products on the energy diagram.

6.4 Reaction Rates

Even though we may not realize it, the rate of chemical processes affects many facets of our lives. Aspirin is an effective pain reliever because it rapidly blocks the synthesis of pain-causing molecules. Butter turns rancid with time because its fat molecules are slowly oxidized by oxygen in the air to undesirable by-products. DDT is a persistent environmental pollutant because it does not react appreciably with water, oxygen, or any other chemical with which it comes into contact. All of these processes occur at different rates, resulting in beneficial or harmful effects.

The energy of activation, the minimum amount of energy needed for a reaction to occur, is a fundamental characteristic of a reaction. Some reactions are fast because they have low energies of activation. Other reactions are slow because the energy of activation is high. Even reactions that form products that are lower in energy than the reactants can have high energies of activation. The combustion of gasoline to form CO_2 and H_2O releases a great deal of energy, but it is a very slow reaction without a spark or flame to initiate the reaction.

ENVIRONMENTAL NOTE

Gasoline can be safely handled in the air because its reaction with O_2 is slow unless there is a spark to provide energy to initiate the reaction.

6.4A How Concentration and Temperature Affect Reaction Rate

As we learned in Section 6.3, chemical reactions occur when molecules collide. The rate of a reaction depends on the number of collisions and the effectiveness of each collision. How do changes in concentration and temperature affect the reaction rate?

- Increasing the concentration of the reactants increases the number of collisions, so the reaction rate increases.
- Increasing the temperature increases the reaction rate.

Increasing the temperature increases the reaction rate for two reasons. First, increasing the temperature increases the kinetic energy, which increases the number of collisions. Second, increasing the temperature increases the *average* kinetic energy of the reactants. Because the kinetic energy of colliding molecules is used for bond cleavage, more molecules have sufficient energy to cause

CONSUMER NOTE

We store food in a cold refrigerator to slow the reactions that cause food to spoil.

bond breaking, and the reaction rate increases. As a general rule, a reaction rate *doubles* for each 10 °C the temperature is *raised*. Similarly, a reaction rate is generally *halved* for each 10 °C the temperature is *lowered*.

PROBLEM 6.12

Consider the reaction of ozone (O_3) with nitrogen monoxide (NO), which occurs in smog. What effect would each of the following changes have on the rate of this reaction?

$$O_3(g) + NO(g) \longrightarrow O_2(g) + NO_2(g)$$

a. increasing the concentration of O_3
b. decreasing the concentration of NO

c. increasing the temperature
d. decreasing the temperature

6.4B Catalysts

Some reactions do not occur in a reasonable period of time unless a **catalyst** is added.

- A *catalyst* is a substance that speeds up the rate of a reaction. A catalyst is recovered unchanged in a reaction, and it does not appear in the product.

Catalysts accelerate a reaction by lowering the energy of activation (Figure 6.2). They have no effect on the energies of the reactants and products. Thus, the addition of a catalyst lowers E_a but does not affect ΔH.

Metals are often used as catalysts in reactions. For example, ethylene ($CH_2{=}CH_2$) does not react appreciably with hydrogen (H_2), but in the presence of palladium (Pd) a rapid reaction occurs and ethane (C_2H_6) is formed as the product. The metal serves as a surface that brings together both reactants, facilitating the reaction. This reaction, called **hydrogenation,** is used in the food industry to prepare margarine, peanut butter, and many other consumer products that contain vegetable oils (Section 13.7).

$$\underset{\text{ethylene}}{\overset{\displaystyle H\quad\quad H}{\underset{\displaystyle H\quad\quad H}{C{=}C}}} \quad + \quad H_2 \quad \xrightarrow[\text{catalyst}]{\text{Pd}} \quad \underset{\text{ethane}}{C_2H_6}$$

Figure 6.2   The Effect of a Catalyst on a Reaction

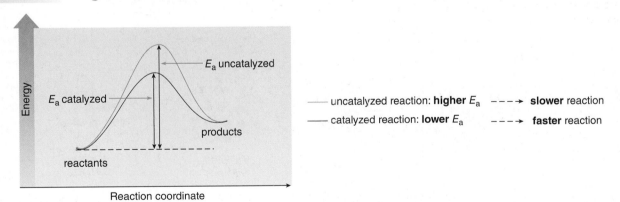

A catalyst lowers the energy of activation, thus increasing the rate of the catalyzed reaction. The energy of the reactants and products is the same in both the uncatalyzed and catalyzed reactions.

6.4C FOCUS ON THE HUMAN BODY
Lactase, a Biological Catalyst

The catalysts that synthesize and break down biological molecules in living organisms are governed by the same principles as the metals in organic reactions. The catalysts in living organisms, however, are protein molecules called **enzymes.**

Enzymes are discussed in greater detail in Section 21.9.

> • *Enzymes* are biological catalysts held together in a very specific three-dimensional shape.

An enzyme contains a region called its **active site** that binds a reactant, which then undergoes a very specific reaction with an enhanced rate. For example, **lactase** is the enzyme that binds **lactose,** the principal carbohydrate in milk (Figure 6.3). Once bound, lactose is converted into two simpler sugars, glucose and galactose. When individuals lack adequate amounts of this enzyme, they are unable to digest lactose, and this causes abdominal cramping and diarrhea.

Figure 6.3   Lactase, an Example of a Biological Catalyst

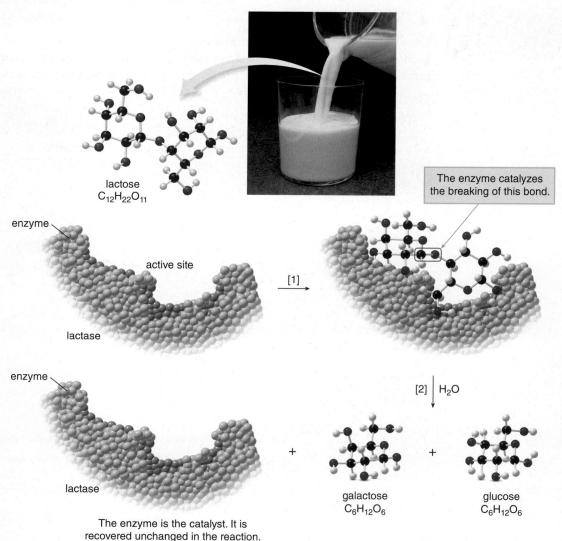

lactose
$C_{12}H_{22}O_{11}$

enzyme

active site

The enzyme catalyzes the breaking of this bond.

[1]

lactase

enzyme

[2] H_2O

lactase

+   galactose
$C_6H_{12}O_6$ +   glucose
$C_6H_{12}O_6$

The enzyme is the catalyst. It is recovered unchanged in the reaction.

The enzyme lactase binds the carbohydrate lactose ($C_{12}H_{22}O_{11}$) in its active site in step [1]. Lactose then reacts with water to break a bond and form two simpler sugars, galactose and glucose, in step [2]. This process is the first step in digesting lactose, the principal carbohydrate in milk. Without the enzyme, individuals are unable to convert lactose to galactose and glucose, lactose cannot be metabolized, and digestive problems result.

There is a direct link between the poor air quality in large metropolitan areas like Los Angeles and an increase in respiratory diseases.

PROBLEM 6.13

The reaction of acetic acid ($C_2H_4O_2$) and ethanol (C_2H_6O) to form ethyl acetate ($C_4H_8O_2$) and water occurs at an appreciable rate only when a small amount of sulfuric acid (H_2SO_4) is added. Is H_2SO_4 a catalyst for this reaction? What effect does H_2SO_4 have on the relative energies of the reactants and products?

6.4D FOCUS ON THE ENVIRONMENT
Catalytic Converters

The combustion of gasoline with oxygen provides a great deal of energy, much like the oxidation reactions of methane and propane discussed in Section 6.2B, and this energy is used to power vehicles. As the number of automobiles increased in the twentieth century, the air pollution they were responsible for became a major problem, especially in congested urban areas.

One problem with the auto engines of the 1970s centered on the carbon- and nitrogen-containing by-products emitted in engine exhaust. In addition to CO_2 and H_2O formed during combustion, auto exhaust also contained unreacted gasoline molecules (general formula C_xH_y), the toxic gas carbon monoxide (CO, Section 5.5), and nitrogen monoxide (NO, Section 5.5, a contributing component of acid rain). **Catalytic converters** were devised to clean up these polluting automobile emissions.

The newest catalytic converters, called three-way catalytic converters, use a metal as a surface to catalyze three reactions, as shown in Figure 6.4. Both the unreacted gasoline molecules and carbon monoxide (CO) are oxidized to CO_2 and H_2O. Nitrogen monoxide is also converted to oxygen and nitrogen. In this way, three molecules that contribute to unhealthy smog levels are removed, and the only materials in the engine exhaust are CO_2, H_2O, N_2, and O_2.

Figure 6.4   How a Catalytic Converter Works

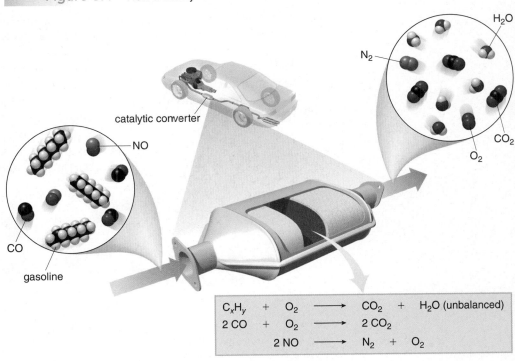

$$C_xH_y + O_2 \longrightarrow CO_2 + H_2O \text{ (unbalanced)}$$
$$2\,CO + O_2 \longrightarrow 2\,CO_2$$
$$2\,NO \longrightarrow N_2 + O_2$$

A catalytic converter uses a metal catalyst—rhodium, platinum, or palladium—to catalyze three reactions that clean up the exhaust from an auto engine.

6.5 Equilibrium

Thus far in discussing reactions we have assumed that the reactants are completely converted to products. A reaction of this sort is said to **go to completion.** Sometimes, however, a reaction is **reversible;** that is, reactants can come together and form products, and products can come together to re-form reactants.

> • A *reversible reaction* can occur in either direction, from reactants to products or from products to reactants.

Consider the reversible reaction of carbon monoxide (CO) with water to form carbon dioxide (CO_2) and hydrogen. Two full-headed arrows ($\rightleftharpoons$) are used to show that the reaction can proceed from left to right and right to left as written.

The **forward** reaction proceeds to the *right.*

$$CO(g) \ + \ H_2O(g) \ \rightleftharpoons \ CO_2(g) \ + \ H_2(g)$$

The **reverse** reaction proceeds to the *left.*

> • The *forward* reaction proceeds from left to right as drawn.
> • The *reverse* reaction proceeds from right to left as drawn.

When CO and H_2O are mixed together they react to form CO_2 and H_2 by the forward reaction. Once CO_2 and H_2 are formed, they can react together to form CO and H_2O by the reverse reaction. The rate of the forward reaction is rapid at first, and then decreases as the concentration of reactants decreases. The rate of the reverse reaction is slow at first, but speeds up as the concentration of the products increases.

> • When the rate of the forward reaction equals the rate of the reverse reaction, the net concentrations of all species do not change and the system is at *equilibrium.*

The forward and reverse reactions do not stop once equilibrium has been reached. The reactants and products continue to react. Since the rates of the forward and reverse reactions are equal, however, the **net concentrations of all reactants and products do *not* change.** Molecular art in Figure 6.5 shows how the reversible reaction A $\rightleftharpoons$ B reaches equilibrium.

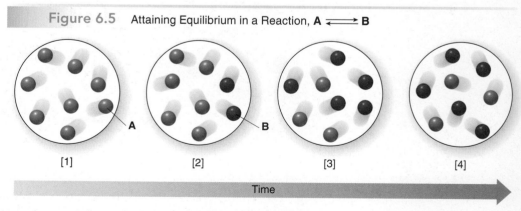

Figure 6.5   Attaining Equilibrium in a Reaction, A $\rightleftharpoons$ B

[1]   [2]   [3]   [4]

Time

The conversion of **A** (shown in blue spheres) to **B** (shown in red spheres) is a reversible reaction. Initially, the reaction contains only **A** (diagram [1]). As **A** reacts to form **B**, the amount of **B** increases (diagram [2]). As **B** is formed, it can be re-converted to **A**. At equilibrium (diagrams [3] and [4]), the amounts of **A** and **B** do not change, but the conversion of **A** to **B** and the conversion of **B** to **A** still occur.

PROBLEM 6.14

Identify the forward and reverse reactions in each of the following reversible reactions.

a. $2 SO_2(g) + O_2(g) \rightleftharpoons 2 SO_3(g)$
b. $N_2(g) + O_2(g) \rightleftharpoons 2 NO(g)$
c. $C_2H_4O_2 + CH_4O \rightleftharpoons C_3H_6O_2 + H_2O$

6.5A The Equilibrium Constant

Because the net concentrations of the reactants and products do not change at equilibrium, they are used to define an expression, the **equilibrium constant, *K*,** which has a characteristic value for a reaction at a given temperature. When discussing equilibrium it is not the absolute number of moles that is the important quantity, but rather it is the *concentration,* **the number of moles in a given volume.** Brackets, [ ], are used to symbolize concentration, which is reported in moles per liter (mol/L).

Consider the following general reaction, where **A** and **B** represent reactants, **C** and **D** represent products, and *a, b, c,* and *d* represent the coefficients in the balanced chemical equation.

$$a\,\mathbf{A} + b\,\mathbf{B} \rightleftharpoons c\,\mathbf{C} + d\,\mathbf{D}$$

The equilibrium constant *K* is the ratio of the concentrations of the products (**C** and **D**) multiplied together, to the concentrations of the reactants (**A** and **B**) multiplied together. Each concentration term is raised to a power equal to the coefficient in the balanced chemical equation.

concentration of each product (mol/L)

$$\text{Equilibrium constant} = K = \frac{[\text{products}]}{[\text{reactants}]}$$

concentration of each reactant (mol/L)

$$K = \frac{[C]^c[D]^d}{[A]^a[B]^b}$$

The expression for the equilibrium constant for any reaction can be written from a balanced equation, as shown for the reaction of N_2 and O_2 to form NO.

above the division line

Balanced equation: $N_2(g) + O_2(g) \rightleftharpoons 2 NO(g)$

below the division line

The coefficient becomes the exponent.

$$\text{Equilibrium constant} = K = \frac{[NO]^2}{[N_2][O_2]}$$

SAMPLE PROBLEM 6.8

Write the expression for the equilibrium constant for the following balanced equation.

$$2 CO(g) + O_2(g) \rightleftharpoons 2 CO_2(g)$$

Analysis

To write an expression for the equilibrium constant, multiply the concentration of the products together and divide this number by the product of the concentrations of the reactants. Each concentration term must be raised to a power equal to the coefficient in the balanced chemical equation.

Solution

The concentration of the sole product, CO_2, is placed in the numerator and raised to the second power since this term has the coefficient "2." The denominator contains concentration terms for the two reactants, CO and O_2, multiplied together. Since the coefficient preceding CO in the balanced equation is "2," this concentration term has an exponent of "2."

$$\text{Equilibrium constant} = K = \frac{[CO_2]^2}{[CO]^2[O_2]}$$

PROBLEM 6.15

Write the expression for the equilibrium constant for each equation.

a. $PCl_3(g) + Cl_2(g) \rightleftharpoons PCl_5(g)$
b. $2\,SO_2(g) + O_2(g) \rightleftharpoons 2\,SO_3(g)$
c. $H_2(g) + Br_2(g) \rightleftharpoons 2\,HBr(g)$
d. $CH_4(g) + 3\,Cl_2(g) \rightleftharpoons CHCl_3(g) + 3\,HCl(g)$

6.5B The Magnitude of the Equilibrium Constant

The magnitude of the equilibrium constant tells us whether the products or reactants are favored once equilibrium is reached.

- When the equilibrium constant is much greater than one ($K > 1$), the concentration of the products is larger than the concentration of the reactants. We say equilibrium lies to the *right* and favors the *products.*

When K is greater than 1: $\dfrac{[products]}{[reactants]}$ The numerator is larger.
($K > 1$)   Equilibrium favors the **products.**

- When the equilibrium constant is much less than one ($K < 1$), the concentration of the reactants is larger than the concentration of the products. We say equilibrium lies to the *left* and favors the *reactants.*

When K is less than 1: $\dfrac{[products]}{[reactants]}$ The denominator is larger.
($K < 1$)   Equilibrium favors the **reactants.**

- When the equilibrium constant is around 1, anywhere in the range of 0.01–100, both reactants and products are present at equilibrium.

When K is approximately equal to 1: $\dfrac{[products]}{[reactants]}$ Both reactants and products are present.
($K \approx 1$)

For example, the equilibrium constant for the reaction of H_2 and O_2 to form water is much greater than one, so the product, H_2O, is highly favored at equilibrium. A reaction with such a large K essentially goes to completion, with little or no reactants left.

$2\,H_2(g) + O_2(g) \rightleftharpoons 2\,H_2O(g) \qquad K = 2.9 \times 10^{82}$

- The product is highly favored since $K > 1$.
- Equilibrium lies to the right.

In contrast, the equilibrium constant for the conversion of O_2 to O_3 is much less than one, so the reactant, O_2, is highly favored at equilibrium, and almost no product, O_3, is formed. The relationship between the equilibrium constant and the direction of equilibrium is summarized in Table 6.4.

$$3\ O_2(g) \ \rightleftharpoons \ 2\ O_3(g) \qquad K \ = \ 2.7 \times 10^{-29}$$

- The reactant is highly favored since $K < 1$.
- Equilibrium lies to the left.

Generally there is a relationship between the equilibrium constant K and the ΔH of a reaction.

> - The products of a reaction are favored when K is much greater than one ($K > 1$), and ΔH is negative. In other words, equilibrium favors the products when they are lower in energy than the reactants.

There is, however, no relationship between K and the reaction rate. Some reactions with very large equilibrium constants are still very slow. Moreover, a catalyst may speed up a reaction, but it does not affect the size of K. With a catalyst, equilibrium is reached more quickly, but the relative concentrations of reactants and products do not change.

Table 6.4 How the Magnitude of K Relates to the Direction of Equilibrium

Value of K	Position of Equilibrium
$K > 1$	Equilibrium favors the products. Equilibrium lies to the right.
$K < 1$	Equilibrium favors the reactants. Equilibrium lies to the left.
$K \approx 1$	Both the reactants and products are present at equilibrium.

SAMPLE PROBLEM 6.9

Consider the reversible reaction **A** $\rightleftharpoons$ **B,** with $K = 10$. Assume the reaction begins with only **A,** and draw a representation for the reaction mixture at equilibrium.

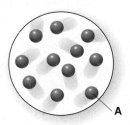

Analysis

Write the expression for the equilibrium constant, and use the value of K to determine the relative amounts of product (**B**) and reactant (**A**).

Solution

In this reaction, $K = [\mathbf{B}]/[\mathbf{A}] = 10$. Since the concentration of the product is in the numerator, this means that there is 10 times as much product (**B**) as reactant (**A**) at equilibrium.

For $K = 10$: $\qquad K \ = \ \dfrac{[\mathbf{B}]}{[\mathbf{A}]} \ = \ \dfrac{10}{1}$ 10 times as much **B** as **A**

To represent equilibrium in this reaction using molecular art, draw 10 times as many **B** spheres (in red) as **A** spheres (in blue).

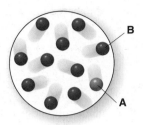

PROBLEM 6.16

Consider the reversible reaction **A** $\rightleftharpoons$ **B**, with $K = 1$. Assuming the reaction begins with only **A**, draw a representation using molecular art for the reaction mixture at equilibrium. Use blue spheres for **A** and red spheres for **B**.

PROBLEM 6.17

Given each equilibrium constant, state whether the reactants are favored, the products are favored, or both the reactants and products are present at equilibrium.

   a. 5.0×10^{-4} b. 4.4×10^{5} c. 350   d. 0.35

PROBLEM 6.18

Predict whether the reactions with the equilibrium constants in Problem 6.17 are endothermic or exothermic.

PROBLEM 6.19

Consider the following reaction: $2\ H_2(g) + S_2(g) \longrightarrow 2\ H_2S(g)$ with $K = 1.1 \times 10^{7}$. (a) Write the expression for the equilibrium constant for this reaction. (b) Are the reactants or products favored at equilibrium? (c) Would you predict ΔH to be positive or negative? (d) Are the reactants or products lower in energy? (e) Would you predict this reaction to be fast or slow? Explain your choice.

6.5C   Calculating the Equilibrium Constant

The equilibrium constant for a reaction is an experimentally determined value, and thus it can be calculated if the concentrations of all substances involved in a reaction are measured at equilibrium. Concentrations are reported in moles per liter (mol/L), symbolized as M.

How To **Calculate the Equilibrium Constant for a Reaction**

Example: Calculate K for the reaction between the general reactants A_2 and B_2. The equilibrium concentrations are as follows: $[A_2] = 0.25$ M; $[B_2] = 0.25$ M; $[AB] = 0.50$ M.

$$A_2 + B_2 \rightleftharpoons 2\ AB$$

Step [1] **Write the expression for the equilibrium constant from the balanced chemical equation, using the coefficients as exponents for the concentration terms.**

$$\text{Equilibrium constant} = K = \frac{[AB]^2}{[A_2][B_2]}$$

Step [2] **Substitute the given concentrations in the equilibrium expression and calculate K.**

   • Since the concentration is always reported in mol/L (M), these units are omitted during the calculation.

$$K = \frac{[AB]^2}{[A_2][B_2]} = \frac{[0.50]^2}{[0.25][0.25]} = \frac{(0.50) \times (0.50)}{0.0625}$$

$$= \frac{0.25}{0.0625} = 4.0$$

Answer

The conversion of nitrogen and hydrogen to ammonia (Sample Problem 6.10) is an exceedingly important reaction since it converts molecular nitrogen from the air to a nitrogen compound (NH_3) that can be used as a fertilizer for plants. In the early twentieth century, German chemist Fritz Haber developed a catalyst that enabled this reaction to proceed quickly to afford favorable yields of NH_3. This process paved the way for large-scale agriculture, which provides food for the world's growing population.

SAMPLE PROBLEM 6.10

Calculate K for the reaction of N_2 and H_2 to form NH_3, with the given balanced equation and the following equilibrium concentrations: $[N_2]$ = 0.12 M; $[H_2]$ = 0.36 M; $[NH_3]$ = 1.1 M.

$$N_2(g) + 3\,H_2(g) \rightleftharpoons 2\,NH_3(g)$$

Analysis

Write an expression for K using the balanced equation and substitute the equilibrium concentrations of all substances in the expression.

Solution

$$K = \frac{[NH_3]^2}{[N_2][H_2]^3} = \frac{(1.1)^2}{(0.12)(0.36)^3} = \frac{1.1 \times 1.1}{0.12 \times 0.36 \times 0.36 \times 0.36}$$

$$= \frac{1.21}{0.0056} = 216 \text{ rounded to } 220$$

Answer

PROBLEM 6.20

Calculate the equilibrium constant for each reaction using the balanced chemical equations and the concentrations of the substances at equilibrium.

a. $CO(g) + H_2O(g) \rightleftharpoons CO_2(g) + H_2(g)$ 　　　$[CO]$ = 0.0236 M; $[H_2O]$ = 0.00240 M; $[CO_2]$ = 0.0164 M; $[H_2]$ = 0.0164 M

b. $2\,NO_2(g) \rightleftharpoons N_2O_4(g)$ 　　　$[NO_2]$ = 0.0760 M; $[N_2O_4]$ = 1.26 M

6.6　Le Châtelier's Principle

What happens when a reaction is at equilibrium and something changes? For example, what happens when the temperature is increased or some additional reactant is added? **Le Châtelier's principle** is a general rule used to explain the effect of a change in reaction conditions on equilibrium. Le Châtelier's principle states:

- If a chemical system at equilibrium is disturbed or stressed, the system will react in the direction that counteracts the disturbance or relieves the stress.

Let's examine the effect of changes in concentration, temperature, and pressure on equilibrium.

6.6A　Concentration Changes

Consider the reaction of carbon monoxide (CO) with oxygen (O_2) to form carbon dioxide (CO_2).

$$2\,CO(g) + O_2(g) \rightleftharpoons 2\,CO_2(g)$$

If the reactants and products are at equilibrium, what happens if the concentration of CO is increased? Now the equilibrium is disturbed and, as a result, the rate of the forward reaction increases to produce more CO_2. We can think of **added reactant as driving the equilibrium to the *right*.**

Adding more reactant…

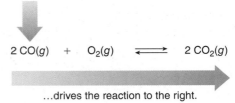

$$2\,CO(g) + O_2(g) \rightleftharpoons 2\,CO_2(g)$$

…drives the reaction to the right.

When the system reaches equilibrium once again, the concentrations of CO_2 and CO are both higher. Since O_2 reacted with the additional CO, its new value at equilibrium is lower. Even though the concentrations of reactants and products are different, the value of K is the same.

If CO is added...

$$2\,CO(g)\ +\ O_2(g)\ \rightleftharpoons\ 2\,CO_2(g)$$

...this decreases...   ...and this increases.

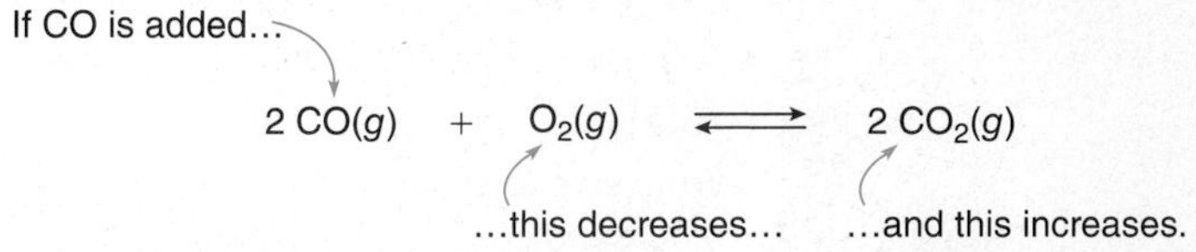

What happens, instead, if the concentration of CO_2 is increased? Now the equilibrium is disturbed but there is more product than there should be. As a result, the rate of the reverse reaction increases to produce more of both reactants, CO and O_2. We can think of **added product as driving the equilibrium to the *left*.**

Adding more product...

$$2\,CO(g)\ +\ O_2(g)\ \rightleftharpoons\ 2\,CO_2(g)$$

...drives the reaction to the left.

When the system reaches equilibrium once again, the concentrations of CO, O_2, and CO_2 are all higher. Even though the concentrations of reactants and products are different, the value of K is the same.

If CO_2 is added...

$$2\,CO(g)\ +\ O_2(g)\ \rightleftharpoons\ 2\,CO_2(g)$$

...this increases...   ...and this increases.

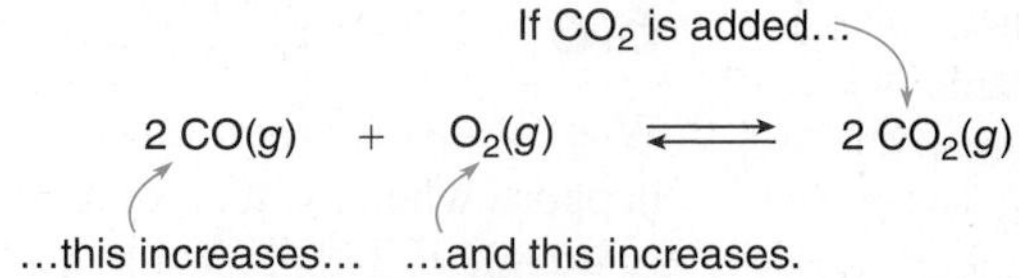

Similar arguments can be made about the effect of decreasing the concentration of a reactant or product. Sometimes, when $K < 1$ and the amount of product at equilibrium is not high, a product is removed from the reaction mixture as it is formed. For example, ethanol (C_2H_6O) can be converted to ethylene ($CH_2{=}CH_2$) and water in the presence of a small amount of acid, but equilibrium does not favor the products.

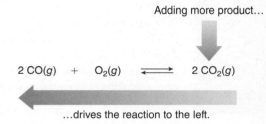

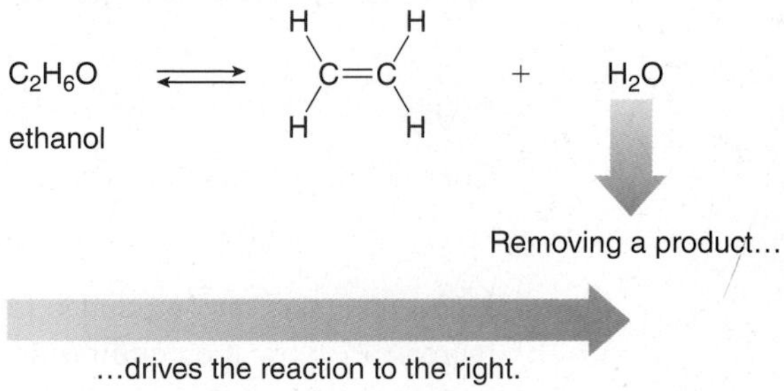

Removing a product...

...drives the reaction to the right.

In this case, water can be removed from the reaction as it is formed. A decrease in concentration of one product results in more of the forward reaction to form more product. **This process drives the equilibrium to the right.** If water is continuously removed, essentially all of the starting material can be converted to product.

SAMPLE PROBLEM 6.11

In which direction is the equilibrium shifted with each of the following concentration changes for the given reaction: (a) increase $[SO_2]$; (b) increase $[SO_3]$; (c) decrease $[O_2]$; (d) decrease $[SO_3]$?

$$2\,SO_2(g)\ +\ O_2(g)\ \rightleftharpoons\ 2\,SO_3(g)$$

Analysis

Use Le Châtelier's principle to predict the effect of a change in concentration on equilibrium. Adding more reactant or removing product drives the equilibrium to the right. Adding more product or removing reactant drives the equilibrium to the left.

Solution

    a. Increasing $[SO_2]$, a reactant, drives the equilibrium to the right to form more product.
    b. Increasing $[SO_3]$, a product, drives the equilibrium to the left to form more reactants.
    c. Decreasing $[O_2]$, a reactant, drives the equilibrium to the left to form more reactants.
    d. Decreasing $[SO_3]$, a product, drives the equilibrium to the right to form more product.

PROBLEM 6.21

In which direction is the equilibrium shifted with each of the following concentration changes for the given reaction: (a) increase $[H_2]$; (b) increase $[HCl]$; (c) decrease $[Cl_2]$; (d) decrease $[HCl]$?

$$H_2(g) + Cl_2(g) \rightleftharpoons 2\ HCl(g)$$

6.6B Temperature Changes

In order to predict what effect a change of temperature has on a reaction, we must know if a reaction is endothermic or exothermic.

> • When temperature is increased, the reaction that removes heat is favored.
> • When temperature is decreased, the reaction that adds heat is favored.

For example, the reaction of N_2 and O_2 to form NO is an endothermic reaction ($\Delta H = +43$ kcal/mol). **Since an endothermic reaction absorbs heat, increasing the temperature increases the rate of the *forward* reaction to form more product.** The equilibrium shifts to the right.

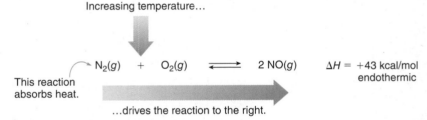

In the exothermic reaction of N_2 and H_2 to form NH_3 ($\Delta H = -22$ kcal/mol), **increasing the temperature increases the rate of the *reverse* reaction to form more reactants.** When temperature is increased, the reaction that absorbs heat, in this case the reverse reaction, predominates and the equilibrium shifts to the left.

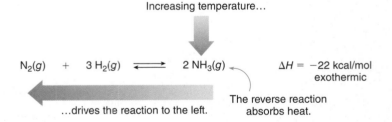

SAMPLE PROBLEM 6.12

The reaction of SO_2 with O_2 to form SO_3 is an exothermic reaction. In which direction is the equilibrium shifted when the temperature is (a) increased; (b) decreased?

Analysis

When temperature is increased, the reaction that removes heat is favored. When temperature is decreased, the reaction that adds heat is favored.

Solution

In an exothermic reaction, the forward reaction releases heat and the reverse reaction absorbs heat. (a) When the temperature is increased, the reverse reaction is favored because it removes heat, so the equilibrium shifts to the reactants (to the left). (b) When the temperature is decreased, the forward reaction is favored because it adds heat, so the equilibrium shifts to the products (to the right).

Pressure, the force per unit area, is discussed in greater detail in Chapter 7.

PROBLEM 6.22

The conversion of H_2O to H_2 and O_2 is an endothermic reaction. In which direction is the equilibrium shifted when the temperature is (a) increased; (b) decreased?

PROBLEM 6.23

The reaction of O_3 with NO to form NO_2 and O_2 is an exothermic reaction. In which direction is the equilibrium shifted when the temperature is (a) increased; (b) decreased?

6.6C   Pressure Changes

When the substances involved in a reaction are gases and the total number of moles of reactants and products differs, a change in pressure has an effect on equilibrium.

- When pressure *increases,* equilibrium shifts in the direction that *decreases* the number of moles in order to decrease pressure.
- When pressure *decreases,* equilibrium shifts in the direction that *increases* the number of moles in order to increase pressure.

In the reaction of N_2 and H_2 to form NH_3, there are four moles of reactants but only two moles of product. When the pressure of the system is increased, the equilibrium shifts to the right since there are fewer moles of product.

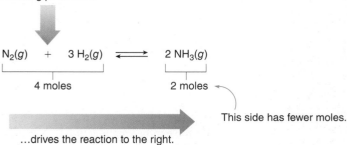

In contrast, when the pressure of the system is decreased, the equilibrium shifts to the left since there are more moles of reactants.

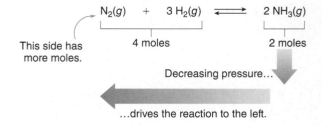

SAMPLE PROBLEM 6.13

In which direction is the equilibrium shifted in the following reaction when the pressure is (a) increased; (b) decreased?

$$H\text{—}C\equiv C\text{—}H(g) + 2\,H_2(g) \rightleftharpoons C_2H_6(g)$$

Analysis

When pressure is increased, the equilibrium shifts in the direction that decreases the number of moles. When pressure is decreased, the equilibrium shifts in the direction that increases the number of moles.

Solution

In this reaction, there are three moles of reactants and only one mole of product. (a) Increasing the pressure shifts the equilibrium to the right, to the side of fewer moles. (b) Decreasing the pressure shifts the equilibrium to the left, to the side of more moles.

Table 6.5 summarizes the effects of changes in reaction conditions on the direction of an equilibrium.

PROBLEM 6.24

In which direction is the equilibrium shifted in the following reaction when the pressure is
(a) increased; (b) decreased?

$$C_2H_4(g) \; - \; Cl_2(g) \; \rightleftharpoons \; C_2H_4Cl_2(g)$$

Table 6.5 The Effects of Changes in Conditions on Equilibrium

Change	Effect on Equilibrium
Concentration	
• Adding reactant	Equilibrium favors the products.
• Removing reactant	Equilibrium favors the reactants.
• Adding product	Equilibrium favors the reactants.
• Removing product	Equilibrium favors the products.
Temperature	
• Increasing temperature	In an endothermic reaction, equilibrium favors the products.
	In an exothermic reaction, equilibrium favors the reactants.
• Decreasing temperature	In an endothermic reaction, equilibrium favors the reactants.
	In an exothermic reaction, equilibrium favors the products.
Pressure	
• Increasing pressure	Equilibrium favors the side that has fewer moles.
• Decreasing pressure	Equilibrium favors the side that has more moles.

6.7 FOCUS ON THE HUMAN BODY
Body Temperature

The human body is an enormously complex organism that illustrates important features of energy and reaction rates. At any moment, millions of reactions occur in the body, when nutrients are metabolized and new cell materials are synthesized.

Normal body temperature, 37 °C, reflects a delicate balance between the amount of heat absorbed and released in all of the reactions and other processes. Since reaction rate increases with increasing temperature, it is crucial to maintain the right temperature for proper body function. When temperature increases, reactions proceed at a faster rate. An individual must breathe more rapidly and the heart must pump harder to supply oxygen for the faster metabolic processes. When temperature decreases, reactions slow down, less heat is generated in exothermic reactions, and it becomes harder and harder to maintain an adequate body temperature.

Thermoregulation—regulating temperature—is a complex mechanism that involves the brain, the circulatory system, and the skin (Figure 6.6). Temperature sensors in the skin and body core signal when there is a temperature change. The hypothalamus region of the brain, in turn, responds to changes in its environment in a process that is reminiscent of Le Châtelier's principle.

When the temperature increases, the body must somehow rid itself of excess heat. Blood vessels near the surface of the skin are dilated to release more heat. Sweat glands are stimulated so the body can be cooled by the evaporation of water from the skin's surface.

When the temperature decreases, the body must generate more heat as well as slow down the loss of heat to the surroundings. Blood vessels constrict to reduce heat loss from the skin and muscles shiver to generate more heat.

Figure 6.6   Temperature Regulation in the Body

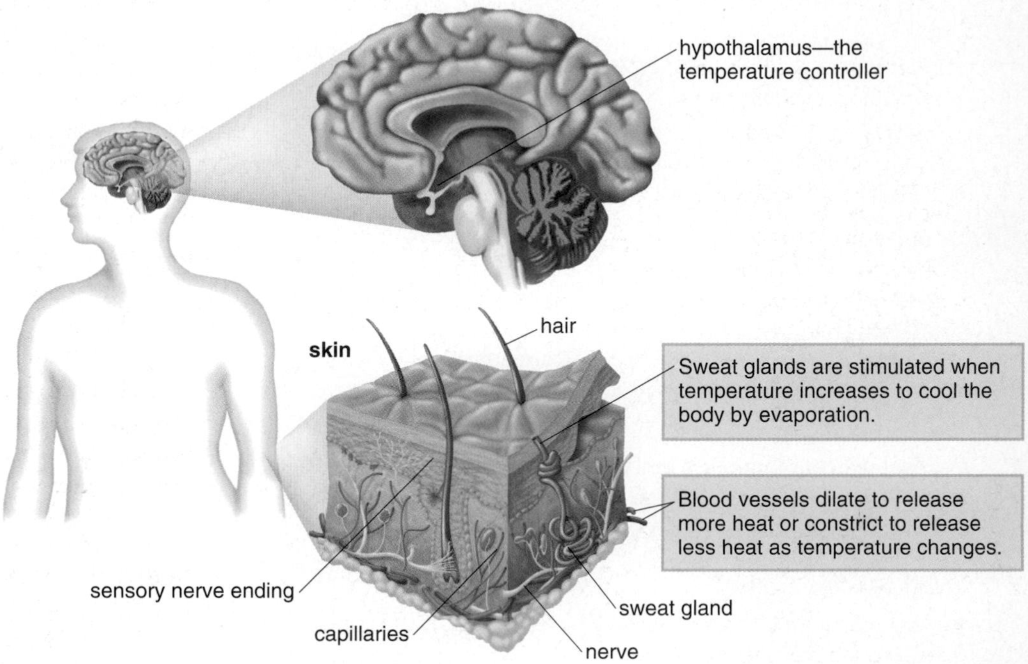

hypothalamus—the
temperature controller

hair

skin

Sweat glands are stimulated when
temperature increases to cool the
body by evaporation.

Blood vessels dilate to release
more heat or constrict to release
less heat as temperature changes.

sensory nerve ending

capillaries

sweat gland

nerve

When the temperature in the environment around the body changes, the body works to counteract
the change, in a method similar to Le Châtelier's principle. The hypothalamus acts as a thermostat,
which signals the body to respond to temperature changes. When the temperature increases, the
body must dissipate excess heat by dilating blood vessels and sweating. When the temperature
decreases, blood vessels constrict and the body shivers.

An infection in the body is often accompanied by a fever; that is, the temperature in the body
increases. A fever is part of the body's response to increase the rates of defensive reactions that
kill bacteria. The respiratory rate and heart rate increase to supply more oxygen needed for faster
reactions.

CHAPTER HIGHLIGHTS
KEY TERMS

Active site (6.4)

Bond dissociation energy (6.2)

Calorie (6.1)

Catalyst (6.4)

Endothermic reaction (6.2)

Energy (6.1)

Energy diagram (6.3)

Energy of activation (6.3)

Enthalpy change (6.2)

Enzyme (6.4)

Equilibrium (6.5)

Equilibrium constant (6.5)

Exothermic reaction (6.2)

Forward reaction (6.5)

Heat of reaction (6.2)

Joule (6.1)

Kinetic energy (6.1)

Law of conservation of energy (6.1)

Le Châtelier's principle (6.6)

Potential energy (6.1)

Reaction rate (6.3)

Reverse reaction (6.5)

Reversible reaction (6.5)

Transition state (6.3)

KEY CONCEPTS

1 **What is energy and what units are used to measure energy? (6.1)**

- Energy is the capacity to do work. Kinetic energy is the energy of motion, whereas potential energy is stored energy.
- Energy is measured in calories (cal) or joules (J), where 1 cal = 4.184 J.
- One nutritional calorie (Cal) = 1 kcal = 1,000 cal.

2 **Define bond dissociation energy and describe its relationship to bond strength. (6.2)**

- The bond dissociation energy is the energy needed to break a covalent bond by equally dividing the electrons between the two atoms in the bond.
- The higher the bond dissociation energy, the stronger the bond.

3 **What is the heat of reaction and what is the difference between an endothermic and an exothermic reaction? (6.2)**

- The heat of reaction, also called the enthalpy change and symbolized by ΔH, is the energy absorbed or released in a reaction.
- In an endothermic reaction, energy is absorbed, ΔH is positive (+), and the products are higher in energy than the reactants. The bonds in the reactants are stronger than the bonds in the products.
- In an exothermic reaction, energy is released, ΔH is negative (–), and the reactants are higher in energy than the products. The bonds in the products are stronger than the bonds in the reactants.

4 **What are the important features of an energy diagram? (6.3)**

- An energy diagram illustrates the energy changes that occur during the course of a reaction. Energy is plotted on the vertical axis and reaction coordinate is plotted on the horizontal axis. The transition state is located at the top of the energy barrier that separates the reactants and products.
- The energy of activation is the energy difference between the reactants and the transition state. The higher the energy of activation, the slower the reaction.
- The difference in energy between the reactants and products is the ΔH.

5 **How do temperature, concentration, and catalysts affect the rate of a reaction? (6.4)**

- Increasing the temperature and concentration increases the reaction rate.
- A catalyst speeds up the rate of a reaction without affecting the energies of the reactants and products. Enzymes are biological catalysts that increase the rate of reactions in living organisms. Catalytic converters use a catalyst to convert automobile engine exhaust to environmentally cleaner products.

6 **What are the basic features of equilibrium? (6.5)**

- At equilibrium, the rates of the forward and reverse reactions in a reversible reaction are equal and the net concentrations of all substances do not change.
- The equilibrium constant for a reaction $aA + bB \rightleftharpoons cC + dD$ is written as $K = ([C]^c[D]^d)/([A]^a[B]^b)$.
- The magnitude of K tells the relative amount of reactants and products. When $K > 1$, the products are favored; when $K < 1$, the reactants are favored; when $K \approx 1$, both reactants and products are present at equilibrium.

7 **How does Le Châtelier's principle predict what happens when equilibrium is disturbed? (6.6)**

- Le Châtelier's principle states that a system at equilibrium reacts in such a way as to counteract any disturbance to the equilibrium. How changes in concentration, temperature, and pressure affect equilibrium are summarized in Table 6.5.
- Catalysts increase the rate at which equilibrium is reached, but do not alter the amount of any substance involved in the reaction.

8 **How can the principles that describe equilibrium and reaction rates be used to understand the regulation of body temperature? (6.7)**

- Increasing temperature increases the rates of the reactions in the body.
- When temperature is increased, the body dissipates excess heat by dilating blood vessels and sweating. When temperature is decreased, blood vessels constrict to conserve heat, and the body shivers to generate more heat.

PROBLEMS

Selected in-chapter and odd-numbered end-of-chapter problems have brief answers in Appendix B. The *Student Study Guide and Solutions Manual* contains detailed solutions to all in-chapter and odd-numbered end-of-chapter problems, as well as additional worked examples and a chapter self-test.

Energy

6.25 What is the difference between kinetic energy and potential energy? Give an example of each type.

6.26 What is the difference between a calorie and a Calorie?

6.27 Riding a bicycle at 12–13 miles per hour uses 563 Calories in an hour. Convert this value to (a) calories; (b) kilocalories; (c) joules; (d) kilojoules.

6.28 Running at a rate of 6 mi/h uses 704 Calories in an hour. Convert this value to (a) calories; (b) kilocalories; (c) joules; (d) kilojoules.

6.29 Carry out each of the following conversions.

    a. 50 cal to kcal   c. 0.96 kJ to cal

    b. 56 cal to kJ   d. 4,230 kJ to cal

6.30 Carry out each of the following conversions.

   a. 5 kcal to cal   c. 1.22 kJ to cal

   b. 2,560 cal to kJ   d. 4,230 J to kcal

6.31 Estimate the number of Calories in two tablespoons of peanut butter, which contains 16 g of protein, 7 g of carbohydrates, and 16 g of fat.

6.32 Estimate the number of Calories in a serving of oatmeal that has 4 g of protein, 19 g of carbohydrates, and 2 g of fat.

6.33 A can of soda contains 120 Calories, and no protein or fat. How many grams of carbohydrates are present in each can?

6.34 Alcohol releases 29.7 kJ/g when it burns. Convert this value to the number of Calories per gram.

6.35 Which food has more Calories: 3 oz of salmon, which contains 17 g of protein and 5 g of fat, or 3 oz of chicken, which contains 20 g of protein and 3 g of fat?

6.36 Which food has more Calories: one egg, which contains 6 g of protein and 6 g of fat, or 1 cup of nonfat milk, which contains 9 g of protein and 12 g of carbohydrates?

Bond Dissociation Energy and ΔH

6.37 What is the difference between an endothermic reaction and an exothermic reaction?

6.38 What is the difference between ΔH and the bond dissociation energy?

6.39 Based on the location of the elements in the periodic table, which species in each pair has the stronger bond?

   a. Br_2 or Cl_2 b. Cl_2 or I_2 c. HF or HBr

6.40 Using the given bond dissociation energies, rank the indicated bonds in order of increasing strength.

$\Delta H = +104$ kcal/mol $\Delta H = +98$ kcal/mol $\Delta H = +125$ kcal/mol

6.41 Do each of the following statements describe an endothermic or exothermic reaction?

   a. ΔH is a negative value.

   b. The energy of the reactants is lower than the energy of the products.

   c. Energy is absorbed in the reaction.

   d. The bonds in the products are stronger than the bonds in the reactants.

6.42 Do each of the following statements describe an endothermic or exothermic reaction?

   a. ΔH is a positive value.

   b. The energy of the products is lower than the energy of the reactants.

   c. Energy is released in the reaction.

   d. The bonds in the reactants are stronger than the bonds in the products.

6.43 The combustion of coal with oxygen forms CO_2 and releases 94 kcal of energy.

$$C(s) + O_2(g) \longrightarrow CO_2(g)$$

   a. How much energy is released when 2.5 mol of C reacts?

   b. How much energy is released when 3.0 mol of O_2 reacts?

   c. How much energy is released when 25.0 g of C reacts?

6.44 Ammonia (NH_3) decomposes to hydrogen and nitrogen and 22.0 kcal/mol of energy is absorbed.

$$2\ NH_3(g) \longrightarrow 3\ H_2(g) + N_2(g)$$

   a. How much energy is absorbed when 1 mol of N_2 is formed?

   b. How much energy is absorbed when 1 mol of NH_3 reacts?

   c. How much energy is absorbed when 3.50 g of NH_3 reacts?

6.45 The metabolism of glucose (molar mass 180.2 g/mol) with oxygen forms CO_2 and H_2O and releases 678 kcal/mol of energy.

$$C_6H_{12}O_6(aq) + 6\ O_2(g) \rightleftharpoons 6\ CO_2(g) + 6\ H_2O(l)$$
glucose

   a. Are the bonds formed in the products stronger or weaker than the bonds broken in the reactants?

   b. How much energy is released when 4.00 mol of glucose is metabolized?

   c. How much energy is released when 3.00 mol of O_2 reacts?

   d. How much energy is released when 10.0 g of glucose reacts?

6.46 Ethanol (C_2H_6O), a gasoline additive, is formed by the reaction of ethylene ($CH_2=CH_2$) with water. The ΔH for this reaction is −9.0 kcal/mol.

   a. How much energy is released when 3.5 mol of ethylene reacts?

   b. How much energy is released when 0.50 mol of H_2O reacts?

   c. How much energy is released when 15.0 g of ethylene reacts?

   d. How much energy is released when 2.5 g of ethanol is formed?

Energy Diagrams

6.47 What is the difference between the energy of activation and the transition state?

6.48 What is the difference between E_a and ΔH?

6.49 Consider the energy diagram drawn below.

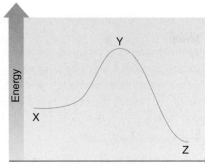

Reaction coordinate

a. Which point on the graph corresponds to reactants?
b. Which point on the graph corresponds to products?
c. Which point on the graph corresponds to the transition state?
d. The difference in energy between which two points equals the energy of activation?
e. The difference in energy between which two points equals the ΔH?
f. Which point is highest in energy?
g. Which point is lowest in energy?

6.50 Compound **A** can be converted to either **B** or **C**. The energy diagrams for both processes are drawn on the graph below.

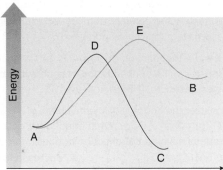

Reaction coordinate

a. Label each reaction as endothermic or exothermic.
b. Which reaction is faster?
c. Which reaction generates the product lower in energy?
d. Which points on the graphs correspond to transition states?
e. Label the energy of activation for each reaction.
f. Label the ΔH for each reaction.

6.51 Draw an energy diagram that fits each description.
a. an endothermic reaction with a high E_a
b. a reaction that has a low E_a and ΔH is negative
c. a slow reaction in which the products are at a lower energy than the reactants

6.52 Draw an energy diagram that fits each description.
a. an exothermic reaction with a high E_a
b. a reaction with a low E_a and a positive value of ΔH
c. a fast reaction in which the products are at a lower energy than the reactants

6.53 Draw an energy diagram for the following reaction in which $\Delta H = -12$ kcal/mol and $E_a = 5$ kcal: $\mathbf{A_2 + B_2 \longrightarrow 2\ AB}$. Label the axes, reactants, products, transition state, E_a, and ΔH. Is the reaction endothermic or exothermic?

6.54 Draw an energy diagram for the following reaction in which $\Delta H = +13$ kcal/mol and $E_a = 21$ kcal: $\mathbf{A + B \longrightarrow C}$. Label the axes, reactants, products, transition state, E_a, and ΔH. Are the products or reactants higher in energy?

Reaction Rates

6.55 How does collision orientation affect the rate of a reaction?

6.56 Explain why a high energy of activation causes a reaction to be slow.

6.57 State two reasons why increasing temperature increases reaction rate.

6.58 Why does decreasing concentration decrease the rate of a chemical reaction?

6.59 Which value (if any) in each pair corresponds to a faster reaction? Explain your choice.
a. $E_a = 10$ kcal or $E_a = 1$ kcal
b. $K = 10$ or $K = 100$
c. $\Delta H = -2$ kcal/mol or $\Delta H = +2$ kcal/mol

6.60 Which value (if any) in each pair corresponds to a faster reaction? Explain your choice.
a. $E_a = 0.10$ kcal or $E_a = 1$ kcal
b. $K = 10$ or $K = 0.001$
c. $\Delta H = -25$ kcal/mol or $\Delta H = -2$ kcal/mol

6.61 Which of the following affect the rate of a reaction: (a) K; (b) E_a; (c) temperature?

6.62 Which of the following affect the rate of a reaction: (a) concentration; (b) ΔH; (c) energy difference between the reactants and the transition state?

6.63 How does a catalyst affect each of the following: (a) reaction rate; (b) ΔH; (c) E_a; (d) K; (e) relative energy of the reactants and products?

6.64 What is the difference between a catalyst and an enzyme?

Equilibrium

6.65 What is the difference between the forward and reverse reactions?

6.66 What is the difference between a reversible reaction and the reverse reaction?

6.67 Given each value of the equilibrium constant, are the reactants or products favored at equilibrium?
a. $K = 5.2 \times 10^3$ c. $K = 0.002$
b. $\Delta H = -27$ kcal/mol   d. $\Delta H = +2$ kcal/mol

6.68 Given each value of the equilibrium constant, are the reactants or products favored at equilibrium?
a. $K = 5.2 \times 10^{-6}$ c. $K = 10,000$
b. $\Delta H = +16$ kcal/mol   d. $\Delta H = -21$ kcal/mol

6.69 How is the magnitude of K related to the sign of ΔH?

6.70 How are the sign and magnitude of ΔH affected by the presence of a catalyst?

6.71 Consider the reversible reaction $A \rightleftharpoons B$, and assume the reaction begins with pure **A**. Using red spheres for **A** and blue spheres for **B**, match each representation to one of the following equilibrium constants: [1] $K = 5$; [2] $K = 1$; [3] $K = 0.5$.

a.   b.   c.

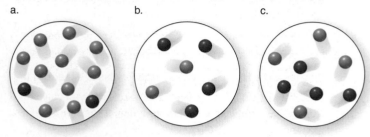

6.72 Consider the reversible reaction $A \rightleftharpoons B$, with $K = 0.1$. Assume the reaction begins with only **A**, and draw a representation using molecular art for the reaction mixture at equilibrium. Use red spheres for **A** and blue spheres for **B**.

6.73 Write an expression for the equilibrium constant for each reaction.
a. $2\,NO(g) + O_2(g) \rightleftharpoons 2\,NO_2(g)$
b. $CH_4(g) + 2\,Br_2(g) \rightleftharpoons CH_2Br_2(g) + 2\,HBr(g)$

6.74 Write an expression for the equilibrium constant for each reaction.
a. $HBr + H_2O \rightleftharpoons H_3O^+ + Br^-$
b. $2\,HCl(g) \rightleftharpoons H_2(g) + Cl_2(g)$

6.75 Use each expression for the equilibrium constant to write a chemical equation.
a. $K = \dfrac{[A_2]}{[A]^2}$ b. $K = \dfrac{[AB_3]^2}{[A_2][B_2]^3}$

6.76 Use each expression for the equilibrium constant to write a chemical equation.
a. $K = \dfrac{[AB_2]^2}{[A_2][B_2]^2}$ b. $K = \dfrac{[A_2B_3]}{[A]^2[B]^3}$

6.77 Consider the following reaction: $2\,HBr(g) \rightleftharpoons H_2(g) + Br_2(g)$ with $K = 5.3 \times 10^{-20}$.
a. Write the expression for the equilibrium constant for this reaction.
b. Are the reactants or products favored at equilibrium?
c. Would you predict ΔH to be positive or negative?
d. Are the reactants or products lower in energy?
e. Would you predict this reaction to be fast or slow? Explain your choice.

6.78 Consider the following reaction: $CO(g) + Cl_2(g) \rightleftharpoons COCl_2(g)$ with $K = 6.6 \times 10^{11}$.
a. Write the expression for the equilibrium constant for this reaction.
b. Are the reactants or products favored at equilibrium?
c. Would you predict ΔH to be positive or negative?
d. Are the reactants or products lower in energy?
e. Would you predict this reaction to be fast or slow? Explain your choice.

6.79 Consider the following reaction.

$$CO(g) + H_2O(g) \rightleftharpoons CO_2(g) + H_2(g)$$

a. Write the expression for the equilibrium constant.
b. Calculate K using the following concentrations of each substance at equilibrium: $[CO] = 0.090\ M$; $[H_2O] = 0.12\ M$; $[CO_2] = 0.15\ M$; $[H_2] = 0.30\ M$.

6.80 Consider the following reaction.

$$H_2(g) + I_2(g) \rightleftharpoons 2\,HI(g)$$

a. Write the expression for the equilibrium constant.
b. Calculate K using the following concentrations of each substance at equilibrium: $[H_2] = 0.95\ M$; $[I_2] = 0.78\ M$; $[HI] = 0.27\ M$.

Le Châtelier's Principle

6.81 Consider the reaction of $N_2(g) + O_2(g) \rightleftharpoons 2\,NO(g)$. What happens to the concentration of each substance when (a) $[O_2]$ is increased; (b) $[NO]$ is increased?

6.82 Consider the reaction of $H_2(g) + F_2(g) \rightleftharpoons 2\,HF(g)$. What happens to the concentration of each substance when (a) $[H_2]$ is decreased; (b) $[HF]$ is increased?

6.83 Consider the endothermic conversion of oxygen to ozone: $3\,O_2(g) \rightleftharpoons 2\,O_3(g)$. What effect does each of the following changes have on the direction of equilibrium?
a. decrease $[O_3]$ d. decrease temperature
b. decrease $[O_2]$ e. add a catalyst
c. increase $[O_3]$ f. increase pressure

6.84 Consider the exothermic reaction: $H_2(g) + I_2(g) \rightleftharpoons 2\,HI(g)$. What effect does each of the following changes have on the direction of equilibrium?
a. decrease $[HI]$ d. increase temperature
b. increase $[H_2]$ e. decrease temperature
c. decrease $[I_2]$ f. increase pressure

6.85 Consider the exothermic reaction: $C_2H_4(g) + Cl_2(g) \rightleftharpoons C_2H_4Cl_2(g)$. What effect does each of the following changes have on the direction of equilibrium?
a. increase $[C_2H_4]$ d. decrease pressure
b. decrease $[Cl_2]$ e. increase temperature
c. decrease $[C_2H_4Cl_2]$ f. decrease temperature

6.86 Consider the endothermic reaction: $2 NH_3(g) \rightleftharpoons$ $3 H_2(g) + N_2(g)$. What effect does each of the following changes have on the direction of equilibrium?

a. increase $[NH_3]$ d. increase temperature

b. decrease $[N_2]$ e. decrease temperature

c. increase $[H_2]$ f. increase pressure

General Problems

6.87 Consider the gas-phase reaction of ethylene ($CH_2\!=\!\!CH_2$) with hydrogen to form ethane (C_2H_6), which occurs in the presence of a palladium catalyst (Section 6.4B).

a. Write the expression for the equilibrium constant for this reaction.

b. If $\Delta H = -28$ kcal/mol, are the products or reactants higher in energy?

c. Which is likely to be true about the equilibrium constant for the reaction: $K > 1$ or $K < 1$?

d. How much energy is released when 20.0 g of ethylene reacts?

e. What happens to the rate of the reaction if the concentration of ethylene is increased?

f. What happens to the equilibrium when each of the following changes occurs: [1] an increase in $[H_2]$; [2] a decrease in $[C_2H_6]$; [3] an increase in temperature; [4] an increase in pressure; [5] removal of the palladium catalyst?

6.88 Methanol (CH_4O), which is used as a fuel in race cars, burns in oxygen (O_2) to form CO_2 and H_2O.

a. Write a balanced equation for this reaction.

b. Write the expression for the equilibrium constant for this reaction.

c. If $\Delta H = -174$ kcal/mol, are the products or reactants higher in energy?

d. How much energy is released when 10.0 g of methanol is burned?

e. Although this reaction is exothermic, the reaction is very slow unless a spark or flame initiates the reaction. Explain how this can be possible.

Applications

6.89 What is the role of lactase and why is it important in the human body?

6.90 How does a catalytic converter clean up automobile emissions?

6.91 A patient receives 2,000 mL of a glucose solution that contains 5 g of glucose in 100 mL. How many Calories does the glucose, a simple carbohydrate, contain?

6.92 The reaction of salicylic acid with acetic acid yields aspirin and water according to the given balanced equation. Since the equilibrium constant for this reaction is close to one, both reactants and products are present at equilibrium. If the reaction has a small negative value of ΔH, suggest ways that this equilibrium could be driven to the right to favor products.

$$C_7H_6O_3 \quad + \quad C_2H_4O_2 \quad \rightleftharpoons \quad C_9H_8O_4 \quad + \quad H_2O$$

salicylic acid   acetic acid   aspirin

6.93 Walking at a brisk pace burns off about 280 Cal/h. How long would you have to walk to burn off the Calories obtained from eating a cheeseburger that contained 32 g of protein, 29 g of fat, and 34 g of carbohydrates?

6.94 How many kilocalories does a runner expend when he runs for 4.5 h and uses 710 Cal/h? How many pieces of pizza that each contain 12 g of protein, 11 g of fat, and 30 g of carbohydrates could be eaten after the race to replenish these Calories?

6.95 The amount of energy released when a fuel burns is called its heat content. The heat content of fuels is often reported in kcal/g not kcal/mol so that fuels with different molar masses can be compared on a mass basis. The heat content of propane (C_3H_8), used as the fuel in gas grills, is 531 kcal/mol, while the heat content of butane (C_4H_{10}), used in lighters, is 688 kcal/mol. Show that the heat content of these two fuels is similar when converted to kcal/g.

6.96 One mole of ethanol (C_2H_6O) releases 327 kcal when burned, whereas one mole of hydrogen (H_2) releases only 68.4 kcal/mol. How many kcal/g are released when each of these fuels is burned? On a per gram basis, which substance would be a better source of energy?

CHALLENGE PROBLEMS

6.97 Let's assume that a gallon of gasoline contains pure octane (C_8H_{18}) and has a density of 0.700 g/mL. When octane is burned, it releases 1,303 kcal/mol of energy. How many kilocalories of energy are released from burning one gallon of gasoline?

6.98 An energy bar contains 4 g of fat, 12 g of protein, and 24 g of carbohydrates. How many kilojoules of energy are obtained from eating two bars per day for a month? Write the answer in scientific notation.

7

Scuba divers must carefully plan the depth and duration of their dives to avoid "the bends," a dangerous condition caused by the formation of nitrogen gas bubbles in the bloodstream.

Gases, Liquids, and Solids

CHAPTER GOALS

In this chapter you will learn how to:

1 Measure pressure and convert one unit of pressure to another

2 Describe the relationship between the pressure, volume, and temperature of a gas using gas laws

3 Describe the relationship between the volume and number of moles of a gas

4 Write the equation for the ideal gas law and use it in calculations

5 Use Dalton's law to determine the partial pressure and total pressure of a gas mixture

6 Determine the types of intermolecular forces in a compound, and how these forces determine a compound's boiling point and melting point

7 Describe the properties of a liquid, including vapor pressure, viscosity, and surface tension

8 Describe the features of different types of solids

9 Describe the energy changes that accompany changes of state

10 Interpret the changes depicted in heating and cooling curves

In Chapter 7 we study the properties of gases, liquids, and solids. Why is air pulled into the lungs when we expand our rib cage and diaphragm? Why does a lid pop off a container of food when it is heated in the microwave? Why does sweating cool down the body? To answer questions of this sort, we must understand the properties of the three states of matter, as well as the energy changes involved when one state is converted to another.

7.1 The Three States of Matter

As we first learned in Section 1.2, matter exists in three common states—**gas, liquid,** and **solid.**

- A gas consists of particles that are far apart and move rapidly and independently from each other.
- A liquid consists of particles that are much closer together but are still somewhat disorganized since they can move about. The particles in a liquid are close enough that they exert a force of attraction on each other.
- A solid consists of particles—atoms, molecules, or ions—that are close to each other and are often highly organized. The particles in a solid have little freedom of motion and are held together by attractive forces.

As shown in Figure 7.1, air is composed largely of N_2 and O_2 molecules, along with small amounts of argon (Ar), carbon dioxide (CO_2), and water molecules that move about rapidly. Liquid water is composed of H_2O molecules that have no particular organization. Sand is a solid composed of SiO_2, which contains a network of covalent silicon–oxygen bonds.

Figure 7.1   The Three States of Matter—Solid, Liquid, and Gas

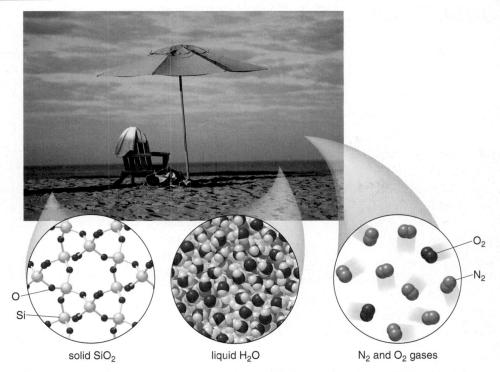

solid SiO_2 liquid H_2O N_2 and O_2 gases

Most sand is composed of silicon dioxide (SiO_2), which forms a three-dimensional network of covalent bonds. Liquid water is composed of H_2O molecules, which can move past each other but are held close together by a force of attraction (Section 7.7). Air contains primarily N_2 and O_2 molecules that move rapidly with no force of attraction for each other.

Whether a substance exists as a gas, liquid, or solid depends on the balance between the kinetic energy of its particles and the strength of the interactions between the particles. In a gas, the kinetic energy of motion is high and the particles are far apart from each other. As a result, the attractive forces between the molecules are negligible and gas molecules move freely. In a liquid, attractive forces hold the molecules much more closely together, so the distance between molecules and the kinetic energy is much less than the gas. In a solid, the attractive forces between molecules are even stronger, so the distance between individual particles is small and there is little freedom of motion. The properties of gases, liquids, and solids are summarized in Table 7.1.

Table 7.1 Properties of Gases, Liquids, and Solids

Property	Gas	Liquid	Solid
Shape and Volume	Expands to fill its container	A fixed volume that takes the shape of the container it occupies	A definite shape and volume
Arrangement of Particles	Randomly arranged, disorganized, and far apart	Randomly arranged but close	Fixed arrangement of very close particles
Density	Low (< 0.01 g/mL)	High (~1 g/mL)[a]	High (1–10 g/mL)
Particle Movement	Very fast	Moderate	Slow
Interaction Between Particles	None	Strong	Very strong

[a]The symbol "~" means approximately.

PROBLEM 7.1

How do gaseous, liquid, and solid methanol (CH_4O) compare in each of the following features: (a) density; (b) the space between the molecules; (c) the attractive force between the molecules?

7.2 Gases and Pressure

Anyone who has ridden a bike against the wind knows that even though we can't see the gas molecules of the air, we can feel them as we move through them.

Simple gases in the atmosphere—oxygen (O_2), carbon dioxide (CO_2), and ozone (O_3)—are vital to life. Oxygen, which constitutes 21% of the earth's atmosphere, is needed for metabolic processes that convert carbohydrates to energy. Green plants use carbon dioxide, a minor component of the atmosphere, to store the energy of the sun in the bonds of carbohydrate molecules during photosynthesis. Ozone forms a protective shield in the upper atmosphere to filter out harmful radiation from the sun, thus keeping it from the surface of the earth.

7.2A Properties of Gases

Helium, a noble gas composed of He atoms, and oxygen, a gas composed of diatomic O_2 molecules, behave differently in chemical reactions. Many of their properties, however, and the properties of all gases, can be explained by the **kinetic-molecular theory of gases,** a set of principles based on the following assumptions:

Figure 7.2

A Barometer—A Device for Measuring Atmospheric Pressure

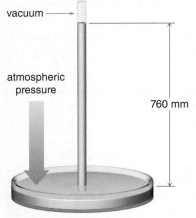

vacuum

atmospheric pressure

760 mm

mercury-filled dish

A barometer measures atmospheric pressure. Air pressure on the Hg in the dish pushes Hg up a sealed glass tube to a height that equals the atmospheric pressure.

- A gas consists of particles—atoms or molecules—that move randomly and rapidly.
- The size of gas particles is small compared to the space between the particles.
- Because the space between gas particles is large, gas particles exert no attractive forces on each other.
- The kinetic energy of gas particles increases with increasing temperature.
- When gas particles collide with each other, they rebound and travel in new directions. When gas particles collide with the walls of a container, they exert a pressure.

Because gas particles move rapidly, two gases mix together quickly. Moreover, when a gas is added to a container, the particles rapidly move to fill the entire container.

7.2B Gas Pressure

When many gas molecules strike a surface, they exert a measurable pressure. **Pressure (P) is the force (F) exerted per unit area (A).**

$$\text{Pressure} = \frac{\text{Force}}{\text{Area}} = \frac{F}{A}$$

All of the gases in the atmosphere collectively exert **atmospheric pressure** on the surface of the earth. The value of the atmospheric pressure varies with location, decreasing with increasing altitude. Atmospheric pressure also varies slightly from day to day, depending on the weather.

Atmospheric pressure is measured with a **barometer** (Figure 7.2). A barometer consists of a column of mercury (Hg) sealed at one end and inverted in a dish of mercury. The downward pressure exerted by the mercury in the column equals the atmospheric pressure on the mercury in the dish. Thus, the height of the mercury in the column measures the atmospheric pressure. Atmospheric pressure at sea level corresponds to a column of mercury 760. mm in height.

Many different units are used for pressure. The two most common units are the **atmosphere (atm),** and **millimeters of mercury (mm Hg),** where **1 atm = 760. mm Hg.** One millimeter of mercury is also called one **torr.** In the United States, the common pressure unit is **pounds per square inch (psi),** where **1 atm = 14.7 psi.** Pressure can also be measured in pascals (Pa), where 1 mm Hg = 133.32 Pa.

$$
\begin{aligned}
1\ \text{atm} &= 760.\ \text{mm Hg} \\
&= 760.\ \text{torr} \\
&= 14.7\ \text{psi} \\
&= 101{,}325\ \text{Pa}
\end{aligned}
$$

To convert a value from one pressure unit to another, set up conversion factors and use the method in Sample Problem 7.1.

SAMPLE PROBLEM 7.1

A scuba diver typically begins a dive with a compressed air tank at 3,000. psi. Convert this value to (a) atmospheres; (b) mm Hg.

Analysis

To solve each part, set up conversion factors that relate the two units under consideration. Use conversion factors that place the unwanted unit, psi, in the denominator to cancel.

A scuba diver's pressure gauge shows the amount of air (usually measured in psi) in his tank before and during a dive.

In part (a), the conversion factor must relate psi and atm:

psi–atm conversion factor

$$\frac{1\ \text{atm}}{14.7\ \text{psi}}$$

unwanted unit

In part (b), the conversion factor must relate psi and mm Hg:

psi–mm Hg conversion factor

$$\frac{760.\ \text{mm Hg}}{14.7\ \text{psi}}$$

unwanted unit

Solution

a. Convert the original unit (3,000. psi) to the desired unit (atm) using the conversion factor:

$$3000.\ \text{psi} \times \frac{1\ \text{atm}}{14.7\ \text{psi}} = 204\ \text{atm}$$

Answer

Psi cancels.

b. Convert the original unit (3,000. psi) to the desired unit (mm Hg) using the conversion factor:

$$3000.\ \text{psi} \times \frac{760.\ \text{mm Hg}}{14.7\ \text{psi}} = 155,000\ \text{mm Hg}$$

Answer

Psi cancels.

PROBLEM 7.2

Typical atmospheric pressure in Denver is 630 mm Hg. Convert this value to (a) atmospheres; (b) psi.

PROBLEM 7.3

Convert each pressure unit to the indicated unit.

a. 3.0 atm to mm Hg   b. 720 mm Hg to psi   c. 424 mm Hg to atm

7.2C FOCUS ON HEALTH & MEDICINE
Blood Pressure

Taking a patient's blood pressure is an important part of most physical examinations. Blood pressure measures the pressure in an artery of the upper arm using a device called a **sphygmomanometer.** A blood pressure reading consists of two numbers such as 120/80, where both values represent pressures in mm Hg. The higher number is the systolic pressure and refers to the maximum pressure in the artery right after the heart contracts. The lower number is the diastolic pressure and represents the minimum pressure when the heart muscle relaxes. A desirable systolic pressure is in the range of 100–120 mm Hg. A desirable diastolic pressure is in the range of 60–80 mm Hg. Figure 7.3 illustrates how a sphygmomanometer records pressure in a blood vessel.

Figure 7.3 Measuring Blood Pressure

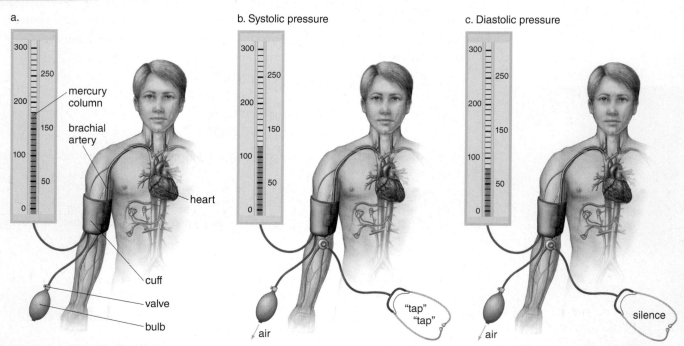

(a) To measure blood pressure, a cuff is inflated around the upper arm and a stethoscope is used to listen to the sound of blood flowing through the brachial artery. When the pressure in the cuff is high, it constricts the artery, so that no blood can flow to the lower arm. (b) Slowly the pressure in the cuff is decreased, and when it gets to the point that blood begins to spurt into the artery, a tapping sound is heard in the stethoscope. This value corresponds to the systolic blood pressure. (c) When the pressure in the cuff is further decreased, so that blood once again flows freely in the artery, the tapping sound disappears and the diastolic pressure is recorded.

When a patient's systolic pressure is routinely 140 mm Hg or greater or diastolic pressure is 90 mm Hg or greater, an individual is said to have **hypertension**—that is, high blood pressure. Consistently high blood pressure leads to increased risk of stroke and heart attacks. Many forms of hypertension can be controlled with medications such as propranolol (trade name Inderal, Problem 15.12).

PROBLEM 7.4

Convert both values in the blood pressure reading 120/80 to atmospheres.

7.3 Gas Laws That Relate Pressure, Volume, and Temperature

Four variables are important in discussing the behavior of gases—pressure (P), volume (V), temperature (T), and number of moles (n). The relationship of these variables is described by equations called **gas laws** that predict the behavior of all gases as conditions change. Three gas laws illustrate the interrelationship of pressure, volume, and temperature.

- Boyle's law relates pressure and volume.
- Charles's law relates volume and temperature.
- Gay–Lussac's law relates pressure and temperature.

7.3A Boyle's Law—How the Pressure and Volume of a Gas Are Related

Boyle's law describes how the volume of a gas changes as the pressure is changed.

- Boyle's law: For a fixed amount of gas at constant temperature, the pressure and volume of a gas are inversely related.

When two quantities are *inversely* related, one quantity *increases* as the other *decreases*. **The product of the two quantities, however, is a *constant*, symbolized by k.**

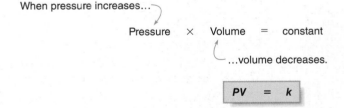

When pressure increases...

Pressure × Volume = constant

...volume decreases.

$$PV = k$$

Thus, if the volume of a cylinder of gas is halved, the pressure of the gas inside the cylinder doubles. **The same number of gas particles occupies half the volume and exerts two times the pressure.**

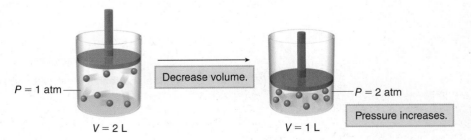

$P = 1$ atm

Decrease volume.

$P = 2$ atm

Pressure increases.

$V = 2$ L

$V = 1$ L

If we know the pressure and volume under an initial set of conditions (P_1 and V_1), we can calculate the pressure or volume under a different set of conditions (P_2 and V_2), since the product of pressure and volume is a constant.

$$\underset{\text{initial conditions}}{P_1V_1} = \underset{\text{new conditions}}{P_2V_2}$$

How To Use Boyle's Law to Calculate a New Gas Volume or Pressure

Example: If a 4.0-L container of helium gas has a pressure of 10.0 atm, what pressure does the gas exert if the volume is increased to 6.0 L?

Step [1] Identify the known quantities and the desired quantity.

- To solve an equation using Boyle's law, we must know three quantities and solve for one quantity. In this case P_1, V_1, and V_2 are known and the final pressure, P_2, must be determined.

$$P_1 = 10.0 \text{ atm}$$

$$\underset{\text{known quantities}}{V_1 = 4.0 \text{ L} \qquad V_2 = 6.0 \text{ L}} \qquad \underset{\text{desired quantity}}{P_2 = ?}$$

Step [2] Write the equation and rearrange it to isolate the desired quantity on one side.

- Rearrange the equation for Boyle's law so that the unknown quantity, P_2, is present alone on one side.

$$P_1V_1 = P_2V_2 \qquad \text{Solve for } P_2 \text{ by dividing both sides by } V_2.$$

$$\frac{P_1V_1}{V_2} = P_2$$

Step [3] Solve the problem.

- Substitute the known quantities into the equation and solve for P_2. Identical units must be used for two similar quantities (liters in this case) so that the units cancel.

$$P_2 = \frac{P_1V_1}{V_2} = \frac{(10.0 \text{ atm})(4.0 \cancel{L})}{6.0 \cancel{L}} = 6.7 \text{ atm}$$

Liters cancel. **Answer**

- In this example, the volume increased so the pressure decreased.

SAMPLE PROBLEM 7.2

A tank of compressed air for scuba diving contains 8.5 L of gas at 204 atm pressure. What volume of air does this gas occupy at 1.0 atm?

Analysis

Boyle's law can be used to solve this problem since an initial pressure and volume (P_1 and V_1) and a final pressure (P_2) are known, and a final volume (V_2) must be determined.

Solution

[1] Identify the known quantities and the desired quantity.

$$P_1 = 204 \text{ atm} \qquad P_2 = 1.0 \text{ atm}$$

$$\underset{\text{known quantities}}{V_1 = 8.5 \text{ L}} \qquad\qquad \underset{\text{desired quantity}}{V_2 = ?}$$

[2] Write the equation and rearrange it to isolate the desired quantity, V_2, on one side.

$$P_1V_1 = P_2V_2 \qquad \text{Solve for } V_2 \text{ by dividing both sides by } P_2.$$

$$\frac{P_1V_1}{P_2} = V_2$$

[3] Solve the problem.

• Substitute the three known quantities into the equation and solve for V_2.

$$V_2 \;=\; \frac{P_1V_1}{P_2} \;=\; \frac{(204 \text{ atm})(8.5 \text{ L})}{1.0 \text{ atm}} \;=\; 1{,}734 \text{ rounded to } 1{,}700 \text{ L}$$

Answer

Atm cancels.

• Thus, the volume increased because the pressure decreased.

PROBLEM 7.5

A sample of helium gas has a volume of 2.0 L at a pressure of 4.0 atm. What is the volume of gas at each of the following pressures?

a. 5.0 atm   b. 2.5 atm   c. 10.0 atm   d. 380 mm Hg

PROBLEM 7.6

A sample of nitrogen gas has a volume of 15.0 mL at a pressure of 0.50 atm. What is the pressure exerted by the gas if the volume is changed to each of the following values?

a. 30.0 mL   b. 5.0 mL   c. 100. mL   d. 1.0 L

Boyle's law explains how air is brought into or expelled from the lungs as the rib cage and diaphragm expand and contract when we breathe (Figure 7.4).

Figure 7.4   Focus on the Human Body: Boyle's Law and Breathing

a.

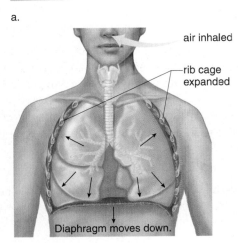

b.

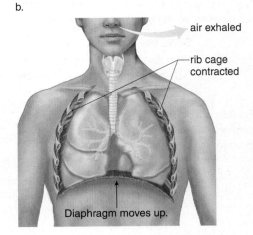

a. When an individual inhales, the rib cage expands and the diaphragm is lowered, thus increasing the volume of the lungs. According to Boyle's law, increasing the volume of the lungs decreases the pressure inside the lungs. The decrease in pressure draws air into the lungs.

b. When an individual exhales, the rib cage contracts and the diaphragm is raised, thus decreasing the volume of the lungs. Since the volume is now decreased, the pressure inside the lungs increases, causing air to be expelled into the surroundings.

7.3B   Charles's Law—How the Volume and Temperature of a Gas Are Related

All gases expand when they are heated and contract when they are cooled. Charles's law describes how the volume of a gas changes as the Kelvin temperature is changed.

• **Charles's law: For a fixed amount of gas at constant pressure, the volume of a gas is proportional to its Kelvin temperature.**

Volume and temperature are *proportional;* that is, as one quantity *increases,* the other *increases* as well. Thus, **dividing volume by temperature is a constant (*k*).**

$$\frac{V}{T} = k$$

Increasing the temperature increases the kinetic energy of the gas particles, and they move faster and spread out, thus occupying a larger volume. Note that **Kelvin temperature** must be used in calculations involving gas laws. Any temperature reported in °C or °F must be converted to kelvins (K) prior to carrying out the calculation.

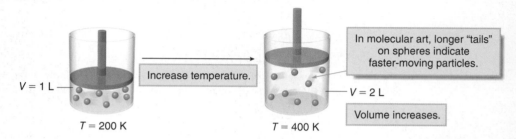

$V = 1$ L

Increase temperature.

In molecular art, longer "tails" on spheres indicate faster-moving particles.

$V = 2$ L

Volume increases.

$T = 200$ K $T = 400$ K

A hot air balloon illustrates Charles's law. Heating the air inside the balloon causes it to expand and fill the balloon. When the air inside the balloon becomes less dense than the surrounding air, the balloon rises.

Since dividing the volume of a gas by the temperature gives a constant, knowing the volume and temperature under an initial set of conditions (V_1 and T_1) means we can calculate the volume or temperature under another set of conditions (V_2 and T_2) when either volume or temperature is changed.

$$\frac{V_1}{T_1} = \frac{V_2}{T_2}$$

initial conditions   new conditions

To solve a problem of this sort, we follow the same three steps listed in the *How To* outlined in Section 7.3A, except we use the equation for Charles's law in step [2] in place of the equation for Boyle's law. This procedure is illustrated in Sample Problem 7.3.

Equations for converting one temperature unit to another are given in Section 1.9.

SAMPLE PROBLEM 7.3

A balloon that contains 0.50 L of air at 25 °C is cooled to –196 °C. What volume does the balloon now occupy?

Analysis

Since this question deals with volume and temperature, Charles's law is used to determine a final volume because three quantities are known—the initial volume and temperature (V_1 and T_1), and the final temperature (T_2).

Solution

[1] Identify the known quantities and the desired quantity.

$V_1 = 0.50$ L

$T_1 = 25$ °C $T_2 = -196$ °C $V_2 = $?

known quantities   desired quantity

- Both temperatures must be converted to Kelvin temperatures using the equation
  K = °C + 273.
- $T_1 = 25$ °C + 273 = 298 K
- $T_2 = -196$ °C + 273 = 77 K

[2] Write the equation and rearrange it to isolate the desired quantity, V_2, on one side.

- Use Charles's law.

$$\frac{V_1}{T_1} = \frac{V_2}{T_2} \qquad \text{Solve for } V_2 \text{ by multiplying both sides by } T_2.$$

$$\frac{V_1 T_2}{T_1} = V_2$$

[3] Solve the problem.

• Substitute the three known quantities into the equation and solve for V_2.

$$V_2 = \frac{V_1 T_2}{T_1} = \frac{(0.50\ \text{L})(77\ \text{K})}{298\ \text{K}} = 0.13\ \text{L}$$

Kelvins cancel.

Answer

• Since the temperature has decreased, the volume of gas must decrease as well.

PROBLEM 7.7

A volume of 0.50 L of air at 37 °C is expelled from the lungs into cold surroundings at 0.0 °C. What volume does the expelled air occupy at this temperature?

PROBLEM 7.8

(a) A volume (25.0 L) of gas at 45 K is heated to 450 K. What volume does the gas now occupy? (b) A volume (50.0 mL) of gas at 400. °C is cooled to 50. °C. What volume does the gas now occupy?

Charles's law can be used to explain how wind currents form at the beach (Figure 7.5). The air above land heats up faster than the air above water. As the temperature of the air above the land increases, the volume that it occupies increases; that is, the air expands, and as a result, its density decreases. This warmer, less dense air then rises, and the cooler denser air above the water moves toward the land as wind, filling the space left vacant by the warm, rising air.

Figure 7.5 Focus on the Environment: How Charles's Law Explains Wind Currents

The same number of air molecules occupy a smaller volume, giving cooler air a higher density.

Warmer air rising

Heated air expands (Charles's law), so its density decreases. The hot air rises.

to take warm air's place

Cooler air moving

Land

Sea

7.3C Gay–Lussac's Law—How the Pressure and Temperature of a Gas Are Related

Gay–Lussac's law describes how the pressure of a gas changes as the Kelvin temperature is changed.

• **Gay–Lussac's law:** For a fixed amount of gas at constant volume, the pressure of a gas is proportional to its Kelvin temperature.

Pressure and temperature are *proportional;* that is, as one quantity *increases*, the other *increases*. Thus, dividing the pressure by the temperature is a constant (*k*).

$$\frac{P}{T} = k$$

Increasing the temperature increases the kinetic energy of the gas particles, and if the volume is kept constant, the pressure exerted by the particles increases.

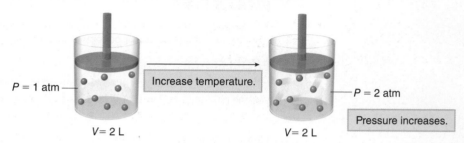

$P = 1$ atm — Increase temperature. — $P = 2$ atm

Pressure increases.

$V = 2$ L $V = 2$ L

Since dividing the pressure of a gas by the temperature gives a constant, knowing the pressure and Kelvin temperature under an initial set of conditions (P_1 and T_1) means we can calculate the pressure or temperature under another set of conditions (P_2 and T_2) when either pressure or temperature is changed.

$$\frac{P_1}{T_1} = \frac{P_2}{T_2}$$

initial conditions   new conditions

We solve this type of problem by following the same three steps in the *How To* in Section 7.3A, using the equation for Gay–Lussac's law in step [2].

SAMPLE PROBLEM 7.4

The tire on a bicycle stored in a cool garage at 18 °C had a pressure of 80. psi. What is the pressure inside the tire after riding the bike at 43 °C?

Analysis

Since this question deals with pressure and temperature, Gay–Lussac's law is used to determine a final pressure because three quantities are known—the initial pressure and temperature (P_1 and T_1), and the final temperature (T_2).

Solution

[1] Identify the known quantities and the desired quantity.

$$P_1 = 80. \text{ psi}$$

$$T_1 = 18 \text{ °C} \qquad T_2 = 43 \text{ °C} \qquad\qquad P_2 = ?$$

known quantities   desired quantity

- Both temperatures must be converted to Kelvin temperatures.
- $T_1 = \text{°C} + 273 = 18 \text{ °C} + 273 = 291 \text{ K}$
- $T_2 = \text{°C} + 273 = 43 \text{ °C} + 273 = 316 \text{ K}$

[2] Write the equation and rearrange it to isolate the desired quantity, P_2, on one side.

- Use Gay–Lussac's law. Since the initial pressure is reported in psi, the final pressure will be calculated in psi.

$$\frac{P_1}{T_1} = \frac{P_2}{T_2} \qquad \text{Solve for } P_2 \text{ by multiplying both sides by } T_2.$$

$$\frac{P_1 T_2}{T_1} = P_2$$

[3] Solve the problem.

- Substitute the three known quantities into the equation and solve for P_2.

$$P_2 = \frac{P_1 T_2}{T_1} = \frac{(80.\text{ psi})(316\text{ K})}{291\text{ K}} = 87\text{ psi}$$

Kelvins cancel.   **Answer**

- Since the temperature has increased, the pressure of the gas must increase as well.

PROBLEM 7.9

CONSUMER NOTE

A pressure cooker is used to cook food in a closed pot. By heating the contents of a pressure cooker at constant volume, the pressure increases. If the steam inside the pressure cooker is initially at 100. °C and 1.00 atm, what is the final temperature of the steam if the pressure is increased to 1.05 atm?

PROBLEM 7.10

The temperature of a 0.50-L gas sample at 25 °C and 1.00 atm is changed to each of the following temperatures. What is the final pressure of the system?

   a. 310. K   b. 150. K   c. 50. °C   d. 200. °C

PROBLEM 7.11

Use Gay–Lussac's law to answer the question posed at the beginning of the chapter: Why does a lid pop off a container of food when it is heated in a microwave?

7.3D The Combined Gas Law

All three gas laws—Boyle's, Charles's, and Gay–Lussac's laws—can be combined in a single equation, the **combined gas law,** that relates pressure, volume, and temperature.

$$\frac{P_1 V_1}{T_1} = \frac{P_2 V_2}{T_2}$$

initial conditions   new conditions

Food cooks faster in a pressure cooker because the reactions involved in cooking occur at a faster rate at a higher temperature.

The combined gas law contains six terms that relate the pressure, volume, and temperature of an initial and final state of a gas. It can be used to calculate one quantity when the other five are known, as long as the number of moles of gas (n) is constant. The combined gas law is used for determining the effect of changing two factors—such as pressure and temperature—on the third factor, volume.

We solve this type of problem by following the same three steps in the *How To* in Section 7.3A, using the equation for the combined gas law in step [2]. Sample Problem 7.5 shows how this is done. Table 7.2 summarizes the equations for the gas laws presented in Section 7.3.

SAMPLE PROBLEM 7.5

A weather balloon contains 222 L of helium at 20. °C and 760 mm Hg. What is the volume of the balloon when it ascends to an altitude where the temperature is −40. °C and the pressure is 540 mm Hg?

Analysis

Since this question deals with pressure, volume, and temperature, the combined gas law is used to determine a final volume (V_2) because five quantities are known—the initial pressure, volume, and temperature (P_1, V_1, and T_1), and the final pressure and temperature (P_2 and T_2).

Solution

[1] Identify the known quantities and the desired quantity.

$P_1 = 760$ mm Hg $P_2 = 540$ mm Hg

$T_1 = 20.$ °C $T_2 = -40.$ °C

$V_1 = 222$ L $V_2 = ?$

known quantities   desired quantity

- Both temperatures must be converted to Kelvin temperatures.
- $T_1 = °C + 273 = 20. °C + 273 = 293$ K
- $T_2 = °C + 273 = -40. °C + 273 = 233$ K

[2] Write the equation and rearrange it to isolate the desired quantity, V_2, on one side.

- Use the combined gas law.

$$\frac{P_1V_1}{T_1} = \frac{P_2V_2}{T_2} \quad \text{Solve for } V_2 \text{ by multiplying both sides by } \frac{T_2}{P_2}.$$

$$\frac{P_1V_1T_2}{T_1P_2} = V_2$$

[3] Solve the problem.

- Substitute the five known quantities into the equation and solve for V_2.

$$V_2 = \frac{P_1V_1T_2}{T_1P_2} = \frac{(760 \text{ mm Hg})(222 \text{ L})(233 \text{ K})}{(293 \text{ K})(540 \text{ mm Hg})} = 248.5 \text{ L rounded to } 250 \text{ L}$$

Answer

Kelvins and mm Hg cancel.

PROBLEM 7.12

The pressure inside a 1.0-L balloon at 25 °C was 750 mm Hg. What is the pressure inside the balloon when it is cooled to −40. °C and expands to 2.0 L in volume?

Table 7.2 Summary of the Gas Laws That Relate Pressure, Volume, and Temperature

Law	Equation	Relationship
Boyle's law	$P_1V_1 = P_2V_2$	As P increases, V decreases for constant T and n.
Charles's law	$\dfrac{V_1}{T_1} = \dfrac{V_2}{T_2}$	As T increases, V increases for constant P and n.
Gay–Lussac's law	$\dfrac{P_1}{T_1} = \dfrac{P_2}{T_2}$	As T increases, P increases for constant V and n.
Combined gas law	$\dfrac{P_1V_1}{T_1} = \dfrac{P_2V_2}{T_2}$	The combined gas law shows the relationship of P, V, and T when two quantities are changed and the number of moles (n) is constant.

7.4 Avogadro's Law—How Volume and Moles Are Related

Each equation in Section 7.3 was written for a constant amount of gas; that is, the number of moles (n) did not change. **Avogadro's law** describes the relationship between the number of moles of a gas and its volume.

- **Avogadro's law: When the pressure and temperature are held constant, the volume of a gas is proportional to the number of moles present.**

As the number of moles of a gas *increases*, its volume *increases* as well. Thus, dividing the volume by the number of moles is a constant (k). **The value of k is the same regardless of the identity of the gas.**

$$\frac{V}{n} = k$$

Thus, if the pressure and temperature of a system are held constant, **increasing the number of moles increases the volume of a gas.**

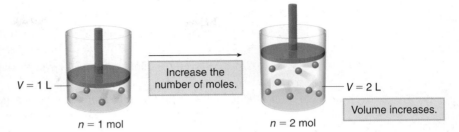

A balloon inflates when someone blows into it because the volume increases with an increased number of moles of air.

Since dividing the volume of a gas by the number of moles is a constant, knowing the volume and number of moles initially (V_1 and n_1) means we can calculate a new volume or number of moles (V_2 and n_2) when one of these quantities is changed.

$$\frac{V_1}{n_1} = \frac{V_2}{n_2}$$

initial conditions   new conditions

To solve a problem of this sort, we follow the same three steps listed in the *How To* outlined in Section 7.3A, using Avogadro's law in step [2].

SAMPLE PROBLEM 7.6

The lungs of an average male hold 0.25 mol of air in a volume of 5.8 L. How many moles of air do the lungs of an average female hold if the volume is 4.6 L?

Analysis

This question deals with volume and number of moles, so Avogadro's law is used to determine a final number of moles when three quantities are known—the initial volume and number of moles (V_1 and n_1), and the final volume (V_2).

Solution

[1] Identify the known quantities and the desired quantity.

$$V_1 = 5.8 \text{ L} \qquad\qquad V_2 = 4.6 \text{ L}$$
$$n_1 = 0.25 \text{ mol} \qquad\qquad\qquad n_2 = ?$$

known quantities   desired quantity

[2] Write the equation and rearrange it to isolate the desired quantity, n_2, on one side.

- Use Avogadro's law. To solve for n_2, we must invert the numerator and denominator on *both* sides of the equation, and then multiply by V_2.

$$\boxed{\frac{V_1}{n_1} = \frac{V_2}{n_2}}$$ Switch V and n on both sides. $\frac{n_1}{V_1} = \frac{n_2}{V_2}$ Solve for n_2 by multiplying both sides by V_2.

$$\frac{n_1 V_2}{V_1} = n_2$$

[3] Solve the problem.

- Substitute the three known quantities into the equation and solve for n_2.

$$n_2 = \frac{n_1 V_2}{V_1} = \frac{(0.25 \text{ mol})(4.6 \cancel{\text{ L}})}{(5.8 \cancel{\text{ L}})} = 0.20 \text{ mol}$$

Liters cancel. **Answer**

PROBLEM 7.13

A sample of nitrogen gas contains 5.0 mol in a volume of 3.5 L. Calculate the new volume of the container if the pressure and temperature are kept constant but the number of moles of nitrogen is changed to each of the following values: (a) 2.5 mol; (b) 3.65 mol; (c) 21.5 mol.

Avogadro's law allows us to compare the amounts of any two gases by comparing their volumes. Often amounts of gas are compared at a set of **standard conditions of temperature and pressure,** abbreviated as **STP.**

> • STP conditions are: 1 atm (760 mm Hg) for pressure
>   273 K (0 °C) for temperature
> • At STP, one mole of any gas has the same volume, 22.4 L, called the *standard molar volume.*

Under STP conditions, one mole of nitrogen gas and one mole of helium gas each contain 6.02×10^{23} molecules of gas and occupy a volume of 22.4 L at 0 °C and 1 atm pressure. Since the molar masses of nitrogen and helium are different (28.0 g for N_2 compared to 4.0 g for He), one mole of each substance has a *different* mass.

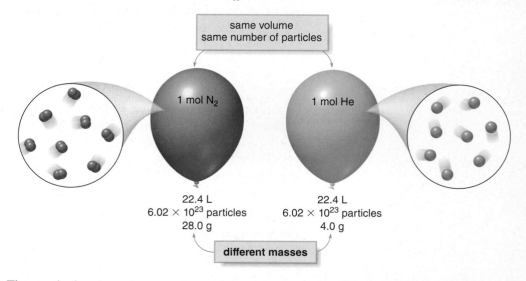

The standard molar volume can be used to set up conversion factors that relate the volume and number of moles of a gas at STP, as shown in the following stepwise procedure.

How To Convert Moles of Gas to Volume at STP

Example: How many moles are contained in 2.0 L of N_2 at standard temperature and pressure?

Step [1] **Identify the known quantities and the desired quantity.**

$$2.0 \text{ L of } N_2 \qquad\qquad ? \text{ moles of } N_2$$

original quantity   desired quantity

Step [2] **Write out the conversion factors.**
- Set up conversion factors that relate the number of moles of a gas to volume at STP. Choose the conversion factor that places the unwanted unit, liters, in the denominator so that the units cancel.

$$\frac{22.4 \text{ L}}{1 \text{ mol}} \quad \text{or} \quad \boxed{\frac{1 \text{ mol}}{22.4 \text{ L}}}$$

Choose this conversion factor to cancel L.

Step [3] **Solve the problem.**
- Multiply the original quantity by the conversion factor to obtain the desired quantity.

$$2.0 \, \cancel{\text{L}} \quad \times \quad \frac{1 \text{ mol}}{22.4 \, \cancel{\text{L}}} \quad = \quad 0.089 \text{ mol of } N_2$$

Liters cancel.   **Answer**

By using the molar mass of a gas, we can determine the volume of a gas from a given number of grams, as shown in Sample Problem 7.7.

SAMPLE PROBLEM 7.7

Burning one mole of propane in a gas grill adds 132 g of carbon dioxide (CO_2) to the atmosphere. What volume of CO_2 does this correspond to at STP?

Analysis

To solve this problem, we must convert the number of grams of CO_2 to moles using the molar mass. The number of moles of CO_2 can then be converted to its volume using a mole–volume conversion factor (1 mol/22.4 L).

Solution

[1] Identify the known quantities and the desired quantity.

132 g CO_2 ? L CO_2

known quantity   desired quantity

[2] Convert the number of grams of CO_2 to the number of moles of CO_2 using the molar mass.

molar mass conversion factor

$$132 \text{ g } CO_2 \times \frac{1 \text{ mol } CO_2}{44.01 \text{ g } CO_2} = 3.00 \text{ mol } CO_2$$

Grams cancel.

[3] Convert the number of moles of CO_2 to the volume of CO_2 using a mole–volume conversion factor.

mole–volume conversion factor

$$3.00 \text{ mol } CO_2 \times \frac{22.4 \text{ L}}{1 \text{ mol}} = 67.2 \text{ L } CO_2$$

Moles cancel.   **Answer**

PROBLEM 7.14

How many liters does each of the following quantities of O_2 occupy at STP: (a) 4.5 mol; (b) 0.35 mol; (c) 18.0 g?

PROBLEM 7.15

How many moles are contained in the following volumes of air at STP: (a) 1.5 L; (b) 8.5 L; (c) 25 mL?

7.5 The Ideal Gas Law

All four properties of gases—pressure, volume, temperature, and number of moles—can be combined into a single equation called the **ideal gas law.** The product of pressure and volume divided by the product of moles and Kelvin temperature is a constant, called the **universal gas constant** and symbolized by R.

$$\frac{PV}{nT} = R \quad \text{universal gas constant}$$

More often the equation is rearranged and written in the following way:

$$PV = nRT$$

Ideal gas law

For atm: R = $0.0821 \dfrac{\text{L} \cdot \text{atm}}{\text{mol} \cdot \text{K}}$

For mm Hg: R = $62.4 \dfrac{\text{L} \cdot \text{mm Hg}}{\text{mol} \cdot \text{K}}$

The value of the universal gas constant R depends on its units. The two most common values of R are given using atmospheres or mm Hg for pressure, liters for volume, and kelvins for temperature. **Be careful to use the correct value of R for the pressure units in the problem you are solving.**

The ideal gas law can be used to find any value—P, V, n, or T—as long as three of the quantities are known. Solving a problem using the ideal gas law is shown in the stepwise *How To* procedure and in Sample Problem 7.8. Although the ideal gas law gives exact answers only for a perfectly "ideal" gas, it gives a good approximation for most real gases, such as the oxygen and carbon dioxide in breathing, as well (Figure 7.6).

Figure 7.6   Focus on the Human Body: The Lungs

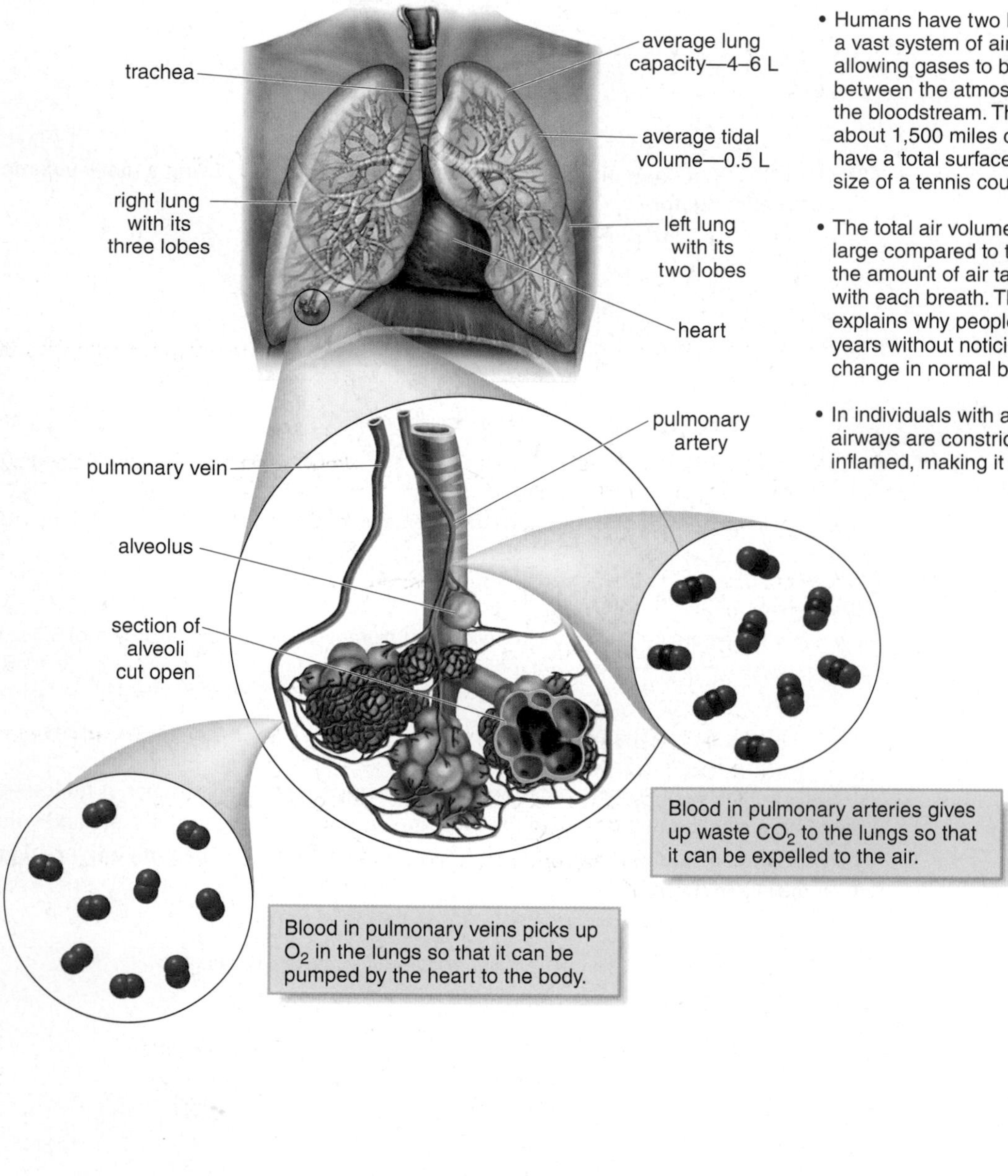

- trachea
- right lung with its three lobes
- average lung capacity—4–6 L
- average tidal volume—0.5 L
- left lung with its two lobes
- heart
- pulmonary vein
- alveolus
- section of alveoli cut open
- pulmonary artery

- Humans have two lungs that contain a vast system of air passages, allowing gases to be exchanged between the atmosphere and with the bloodstream. The lungs contain about 1,500 miles of airways that have a total surface area about the size of a tennis court.

- The total air volume of the lungs is large compared to the tidal volume, the amount of air taken in or expelled with each breath. This large reserve explains why people can smoke for years without noticing any significant change in normal breathing.

- In individuals with asthma, small airways are constricted and inflamed, making it difficult to breathe.

Blood in pulmonary arteries gives up waste CO_2 to the lungs so that it can be expelled to the air.

Blood in pulmonary veins picks up O_2 in the lungs so that it can be pumped by the heart to the body.

How To Carry Out Calculations with the Ideal Gas Law

Example: How many moles of gas are contained in a typical human breath that takes in 0.50 L of air at 1.0 atm pressure and 37 °C?

Step [1] Identify the known quantities and the desired quantity.

$$P = 1.0 \text{ atm}$$
$$V = 0.50 \text{ L}$$
$$T = 37 \text{ °C} \qquad\qquad n = ? \text{ mol}$$

known quantities   desired quantity

Step [2] Convert all values to proper units and choose the value of R that contains these units.
- Convert °C to K. K = °C + 273 = 37 °C + 273 = 310. K
- Use the value of R in atm since the pressure is given in atm; that is, $R = 0.0821 \text{ L} \cdot \text{atm}/(\text{mol} \cdot \text{K})$.

Step [3] Write the equation and rearrange it to isolate the desired quantity on one side.
- Use the ideal gas law and solve for n by dividing both sides by RT.

$$PV \quad = \quad nRT \qquad \text{Solve for } n \text{ by dividing both sides by } RT.$$

$$\frac{PV}{RT} \quad = \quad n$$

Step [4] Solve the problem.
- Substitute the known quantities into the equation and solve for n.

$$n \quad = \quad \frac{PV}{RT} \quad = \quad \frac{(1.0 \text{ atm})(0.50 \text{ L})}{\left(0.0821 \dfrac{\text{L} \cdot \text{atm}}{\text{mol} \cdot \text{K}}\right)(310. \text{ K})} \quad = \quad 0.0196 \text{ rounded to } 0.020 \text{ mol}$$

Answer

SAMPLE PROBLEM 7.8

If a person exhales 25.0 g of CO_2 in an hour, what volume does this amount occupy at 1.00 atm and 37 °C?

Analysis

Use the ideal gas law to calculate V, since P and T are known and n can be determined by using the molar mass of CO_2 (44.01 g/mol).

Solution

[1] Identify the known quantities and the desired quantity.

$$P = 1.00 \text{ atm}$$
$$T = 37 \text{ °C} \qquad 25.0 \text{ g } CO_2 \qquad\qquad V = ? \text{ L}$$

known quantities   desired quantity

[2] Convert all values to proper units and choose the value of R that contains these units.
- Convert °C to K. K = °C + 273 = 37 °C + 273 = 310. K
- Use the value of R with atm since the pressure is given in atm; that is, $R = 0.0821 \text{ L} \cdot \text{atm}/(\text{mol} \cdot \text{K})$.
- Convert the number of grams of CO_2 to the number of moles of CO_2 using the molar mass (44.01 g/mol).

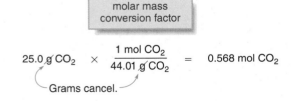

$$25.0 \text{ g } CO_2 \quad \times \quad \frac{1 \text{ mol } CO_2}{44.01 \text{ g } CO_2} \quad = \quad 0.568 \text{ mol } CO_2$$

Grams cancel.

[3] **Write the equation and rearrange it to isolate the desired quantity, *V*, on one side.**

- Use the ideal gas law and solve for *V* by dividing both sides by *P*.

$$PV = nRT \qquad \text{Solve for } V \text{ by dividing both sides by } P.$$

$$V = \frac{nRT}{P}$$

[4] **Solve the problem.**

- Substitute the three known quantities into the equation and solve for *V*.

$$V = \frac{nRT}{P} = \frac{(0.568 \text{ mol})\left(0.0821 \ \dfrac{\text{L} \cdot \text{atm}}{\text{mol} \cdot \text{K}}\right)(310. \text{ K})}{1.0 \text{ atm}} = 14.5 \text{ L}$$

Answer

PROBLEM 7.16

How many moles of oxygen (O_2) are contained in a 5.0-L cylinder that has a pressure of 175 atm and a temperature of 20. °C?

PROBLEM 7.17

Determine the pressure of N_2 under each of the following conditions.

  a. 0.45 mol at 25 °C in 10.0 L   b. 10.0 g at 20. °C in 5.0 L

7.6 Dalton's Law and Partial Pressures

Since gas particles are very far apart compared to the size of an individual particle, gas particles behave independently. As a result, the identity of the components of a gas mixture does not matter, and **a mixture of gases behaves like a pure gas.** Each component of a gas mixture is said to exert a pressure called its **partial pressure. Dalton's law** describes the relationship between the partial pressures of the components and the total pressure of a gas mixture.

- Dalton's law: The *total pressure* (P_{total}) of a gas mixture is the sum of the partial pressures of its component gases.

Since the partial pressure of O_2 is low at very high altitudes, most mountain climbers use supplemental O_2 tanks above about 24,000 ft.

Thus, if a mixture has two gases (**A** and **B**) with partial pressures P_A and P_B, respectively, the total pressure of the system (P_{total}) is the sum of the two partial pressures. The partial pressure of a component of a mixture is the same pressure that the gas would exert if it were a pure gas.

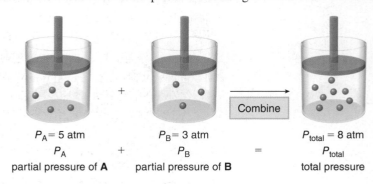

$P_A = 5$ atm		$P_B = 3$ atm		$P_{total} = 8$ atm
P_A	+	P_B	=	P_{total}
partial pressure of **A**		partial pressure of **B**		total pressure

SAMPLE PROBLEM 7.9

A sample of exhaled air from the lungs contains four gases with the following partial pressures: N_2 (563 mm Hg), O_2 (118 mm Hg), CO_2 (30. mm Hg), and H_2O (50. mm Hg). What is the total pressure of the sample?

Analysis

Using Dalton's law, the total pressure is the sum of the partial pressures.

Solution

Adding up the four partial pressures gives the total:

$$563 + 118 + 30. + 50. = 761 \text{ mm Hg (total pressure)}$$

PROBLEM 7.18

CO_2 was added to a cylinder containing 2.5 atm of O_2 to give a total pressure of 4.0 atm of gas. What is the partial pressure of O_2 and CO_2 in the final mixture?

We can also calculate the partial pressure of each gas in a mixture if two quantities are known—[1] the total pressure and [2] the percent of each component—as shown in Sample Problem 7.10.

SAMPLE PROBLEM 7.10

Air is a mixture of 21% O_2, 78% N_2, and 1% argon by volume. What is the partial pressure of each gas at sea level, where the total pressure is 760 mm Hg?

Analysis

Convert each percent to a decimal by moving the decimal point two places to the left. Multiply each decimal by the total pressure to obtain the partial pressure for each component.

Solution

		Partial pressure
Fraction O_2:	21% = 0.21	0.21 × 760 mm Hg = 160 mm Hg (O_2)
Fraction N_2:	78% = 0.78	0.78 × 760 mm Hg = 590 mm Hg (N_2)
Fraction Ar:	1% = 0.01	0.01 × 760 mm Hg = $\underline{\quad 8 \text{ mm Hg (Ar)} \quad}$
		758 rounded to 760 mm Hg

PROBLEM 7.19

A sample of natural gas at 750 mm Hg contains 85% methane, 10.% ethane, and 5.0% propane. What are the partial pressures of each gas in this mixture?

HEALTH NOTE

The high pressures of a hyperbaric chamber can be used to treat patients fighting infections and scuba divers suffering from the bends.

The composition of the atmosphere does not change with location, even though the total atmospheric pressure decreases with increasing altitude. At high altitudes, therefore, the partial pressure of oxygen is much lower than it is at sea level, making breathing difficult. This is why mountain climbers use supplemental oxygen at altitudes above 8,000 meters.

In contrast, a hyperbaric chamber is a device that maintains air pressure two to three times higher than normal. Hyperbaric chambers have many uses. At this higher pressure the partial pressure of O_2 is higher. For burn patients, the higher pressure of O_2 increases the amount of O_2 in the blood, where it can be used by the body for reactions that fight infections.

When a scuba diver surfaces too quickly, the N_2 dissolved in the blood can form microscopic bubbles that cause pain in joints and can occlude small blood vessels, causing organ injury. This condition, called the bends, is treated by placing a diver in a hyperbaric chamber, where the elevated pressure decreases the size of the N_2 bubbles, which are then eliminated as N_2 gas from the lungs as the pressure is slowly decreased.

PROBLEM 7.20

In which hyperbaric chamber is the pressure due to O_2 higher: chamber **A** with pure O_2 at 2.5 atm pressure, or chamber **B,** which has a total pressure of 5.5 atm and contains 40.% O_2?

7.7 Intermolecular Forces, Boiling Point, and Melting Point

Unlike gases, the behavior of liquids and solids cannot be described by a set of laws that can be applied regardless of the identity of the substance. Since liquids and solids are composed of particles that are much closer together, **a force of attraction exists between them.**

Ionic compounds are composed of extensive arrays of oppositely charged ions that are held together by strong electrostatic interactions. These ionic interactions are much stronger than the forces between covalent molecules, so it takes a great deal of energy to separate ions from each other (Section 3.5).

In covalent compounds, the nature and strength of the attraction between individual molecules depend on the identity of the atoms.

> • Intermolecular forces are the attractive forces that exist *between* molecules.

There are three different types of intermolecular forces in covalent molecules, presented in order of *increasing strength:*

> • London dispersion forces
> • Dipole–dipole interactions
> • Hydrogen bonding

The strength of the intermolecular forces determines whether a compound has a high or low melting point and boiling point, and thus if the compound is a solid, liquid, or gas at a given temperature.

7.7A London Dispersion Forces

> • London dispersion forces are very weak interactions due to the momentary changes in electron density in a molecule.

For example, although a nonpolar methane molecule (CH_4) has no net dipole, at any one instant its electron density may not be completely symmetrical. If more electron density is present in one region of the molecule, less electron density must be present some place else, and this creates a *temporary* dipole. A temporary dipole in one CH_4 molecule induces a temporary dipole in another CH_4 molecule, with the partial positive and negative charges arranged close to each other. **The weak interaction between these temporary dipoles constitutes London dispersion forces.**

London dispersion forces can also be called van der Waals forces.

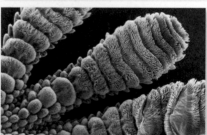

Although any single interaction is weak, a large number of London dispersion forces creates a strong force. For example, geckos stick to walls and ceilings by London dispersion forces between the surfaces and the 500,000 tiny hairs on each foot.

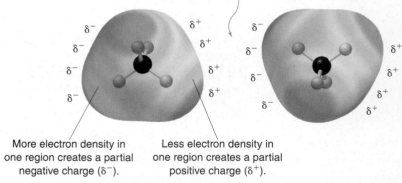

London dispersion force between two CH_4 molecules

More electron density in one region creates a partial negative charge (δ^-).

Less electron density in one region creates a partial positive charge (δ^+).

All **covalent compounds exhibit London dispersion forces.** These intermolecular forces are the only intermolecular forces present in nonpolar compounds. The strength of these forces is related to the size of the molecule.

> • The larger the molecule, the larger the attractive force between two molecules, and the stronger the intermolecular forces.

PROBLEM 7.21

Which of the following compounds exhibit London dispersion forces: (a) NH_3; (b) H_2O; (c) HCl; (d) ethane (C_2H_6)?

7.7B Dipole–Dipole Interactions

How to determine whether a molecule is polar is shown in Section 4.8.

> • Dipole–dipole interactions are the attractive forces between the permanent dipoles of two polar molecules.

For example, the carbon–oxygen bond in formaldehyde, $H_2C{=}O$, is polar because oxygen is more electronegative than carbon. This polar bond gives formaldehyde a permanent dipole, making it a polar molecule. The dipoles in adjacent formaldehyde molecules can align so that the partial positive and partial negative charges are close to each other. These attractive forces due to permanent dipoles are much stronger than London dispersion forces.

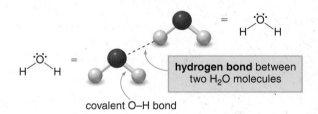

formaldehyde

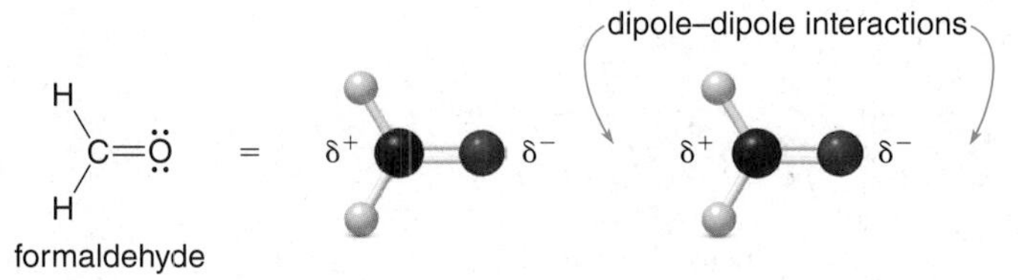

PROBLEM 7.22

Draw the individual dipoles of two H—Cl molecules and show how the dipoles are aligned in a dipole–dipole interaction.

7.7C Hydrogen Bonding

> • Hydrogen bonding occurs when a hydrogen atom bonded to O, N, or F is electrostatically attracted to an O, N, or F atom in another molecule.

hydrogen bond between two H_2O molecules

covalent O–H bond

Hydrogen bonding is only possible between two molecules that contain a hydrogen atom bonded to a very electronegative atom—that is, oxygen, nitrogen, or fluorine. For example, two H_2O molecules can hydrogen bond to each other: a hydrogen atom is covalently bonded to oxygen in one water molecule, and hydrogen-bonded to an oxygen atom in another water molecule. **Hydrogen bonds are the strongest of the three types of intermolecular forces.** Table 7.3 summarizes the three types of intermolecular forces.

Hydrogen bonding is important in many biological molecules, including proteins and DNA. DNA, which is contained in the chromosomes of the nucleus of a cell, is responsible for the storage of all genetic information. DNA is composed of two long strands of atoms that are held together by hydrogen bonding as shown in Figure 7.7. A detailed discussion of DNA appears in Chapter 22.

Table 7.3 Summary of the Types of Intermolecular Forces

Type of Force	Relative Strength	Exhibited by	Example
London dispersion	Weak	All molecules	CH_4, H_2CO, H_2O
Dipole–dipole	Moderate	Molecules with a net dipole	H_2CO, H_2O
Hydrogen bonding	Strong	Molecules with an O—H, N—H, or H—F bond	H_2O

Figure 7.7

Hydrogen Bonding and DNA

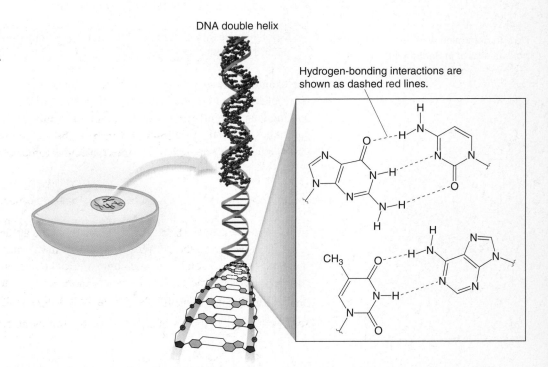

DNA double helix

Hydrogen-bonding interactions are shown as dashed red lines.

DNA is composed of two long strands of atoms that wind around each other in an arrangement called a double helix. The two strands are held together by an extensive network of hydrogen bonds. In each hydrogen bond, an H atom of an N—H bond on one chain is intermolecularly hydrogen bonded to an oxygen or nitrogen atom on an adjacent chain. Five hydrogen bonds are indicated.

SAMPLE PROBLEM 7.11

What types of intermolecular forces are present in each compound: (a) HCl; (b) C_2H_6 (ethane); (c) NH_3?

Analysis

- London dispersion forces are present in all covalent compounds.
- Dipole–dipole interactions are present only in polar compounds with a permanent dipole.
- Hydrogen bonding occurs only in compounds that contain an O—H, N—H, or H—F bond.

Solution

a.

polar bond

$\overset{\delta^+}{H}-\overset{\delta^-}{Cl}$

- HCl has London forces like all covalent compounds.
- HCl has a polar bond, so it exhibits dipole–dipole interactions.
- HCl has no H atom on an O, N, or F, so it has no intermolecular hydrogen bonding.

b.

nonpolar molecule

- C_2H_6 is a nonpolar molecule since it has only nonpolar C—C and C—H bonds. Thus, it exhibits only London forces.

c.

- NH_3 has London forces like all covalent compounds.
- NH_3 has a net dipole from its three polar bonds (Section 4.8), so it exhibits dipole–dipole interactions.
- NH_3 has a H atom bonded to N, so it exhibits intermolecular hydrogen bonding.

PROBLEM 7.23

What types of intermolecular forces are present in each molecule?

a. Cl_2 b. HCN   c. HF   d. CH_3Cl e. H_2

PROBLEM 7.24

Which of the compounds in each pair has stronger intermolecular forces?

a. CO_2 or H_2O b. CO_2 or HBr   c. HBr or H_2O d. CH_4 or C_2H_6

7.7D Boiling Point and Melting Point

The **boiling point (bp)** of a compound is the temperature at which a liquid is converted to the gas phase, while the **melting point (mp)** is the temperature at which a solid is converted to the liquid phase. The strength of the intermolecular forces determines the boiling point and melting point of compounds.

- The *stronger* the intermolecular forces, the *higher* the boiling point and melting point.

In boiling, energy must be supplied to overcome the attractive forces of the liquid state and separate the molecules to the gas phase. Similarly, in melting, energy must be supplied to overcome the highly ordered solid state and convert it to the less ordered liquid phase. A stronger force of attraction between molecules means that more energy must be supplied to overcome those intermolecular forces, increasing the boiling point and melting point.

In comparing compounds of similar size, the following trend is observed:

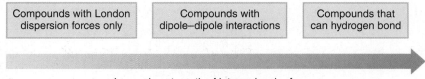

| Compounds with London dispersion forces only | Compounds with dipole–dipole interactions | Compounds that can hydrogen bond |

Increasing strength of intermolecular forces
Increasing boiling point
Increasing melting point

Methane (CH_4) and water (H_2O) are both small molecules with hydrogen atoms bonded to a second-row element, so you might expect them to have similar melting points and boiling points. Methane, however, is a nonpolar molecule that exhibits only London dispersion forces, whereas water is a polar molecule that can form intermolecular hydrogen bonds. As a result, the melting point and boiling point of water are *much higher* than those of methane. In fact, the hydrogen bonds in water are so strong that it is a liquid at room temperature, whereas methane is a gas.

methane

London forces only
bp = −162 °C
mp = −183 °C

water

hydrogen bonding
bp = 100 °C ← stronger forces
mp = 0 °C ← higher bp and mp

In comparing two compounds with similar types of intermolecular forces, the higher molecular weight compound generally has more surface area and therefore a larger force of attraction, giving it the higher boiling point and melting point. Thus, propane (C_3H_8) and butane (C_4H_{10}) have only nonpolar bonds and London forces, but butane is larger and therefore has the higher boiling point and melting point.

propane

bp $= -42\,°C$
mp $= -190\,°C$

butane

bp $= -0.5\,°C$
mp $= -138\,°C$

larger molecule
stronger forces
higher bp and mp

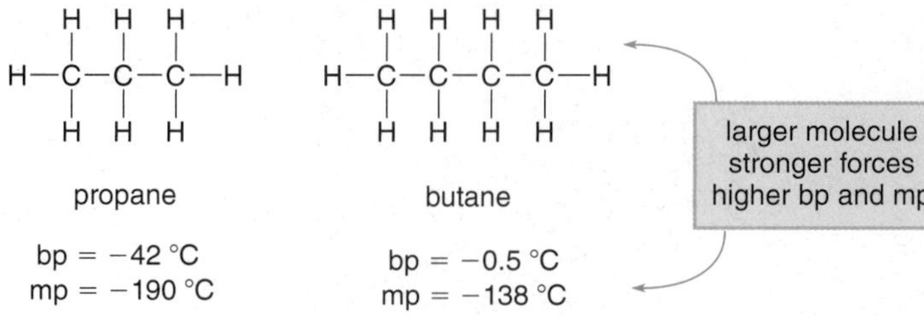

SAMPLE PROBLEM 7.12

(a) Which compound, **A** or **B,** has the higher boiling point? (b) Which compound, **C** or **D,** has the higher melting point?

NH_3

ammonia

A

CH_4

methane

B

methanol

C

chloromethane

D

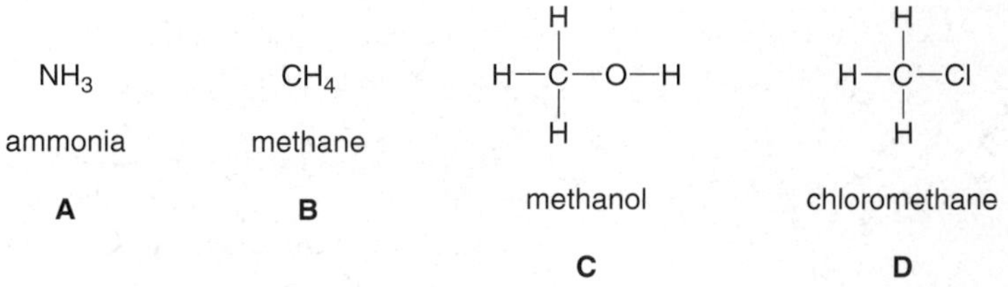

Analysis

Determine the types of intermolecular forces in each compound. The compound with the stronger forces has the higher boiling point or melting point.

Solution

a. NH_3 (**A**) has an N—H bond, so it exhibits intermolecular hydrogen bonding. CH_4 (**B**) has only London forces since it has only nonpolar C—H bonds. NH_3 has stronger forces and the higher boiling point.

b. Methanol (**C**) has an O—H bond, so it can intermolecularly hydrogen bond. Chloromethane (**D**) has a polar C—Cl bond, so it has dipole–dipole interactions, but it cannot hydrogen bond. **C** has stronger forces, so **C** has the higher melting point.

PROBLEM 7.25

Which compound in each pair has the higher boiling point? Which compound in each pair has the higher melting point?

a. CH_4 or C_2H_6 b. C_2H_6 or CH_3OH c. HBr or HCl   d. C_2H_6 or CH_3Br

PROBLEM 7.26

Explain why CO_2 is a gas at room temperature but H_2O is a liquid.

7.8   The Liquid State

Since liquid molecules are much closer together than gas molecules, many properties of a liquid are determined by the strength of its intermolecular forces. The molecules in a liquid are still much more mobile than those of a solid, though, making liquids fluid and giving them no definite shape. Some liquid molecules move fast enough that they escape the liquid phase altogether and become gas molecules that are very far apart from each other.

HEALTH NOTE

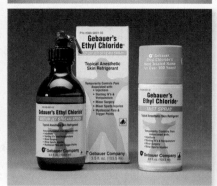

Chloroethane (CH_3CH_2Cl), commonly called ethyl chloride, is a local anesthetic. When chloroethane is sprayed on a wound it quickly evaporates, causing a cooling sensation that numbs the site of an injury.

7.8A   Vapor Pressure

When a liquid is placed in an open container, liquid molecules near the surface that have enough kinetic energy to overcome the intermolecular forces escape to the gas phase. This process, **evaporation,** will continue until all of the liquid has become gas. A puddle of water formed after a rainstorm evaporates as all of the liquid water is converted to gas molecules called water **vapor. Evaporation is an** *endothermic* **process**—it absorbs heat from the surroundings. This explains why the skin is cooled as sweat evaporates.

evaporation

In a closed container, some liquid molecules evaporate from the surface and enter the gas phase. As more molecules accumulate in the gas phase, some molecules re-enter the liquid phase in the process of **condensation. Condensation is an** *exothermic* **process**—it gives off heat to the surroundings. At equilibrium, the rate of evaporation and the rate of condensation are equal.

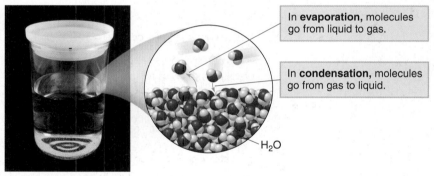

In **evaporation,** molecules go from liquid to gas.

In **condensation,** molecules go from gas to liquid.

H_2O

liquid in a closed container

The gas laws we have already learned can describe the behavior of the gas molecules above a liquid. In particular, these gas molecules exert pressure, called **vapor pressure.**

- Vapor pressure is the pressure exerted by gas molecules in equilibrium with the liquid phase.

The vapor pressure exerted by a particular liquid depends on the identity of the liquid and the temperature. As the temperature is increased, the kinetic energy of the molecules increases and more molecules escape into the gas phase.

- Vapor pressure increases with increasing temperature.

When the temperature is high enough that the vapor pressure above the liquid equals the atmospheric pressure, even molecules below the surface of the liquid have enough kinetic energy to enter the gas phase and the liquid boils. **The** *normal boiling point* **of a liquid is the temperature at which its vapor pressure equals 760 mm Hg.**

The boiling point depends on the atmospheric pressure. At the lower atmospheric pressure of higher altitudes, a liquid has a lower boiling point because the vapor pressure above the liquid equals the atmospheric pressure at a lower temperature. In Denver, Colorado (elevation 1,609 m or 5,280 ft), where atmospheric pressure is typically 630 mm Hg, water boils at 93 °C.

How is the strength of the intermolecular forces related to the vapor pressure? The stronger the intermolecular forces, the less readily a compound escapes from the liquid to the gas phase. Thus,

- **The stronger the intermolecular forces, the lower the vapor pressure at a given temperature.**

Compounds with strong intermolecular forces have high boiling points and low vapor pressures at a given temperature. In Section 7.7 we learned that water has a *higher* boiling point than methane (CH_4) because water can hydrogen bond while methane cannot. At any given temperature, water has a *lower* vapor pressure because its molecules are held more tightly and remain in the liquid phase.

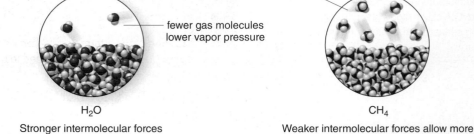

more gas molecules
higher vapor pressure

fewer gas molecules
lower vapor pressure

H_2O

CH_4

Stronger intermolecular forces
keep the H_2O molecules as a liquid.

Weaker intermolecular forces allow more
CH_4 molecules to escape to the gas phase.

SAMPLE PROBLEM 7.13

Which compound, H_2O or H_2S, has the higher boiling point? Which compound has the higher vapor pressure at a given temperature?

Analysis

Determine which compound has the stronger intermolecular forces. Stronger forces mean a higher boiling point and a lower vapor pressure.

Solution

Since H_2O contains an O atom bonded to H, H_2O exhibits hydrogen bonding, the strongest of the intermolecular forces. H_2S has no hydrogen bonding since it has no hydrogen bonded to O, N, or F. The stronger intermolecular forces in H_2O give it a higher boiling point. The weaker intermolecular forces in H_2S mean that the molecules escape into the gas phase more readily, giving H_2S the higher vapor pressure.

PROBLEM 7.27

Which molecule in each pair has the higher vapor pressure at a given temperature?

a. CH_4 or NH_3 b. CH_4 or C_2H_6 c. C_2H_6 or CH_3OH

PROBLEM 7.28

Explain why you feel cool when you get out of a swimming pool, even when the air temperature is quite warm. Then explain why the water feels warmer when you get back into the swimming pool.

7.8B Viscosity and Surface Tension

Viscosity and surface tension are two more properties of liquids that can be explained at least in part by the strength of the intermolecular forces.

***Viscosity* is a measure of a fluid's resistance to flow freely.** A viscous liquid is one that feels "thicker." Compounds with stronger intermolecular forces tend to be more viscous than

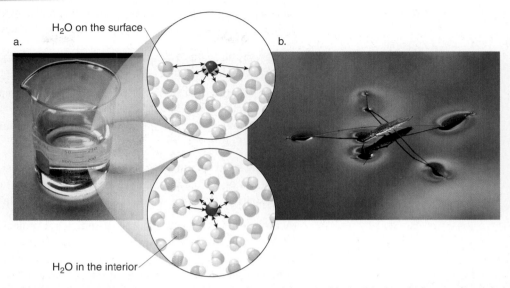

Figure 7.8 Surface Tension

H$_2$O on the surface

a.

b.

H$_2$O in the interior

(a) Interior molecules experience intermolecular forces (shown with double-headed arrows) evenly in all directions, whereas surface molecules experience uneven interactions and are pulled downward towards the interior. (b) Water's high surface tension allows a water strider to walk on the surface.

compounds with weaker forces. Thus water is more viscous than gasoline, which is composed of nonpolar molecules with weak intermolecular forces. The size of molecules also plays a role. Large molecules do not slide past each other as freely, so substances composed of large molecules tend to be more viscous. Olive oil, for example, is more viscous than water because olive oil is composed of compounds with three long floppy chains that contain more than 50 atoms in each chain.

Surface tension **is a measure of the resistance of a liquid to spread out.** Molecules in the interior of a liquid are surrounded by intermolecular forces on all sides, making them more stable than surface molecules that only experience intermolecular forces from neighbors on the side and below [Figure 7.8a]. This makes surface molecules less stable. **The *stronger* the intermolecular forces, the stronger surface molecules are pulled down toward the interior of a liquid and the *higher* the surface tension.** Because water has strong intermolecular hydrogen bonding, its surface tension is high. This explains why water striders can walk across the surface [Figure 7.8b], and why a paper clip can "float" on water.

PROBLEM 7.29

Explain why benzene is less viscous than water, but ethylene glycol is more viscous than water.

benzene   ethylene glycol

PROBLEM 7.30

Would you predict the surface tension of gasoline, composed of molecules containing only carbon and hydrogen atoms, to be higher or lower than the surface tension of water?

7.9 The Solid State

When a liquid is cooled so that the intermolecular forces are stronger than the kinetic energy of the particles, a solid is formed. Solids can be either **crystalline** or **amorphous.**

- A crystalline solid has a regular arrangement of particles—atoms, molecules, or ions—with a repeating structure.
- An amorphous solid has no regular arrangement of its closely packed particles.

There are four different types of crystalline solids—**ionic, molecular, network,** and **metallic**—as shown in Figure 7.9.

An **ionic solid** is composed of oppositely charged ions. For example, sodium chloride, NaCl, is composed of Na^+ cations and Cl^- anions, arranged so that each Na^+ cation is surrounded by six Cl^- anions and each Cl^- anion is surrounded by six Na^+ cations.

A **molecular solid** is composed of individual molecules arranged regularly. Ice, for example, contains a hexagonal arrangement of water molecules that are extensively hydrogen bonded to each other. In fact, the crystalline structure of water accounts for one of its unique properties. Water is one of the few substances whose solid phase is *less* dense than its liquid phase. As a result, solid ice floats on liquid water. A sheet of ice freezes on top of a lake, allowing plant and animal life to survive beneath the surface.

A **network solid** is composed of a vast number of atoms covalently bonded together, forming sheets or three-dimensional arrays. Quartz sand, SiO_2, contains an infinite network of silicon and oxygen atoms. Each silicon atom is bonded to four oxygen atoms and each oxygen is bonded to two silicon atoms, so that there are twice as many oxygen atoms as silicon. Other examples include diamond and graphite, two elemental forms of carbon, whose structures appeared in Figure 2.6.

Since metals are atoms that readily give up their electrons, a **metallic solid** such as copper or silver can be thought of as a lattice of metal cations surrounded by a cloud of electrons that move freely. Because of their loosely held, delocalized electrons, metals conduct electricity and heat.

Figure 7.9 Four Examples of Crystalline Solids

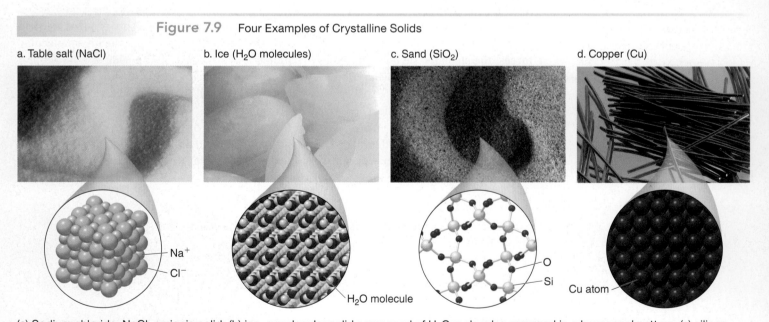

a. Table salt (NaCl) b. Ice (H_2O molecules) c. Sand (SiO_2) d. Copper (Cu)

Na^+
Cl^-

H_2O molecule

O
Si

Cu atom

(a) Sodium chloride, NaCl, an ionic solid; (b) ice, a molecular solid composed of H_2O molecules arranged in a hexagonal pattern; (c) silicon dioxide, SiO_2, a network solid that comprises sand; (d) metallic copper.

A polycarbonate helmet, polyethylene water bottle, and rubber tires are all examples of amorphous solids.

In contrast to crystalline solids, **amorphous solids have no regular arrangement of particles.** Amorphous solids can be formed when a liquid cools too quickly to allow the regular crystalline pattern to form. Substances composed of very large strands of covalent molecules also tend to form amorphous solids, because the chains can become folded and intertwined, making an organized regular arrangement impossible. Examples of amorphous solids include rubber, glass, and most plastics.

PROBLEM 7.31

Which type of crystalline solid is formed by each substance: (a) $CaCl_2$; (b) Fe (iron); (c) sugar $(C_{12}H_{22}O_{11})$; (d) $NH_3(s)$?

7.10 Energy and Phase Changes

In Section 7.7 we learned how the strength of intermolecular forces in a liquid and solid affect a compound's boiling point and melting point. Let's now look in more detail at the energy changes that occur during phase changes.

7.10A Converting a Solid to a Liquid

Converting a solid to a liquid is called *melting*. Melting is an *endothermic* process. Energy must be absorbed to overcome some of the attractive intermolecular forces that hold the organized solid molecules together to form the more random liquid phase. The amount of energy needed to melt 1 g of a substance is called its **heat of fusion.**

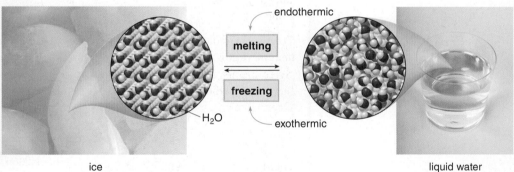

ice   liquid water

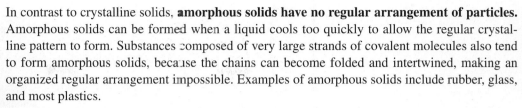

When an ice cube is added to a liquid at room temperature, the ice cube melts. The energy needed for melting is "pulled" from the warmer liquid molecules and the liquid cools down.

Freezing is the opposite of melting; that is, ***freezing* converts a liquid to a solid.** Freezing is an *exothermic* process because energy is released as the faster moving liquid molecules form an organized solid in which particles have little freedom of motion. For a given mass of a particular substance, the amount of energy released in freezing is the same as the amount of energy absorbed during melting.

Heats of fusion are reported in calories per gram (cal/g). A heat of fusion can be used as a conversion factor to determine how much energy is absorbed when a particular amount of a substance melts, as shown in Sample Problem 7.14.

SAMPLE PROBLEM 7.14

How much energy in calories is absorbed when 50.0 g of ice cubes melt? The heat of fusion of H_2O is 79.7 cal/g.

Analysis

Use the heat of fusion as a conversion factor to determine the amount of energy absorbed in melting.

Solution

[1] Identify the original quantity and the desired quantity.

50.0 g   ? calories

original quantity   desired quantity

[2] Write out the conversion factors.

- Use the heat of fusion as a conversion factor to convert grams to calories.

g–cal conversion factors

$$\frac{1\text{ g}}{79.7\text{ cal}} \quad \text{or} \quad \boxed{\frac{79.7\text{ cal}}{1\text{ g}}} \quad \begin{array}{l}\text{Choose this conversion factor}\\ \text{to cancel the unwanted unit, g.}\end{array}$$

[3] Solve the problem.

$$50.0\text{ g} \quad \times \quad \frac{79.7\text{ cal}}{1\text{ g}} \quad = \quad 3{,}985\text{ cal rounded to } 3{,}990\text{ cal}$$

Grams cancel.

Answer

PROBLEM 7.32

Use the heat of fusion of water from Sample Problem 7.14 to answer each question.

a. How much energy in calories is released when 50.0 g of water freezes?
b. How much energy in calories is absorbed when 35.0 g of water melts?
c. How much energy in kilocalories is absorbed when 35.0 g of water melts?
d. How much energy in calories is absorbed when 1.00 mol of water melts?

7.10B Converting a Liquid to a Gas

Converting a liquid to a gas is called *vaporization.* Vaporization is an *endothermic* process. Energy must be absorbed to overcome the attractive intermolecular forces of the liquid phase to form gas molecules. The amount of energy needed to vaporize 1 g of a substance is called its **heat of vaporization.**

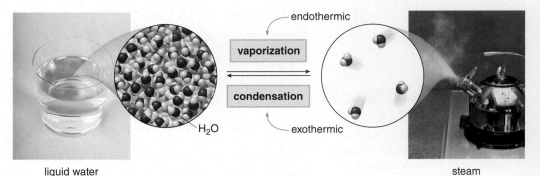

liquid water　　　　　　　　　　　　　　　　　　　　　　　　　　　　　　steam

Condensation is the opposite of vaporization; that is, *condensation* **converts a gas to a liquid.** Condensation is an *exothermic* process because energy is released as the faster moving gas molecules form the more organized liquid phase. For a given mass of a particular substance, the amount of energy released in condensation equals the amount of energy absorbed during vaporization.

Heats of vaporization are reported in calories per gram (cal/g). A high heat of vaporization means that a substance absorbs a great deal of energy as it is converted from a liquid to a gas. **Water has a high heat of vaporization.** As a result, the evaporation of sweat from the skin is a very effective cooling mechanism for the body. The heat of vaporization can be used as a conversion factor to determine how much energy is absorbed when a particular amount of a substance vaporizes, as shown in Sample Problem 7.15.

SAMPLE PROBLEM 7.15

How much heat in kilocalories is absorbed when 22.0 g of 2-propanol, rubbing alcohol, evaporates after being rubbed on the skin? The heat of vaporization of 2-propanol is 159 cal/g.

Analysis

Use the heat of vaporization to convert grams to an energy unit, calories. Calories must also be converted to kilocalories using a cal–kcal conversion factor.

Solution

[1] Identify the original quantity and the desired quantity.

$$22.0 \text{ g} \qquad\qquad ? \text{ kilocalories}$$

original quantity   desired quantity

[2] Write out the conversion factors.

- We have no conversion factor that relates grams and kilocalories directly. We do know, however, how to relate grams to calories using the heat of vaporization, and calories to kilocalories.

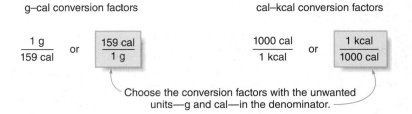

g–cal conversion factors   cal–kcal conversion factors

$$\frac{1 \text{ g}}{159 \text{ cal}} \quad \text{or} \quad \boxed{\frac{159 \text{ cal}}{1 \text{ g}}} \qquad\qquad \frac{1000 \text{ cal}}{1 \text{ kcal}} \quad \text{or} \quad \boxed{\frac{1 \text{ kcal}}{1000 \text{ cal}}}$$

Choose the conversion factors with the unwanted units—g and cal—in the denominator.

[3] Solve the problem.

$$22.0 \text{ g} \quad \times \quad \frac{159 \text{ cal}}{1 \text{ g}} \quad \times \quad \frac{1 \text{ kcal}}{1000 \text{ cal}} \quad = \quad 3.50 \text{ kcal}$$

Grams cancel.   Calories cancel.   **Answer**

PROBLEM 7.33

Answer the following questions about water, which has a heat of vaporization of 540 cal/g.

- a. How much energy in calories is absorbed when 42 g of water is vaporized?
- b. How much energy in calories is released when 42 g of water is condensed?
- c. How much energy in kilocalories is absorbed when 1.00 mol of water is vaporized?
- d. How much energy in kilocalories is absorbed when 3.5 mol of water is vaporized?

7.10C Converting a Solid to a Gas

Occasionally a solid phase forms a gas phase without passing through the liquid state. This process is called **sublimation.** The reverse process, conversion of a gas directly to a solid, is called **deposition.** Carbon dioxide is called *dry ice* because solid carbon dioxide (CO_2) sublimes to gaseous CO_2 without forming liquid CO_2.

CONSUMER NOTE

Freeze-drying removes water from foods by the process of sublimation. These products can be stored almost indefinitely, since bacteria cannot grow in them without water.

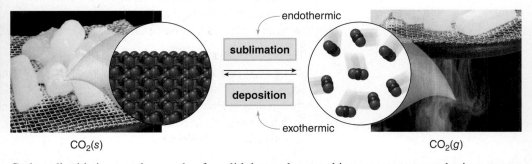

$CO_2(s)$ $CO_2(g)$

Carbon dioxide is a good example of a solid that undergoes this process at atmospheric pressure. At reduced pressure other substances sublime. For example, freeze-dried foods are prepared by subliming water from a food product at low pressure.

Table 7.4 summarizes the phase changes in Section 7.10.

Table 7.4 Summary of Energy and Phase Changes

Process	Phases	Energy Change
Melting	Solid ⟶ liquid	Endothermic process—Energy is absorbed.
Freezing	Liquid ⟶ solid	Exothermic process—Energy is released.
Vaporization	Liquid ⟶ gas	Endothermic process—Energy is absorbed.
Condensation	Gas ⟶ liquid	Exothermic process—Energy is released.
Sublimation	Solid ⟶ gas	Endothermic process—Energy is absorbed.
Deposition	Gas ⟶ solid	Exothermic process—Energy is released.

SAMPLE PROBLEM 7.16

Is the process depicted in the molecular art endothermic or exothermic?

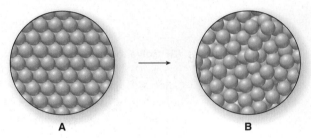

A   B

Analysis

Identify the phase by the distance between the spheres and their level of organization. A solid has closely packed spheres that are well organized; a liquid has closely packed but randomly arranged spheres; a gas has randomly arranged spheres that are far apart. Then, classify the transformation as melting, freezing, vaporization, condensation, sublimation, or deposition, depending on the phases depicted.

Solution

A represents a solid and **B** represents a liquid, so the molecular art represents melting. Melting is an endothermic process because energy must be absorbed to convert the more ordered solid state to the less ordered liquid state.

PROBLEM 7.34

Is the process depicted in the molecular art endothermic or exothermic?

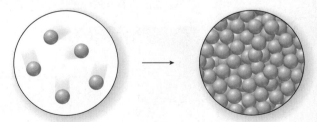

7.11 Heating and Cooling Curves

The changes of state described in Section 7.10 can be illustrated on a single graph called a **heating curve.** A heating curve shows how the temperature of a substance (plotted on the vertical axis) changes as heat is *added*. A general heating curve is shown in Figure 7.10.

Figure 7.10

Heating Curve

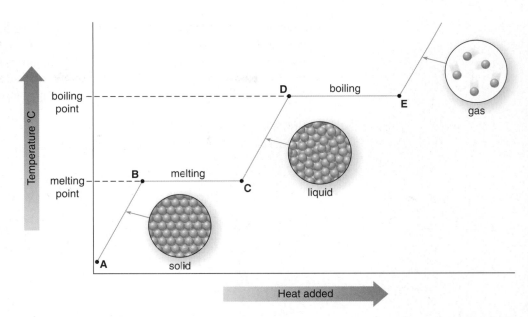

A heating curve shows how the temperature of a substance changes as heat is added. The plateau **B** ⟶ **C** occurs at the melting point, while the plateau **D** ⟶ **E** occurs at the boiling point.

A solid is present at point **A.** As the solid is heated it increases in temperature until its melting point is reached at **B.** More heat causes the solid to melt to a liquid, without increasing its temperature (the plateau from **B** ⟶ **C**). Added heat increases the temperature of the liquid until its boiling point is reached at **D.** More heat causes the liquid to boil to form a gas, without increasing its temperature (the plateau from **D** ⟶ **E**). Additional heat then increases the temperature of the gas. Each diagonal line corresponds to the presence of a single phase—solid, liquid, or gas—while horizontal lines correspond to phase changes—solid to liquid or liquid to gas.

A **cooling curve** illustrates how the temperature of a substance (plotted on the vertical axis) changes as heat is *removed*. A cooling curve for water is shown in Figure 7.11.

Figure 7.11

Cooling Curve for Water

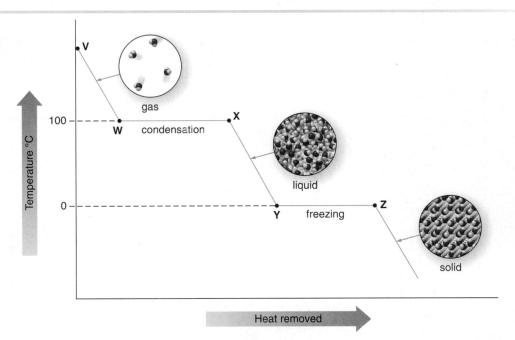

The cooling curve shows how the temperature of water changes as heat is removed. The plateau **W** ⟶ **X** occurs at the boiling point, while the plateau **Y** ⟶ **Z** occurs at the freezing point.

Gaseous water is present at point **V.** As the gas is cooled it decreases in temperature until its boiling point is reached at **W.** Condensation at 100 °C forms liquid water, represented by the plateau from **W** → **X.** Further cooling of the liquid water takes place until its freezing point (melting point) is reached at **Y.** Freezing water forms ice at 0 °C, represented by the plateau from **Y** → **Z.** Cooling the ice further decreases its temperature below its freezing point.

PROBLEM 7.35

Answer the following questions about the graph.

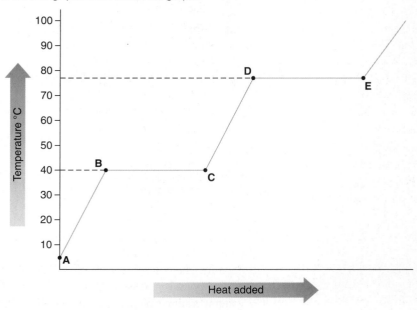

a. Does the graph illustrate a heating curve or a cooling curve?

b. What is the melting point of the substance?

c. What is the boiling point of the substance?

d. What phase(s) are present at plateau **B** → **C?**

e. What phase(s) are present along the diagonal **C** → **D?**

PROBLEM 7.36

If the substance shown in the heating curve in Figure 7.10 has a melting point of 50 °C and a boiling point of 75 °C, what state or states of matter are present at each temperature?

a. 85 °C   b. 50 °C   c. 65 °C   d. 10 °C   e. 75 °C

CHAPTER HIGHLIGHTS

KEY TERMS

Amorphous solid (7.9)

Atmosphere (7.2)

Avogadro's law (7.4)

Barometer (7.2)

Boiling point (bp, 7.7)

Boyle's law (7.3)

Charles's law (7.3)

Combined gas law (7.3)

Condensation (7.8, 7.10)

Cooling curve (7.11)

Crystalline solid (7.9)

Dalton's law (7.6)

Deposition (7.10)

Dipole–dipole interactions (7.7)

Evaporation (7.8)

Freezing (7.10)

Gas laws (7.3)

Gay–Lussac's law (7.3)

Heating curve (7.11)

Heat of fusion (7.10)

Heat of vaporization (7.10)

Hydrogen bonding (7.7)

Ideal gas law (7.5)

Intermolecular forces (7.7)

Ionic solid (7.9)

Kinetic-molecular theory (7.2)

London dispersion forces (7.7)

Melting (7.10)

Melting point (mp, 7.7)

Metallic solid (7.9)

Millimeters of mercury (7.2)

Molecular solid (7.9)

Network solid (7.9)

Normal boiling point (7.8)

Partial pressure (7.6)

Pressure (7.2)

Standard molar volume (7.4)

STP (7.4)

Sublimation (7.10)

Surface tension (7.8)

Universal gas constant (7.5)

Vapor (7.8)

Vapor pressure (7.8)

Vaporization (7.10)

Viscosity (7.8)

KEY CONCEPTS

❶ What is pressure and what units are used to measure it? (7.2)

- Pressure is the force per unit area. The pressure of a gas is the force exerted when gas particles strike a surface. Pressure is measured by a barometer and recorded in atmospheres (atm), millimeters of mercury (mm Hg), or pounds per square inch (psi).
- 1 atm = 760 mm Hg = 14.7 psi.

❷ What are gas laws and how are they used to describe the relationship between the pressure, volume, and temperature of a gas? (7.3)

- Because gas particles are far apart and behave independently, a set of gas laws describes the behavior of all gases regardless of their identity. Three gas laws—Boyle's law, Charles's law, and Gay–Lussac's law—describe the relationship between the pressure, volume, and temperature of a gas. These gas laws are summarized in "Key Equations— The Gas Laws" on page 234.
- For a constant amount of gas, the following relationships exist.
  - The pressure and volume of a gas are inversely related, so increasing the pressure decreases the volume at constant temperature.
  - The volume of a gas is proportional to its Kelvin temperature, so increasing the temperature increases the volume at constant pressure.
  - The pressure of a gas is proportional to its Kelvin temperature, so increasing the temperature increases the pressure at constant volume.

❸ Describe the relationship between the volume and number of moles of a gas. (7.4)

- Avogadro's law states that when temperature and pressure are held constant, the volume of a gas is proportional to its number of moles.
- One mole of any gas has the same volume, the standard molar volume of 22.4 L, at 1 atm and 273 K (STP).

❹ What is the ideal gas law? (7.5)

- The ideal gas law is an equation that relates the pressure (P), volume (V), temperature (T), and number of moles (n) of a gas; $PV = nRT$, where R is the universal gas constant. The ideal gas law can be used to calculate any one of the four variables, as long as the other three variables are known.

❺ What is Dalton's law and how is it used to relate partial pressures and the total pressure of a gas mixture? (7.6)

- Dalton's law states that the total pressure of a gas mixture is the sum of the partial pressures of its component gases. The partial pressure is the pressure exerted by each component of a mixture.

❻ What types of intermolecular forces exist and how do they determine a compound's boiling point and melting point? (7.7)

- Intermolecular forces are the forces of attraction between molecules. Three types of intermolecular forces exist in covalent compounds. London dispersion forces are due to momentary changes in electron density in a molecule. Dipole–dipole interactions are due to permanent dipoles. Hydrogen bonding, the strongest intermolecular force, results when a H atom bonded to an O, N, or F, is attracted to an O, N, or F atom in another molecule.
- The stronger the intermolecular forces, the higher the boiling point and melting point of a compound.

7 Describe three features of the liquid state—vapor pressure, viscosity, and surface tension. (7.8)

- Vapor pressure is the pressure exerted by gas molecules in equilibrium with the liquid phase. Vapor pressure increases with increasing temperature. The higher the vapor pressure at a given temperature, the lower the boiling point of a compound.
- Viscosity measures a liquid's resistance to flow. More viscous compounds tend to have stronger intermolecular forces or they have high molecular weights.
- Surface tension measures a liquid's resistance to spreading out. The stronger the intermolecular forces, the higher the surface tension.

8 Describe the features of different types of solids. (7.9)

- Solids can be amorphous or crystalline. An amorphous solid has no regular arrangement of particles. A crystalline solid has a regular arrangement of particles in a repeating pattern. There are four types of crystalline solids. Ionic solids are composed of ions. Molecular solids are composed of individual molecules. Network solids are composed of vast repeating arrays of covalently bonded atoms in a regular three-dimensional arrangement. Metallic solids are composed of metal cations with a cloud of delocalized electrons.

9 Describe the energy changes that accompany changes of state. (7.10)

- A phase change converts one state to another. Energy is absorbed when a more organized state is converted to a less organized state. Thus, energy is absorbed when a solid melts to form a liquid, or when a liquid vaporizes to form a gas.
- Energy is released when a less organized state is converted to a more organized state. Thus, energy is released when a gas condenses to form a liquid, or a liquid freezes to form a solid.
- The heat of fusion is the energy needed to melt 1 g of a substance, while the heat of vaporization is the energy needed to vaporize 1 g of a substance.

10 What changes are depicted on heating and cooling curves? (7.11)

- A heating curve shows how the temperature of a substance changes as heat is added. Diagonal lines show the temperature increase of a single phase. Horizontal lines correspond to phase changes—solid to liquid or liquid to gas.
- A cooling curve shows how the temperature of a substance changes as heat is removed. Diagonal lines show the temperature decrease of a single phase. Horizontal lines correspond to phase changes—gas to liquid or liquid to solid.

KEY EQUATIONS—THE GAS LAWS

Name	Equation	Variables Related	Constant Terms
Boyle's law	$P_1V_1 = P_2V_2$	P, V	T, n
Charles's law	$\dfrac{V_1}{T_1} = \dfrac{V_2}{T_2}$	V, T	P, n
Gay–Lussac's law	$\dfrac{P_1}{T_1} = \dfrac{P_2}{T_2}$	P, T	V, n
Combined gas law	$\dfrac{P_1V_1}{T_1} = \dfrac{P_2V_2}{T_2}$	P, V, T	n
Avogadro's law	$\dfrac{V_1}{n_1} = \dfrac{V_2}{n_2}$	V, n	P, T
Ideal gas law	$PV = nRT$	P, V, T, n	R

PROBLEMS

Selected in-chapter and odd-numbered end-of-chapter problems have brief answers in Appendix B. The *Student Study Guide and Solutions Manual* contains detailed solutions to all in-chapter and odd-numbered end-of-chapter problems, as well as additional worked examples and a chapter self-test.

Pressure

7.37 The highest atmospheric pressure ever measured is 814.3 mm Hg, recorded in Mongolia in December, 2001. Convert this value to atmospheres.

7.38 The lowest atmospheric pressure ever measured is 652.5 mm Hg, recorded during Typhoon Tip on October 12, 1979. Convert this value to atmospheres.

7.39 Convert each quantity to the indicated unit.
   a. 2.8 atm to psi
   b. 520 mm Hg to atm
   c. 20.0 atm to torr
   d. 100. mm Hg to Pa

7.40 The compressed air tank of a scuba diver reads 3,200 psi at the beginning of a dive and 825 psi at the end of a dive. Convert each of these values to atm and mm Hg.

General Gas Law Problems

7.41 **X** consists of a flexible container with eight particles of a gas as shown. What happens to the pressure of the system when **X** is converted to the representations in parts (a), (b), and (c)?

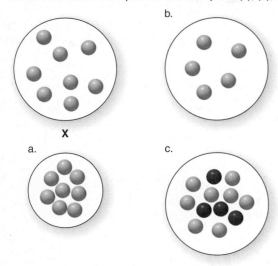

7.42 Suppose **A** represents a balloon that can expand or contract. **A** contains 10 particles of a gas as shown. Draw a diagram that shows the volume of **A** when each change occurs.

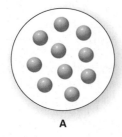

A

a. The volume is halved and the temperature and number of particles remain the same.
b. The pressure is doubled and the temperature and number of particles remain the same.
c. The temperature is increased and the pressure and number of particles remain the same.
d. The number of particles is doubled and the pressure and temperature remain the same.

7.43 Draw a picture that represents the given balloon when each of the following changes occurs.

a. The balloon is inflated outside on a cold winter day and then taken inside a building at 75 °F.
b. The balloon is taken to the top of Mauna Kea, Hawaii (elevation 13,796 ft). Assume the temperature is constant.
c. The balloon is taken inside an airplane pressurized at 0.8 atm.

7.44 Which representation ([1], [2], or [3]) shows what balloon **Z** resembles after each change occurs?

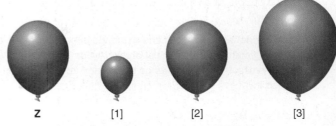

a. The balloon is cooled to a lower temperature.
b. Some gas leaks out.
c. The balloon is allowed to rise to a higher altitude.

7.45 A balloon is filled with helium at sea level. What happens to the volume of the balloon in each instance? Explain each answer.

a. The balloon floats to a higher altitude.
b. The balloon is placed in a bath of liquid nitrogen at −196 °C.
c. The balloon is placed inside a hyperbaric chamber at a pressure of 2.5 atm.
d. The balloon is heated inside a microwave.

7.46 Suppose you have a fixed amount of gas in a container with a movable piston, as drawn. Re-draw the container and piston to illustrate what it looks like after each of the following changes takes place.

—piston

a. The temperature is held constant and the pressure is doubled.
b. The pressure is held constant and the Kelvin temperature is doubled.
c. The pressure is halved and the Kelvin temperature is halved.

Boyle's Law

7.47 Assuming a fixed amount of gas at constant temperature, complete the following table.

	P_1	V_1	P_2	V_2
a.	2.0 atm	3.0 L	8.0 atm	?
b.	55 mm Hg	0.35 L	18 mm Hg	?
c.	705 mm Hg	215 mL	?	1.52 L

7.48 Assuming a fixed amount of gas at constant temperature, complete the following table.

	P_1	V_1	P_2	V_2
a.	2.5 atm	1.5 L	3.8 atm	?
b.	2.0 atm	350 mL	750 mm Hg	?
c.	75 mm Hg	9.1 mL	?	890 mL

7.49 If a scuba diver releases a 10.-mL air bubble below the surface where the pressure is 3.5 atm, what is the volume of the bubble when it rises to the surface and the pressure is 1.0 atm?

7.50 If someone takes a breath and the lungs expand from 4.5 L to 5.6 L in volume, and the initial pressure was 756 mm Hg, what is the pressure inside the lungs before any additional air is pulled in?

Charles's Law

7.51 Assuming a fixed amount of gas at constant pressure, complete the following table.

	V_1	T_1	V_2	T_2
a.	5.0 L	310 K	?	250 K
b.	150 mL	45 K	?	45 °C
c.	60.0 L	0.0 °C	180 L	?

7.52 Assuming a fixed amount of gas at constant pressure, complete the following table.

	V_1	T_1	V_2	T_2
a.	10.0 mL	210 K	?	450 K
b.	255 mL	55 °C	?	150 K
c.	13 L	−150 °C	52 L	?

7.53 If a balloon containing 2.2 L of gas at 25 °C is cooled to −78 °C, what is its new volume?

7.54 How hot must the air in a balloon be heated if initially it has a volume of 750. L at 20 °C and the final volume must be 1,000. L?

Gay–Lussac's Law

7.55 Assuming a fixed amount of gas at constant volume, complete the following table.

	P_1	T_1	P_2	T_2
a.	3.25 atm	298 K	?	398 K
b.	550 mm Hg	273 K	?	−100. °C
c.	0.50 atm	250 °C	955 mm Hg	?

7.56 Assuming a fixed amount of gas at constant volume, complete the following table.

	P_1	T_1	P_2	T_2
a.	1.74 atm	120 °C	?	20. °C
b.	220 mm Hg	150 °C	?	300. K
c.	0.75 atm	198 °C	220 mm Hg	?

7.57 An autoclave is a pressurized container used to sterilize medical equipment by heating it to a high temperature under pressure. If an autoclave containing steam at 100. °C and 1.0 atm pressure is then heated to 150. °C, what is the pressure inside it?

7.58 If a plastic container at 1.0 °C and 750. mm Hg is heated in a microwave oven to 80. °C, what is the pressure inside the container?

Combined Gas Law

7.59 Assuming a fixed amount of gas, complete the following table.

	P_1	V_1	T_1	P_2	V_2	T_2
a.	0.90 atm	4.0 L	265 K	?	3.0 L	310 K
b.	1.2 atm	75 L	5.0 °C	700. mm Hg	?	50 °C
c.	200. mm Hg	125 mL	298 K	100. mm Hg	0.62 L	?

7.60 Assuming a fixed amount of gas, complete the following table.

	P_1	V_1	T_1	P_2	V_2	T_2
a.	0.55 atm	1.1 L	340 K	?	3.0 L	298 K
b.	735 mm Hg	1.2 L	298 K	1.1 atm	?	0.0 °C
c.	7.5 atm	230 mL	−120 °C	15 atm	0.45 L	?

7.61 If a compressed air cylinder for scuba diving contains 6.0 L of gas at 18 °C and 200. atm pressure, what volume does the gas occupy at 1.0 atm and 25 °C?

7.62 What happens to the pressure of a sample with each of the following changes?
   a. Double the volume and halve the Kelvin temperature.
   b. Double the volume and double the Kelvin temperature.
   c. Halve the volume and double the Kelvin temperature.

Avogadro's Law

7.63 What is the difference between STP and standard molar volume?

7.64 Given the same number of moles of two gases at STP conditions, how do the volumes of two gases compare? How do the masses of the two gas samples compare?

7.65 How many moles of helium are contained in each volume at STP: (a) 5.0 L; (b) 11.2 L; (c) 50.0 mL?

7.66 How many moles of argon are contained in each volume at STP: (a) 4.0 L; (b) 31.2 L; (c) 120 mL?

7.67 Calculate the volume of each substance at STP.
   a. 4.2 mol Ar   b. 3.5 g CO_2 c. 2.1 g N_2

7.68 What volume does 3.01×10^{21} molecules of N_2 occupy at STP?

Ideal Gas Law

7.69 How many moles of gas are contained in a human breath that occupies 0.45 L and has a pressure of 747 mm Hg at 37 °C?

7.70 How many moles of gas are contained in a compressed air tank for scuba diving that has a volume of 7.0 L and a pressure of 210 atm at 25 °C?

7.71 How many moles of air are present in the lungs if they occupy a volume of 5.0 L at 37 °C and 740 mm Hg? How many molecules of air does this correspond to?

7.72 If a cylinder contains 10.0 g of CO_2 in 10.0 L at 325 K, what is the pressure?

7.73 Which sample contains more moles: 2.0 L of O_2 at 273 K and 500. mm Hg, or 1.5 L of N_2 at 298 K and 650 mm Hg? Which sample has more mass?

7.74 An unknown amount of gas occupies 30.0 L at 2.1 atm and 298 K. How many moles does the sample contain? What is the mass if the gas is helium? What is the mass if the gas is argon?

Dalton's Law and Partial Pressure

7.75 The molecular art shows a closed container with two gases, **A** (red spheres) and **B** (blue spheres) at a pressure of 630 mm Hg. What is the partial pressure of **A** and **B**?

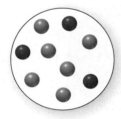

7.76 If the pressure due to the red spheres in the molecular art is 480 mm Hg, what is the pressure due to the blue spheres? What is the total pressure of the system?

7.77 Air pressure on the top of Mauna Loa, a 13,000-ft mountain in Hawaii, is 460 mm Hg. What are the partial pressures of O_2 and N_2, which compose 21% and 78% of the atmosphere, respectively?

7.78 If air contains 21% O_2, what is the partial pressure of O_2 in a cylinder of compressed air at 175 atm?

7.79 The partial pressure of N_2 in the air is 593 mm Hg at 1 atm. What is the partial pressure of N_2 in a bubble of air a scuba diver breathes when he is 66 ft below the surface of the water where the pressure is 3 atm?

7.80 If N_2 is added to a balloon that contains O_2 (partial pressure 450 mm Hg) and CO_2 (partial pressure 150 mm Hg) to give a total pressure of 850 mm Hg, what is the partial pressure of each gas in the final mixture?

Intermolecular Forces

7.81 Why is H_2O a liquid at room temperature, but H_2S, which has a higher molecular weight and a larger surface area, is a gas at room temperature?

7.82 Why is Cl_2 a gas, Br_2 a liquid, and I_2 a solid at room temperature?

7.83 What types of intermolecular forces are exhibited by each compound? Chloroethane is a local anesthetic and cyclopropane is a general anesthetic.

a.
```
    H  H
    |  |
H—C—C—Cl
    |  |
    H  H
```
chloroethane

b.
```
      H  H
       \ /
        C
       / \
  H—C———C—H
    |       |
    H       H
```
cyclopropane

7.84 What types of intermolecular forces are exhibited by each compound? Acetaldehyde is formed when ethanol, the alcohol in alcoholic beverages, is metabolized, and acetic acid gives vinegar its biting odor and taste.

a.
```
    H  O
    |  ‖
H—C—C—H
    |
    H
```
acetaldehyde

b.
```
    H  O
    |  ‖
H—C—C—O—H
    |
    H
```
acetic acid

7.85 Which molecules are capable of intermolecular hydrogen bonding?

a. $H—C\equiv C—H$ b. CO_2 c. Br_2 d.
```
    H  H
    |  |
H—C—N—H
    |
    H
```

7.86 Which molecules are capable of intermolecular hydrogen bonding?

a. N_2 b.
```
    H
    |
H—C—F
    |
    H
```
    c. HI   d.
```
    H
    |
H—C—O—H
    |
    H
```

7.87 Can two molecules of formaldehyde ($H_2C{=}O$) intermolecularly hydrogen bond to each other? Explain why or why not.

7.88 Why is the melting point of NaCl (801 °C) much higher than the melting point of water (0 °C)?

7.89 Ethylene and methanol have approximately the same molar mass.

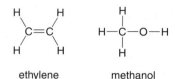

ethylene   methanol

a. What types of intermolecular forces are present in each compound?
b. Which compound has the higher boiling point?
c. Which compound has the higher vapor pressure at a given temperature?

7.90 Ethanol and dimethyl ether have the same molecular formula.

ethanol   dimethyl ether

a. What types of intermolecular forces are present in each compound?
b. Which compound has the higher boiling point?
c. Which compound has the higher vapor pressure at a given temperature?

Liquids and Solids

7.91 Given the following vapor pressures at 20 °C, arrange the compounds in order of increasing boiling point: butane, 1,650 mm Hg; acetaldehyde, 740 mm Hg; Freon-113, 284 mm Hg.

7.92 Using the given boiling points, predict which compound has the higher vapor pressure at a given temperature.
a. ethanol (C_2H_6O, bp 78 °C) or 1-propanol (C_3H_8O, bp 97 °C)
b. hexane (C_6H_{14}, bp 69 °C) or octane (C_8H_{18}, bp 125 °C)

7.93 Explain why glycerol is *more* viscous than water, but acetone is *less* viscous than water. Glycerol is a component of skin lotions and creams. Acetone is the main ingredient in nail polish remover.

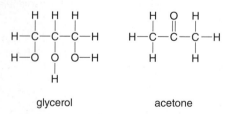

glycerol   acetone

7.94 Explain the following observation. When a needle is carefully placed on the surface of water, it floats, yet when its tip is pushed below the surface, it sinks to the bottom.

7.95 Classify each solid as amorphous, ionic, molecular, network, or metallic.
a. KI
b. CO_2
c. bronze, an alloy of Cu and Sn
d. diamond
e. the plastic polyethylene

7.96 Classify each solid as amorphous, ionic, molecular, network, or metallic.
a. $CaCO_3$
b. CH_3COOH (acetic acid)
c. Ag
d. graphite
e. the plastic polypropylene

Energy and Phase Changes

7.97 What is the difference between evaporation and condensation?

7.98 What is the difference between sublimation and deposition?

7.99 What phase change is shown in the accompanying molecular art? Is energy absorbed or released during the process?

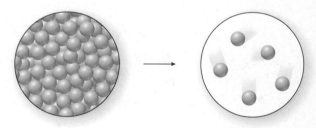

7.100 What phase change is shown in the accompanying molecular art? Is energy absorbed or released during the process?

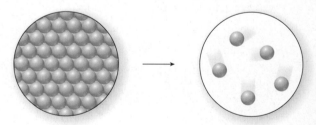

7.101 Indicate whether heat is absorbed or released in each process.
a. melting 100 g of ice
b. freezing 25 g of water
c. condensing 20 g of steam
d. vaporizing 30 g of water

7.102 What is the difference between the heat of fusion and the heat of vaporization?

7.103 Which process requires more energy, melting 250 g of ice or vaporizing 50.0 g of water? The heat of fusion of water is 79.7 cal/g and the heat of vaporization is 540 cal/g.

7.104 How much energy in kilocalories is needed to vaporize 255 g of water? The heat of vaporization of water is 540 cal/g.

Heating and Cooling Curves

7.105 Consider the cooling curve drawn below.

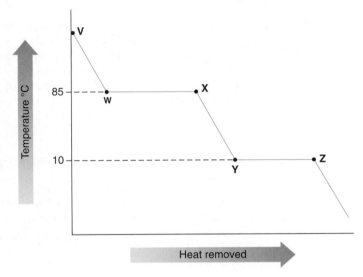

a. Which line segment corresponds to the following changes of state?

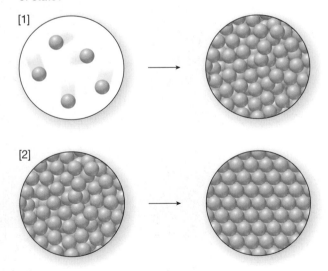

[1]

[2]

b. What is the melting point of the substance?
c. What is the boiling point of the substance?

7.106 Which line segments on the cooling curve in Problem 7.105 correspond to each of the following physical states?

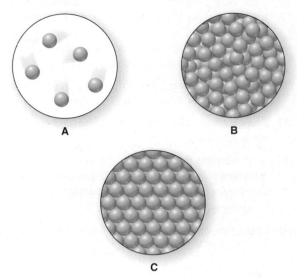

7.107 Draw the heating curve that is observed when octane is warmed from –70 °C to 130 °C. Octane, a component of gasoline, has a melting point of –57 °C and a boiling point of 126 °C.

7.108 Draw the heating curve that is observed when ice is warmed from –20 °C to 120 °C. Which sections of the curve correspond to the molecular art in **A, B,** and **C?**

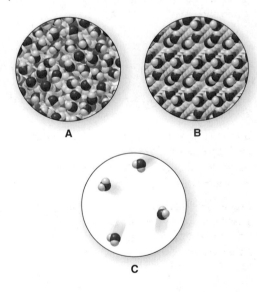

Applications

7.109 If you pack a bag of potato chips for a snack on a plane ride, the bag appears to have inflated when you take it out to open. Explain why this occurs. If the initial volume of air in the bag was 250 mL at 760 mm Hg, and the plane is pressurized at 650 mm Hg, what is the final volume of the bag?

7.110 Why does a bubble at the bottom of a glass of a soft drink get larger as it rises to the surface?

7.111 Explain why cooling a full glass water bottle to −10 °C causes the bottle to crack.

7.112 What happens to the density of a gas if the temperature is increased but the pressure is held constant? Use this information to explain how wind currents arise.

7.113 A common laboratory test for a patient is to measure blood gases—that is, the partial pressures of O_2 and CO_2 in oxygenated blood. Normal values are 100 mm Hg for O_2 and 40 mm Hg for CO_2. A high or low level of one or both readings has some underlying cause. Offer an explanation for each of the following situations.

a. If a patient comes in agitated and hyperventilating—breathing very rapidly—the partial pressure of O_2 is normal but the partial pressure of CO_2 is 22 mm Hg.

b. A patient with chronic lung disease has a partial pressure of O_2 of 60 mm Hg and a partial pressure of CO_2 of 60 mm Hg.

7.114 If a scuba diver inhales 0.50 L of air at a depth of 100. ft and 4.0 atm pressure, what volume does this air occupy at the surface of the water, assuming air pressure is 1.0 atm? When a scuba diver must make a rapid ascent to the surface, he is told to exhale slowly as he ascends. How does your result support this recommendation?

CHALLENGE PROBLEMS

7.115 A gas (4.0 g) occupies 11.2 L at 2 atm and 273 K. What is the molar mass of the gas? What is the identity of the gas?

7.116 As we learned in Chapter 5, an automobile airbag inflates when NaN_3 is converted to Na and N_2 according to the equation, $2\ NaN_3 \longrightarrow 2\ Na + 3\ N_2$. What volume of N_2 would be produced if 100. g of NaN_3 completely reacted at STP?

8

A sports drink is a solution of dissolved ions and carbohydrates, used to provide energy and hydration during strenuous exercise.

Solutions

CHAPTER GOALS

In this chapter you will learn how to:

1 Describe the fundamental properties of a solution

2 Predict whether a substance is soluble in water or a nonpolar solvent

3 Predict the effect of temperature and pressure on solubility

4 Calculate the concentration of a solution

5 Prepare a dilute solution from a more concentrated solution

6 Describe the effect of dissolved particles on the boiling point and melting point of a solution

7 Describe the process of osmosis and how it relates to biological membranes and dialysis

A pepperoni pizza is a heterogeneous mixture, while a soft drink is a homogeneous solution.

The particles in a colloid are typically between 1 and 1,000 nm in diameter.

In Chapter 8 we study **solutions**—homogeneous mixtures of two or more substances. Why are table salt (NaCl) and sugar (sucrose) soluble in water but vegetable oil and gasoline are not? How does a healthcare professional take a drug as supplied by the manufacturer and prepare a dilute solution to administer a proper dose to a patient? An understanding of solubility and concentration is needed to explain each of these phenomena.

8.1 Introduction

Thus far we have concentrated primarily on **pure substances**—elements, covalent compounds, and ionic compounds. Most matter with which we come into contact, however, is a **mixture** composed of two or more pure substances. The air we breathe is composed of nitrogen and oxygen, together with small amounts of argon, water vapor, carbon dioxide, and other gases. Seawater is composed largely of sodium chloride and water. A mixture may be **heterogeneous** or **homogeneous.**

- A *heterogeneous* mixture does not have a uniform composition throughout a sample.
- A *homogeneous* mixture has a uniform composition throughout a sample.

Homogeneous mixtures are either **solutions** or **colloids.**

- A *solution* is a homogeneous mixture that contains small particles. Liquid solutions are transparent.
- A *colloid* is a homogeneous mixture with larger particles, often having an opaque appearance.

A cup of hot coffee, vinegar, and gasoline are transparent solutions, whereas milk is an opaque colloid that contains undissolved particles of fat and proteins. Any phase of matter can form a solution (Figure 8.1). Air is a solution of gases. An intravenous saline solution contains solid sodium chloride (NaCl) in liquid water. A dental filling contains liquid mercury (Hg) in solid silver.

Figure 8.1   Three Different Types of Solutions

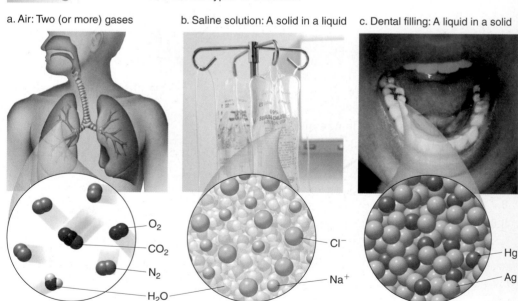

a. Air is a solution of gases, primarily N_2 and O_2. The lungs contain significant amounts of H_2O and CO_2 as well.

b. An IV saline solution contains solid sodium chloride (NaCl) dissolved in liquid water.

c. A dental filling contains a liquid, mercury (Hg), dissolved in solid silver (Ag).

When two substances form a solution, the substance present in the lesser amount is called the **solute,** and the substance present in the larger amount is the **solvent.** A solution with water as the solvent is called an **aqueous solution.**

Although a solution can be separated into its pure components, one component of a solution cannot be filtered away from the other component. For a particular solute and solvent, solutions having different compositions are possible. For example, 1.0 g of NaCl can be mixed with 50.0 g of water or 10.0 g of NaCl can be mixed with 50.0 g of water.

An aqueous solution that contains ions conducts electricity, whereas one that contains only neutral molecules does not. Thus, an aqueous solution of sodium chloride, NaCl, contains Na^+ cations and Cl^- anions and conducts electricity. An aqueous solution of hydrogen peroxide, H_2O_2, contains only neutral H_2O_2 molecules in H_2O, so it does not conduct electricity.

- A substance that conducts an electric current in water is called an *electrolyte.* NaCl is an electrolyte.
- A substance that does not conduct an electric current in water is called a *nonelectrolyte.* H_2O_2 is a nonelectrolyte.

Figure 8.2 summarizes the classification of matter.

PROBLEM 8.1

Classify each substance as a heterogeneous mixture, solution, or colloid: (a) Cherry Garcia ice cream (cherry ice cream + chocolate bits + cherries); (b) mayonnaise; (c) seltzer water; (d) nail polish remover; (e) brass (an alloy of Cu and Zn).

PROBLEM 8.2

Classify each solution as an electrolyte or nonelectrolyte: (a) KCl in H_2O; (b) sucrose ($C_{12}H_{22}O_{11}$) in H_2O; (c) KI in H_2O.

Figure 8.2   Classification of Matter

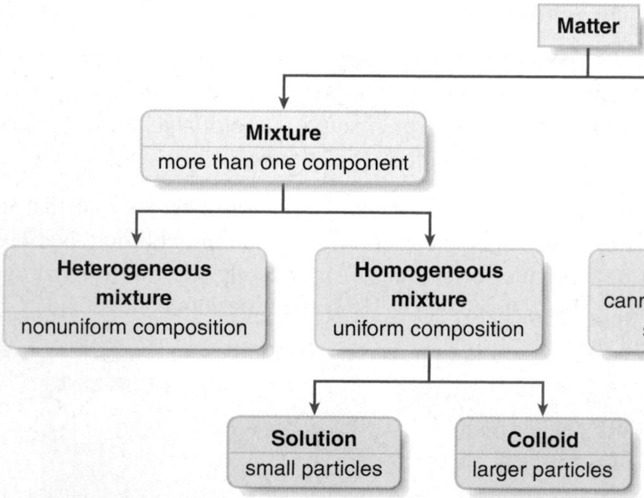

8.2 Solubility—General Features

Solubility is the amount of solute that dissolves in a given amount of solvent, usually reported in grams of solute per 100 mL of solution (g/100 mL). A solution that has less than the maximum number of grams of solute is said to be **unsaturated.** A solution that has the maximum number of grams of solute that can dissolve is said to be **saturated.** If we added more solute to a saturated solution, the additional solute would remain undissolved in the flask.

8.2A Basic Principles

What determines if a compound dissolves in a particular solvent? Whether a compound is soluble in a given solvent depends on the strength of the interactions between the compound and the solvent. As a result, compounds are soluble in solvents to which they are strongly attracted. Solubility is often summed up in three words: **"Like dissolves like."**

- Most ionic and polar covalent compounds are soluble in water, a polar solvent.
- Nonpolar compounds are soluble in nonpolar solvents.

Water-soluble compounds are ionic or are small polar molecules that can hydrogen bond with the water solvent. For example, solid sodium chloride (NaCl) is held together by very strong electrostatic interactions of the oppositely charged ions. When it is mixed with water, the Na^+ and Cl^- ions are separated from each other and surrounded by polar water molecules (Figure 8.3). Each Na^+ is surrounded by water molecules arranged with their O atoms (which bear a partial negative charge) in close proximity to the positive charge of the cation. Each Cl^- is surrounded by water molecules arranged with their H atoms (which bear a partial positive charge) in close proximity to the negative charge of the anion.

- The attraction of an ion with a dipole in a molecule is called an ion–dipole interaction.

Figure 8.3   Dissolving Sodium Chloride in Water

When ionic NaCl dissolves in water, the Na$^+$ and Cl$^-$ interactions of the crystal are replaced by new interactions of Na$^+$ and Cl$^-$ ions with the solvent. Each ion is surrounded by a loose shell of water molecules arranged so that oppositely charged species are close to each other.

The ion–dipole interactions between Na$^+$, Cl$^-$, and water provide the energy needed to break apart the ions from the crystal lattice. The water molecules form a loose shell of solvent around each ion. The process of surrounding particles of a solute with solvent molecules is called **solvation.**

Small neutral molecules that can hydrogen bond with water are also soluble. Thus, ethanol (C_2H_5OH), which is present in alcoholic beverages, dissolves in water because hydrogen bonding occurs between the OH group in ethanol and the OH group of water.

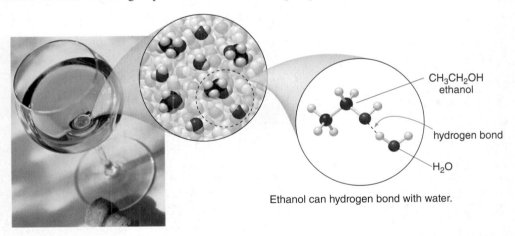

CH$_3$CH$_2$OH
ethanol

hydrogen bond

H$_2$O

Ethanol can hydrogen bond with water.

The basic principles of solubility explain why some vitamins are fat soluble while others are water soluble, as discussed in Chapter 11.

Water solubility for neutral molecules occurs only with small polar molecules or those with many O or N atoms that can hydrogen bond to water. Thus, stearic acid ($C_{18}H_{36}O_2$), a component of animal fats, is *insoluble* in water because its nonpolar part (C—C and C—H bonds) is large compared to its polar part (C—O and O—H bonds). On the other hand, glucose ($C_6H_{12}O_6$), a simple carbohydrate, is *soluble* in water because it has many OH groups and thus many opportunities for hydrogen bonding with water.

Stearic acid–Water insoluble

many nonpolar C–C and C–H bonds

Most of the molecule is nonpolar, so it is not attracted to a polar solvent like H_2O.

polar C–O and O–H bonds

Glucose–Water soluble

many O–H bonds for hydrogen bonding to H_2O

Nonpolar compounds are soluble in nonpolar solvents. As a result, octane (C_8H_{18}), a component of gasoline, dissolves in the nonpolar solvent carbon tetrachloride (CCl_4), as shown in Figure 8.4. Animal fat and vegetable oils, which are composed largely of nonpolar C—C and C—H bonds, are soluble in CCl_4, but are insoluble in a polar solvent like water. These solubility properties explain why "oil and water don't mix."

Dissolving a solute in a solvent is a physical process that is accompanied by an energy change. Breaking up the particles of the solute requires energy, and forming new attractive forces between the solute and the solvent releases energy.

Figure 8.4   Solubility—A Nonpolar Compound in a Nonpolar Solvent

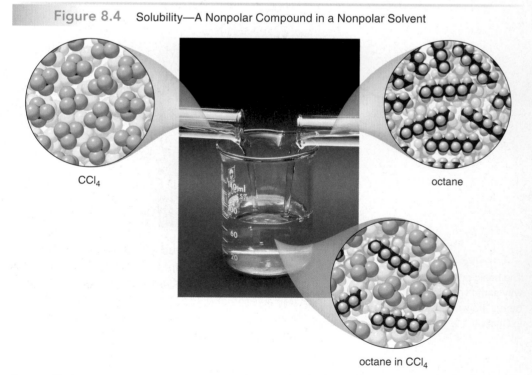

CCl_4

octane

octane in CCl_4

Octane (C_8H_{18}) dissolves in CCl_4 because both are nonpolar liquids that exhibit only London dispersion forces.

- When solvation releases more energy than that required to separate particles, the overall process is exothermic (heat is released).
- When the separation of particles requires more energy than is released during solvation, the process is endothermic (heat is absorbed).

These energy changes are used to an advantage in commercially available hot packs and cold packs. A hot pack, sometimes used for pain relief of sore muscles, contains calcium chloride ($CaCl_2$) or magnesium sulfate ($MgSO_4$) and water. Breaking the seal that separates them allows the salt to dissolve in the water, releasing heat, and the pouch gets warm. In contrast, ammonium nitrate (NH_4NO_3) absorbs heat on mixing with water, so this salt is found in instant cold packs used to reduce swelling.

SAMPLE PROBLEM 8.1

Predict the water solubility of each compound: (a) KCl; (b) methanol (CH_3OH); (c) hexane (C_6H_{14}).

Analysis

Use the general solubility rule—"like dissolves like." Generally, ionic and small polar compounds that can hydrogen bond are soluble in water. Nonpolar compounds are soluble in nonpolar solvents.

Solution

a. KCl is an ionic compound, so it dissolves in water, a polar solvent.
b. CH_3OH is a small polar molecule that contains an OH group. As a result, it can hydrogen bond to water, making it soluble.
c. Hexane (C_6H_{14}) has only nonpolar C—C and C—H bonds, making it a nonpolar molecule that is therefore water insoluble.

PROBLEM 8.3

Which compounds are water soluble?

a. $NaNO_3$ b. CH_4 c. $HO-\overset{\displaystyle H}{\underset{\displaystyle H}{C}}-\overset{\displaystyle H}{\underset{\displaystyle H}{C}}-OH$ d. KBr   e. NH_2OH

PROBLEM 8.4

Which pairs of compounds will form a solution?

a. benzene (C_6H_6) and hexane (C_6H_{14})   c. NaCl and hexane (C_6H_{14})
b. Na_2SO_4 and H_2O d. H_2O and CCl_4

8.2B Ionic Compounds—Additional Principles

Although ionic compounds are generally water soluble, some are not. If the attraction between the ions in a crystalline solid is stronger than the forces of attraction between the ions and water, the ionic compound does not dissolve. The identity of the cation and anion in the ionic compound determines its water solubility. Two rules can be used to predict water solubility.

General Rules for the Solubility of Ionic Compounds

Rule [1]   A compound is soluble if it contains one of the following cations:
  - Group 1A cations: Li^+, Na^+, K^+, Rb^+, Cs^+
  - Ammonium, NH_4^+

Rule [2]   A compound is soluble if it contains one of the following anions:
  - Halide: Cl^-, Br^-, I^-, except for salts with Ag^+, Hg_2^{2+}, and Pb^{2+}
  - Nitrate, NO_3^-
  - Acetate, $CH_3CO_2^-$
  - Sulfate, SO_4^{2-}, except for salts with Ba^{2+}, Hg_2^{2+}, and Pb^{2+}

Thus, Na_2CO_3 is water soluble because it contains a Na^+ cation (rule [1]), but $CaCO_3$ is water insoluble because it contains none of the ions listed in rules [1] and [2]. In dealing with the solubility of ionic compounds in this text, we will assume the compound to be water soluble unless specifically asked to consider the solubility rules just mentioned.

SAMPLE PROBLEM 8.2

Use the solubility rules to predict whether the following ionic compounds are soluble in water:
(a) Na_3PO_4; (b) $Mg_3(PO_4)_2$; (c) KOH.

Analysis

Identify the cation and anion and use the solubility rules to predict if the ionic compound is water soluble.

Solution

a. Na_3PO_4 contains a Na^+ cation, and all Na^+ salts are soluble regardless of the anion.
b. $Mg_3(PO_4)_2$ contains none of the cations or anions listed under the solubility rules, so it is water insoluble.
c. KOH contains a K^+ cation, and all K^+ salts are soluble regardless of the anion.

PROBLEM 8.5

Use the solubility rules to predict whether the following ionic compounds are soluble in water:
(a) Li_2CO_3; (b) $MgCO_3$; (c) KBr; (d) $PbSO_4$; (e) $CaCl_2$; (f) $MgCl_2$.

PROBLEM 8.6

Use the solubility rules for ionic compounds to explain why milk of magnesia, which contains $Mg(OH)_2$ and water, is a heterogeneous mixture rather than a solution.

8.3 Solubility—Effects of Temperature and Pressure

Both temperature and pressure can affect solubility.

8.3A Temperature Effects

For most ionic and molecular solids, solubility generally increases as temperature increases. Thus, sugar is much more soluble in a cup of hot coffee than in a glass of iced tea. If a solid is dissolved in a solvent at high temperature and then the solution is slowly cooled, the solubility of the solute decreases and it precipitates from the solution. Sometimes, however, if cooling is very slow, the solution becomes **supersaturated** with solute; that is, the solution contains more than the predicted maximum amount of solute at a given temperature. Such a solution is unstable, and when it is disturbed, the solute precipitates rapidly.

In contrast, **the solubility of gases *decreases* with increasing temperature.** Because increasing temperature increases the kinetic energy, more gas particles escape into the gas phase and fewer remain in solution. Increasing temperature decreases the solubility of oxygen in lakes and streams. In cases where industrial plants operating near lakes or streams have raised water temperature, marine life dies from lack of sufficient oxygen in solution.

PROBLEM 8.7

Why does a soft drink become "flat" faster when it is left open at room temperature compared to when it is left open in the refrigerator?

Figure 8.5 Henry's Law and Carbonated Beverages

The air pressure in a closed can of soda is approximately 2 atm. When the can is opened, the pressure above the liquid in the can decreases to 1 atm, so the CO_2 concentration in the soda decreases as well, and the gas fizzes from the soda.

Scuba divers often hold onto a rope so that they ascend to the surface slowly after a dive, in order to avoid forming bubbles of nitrogen gas in joints and blood vessels.

8.3B Pressure Effects

Pressure changes do not affect the solubility of liquids and solids, but pressure affects the solubility of gases a great deal. **Henry's law** describes the effect of pressure on gas solubility.

> • Henry's law: The solubility of a gas in a liquid is proportional to the partial pressure of the gas above the liquid.

Thus, the **higher the pressure, the higher the solubility of a gas in a solvent.** A practical demonstration of Henry's law occurs whenever we open a carbonated soft drink. Soft drinks containing dissolved CO_2 are sealed under greater than 1 atm pressure. When a can is opened, the pressure above the liquid decreases to 1 atm, so the solubility of the CO_2 in the soda decreases as well and some of the dissolved CO_2 fizzes out of solution (Figure 8.5).

As we learned in Section 7.6, increasing gas solubility affects scuba divers because more N_2 is dissolved in the blood under the higher pressures experienced under water. Divers must ascend slowly to avoid forming bubbles of N_2 in joints and small blood vessels. If a diver ascends slowly, the external pressure around the diver slowly decreases and by Henry's law, the solubility of the gas in the diver's blood slowly decreases as well.

PROBLEM 8.8

Predict the effect each change has on the solubility of [1] $Na_2CO_3(s)$; [2] $N_2(g)$.

a. increasing the temperature   c. increasing the pressure
b. decreasing the temperature   d. decreasing the pressure

8.4 Concentration Units—Percent Concentration

In using a solution in the laboratory or in administering the proper dose of a liquid medication, we must know its *concentration*—**how much solute is dissolved in a given amount of solution.** Concentration can be measured in several different ways that use mass, volume, or moles. Two useful measures of concentration are reported as percentages—that is, the number of grams or milliliters of solute per 100 mL of solution.

HEALTH NOTE

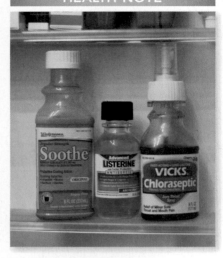

Mouthwash, sore throat spray, and many other over-the-counter medications contain ingredients whose concentrations are reported in (w/v)%.

8.4A   Weight/Volume Percent

One of the most common measures of concentration is **weight/volume percent concentration, (w/v)%—that is, the number of grams of solute dissolved in 100 mL of solution.** Mathematically, weight/volume percent is calculated by dividing the number of grams of solute in a given number of milliliters of solution, and multiplying by 100%.

$$\boxed{\text{Weight/volume percent concentration}} \quad (\text{w/v})\% = \frac{\text{mass of solute (g)}}{\text{volume of solution (mL)}} \times 100\%$$

For example, vinegar contains 5 g of acetic acid dissolved in 100 mL of solution, so the acetic acid concentration is 5% (w/v).

$$(\text{w/v})\% = \frac{5 \text{ g acetic acid}}{100 \text{ mL vinegar solution}} \times 100\% = 5\% \ (\text{w/v}) \text{ acetic acid}$$

Note that the volume used to calculate concentration is the *final* volume of the solution, not the volume of solvent added to make the solution. A special flask called a **volumetric flask** is used to make a solution of a given concentration (Figure 8.6). The solute is placed in the flask and then enough solvent is added to dissolve the solute by mixing. Next, additional solvent is added until it reaches a calibrated line that measures the final volume of the solution.

Figure 8.6   Making a Solution with a Particular Concentration

a. Add the solute.   b. Add the solvent.

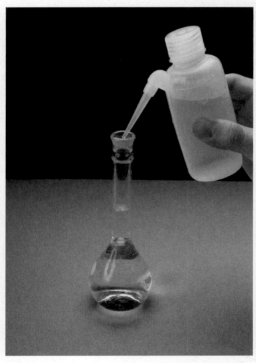

To make a solution of a given concentration, (a) add a measured number of grams of solute to a volumetric flask; (b) then add solvent to dissolve the solid, bringing the level of the solvent to the calibrated mark on the neck of the flask.

SAMPLE PROBLEM 8.3

Chloraseptic sore throat spray contains 0.35 g of the antiseptic phenol dissolved in 25 mL of solution. What is the weight/volume percent concentration of phenol?

Analysis

Use the formula (w/v)% = (grams of solute)/(mL of solution) × 100%.

Solution

$$(w/v)\% = \frac{0.35 \text{ g phenol}}{25 \text{ mL solution}} \times 100\% = 1.4\% \text{ (w/v) phenol}$$

Answer

PROBLEM 8.9

Pepto-Bismol, an over-the-counter medication used for upset stomach and diarrhea, contains 525 mg of bismuth subsalicylate in each 15-mL tablespoon. What is the weight/volume percent concentration of bismuth subsalicylate?

PROBLEM 8.10

A commercial mouthwash contains 4.3 g of ethanol and 0.021 g of antiseptic in each 30.-mL portion. Calculate the weight/volume percent concentration of each component.

8.4B   Volume/Volume Percent

When the solute in a solution is a liquid, its concentration is often reported using **volume/volume percent concentration, (v/v)%—that is, the number of milliliters of solute dissolved in 100 mL of solution.** Mathematically, volume/volume percent is calculated by dividing the number of milliliters of solute in a given number of milliliters of solution, and multiplying by 100%.

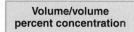

$$(v/v)\% = \frac{\text{volume of solute (mL)}}{\text{volume of solution (mL)}} \times 100\%$$

For example, a bottle of rubbing alcohol that contains 70 mL of 2-propanol in 100 mL of solution has a 70% (v/v) concentration of 2-propanol.

$$(v/v)\% = \frac{70 \text{ mL 2-propanol}}{100 \text{ mL rubbing alcohol}} \times 100\% = 70\% \text{ (v/v) 2-propanol}$$

SAMPLE PROBLEM 8.4

A 750-mL bottle of wine contains 101 mL of ethanol. What is the volume/volume percent concentration of ethanol?

Analysis

Use the formula (v/v)% = (mL of solute)/(mL of solution) × 100%.

Solution

$$(v/v)\% = \frac{101 \text{ mL ethanol}}{750 \text{ mL wine}} \times 100\% = 14\% \text{ (v/v) ethanol}$$

Answer

PROBLEM 8.11

A 250-mL bottle of mouthwash contains 21 mL of ethanol. What is the volume/volume percent concentration of ethanol?

The alcohol (ethanol) content of wine, beer, and other alcoholic beverages is reported using volume/volume percent concentration. Wines typically contain 10–13% (v/v) ethanol, whereas beer usually contains 3–5%.

8.4C Using a Percent Concentration as a Conversion Factor

Percent concentration can be used as a conversion factor to relate the amount of solute (either grams or milliliters) to the amount of solution. For example, ketamine, an anesthetic especially useful for children, is supplied as a 5.0% (w/v) solution, meaning that 5.0 g of ketamine are present in 100 mL of solution. Two conversion factors derived from the percent concentration can be written.

$$5.0\% \text{ (w/v) ketamine} \quad \frac{5.0 \text{ g ketamine}}{100 \text{ mL solution}} \quad \text{or} \quad \frac{100 \text{ mL solution}}{5.0 \text{ g ketamine}}$$

weight/volume
percent concentration

We can use these conversion factors to determine the amount of solute contained in a given volume of solution (Sample Problem 8.5), or to determine how much solution contains a given number of grams of solute (Sample Problem 8.6).

SAMPLE PROBLEM 8.5

A saline solution used in intravenous drips for patients who cannot take oral fluids contains 0.92% (w/v) NaCl in water. How many grams of NaCl are contained in 250 mL of this solution?

Analysis and Solution

[1] Identify the known quantities and the desired quantity.

0.92% (w/v) NaCl solution

250 mL   ? g NaCl

known quantities   desired quantity

[2] Write out the conversion factors.

- Set up conversion factors that relate grams of NaCl to the volume of the solution using the weight/volume percent concentration.

$$\frac{100 \text{ mL solution}}{0.92 \text{ g NaCl}} \quad \text{or} \quad \boxed{\frac{0.92 \text{ g NaCl}}{100 \text{ mL solution}}}$$

Choose this conversion factor to cancel mL.

[3] Solve the problem.

- Multiply the original quantity by the conversion factor to obtain the desired quantity.

$$250 \text{ mL} \times \frac{0.92 \text{ g NaCl}}{100 \text{ mL solution}} = 2.3 \text{ g NaCl}$$

Answer

SAMPLE PROBLEM 8.6

What volume of a 5.0% (w/v) solution of ketamine contains 75 mg?

Analysis and Solution

[1] Identify the known quantities and the desired quantity.

5.0% (w/v) ketamine solution

75 mg   ? mL ketamine

known quantities   desired quantity

[2] Write out the conversion factors.

- Use the weight/volume percent concentration to set up conversion factors that relate grams of ketamine to mL of solution. Since percent concentration is expressed in grams, a mg–g conversion factor is needed as well.

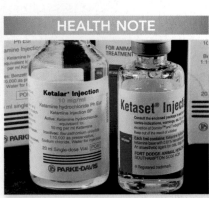

HEALTH NOTE

Ketamine is a widely used anesthetic in both human and veterinary medicine. It has been illegally used as a recreational drug because it can produce hallucinations.

CONCENTRATION UNITS—PERCENT CONCENTRATION

mg–g conversion factors   g–mL solution conversion factors

$$\frac{1000 \text{ mg}}{1 \text{ g}} \quad \text{or} \quad \boxed{\frac{1 \text{ g}}{1000 \text{ mg}}} \qquad \frac{5.0 \text{ g ketamine}}{100 \text{ mL solution}} \quad \text{or} \quad \boxed{\frac{100 \text{ mL solution}}{5.0 \text{ g ketamine}}}$$

Choose the conversion factors with the unwanted units—mg and g—in the denominator.

[3] Solve the problem.

- Multiply the original quantity by the conversion factors to obtain the desired quantity.

$$75 \text{ mg ketamine} \times \frac{1 \text{ g}}{1000 \text{ mg}} \times \frac{100 \text{ mL solution}}{5.0 \text{ g ketamine}} = 1.5 \text{ mL solution}$$

Answer

PROBLEM 8.12

How many mL of ethanol are contained in a 30.-mL portion of a mouthwash that has 8.0% (v/v) of ethanol?

PROBLEM 8.13

A drink sold in a health food store contains 0.50% (w/v) of vitamin C. What volume would you have to ingest to obtain 1,000. mg of vitamin C?

PROBLEM 8.14

A cough medicine contains 0.20% (w/v) dextromethorphan, a cough suppressant, and 2.0% (w/v) guaifenisin, an expectorant. How many milligrams of each drug would you obtain from 3.0 tsp of cough syrup? (1 tsp = 5 mL.)

8.4D Parts Per Million

ENVIRONMENTAL NOTE

Seabirds such as osprey that feed on fish contaminated with the pesticide DDT accumulate an average of 25 parts per million of DDT in their fatty tissues. When DDT concentration is high, mother osprey produce eggs with very thin shells that are easily crushed, so fewer osprey chicks hatch.

When a solution contains a very small concentration of solute, concentration is often expressed in **parts per million (ppm)**. Whereas percent concentration is the number of "parts"—grams or milliliters—in 100 parts (100 mL) of solution, parts per million is the number of "parts" in 1,000,000 parts of solution. The "parts" may be expressed in either mass or volume units as long as the *same* unit is used for both the numerator and denominator.

Parts per million $\text{ppm} = \dfrac{\text{mass of solute (g)}}{\text{mass of solution (g)}} \times 10^6$

or

$$\text{ppm} = \dfrac{\text{volume of solute (mL)}}{\text{volume of solution (mL)}} \times 10^6$$

A sample of seawater that contains 1.3 g of magnesium ions in 10^6 g of solution contains 1.3 ppm of magnesium.

$$\text{ppm} = \frac{1.3 \text{ g magnesium}}{10^6 \text{ g seawater}} \times 10^6 = 1.3 \text{ ppm magnesium}$$

Parts per million is used as a concentration unit for very dilute solutions. When water is the solvent, the density of the solution is close to the density of pure water, which is 1.0 g/mL at room temperature. In this case, the numerical value of the denominator is the same no matter if the unit is grams or milliliters. Thus, an aqueous solution that contains 2 ppm of MTBE, a gasoline additive and environmental pollutant, can be written in the following ways:

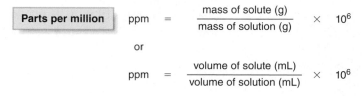

$$\frac{2 \text{ g MTBE}}{10^6 \text{ g solution}} \times 10^6 = \frac{2 \text{ g MTBE}}{10^6 \text{ mL solution}} \times 10^6 = 2 \text{ ppm MTBE}$$

10^6 mL has a mass of 10^6 g.

SAMPLE PROBLEM 8.7

What is the concentration in parts per million of DDT in the tissues of a seabird that contains 50. mg of DDT in 1,900 g of tissue? DDT, a nonbiodegradable pesticide that is a persistent environmental pollutant, has been banned from use in the United States since 1973.

Analysis

Use the formula ppm = (g of solute)/(g of solution) $\times$ 10^6.

Solution

[1] Convert milligrams of DDT to grams of DDT so that both the solute and solution have the same unit.

$$50. \text{ mg DDT} \times \frac{1 \text{ g}}{1000 \text{ mg}} = 0.050 \text{ g DDT}$$

[2] Use the formula to calculate parts per million.

$$\frac{0.050 \text{ g DDT}}{1900 \text{ g tissue}} \times 10^6 = 26 \text{ ppm DDT}$$

Answer

PROBLEM 8.15

What is the concentration in parts per million of DDT in each of the following?

a. 0.042 mg in 1,400 g plankton
b. 5×10^{-4} g in 1.0 kg minnow tissue

c. 2.0 mg in 1.0 kg needlefish tissue
d. 225 µg in 1.0 kg breast milk

8.5 Concentration Units—Molarity

The most common measure of concentration in the laboratory is *molarity*—**the number of moles of solute per liter of solution,** abbreviated as M.

$$\text{Molarity} \;=\; \text{M} \;=\; \frac{\text{moles of solute (mol)}}{\text{liter of solution (L)}}$$

A solution that is formed from 1.00 mol (58.4 g) of NaCl in enough water to give 1.00 L of solution has a molarity of 1.00 M. A solution that is formed from 2.50 mol (146 g) of NaCl in enough water to give 2.50 L of solution is also a 1.00 M solution. Both solutions contain the *same number of moles per unit volume.*

$$\text{M} = \frac{\text{moles of solute (mol)}}{V \text{ (L)}} = \frac{1.00 \text{ mol NaCl}}{1.00 \text{ L solution}} = 1.00 \text{ M}$$

$$\text{M} = \frac{\text{moles of solute (mol)}}{V \text{ (L)}} = \frac{2.50 \text{ mol NaCl}}{2.50 \text{ L solution}} = 1.00 \text{ M}$$

same concentration
same number of moles per unit volume (*V*)

Since quantities in the laboratory are weighed on a balance, we must learn how to determine molarity beginning with a particular number of grams of a substance, as shown in the accompanying stepwise procedure.

How To Calculate Molarity from a Given Number of Grams of Solute

Example: Calculate the molarity of a solution made from 20.0 g of NaOH in 250 mL of solution.

Step [1] Identify the known quantities and the desired quantity.

20.0 g NaOH

250 mL solution   ? M (mol/L)

known quantities   desired quantity

Step [2] Convert the number of grams of solute to the number of moles. Convert the volume of the solution to liters, if necessary.

- Use the molar mass to convert grams of NaOH to moles of NaOH (molar mass 40.00 g/mol).

molar mass
conversion factor

$$20.0 \text{ g NaOH} \quad \times \quad \frac{1 \text{ mol}}{40.00 \text{ g NaOH}} \quad = \quad 0.500 \text{ mol NaOH}$$

Grams cancel.

- Convert milliliters of solution to liters of solution using a mL–L conversion factor.

mL–L
conversion factor

$$250 \text{ mL solution} \quad \times \quad \frac{1 \text{ L}}{1000 \text{ mL}} \quad = \quad 0.25 \text{ L solution}$$

Milliliters cancel.

Step [3] Divide the number of moles of solute by the number of liters of solution to obtain the molarity.

$$M \quad = \quad \frac{\text{moles of solute (mol)}}{V \text{ (L)}} \quad = \quad \frac{0.500 \text{ mol NaOH}}{0.25 \text{ L solution}} \quad = \quad 2.0 \text{ M}$$

molarity   **Answer**

SAMPLE PROBLEM 8.8

What is the molarity of an intravenous glucose solution prepared from 108 g of glucose in 2.0 L of solution?

Analysis and Solution

[1] Identify the known quantities and the desired quantity.

108 g glucose

2.0 L solution   ? M (mol/L)

known quantities   desired quantity

[2] Convert the number of grams of glucose to the number of moles using the molar mass (180.2 g/mol).

$$108 \text{ g glucose} \quad \times \quad \frac{1 \text{ mol}}{180.2 \text{ g}} \quad = \quad 0.599 \text{ mol glucose}$$

Grams cancel.

- Since the volume of the solution is given in liters, no conversion is necessary for volume.

[3] Divide the number of moles of solute by the number of liters of solution to obtain the molarity.

$$M = \frac{\text{moles of solute (mol)}}{V\ (L)} = \frac{0.599\ \text{mol glucose}}{2.0\ \text{L solution}} = 0.30\ M$$

molarity   **Answer**

PROBLEM 8.16

Calculate the molarity of each aqueous solution with the given amount of NaCl (molar mass 58.44 g/mol) and final volume.

a. 1.0 mol in 0.50 L   c. 0.050 mol in 5.0 mL   e. 24.4 g in 350 mL
b. 2.0 mol in 250 mL   d. 12.0 g in 2.0 L   f. 60.0 g in 750 mL

PROBLEM 8.17

Which solution has the higher concentration, one prepared from 10.0 g of NaOH in a final volume of 150 mL, or one prepared from 15.0 g of NaOH in a final volume of 250 mL of solution?

Molarity is a conversion factor that relates the number of moles of solute to the volume of solution it occupies. Thus, if we know the molarity and volume of a solution, we can calculate the number of moles it contains. If we know the molarity and number of moles, we can calculate the volume in liters.

To calculate the moles of solute…   …rearrange the equation for molarity (M):

$$\frac{\text{moles of solute (mol)}}{V\ (L)} = M \qquad\qquad \boxed{\text{moles of solute (mol)} = M \times V\ (L)}$$

To calculate the volume of solution…   …rearrange the equation for molarity (M):

$$\frac{\text{moles of solute (mol)}}{V\ (L)} = M \qquad\qquad \boxed{V\ (L) = \frac{\text{moles of solute (mol)}}{M}}$$

SAMPLE PROBLEM 8.9

What volume in milliliters of a 0.30 M solution of glucose contains 0.025 mol of glucose?

Analysis

Use the equation, $V = (\text{moles of solute})/M$, to find the volume in liters, and then convert the liters to milliliters.

Solution

[1] Identify the known quantities and the desired quantity.

0.30 M   ? V (mL) solution
0.025 mol glucose

known quantities   desired quantity

[2] Divide the number of moles by molarity to obtain the volume in liters.

$$V\ (L) = \frac{\text{moles of solute (mol)}}{M}$$

$$= \frac{0.025\ \text{mol glucose}}{0.30\ \text{mol/L}} = 0.083\ \text{L solution}$$

[3] Use a mL–L conversion factor to convert liters to milliliters.

mL–L conversion factor

$$0.083\ \text{L solution} \times \frac{1000\ \text{mL}}{1\ L} = 83\ \text{mL glucose solution}$$

Liters cancel.   **Answer**

PROBLEM 8.18

How many milliliters of a 1.5 M glucose solution contain each of the following number of moles?

a. 0.15 mol   b. 0.020 mol   c. 0.0030 mol   d. 3.0 mol

PROBLEM 8.19

How many moles of NaCl are contained in each volume of aqueous NaCl solution?

a. 2.0 L of a 2.0 M solution   c. 25 mL of a 2.0 M solution
b. 2.5 L of a 0.25 M solution   d. 250 mL of a 0.25 M solution

Since the number of grams and moles of a substance is related by the molar mass, we can convert a given volume of solution to the number of grams of solute it contains by carrying out the step-wise calculation shown in Sample Problem 8.10.

SAMPLE PROBLEM 8.10

How many grams of aspirin are contained in 50.0 mL of a 0.050 M solution?

Analysis

Use the molarity to convert the volume of the solution to moles of solute. Then use the molar mass to convert moles to grams.

Solution

[1] Identify the known quantities and the desired quantity.

$$0.050 \text{ M}$$

$$50.0 \text{ mL solution} \qquad ? \text{ g aspirin}$$

$$\text{known quantities} \qquad \text{desired quantity}$$

[2] Determine the number of moles of aspirin using the molarity.

volume   molarity   mL–L conversion factor

$$50.0 \text{ mL solution} \quad \times \quad \frac{0.050 \text{ mol aspirin}}{1 \text{ L}} \quad \times \quad \frac{1 \text{ L}}{1000 \text{ mL}} \quad = \quad 0.0025 \text{ mol aspirin}$$

[3] Convert the number of moles of aspirin to grams using the molar mass (180.2 g/mol).

molar mass conversion factor

$$0.0025 \text{ mol aspirin} \quad \times \quad \frac{180.2 \text{ g aspirin}}{1 \text{ mol aspirin}} \quad = \quad 0.45 \text{ g aspirin}$$

Moles cancel.   **Answer**

PROBLEM 8.20

How many grams of NaCl are contained in each of the following volumes of a 1.25 M solution?

a. 0.10 L   b. 2.0 L   c. 0.55 L   d. 50. mL

PROBLEM 8.21

How many milliliters of a 0.25 M sucrose solution contain each of the following number of grams? The molar mass of sucrose ($C_{12}H_{22}O_{11}$) is 342.3 g/mol.

a. 0.500 g   b. 2.0 g   c. 1.25 g   d. 50.0 mg

8.6 Dilution

CONSUMER NOTE

Some cleaning products are sold as concentrated solutions, which are then diluted prior to use.

Sometimes a solution has a higher concentration than is needed. ***Dilution* is the addition of solvent to decrease the concentration of the solution.** For example, a stock solution of a drug is often supplied in a concentrated form to take up less space on a pharmacy shelf, and then it is diluted so that it can be administered in a reasonable volume and lower concentration that allows for more accurate dosing.

A key fact to keep in mind is that the **amount of solute is *constant*.** Only the volume of the solution is changed by adding solvent.

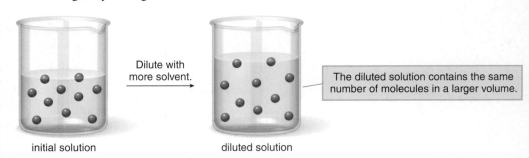

Dilute with more solvent.

The diluted solution contains the same number of molecules in a larger volume.

initial solution   diluted solution

In using molarity as a measure of concentration in Section 8.5, we learned that the number of moles of solute can be calculated from the molarity and volume of a solution.

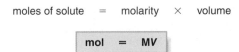

$$\text{moles of solute} = \text{molarity} \times \text{volume}$$

$$\text{mol} = MV$$

Thus, if we have initial values for the molarity and volume (M_1 and V_1), we can calculate a new value for the molarity or volume (M_2 or V_2), since the product of the molarity and volume equals the number of moles, a constant.

$$\underset{\text{initial values}}{M_1 V_1} = \underset{\text{final values}}{M_2 V_2}$$

Although molarity is the most common concentration measure in the laboratory, the same facts hold in diluting solutions reported in other concentration units—percent concentration and parts per million—as well. In general, therefore, if we have initial values for the concentration and volume (C_1 and V_1), we can calculate a new value for the concentration or volume (C_2 or V_2), since the product of the concentration and volume is a constant.

$$\underset{\text{initial values}}{C_1 V_1} = \underset{\text{final values}}{C_2 V_2}$$

SAMPLE PROBLEM 8.11

What is the concentration of a solution formed by diluting 5.0 mL of a 3.2 M glucose solution to 40.0 mL?

Analysis

Since we know an initial molarity and volume (M_1 and V_1) and a final volume (V_2), we can calculate a new molarity (M_2) using the equation $M_1 V_1 = M_2 V_2$.

Solution

[1] Identify the known quantities and the desired quantity.

$$M_1 = 3.2 \text{ M}$$

$$\underset{\text{known quantities}}{V_1 = 5.0 \text{ mL} \qquad V_2 = 40.0 \text{ mL}} \qquad \underset{\text{desired quantity}}{M_2 = ?}$$

[2] Write the equation and rearrange it to isolate the desired quantity, M_2, on one side.

$$M_1V_1 = M_2V_2 \quad \text{Solve for } M_2 \text{ by dividing both sides by } V_2.$$

$$\frac{M_1V_1}{V_2} = M_2$$

[3] Solve the problem.

- Substitute the three known quantities into the equation and solve for M_2.

$$M_2 = \frac{M_1V_1}{V_2} = \frac{(3.2 \text{ M})(5.0 \text{ mL})}{(40.0 \text{ mL})} = 0.40 \text{ M glucose solution}$$

Answer

PROBLEM 8.22

What is the concentration of a solution formed by diluting 25.0 mL of a 3.8 M glucose solution to 275 mL?

SAMPLE PROBLEM 8.12

Dopamine is a potent drug administered intravenously to increase blood pressure in seriously ill patients. How many milliliters of a 4.0% (w/v) solution must be used to prepare 250 mL of a 0.080% (w/v) solution?

Analysis

Since we know an initial concentration (C_1), a final concentration (C_2), and a final volume (V_2), we can calculate the volume (V_1) of the initial solution that must be used with the equation, $C_1V_1 = C_2V_2$.

Solution

[1] Identify the known quantities and the desired quantity.

$$C_1 = 4.0\% \text{ (w/v)} \qquad C_2 = 0.080\% \text{ (w/v)}$$
$$V_2 = 250 \text{ mL} \qquad\qquad V_1 = ?$$

known quantities $\qquad$ desired quantity

[2] Write the equation and rearrange it to isolate the desired quantity, V_1, on one side.

$$C_1V_1 = C_2V_2 \quad \text{Solve for } V_1 \text{ by dividing both sides by } C_1.$$

$$V_1 = \frac{C_2V_2}{C_1}$$

[3] Solve the problem.

- Substitute the three known quantities into the equation and solve for V_1.

$$V_1 = \frac{(0.080\%)(250 \text{ mL})}{4.0\%} = 5.0 \text{ mL dopamine solution}$$

Answer

PROBLEM 8.23

How many milliliters of a 6.0 M NaOH solution would be needed to prepare each solution?

a. 525 mL of a 2.5 M solution

b. 750 mL of a 4.0 M solution

c. 450 mL of a 0.10 M solution

d. 25 mL of a 3.5 M solution

PROBLEM 8.24

Ketamine, an anesthetic, is supplied in a solution of 100. mg/mL. If 2.0 mL of this solution is diluted to a volume of 10.0 mL, how much of the diluted solution should be administered to supply a dose of 75 mg?

8.7 Colligative Properties

Although many properties of a solution are similar to those of a pure solvent, the boiling point and melting point of a solution differ from the boiling point and melting point of the solvent used to make it.

- *Colligative properties* are properties of a solution that depend on the concentration of the solute but not its identity.

Thus, the *number* of dissolved particles of solute affects the properties of the solution, but the identity of the solute does not. In this section we examine how a dissolved solute increases the boiling point and decreases the melting point of a solution. In Section 8.8, we look at **osmosis,** a process that involves the diffusion of solvent across a semipermeable membrane.

8.7A Boiling Point Elevation

A solute in a solution can be **volatile** or **nonvolatile.**

- A volatile solute readily escapes into the vapor phase.
- A nonvolatile solute does not readily escape into the vapor phase, and thus it has a negligible vapor pressure at a given temperature.

Figure 8.7 compares the vapor pressure above a pure liquid (water) with the vapor pressure above a solution made by dissolving a nonvolatile solute in water. The vapor pressure of a solution composed of a nonvolatile solute and a liquid solvent consists solely of gas molecules derived from the solvent. Since there are fewer solvent molecules in the solution than there are in the pure liquid, there are fewer molecules in the gas phase as well. **As a result, the vapor pressure above the solution is *lower* than the vapor pressure of the pure solvent.**

What effect does this lower vapor pressure have on the boiling point of the solution? The boiling point is the temperature at which the vapor pressure equals the atmospheric pressure. A lower vapor pressure means that the solution must be heated to a higher temperature to get the vapor pressure to equal the atmospheric pressure. This results in **boiling point elevation.**

- A liquid solution that contains a nonvolatile solute has a higher boiling point than the solvent alone.

The amount that the boiling point increases depends only on the number of dissolved particles. For example,

- One mole of any nonvolatile solute raises the boiling point of one kilogram of water by 0.51 °C.

Figure 8.7

Vapor Pressure Above a Liquid Solution

H$_2$O   pure liquid   solution   solute   H$_2$O

When a nonvolatile solute is added to a solvent, there are fewer molecules of solvent in the gas phase, so the vapor pressure of the solution above the solvent is lower.

Thus, one mole of glucose molecules raises the boiling point of 1 kg of water by 0.51 °C, to 100.51 °C. Since NaCl contains two particles—Na$^+$ cations and Cl$^-$ anions—per mole, one mole of NaCl raises the boiling point of 1 kg of water by 2 × 0.51 °C or 1.02 °C, to 101.02 °C, rounded to 101.0 °C.

SAMPLE PROBLEM 8.13

What is the boiling point of a solution that contains 0.45 mol of KCl in 1.00 kg of water?

Analysis

Determine the number of "particles" contained in the solute. Use 0.51 °C/mol as a conversion factor to relate the temperature change to the number of moles of solute particles.

Solution

Each KCl provides two "particles," K$^+$ and Cl$^-$.

$$\text{temperature increase} = \frac{0.51\ °C}{\text{mol particles}} \times 0.45\ \text{mol KCl} \times \frac{2\ \text{mol particles}}{\text{mol KCl}} = 0.46\ °C$$

The boiling point of the solution is 100.0 °C + 0.46 °C = 100.46 °C, rounded to 100.5 °C.

PROBLEM 8.25

What is the boiling point of a solution prepared from the given quantity of solute in 1.00 kg of water?

  a. 2.0 mol of sucrose molecules   c. 2.0 mol of CaCl$_2$
  b. 2.0 mol of KNO$_3$ d. 20.0 g of NaCl

8.7B Freezing Point Depression

In a similar manner, a dissolved solute lowers the freezing point of a solvent. The presence of solute molecules makes it harder for solvent molecules to form an organized crystalline solid, thus lowering the temperature at which the liquid phase becomes solid. This results in **freezing point depression.**

- A liquid solution that contains a nonvolatile solute has a lower freezing point than the solvent alone.

The amount of freezing point depression depends only on the number of dissolved particles. For example,

- One mole of any nonvolatile solute lowers the freezing point of one kilogram of water by 1.86 °C.

Thus, one mole of glucose molecules lowers the freezing point of 1 kg of water to –1.86 °C. Since NaCl contains two particles—Na$^+$ cations and Cl$^-$ anions—per mole, one mole of NaCl lowers the freezing point of 1 kg of water by 2 × (–1.86 °C) or –3.72 °C.

Several practical applications exploit freezing point depression. Antifreeze, which contains nonvolatile ethylene glycol, is added to automobile radiators to lower the freezing point of the water in the cooling system, so it does not freeze in cold climates. Fish that inhabit cold environments produce large amounts of glycerol, $C_3H_8O_3$, which lowers the freezing point of their blood, thus allowing it to remain fluid in very cold water.

Airplane wings are de-iced with a solution that contains ethylene glycol, which lowers the freezing point, so the ice melts.

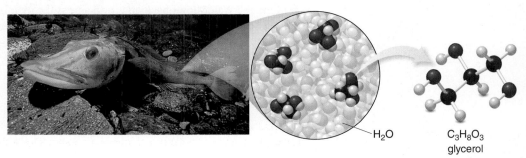

H$_2$O   C$_3$H$_8$O$_3$
glycerol

SAMPLE PROBLEM 8.14

What is the melting point of a solution that contains 3.00 mol of $CaCl_2$ dissolved in 1.00 kg of water? $CaCl_2$ is used in rock salt to melt ice and snow on highways and sidewalks in the winter.

Analysis

Determine the number of "particles" contained in the solute. Use 1.86 °C/mol as a conversion factor to relate the temperature change to the number of moles of solute particles.

Solution

Each $CaCl_2$ provides three "particles," Ca^+ and 2 Cl^-.

$$\text{temperature decrease} = \frac{1.86\ °C}{\text{mol particles}} \times 3.00\ \text{mol } CaCl_2 \times \frac{3\ \text{mol particles}}{\text{mol } CaCl_2} = 16.7\ °C$$

The melting point of the solution is 0.0 °C + −16.7 °C = −16.7 °C.

PROBLEM 8.26

What is the melting point of a solution prepared from the given quantity of solute in 1.00 kg of water?

a. 2.0 mol of sucrose molecules   c. 2.0 mol of $CaCl_2$
b. 2.0 mol of KNO_3 d. 20.0 g of NaCl

PROBLEM 8.27

What is the melting point of a solution that is formed when 250 g of ethylene glycol ($C_2H_6O_2$) is dissolved in 1.00 kg of water?

8.8 Osmosis and Dialysis

The membrane that surrounds living cells is an example of a **semipermeable membrane**—a membrane that allows water and small molecules to pass across, but ions and large molecules cannot.

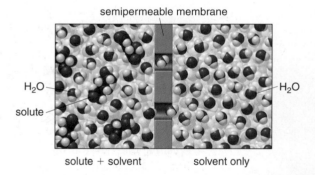

semipermeable membrane

H_2O H_2O

solute

solute + solvent   solvent only

- *Osmosis* is the passage of solvent, usually water, across a semipermeable membrane from a solution of low solute concentration to a solution of higher solute concentration.

8.8A Osmotic Pressure

What happens when water and an aqueous glucose solution are separated by a semipermeable membrane? Water flows back and forth across the membrane, but more water flows from the side that has pure solvent towards the side that has dissolved glucose. This decreases the volume of pure solvent on one side of the membrane and increases the volume of the glucose solution on the other side.

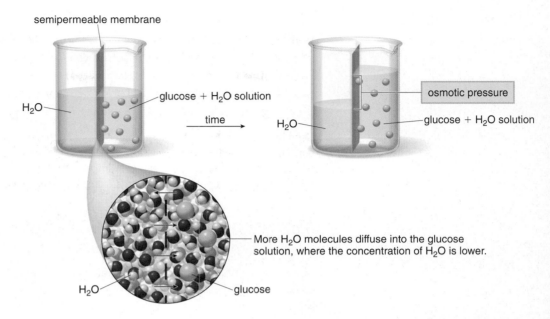

semipermeable membrane

H_2O

glucose + H_2O solution

time

osmotic pressure

H_2O

glucose + H_2O solution

More H_2O molecules diffuse into the glucose solution, where the concentration of H_2O is lower.

H_2O

glucose

The increased volume of the glucose solution creates increased pressure on one side of the membrane. When the increased pressure gets to a certain point, it prevents more water movement to further dilute the glucose solution. Water continues to diffuse back and forth across the membrane, but the level of the two liquids does not change any further.

- *Osmotic pressure* is the pressure that prevents the flow of additional solvent into a solution on one side of a semipermeable membrane.

Osmotic pressure is a colligative property, so it depends only on the number of particles in a solution. **The greater the number of dissolved particles, the greater the osmotic pressure.** A 0.1 M NaCl solution has twice the osmotic pressure as a 0.1 M glucose solution, since each NaCl is composed of two particles, Na^+ cations and Cl^- anions.

If, instead of having pure water on one side of the membrane, there were two solutions of different concentrations, water would flow from the side of the *less* concentrated solution to dilute the *more* concentrated solution.

SAMPLE PROBLEM 8.15

A 0.1 M glucose solution is separated from a 0.2 M glucose solution by a semipermeable membrane. (a) Which solution exerts the greater osmotic pressure? (b) In which direction will water flow between the two solutions? (c) Describe the level of the two solutions when equilibrium is reached.

Analysis

The solvent (water) flows from the less concentrated solution to the more concentrated solution.

Solution

a. The greater the number of dissolved particles, the higher the osmotic pressure, so the 0.2 M glucose solution exerts the greater pressure.

b. Water will flow from the less concentrated solution (0.1 M) to the more concentrated solution (0.2 M).

c. Since water flows into the 0.2 M solution, its height will increase, and the height of the 0.1 M glucose solution will decrease.

Which solution in each pair exerts the greater osmotic pressure?

  a. 1.0% sugar solution or 5.0% sugar solution

  b. 3.0 M NaCl solution or a 4.0 M NaCl solution

  c. 1.0 M glucose solution or a 0.75 M NaCl solution

Describe the process that occurs when a 1.0 M NaCl solution is separated from a 1.5 M NaCl solution by a semipermeable membrane in terms of each of the following: (a) the identity of the substances that flow across the membrane; (b) the direction of flow before and after equilibrium is achieved; (c) the height of the solutions after equilibrium is achieved.

8.8B FOCUS ON THE HUMAN BODY
Osmosis and Biological Membranes

Since cell membranes are semipermeable and biological fluids contain dissolved ions and molecules, osmosis is an ongoing phenomenon in living cells. Fluids on both sides of a cell membrane must have the same osmotic pressure to avoid pressure buildup inside or outside the cell. Any intravenous solution given to a patient, therefore, must have the same osmotic pressure as the fluids in the body.

- Two solutions with the same osmotic pressure are said to be *isotonic*.

Isotonic solutions used in hospitals include 0.92% (w/v) NaCl solution (or 0.15 M NaCl solution) and 5.0% (w/v) glucose solution. Although these solutions do not contain exactly the same ions or molecules present in body fluids, they exert the same osmotic pressure. *Remember:* **With a colligative property the concentration of particles is important, but not the identity of those particles.**

If a red blood cell is placed in an isotonic NaCl solution, called physiological saline solution, the red blood cells retain their same size and shape because the osmotic pressure inside and outside the cell is the same (Figure 8.8a). What happens if a red blood cell is placed in a solution having a different osmotic pressure?

- A *hypotonic* solution has a lower osmotic pressure than body fluids.
- A *hypertonic* solution has a higher osmotic pressure than body fluids.

In a hypotonic solution, the concentration of particles outside the cell is lower than the concentration of particles inside the cell. In other words, the concentration of water outside the cell is *higher* than the concentration of water inside the cell, so water diffuses inside (Figure 8.8b). As a result, the cell swells and eventually bursts. This swelling and rupture of red blood cells is called **hemolysis.**

In a hypertonic solution, the concentration of particles outside the cell is higher than the concentration of particles inside the cell. In other words, the concentration of water inside the cell is *higher* than the concentration of water outside the cell, so water diffuses out of the cell (Figure 8.8c). As a result, the cell shrinks. This process is called **crenation.**

What happens to a red blood cell when it is placed in each of the following solutions: (a) 3% (w/v) glucose solution; (b) 0.15 M KCl solution; (c) 0.15 M Na_2CO_3 solution?

Figure 8.8

The Effect of Osmotic Pressure Differences on Red Blood Cells

a.

b.

c.

isotonic
solution

hypotonic
solution

hypertonic
solution

(a) In an isotonic solution, the movement of water into and out of the red blood cell occurs to an equal extent and the red blood cell keeps its normal volume. (b) In a hypotonic solution, more water moves into the cell than diffuses out, so the cell swells and eventually it can rupture (hemolysis). (c) In a hypertonic solution, more water moves out of the cell than diffuses in, so the cell shrivels (crenation).

8.8C FOCUS ON HEALTH & MEDICINE
Dialysis

Dialysis is also a process that involves the selective passage of substances across a semipermeable membrane, called a dialyzing membrane. In dialysis, however, water, small molecules, and ions can travel across the membrane; only large biological molecules like proteins and starch cannot.

In the human body, blood is filtered through the kidneys by the process of dialysis (Figure 8.9). Each kidney contains over a million nephrons, tubelike structures with filtration membranes.

Figure 8.9

Dialysis of Body Fluids by the Kidneys

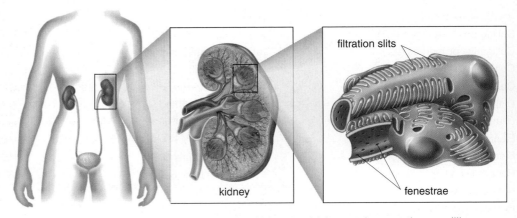

filtration slits

kidney

fenestrae

Body fluids are dialyzed by passage through the kidneys, which contain more than a million nephrons that filter out small molecules and ions from the blood. Useful materials are then reabsorbed while urea and other waste products are eliminated in urine.

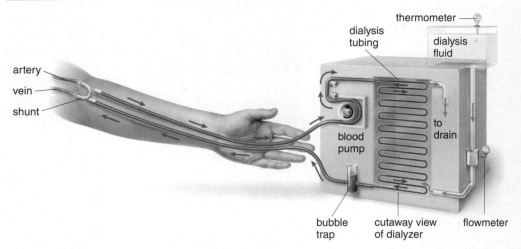

Figure 8.10   Hemodialysis

When a patient's kidneys no longer function properly, periodic dialysis treatments are used to remove waste products from the blood. Blood is passed through a dialyzer, which contains a membrane that allows small molecules to pass through, thus acting as an artificial kidney. Each treatment takes several hours. Patients usually require two to three treatments per week.

These membranes filter small molecules—glucose, amino acids, urea, ions, and water—from the blood. Useful materials are then reabsorbed, but urea and other waste products are eliminated in urine.

When an individual's kidneys are incapable of removing waste products from the blood, **hemodialysis** is used (Figure 8.10). A patient's blood flows through a long tube connected to a cellophane membrane suspended in an isotonic solution that contains NaCl, KCl, NaHCO$_3$, and glucose. Small molecules like urea cross the membrane into the solution, thus removing them from the blood. Red blood cells and large molecules are not removed from the blood because they are too big to cross the dialyzing membrane.

CHAPTER HIGHLIGHTS

KEY TERMS

Aqueous solution (8.1)

Boiling point elevation (8.7)

Colligative properties (8.7)

Colloid (8.1)

Concentration (8.4)

Dialysis (8.8)

Dilution (8.6)

Electrolyte (8.1)

Freezing point depression (8.7)

Henry's law (8.3)

Heterogeneous mixture (8.1)

Homogeneous mixture (8.1)

Hypertonic solution (8.8)

Hypotonic solution (8.8)

Ion–dipole interaction (8.2)

Isotonic solution (8.8)

Molarity (8.5)

Nonelectrolyte (8.1)

Nonvolatile (8.7)

Osmosis (8.8)

Osmotic pressure (8.8)

Parts per million (8.4)

Saturated solution (8.2)

Semipermeable membrane (8.8)

Solubility (8.2)

Solute (8.1)

Solution (8.1)

Solvation (8.2)

Solvent (8.1)

Supersaturated solution (8.3)

Unsaturated solution (8.2)

Volatile (8.7)

Volume/volume percent concentration (8.4)

Weight/volume percent concentration (8.4)

KEY CONCEPTS

1 What are the fundamental features of a solution? (8.1)

- A solution is a homogeneous mixture that contains small dissolved particles. Any phase of matter can form solutions. The substance present in the lesser amount is called the solute, and the substance present in the larger amount is the solvent.
- A solution conducts electricity if it contains dissolved ions, but does not conduct electricity if it contains atoms or neutral molecules.

2 What determines whether a substance is soluble in water or a nonpolar solvent? (8.2)

- One rule summarizes solubility: "Like dissolves like."
- Most ionic compounds are soluble in water. If the attractive forces between the ions and water are stronger than the attraction between the ions in the crystal, an ionic compound dissolves in water.
- Small polar compounds that can hydrogen bond are soluble in water.
- Nonpolar compounds are soluble in nonpolar solvents. Compounds with many nonpolar C—C and C—H bonds are soluble in nonpolar solvents.

3 What effect do temperature and pressure have on solubility? (8.3)

- The solubility of solids in a liquid solvent generally increases with increasing temperature. The solubility of gases decreases with increasing temperature.
- Increasing pressure increases the solubility of a gas in a solvent. Pressure changes do not affect the solubility of liquids and solids.

4 How is the concentration of a solution expressed? (8.4, 8.5)

- Concentration is a measure of how much solute is dissolved in a given amount of solution, and can be measured using mass, volume, or moles.

- Weight/volume (w/v) percent concentration is the number of grams of solute dissolved in 100 mL of solution.
- Volume/volume (v/v) percent concentration is the number of milliliters of solute dissolved in 100 mL of solution.
- Parts per million (ppm) is the number of parts of solute in 1,000,000 parts of solution, where the units for both the solute and the solution are the same.
- Molarity (M) is the number of moles of solute per liter of solution.

5 How are dilutions performed? (8.6)

- Dilution is the addition of solvent to decrease the concentration of a solute. Since the number of moles of solute is constant in carrying out a dilution, a new molarity or volume (M_2 and V_2) can be calculated from a given molarity and volume (M_1 and V_1) using the equation $M_1V_1 = M_2V_2$, as long as three of the four quantities are known.

6 How do dissolved particles affect the boiling point and melting point of a solution? (8.7)

- A nonvolatile solute lowers the vapor pressure above a solution, thus increasing its boiling point.
- A nonvolatile solute makes it harder for solvent molecules to form a crystalline solid, thus decreasing its melting point.

7 What is osmosis? (8.8)

- Osmosis is the passage of solvent, usually water, across a semipermeable membrane. Solvent always moves from the less concentrated solution to the more concentrated solution, until the osmotic pressure prevents additional flow of solvent.
- Since living cells contain and are surrounded by biological solutions separated by a semipermeable membrane, the osmotic pressure must be the same on both sides of the membrane. Dialysis is similar to osmosis in that it involves the selective passage of several substances—water, small molecules, and ions—across a dialyzing membrane.

KEY EQUATIONS—CONCENTRATION

Weight/volume percent concentration

$$(\text{w/v})\% = \frac{\text{mass of solute (g)}}{\text{volume of solution (mL)}} \times 100\%$$

Volume/volume percent concentration

$$(\text{v/v})\% = \frac{\text{volume of solute (mL)}}{\text{volume of solution (mL)}} \times 100\%$$

Parts per million

$$\text{ppm} = \frac{\text{parts of solute (g or mL)}}{\text{parts of solution (g or mL)}} \times 10^6$$

Molarity

$$M = \frac{\text{moles of solute (mol)}}{\text{liter of solution (L)}}$$

PROBLEMS

Selected in-chapter and odd-numbered end-of-chapter problems have brief answers in Appendix B. The *Student Study Guide and Solutions Manual* contains detailed solutions to all in-chapter and odd-numbered end-of-chapter problems, as well as additional worked examples and a chapter self-test.

Mixtures and Solutions

8.31 Which representation of molecular art better shows a solution of KI dissolved in water? Explain your choice. Will this solution conduct an electric current?

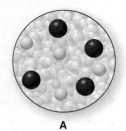 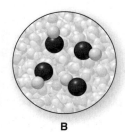

A   B

8.32 Which representation of molecular art better shows a solution of NaF dissolved in water? Explain your choice. Will this solution conduct an electric current?

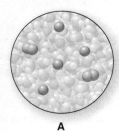 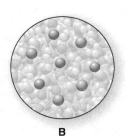

A   B

8.33 Classify each of the following as a heterogeneous mixture, a solution, or a colloid.
   a. bronze (an alloy of Sn and Cu)
   b. diet soda
   c. orange juice with pulp
   d. household ammonia
   e. gasoline
   f. fog

8.34 Classify each of the following as a heterogeneous mixture, a solution, or a colloid.
   a. soft drink   c. wine   e. bleach
   b. cream   d. lava rock   f. apple juice

Solubility

8.35 If the solubility of KCl in 100 mL of H_2O is 34 g at 20 °C and 43 g at 50 °C, label each of the following solutions as unsaturated, saturated, or supersaturated. If more solid is added than can dissolve in the solvent, assume that undissolved solid remains at the bottom of the flask.
   a. adding 30 g to 100 mL of H_2O at 20 °C
   b. adding 65 g to 100 mL of H_2O at 50 °C
   c. adding 20 g to 50 mL of H_2O at 20 °C
   d. adding 42 g to 100 mL of H_2O at 50 °C and slowly cooling to 20 °C to give a clear solution with no precipitate

8.36 If the solubility of sucrose in 100 mL of H_2O is 204 g at 20 °C and 260 g at 50 °C, label each of the following solutions as unsaturated, saturated, or supersaturated. If more solid is added than can dissolve in the solvent, assume that undissolved solid remains at the bottom of the flask.
   a. adding 200 g to 100 mL of H_2O at 20 °C
   b. adding 245 g to 100 mL of H_2O at 50 °C
   c. adding 110 g to 50 mL of H_2O at 20 °C
   d. adding 220 g to 100 mL of H_2O at 50 °C and slowly cooling to 20 °C to give a clear solution with no precipitate

8.37 Which compounds are soluble in water?

   a. LiCl

   c.

   b.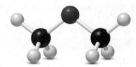

   d. Na_3PO_4

8.38 Which compounds are soluble in water?

   a. C_5H_{12} b. $CaCl_2$ c. H—C—N—H   d. CH_3Br

8.39 Using the ball-and-stick model for methanol (CH_3OH), draw a representation for the solution that results when methanol is dissolved in water.

8.40 Using the ball-and-stick model for dimethyl ether [$(CH_3)_2O$], draw a representation for the solution that results when dimethyl ether is dissolved in water.

8.41 Explain the statement, "Oil and water don't mix."

8.42 Explain why a bottle of salad dressing that contains oil and vinegar has two layers.

8.43 Predict the solubility of solid I_2 in water and in CCl_4. Explain your choices.

8.44 Glycine is a covalent compound that contains two charged atoms. Explain why glycine, an amino acid used to make proteins, is soluble in water.

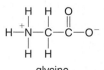

glycine

8.45 Explain why cholesterol, a compound with molecular formula $C_{27}H_{46}O$ and one OH group, is soluble in CCl_4 but insoluble in water.

8.46 Which of the following pairs of compounds form a solution?
   a. KCl and CCl_4
   b. 1-propanol (C_3H_8O) and H_2O
   c. cyclodecanone ($C_{10}H_{18}O$) and H_2O
   d. pentane (C_5H_{12}) and hexane (C_6H_{14})

8.47 The molecular art represents O_2 molecules dissolved in water at 25 °C. Draw a representation for the solution that results (a) after heating to 50 °C; (b) after cooling to 10 °C.

8.48 The molecular art represents NaCl dissolved in water at 25 °C. Assume that this solution is saturated in NaCl and that solid NaCl remains at the bottom of the flask in which the solution is stored. Draw a representation for the solution that results (a) after heating to 50 °C; (b) after cooling to 10 °C.

8.49 How is the solubility of solid NaCl in water affected by each of the following changes?
   a. increasing the temperature from 25 °C to 50 °C
   b. decreasing the temperature from 25 °C to 0 °C
   c. increasing the pressure from 1 atm to 2 atm
   d. decreasing the pressure from 5 atm to 1 atm

8.50 How is the solubility of helium gas in water affected by each of the following changes?
   a. increasing the temperature from 25 °C to 50 °C
   b. decreasing the temperature from 25 °C to 0 °C
   c. increasing the pressure from 1 atm to 2 atm
   d. decreasing the pressure from 5 atm to 1 atm

8.51 Explain the effect of a decrease in temperature on the solubility of each type of solute in a liquid solvent: (a) gas; (b) solid.

8.52 Explain the effect of a decrease in pressure on the solubility of each type of solute in a liquid solvent: (a) gas; (b) solid.

8.53 Explain why many ionic compounds are soluble in water.

8.54 Explain why some ionic compounds are insoluble in water.

8.55 Use the solubility rules listed in Section 8.2B to predict whether each of the following ionic compounds is soluble in water.
   a. K_2SO_4 e. $Fe(NO_3)_3$
   b. $MgSO_4$ f. $PbCl_2$
   c. $ZnCO_3$ g. CsCl
   d. KI   h. $Ni(HCO_3)_2$

8.56 Use the solubility rules listed in Section 8.2B to predict whether each of the following ionic compounds is soluble in water.
   a. $Al(NO_3)_3$ e. $CuCO_3$
   b. $NaHCO_3$ f. $(NH_4)_2SO_4$
   c. $Cr(OH)_2$ g. $Fe(OH)_3$
   d. LiOH   h. $(NH_4)_3PO_4$

Concentration

8.57 Write two conversion factors for each concentration.
   a. 5% (w/v)   b. 6.0 M   c. 10 ppm

8.58 Write two conversion factors for each concentration.
   a. 15% (v/v)   b. 12.0 M   c. 15 ppm

8.59 What is the weight/volume percent concentration using the given amount of solute and total volume of solution?
   a. 10.0 g of LiCl in 750 mL of solution
   b. 25 g of $NaNO_3$ in 150 mL of solution
   c. 40.0 g of NaOH in 500. mL of solution

8.60 What is the weight/volume percent concentration using the given amount of solute and total volume of solution?
   a. 5.5 g of LiCl in 550 mL of solution
   b. 12.5 g of $NaNO_3$ in 250 mL of solution
   c. 20.0 g of NaOH in 400. mL of solution

8.61 What is the volume/volume percent concentration of a solution prepared from 25 mL of ethyl acetate in 150 mL of solution?

8.62 What is the volume/volume percent concentration of a solution prepared from 75 mL of acetone in 250 mL of solution?

8.63 What is the molarity of a solution prepared using the given amount of solute and total volume of solution?
   a. 3.5 mol of KCl in 1.50 L of solution
   b. 0.44 mol of $NaNO_3$ in 855 mL of solution
   c. 25.0 g of NaCl in 650 mL of solution
   d. 10.0 g of $NaHCO_3$ in 3.3 L of solution

8.64 What is the molarity of a solution prepared using the given amount of solute and total volume of solution?
   a. 2.4 mol of NaOH in 1.50 L of solution
   b. 0.48 mol of KNO_3 in 750 mL of solution
   c. 25.0 g of KCl in 650 mL of solution
   d. 10.0 g of Na_2CO_3 in 3.8 L of solution

8.65 How would you use a 250-mL volumetric flask to prepare each of the following solutions?
   a. 4.8% (w/v) acetic acid in water
   b. 22% (v/v) ethyl acetate in water
   c. 2.5 M NaCl solution

8.66 How would you use a 250-mL volumetric flask to prepare each of the following solutions?
    a. 2.0% (w/v) KCl in water
    b. 34% (v/v) ethanol in water
    c. 4.0 M NaCl solution

8.67 How many moles of solute are contained in each solution?
    a. 150 mL of a 0.25 M $NaNO_3$ solution
    b. 45 mL of a 2.0 M HNO_3 solution
    c. 2.5 L of a 1.5 M HCl solution

8.68 How many moles of solute are contained in each solution?
    a. 250 mL of a 0.55 M $NaNO_3$ solution
    b. 145 mL of a 4.0 M HNO_3 solution
    c. 6.5 L of a 2.5 M HCl solution

8.69 How many grams of solute are contained in each solution in Problem 8.67?

8.70 How many grams of solute are contained in each solution in Problem 8.68?

8.71 How many mL of ethanol are contained in a 750-mL bottle of wine that contains 11.0% (v/v) of ethanol?

8.72 What is the molarity of a 20.0% (v/v) aqueous ethanol solution? The density of ethanol (C_2H_6O, molar mass 46.07 g/mol) is 0.790 g/mL.

8.73 A 1.89-L bottle of vinegar contains 5.0% (w/v) of acetic acid ($C_2H_4O_2$, molar mass 60.05 g/mol) in water.
    a. How many grams of acetic acid are present in the container?
    b. How many moles of acetic acid are present in the container?
    c. Convert the weight/volume percent concentration to molarity.

8.74 What is the molarity of a 15% (w/v) glucose solution?

8.75 The maximum safe level of each compound in drinking water is given below. Convert each value to parts per million.
    a. chloroform ($CHCl_3$, a solvent), 80 µg/kg
    b. glyphosate (a pesticide), 700 µg/kg

8.76 The maximum safe level of each metal in drinking water is given below. Convert each value to parts per million.
    a. copper, 1,300 µg/kg
    b. arsenic, 10 µg/kg
    c. chromium, 100 µg/kg

Dilution

8.77 If the solution in **X** is diluted, which representation (**A–C**) represents the final solution?

    X   A   B   C

8.78 Consider solutions **A, B,** and **C** in Problem 8.77. If the volumes of **A** and **B** are twice the volume of **C**, which solution is most concentrated? Which solution is least concentrated?

8.79 (a) If **A** represents a 0.1 M aqueous NaCl solution, what is the concentration of **B,** a solution formed by dilution of **A** with water? (b) If the volume of **A** is 50.0 mL, how much water is added to form **B**?

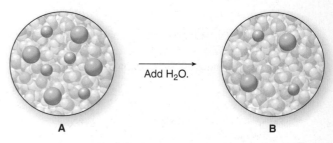

    A   B

8.80 (a) If **C** represents a 2.0 M aqueous NaCl solution, what is the concentration of **D,** a solution formed by dilution of **C** with water? (b) If the volume of **C** is 100. mL, how much water is added to form **D**?

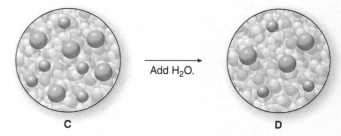

    C   D

8.81 How are the concepts of concentration and dilution related?

8.82 Explain why it is impossible to prepare 200 mL of a 5.0 M NaOH solution by diluting a 2.5 M NaOH solution.

8.83 What is the weight/volume percent concentration of a 30.0% (w/v) solution of vitamin C after each of the following dilutions?
    a. 100. mL diluted to 200. mL
    b. 100. mL diluted to 500. mL
    c. 250 mL diluted to 1.5 L
    d. 0.35 L diluted to 750 mL

8.84 One gram (1.00 g) of vitamin B_3 (niacin) is dissolved in water to give 10.0 mL of solution. (a) What is the weight/volume percent concentration of this solution? (b) What is the concentration of a solution formed by diluting 1.0 mL of this solution to each of the following volumes: [1] 10.0 mL; [2] 2.5 mL; [3] 50.0 mL; [4] 120 mL?

8.85 What is the concentration of a solution formed by diluting 125 mL of 12.0 M HCl solution to 850 mL?

8.86 What is the concentration of a solution formed by diluting 250 mL of 6.0 M NaOH solution to 0.45 L?

8.87 How many milliliters of a 2.5 M NaCl solution would be needed to prepare each solution?
    a. 25 mL of a 1.0 M solution
    b. 1.5 L of a 0.75 M solution
    c. 15 mL of a 0.25 M solution
    d. 250 mL of a 0.025 M solution

8.88 How many milliliters of a 5.0 M sucrose solution would be needed to prepare each solution?
    a. 45 mL of a 4.0 M solution
    b. 150 mL of a 0.5 M solution
    c. 1.2 L of a 0.025 M solution
    d. 750 mL of a 1.0 M solution

Colligative Properties

8.89 Why is the boiling point of ocean water higher than the boiling point of tap water?

8.90 Does pure water have osmotic pressure? Explain why or why not.

8.91 What is the boiling point of a solution that contains each of the following quantities of solute in 1.00 kg of water?
    a. 3.0 mol of fructose molecules
    b. 1.2 mol of KI
    c. 1.5 mol of Na_3PO_4

8.92 What is the freezing point of each solution in Problem 8.91?

8.93 If 150 g of ethylene glycol ($C_2H_6O_2$) is added to 1,000. g of water, what is the freezing point?

8.94 How many grams of ethylene glycol must be added to 1,000. g of water to form a solution that has a freezing point of –10. °C?

8.95 In comparing a 1.0 M NaCl solution and a 1.0 M glucose solution, which solution has the higher: (a) boiling point; (b) melting point; (c) osmotic pressure; (d) vapor pressure at a given temperature?

8.96 In comparing a 1.0 M NaCl solution and a 1.0 M $CaCl_2$ solution, which solution has the higher: (a) boiling point; (b) melting point; (c) osmotic pressure; (d) vapor pressure at a given temperature?

8.97 Which solution in each pair has the higher melting point?
    a. 0.10 M NaOH or 0.10 M glucose
    b. 0.20 M NaCl or 0.15 M $CaCl_2$
    c. 0.10 M Na_2SO_4 or 0.10 M Na_3PO_4
    d. 0.10 M glucose or 0.20 M glucose

8.98 Which solution in each pair in Problem 8.97 has the higher boiling point?

Osmosis

8.99 A flask contains two compartments (**A** and **B**) with equal volumes of solution separated by a semipermeable membrane. Describe the final level of the liquids when **A** and **B** contain each of the following solutions.

	A	**B**
a.	1% (w/v) glucose solution	pure water
b.	0.10 M glucose solution	0.20 M glucose solution
c.	0.10 M NaCl solution	0.10 M NaI solution
d.	0.10 M $CaCl_2$ solution	0.10 M NaCl solution
e.	0.20 M glucose solution	0.10 M NaCl solution

8.100 A flask contains two compartments (**A** and **B**) with equal volumes of solution separated by a semipermeable membrane. Which diagram represents the final level of the liquids when **A** and **B** contain each of the following solutions?

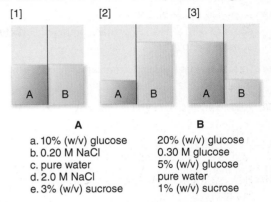

[1]   [2]   [3]

	A	**B**
a.	10% (w/v) glucose	20% (w/v) glucose
b.	0.20 M NaCl	0.30 M glucose
c.	pure water	5% (w/v) glucose
d.	2.0 M NaCl	pure water
e.	3% (w/v) sucrose	1% (w/v) sucrose

Applications

8.101 Explain why opening a warm can of soda causes a louder "whoosh" and more fizzing than opening a cold can of soda.

8.102 Explain why more sugar dissolves in a cup of hot coffee than a glass of iced coffee.

8.103 If the concentration of glucose in the blood is 90 mg/100 mL, what is the weight/volume percent concentration of glucose? What is the molarity of glucose (molar mass 180.2 g/mol) in the blood?

8.104 If the human body contains 5.0 L of blood, how many grams of glucose are present in the blood if the concentration is 90. mg/100. mL?

8.105 Mannitol, a carbohydrate, is supplied as a 25% (w/v) solution. This hypertonic solution is given to patients who have sustained a head injury with associated brain swelling. (a) What volume should be given to provide a dose of 70. g? (b) How does the hypertonic mannitol benefit brain swelling?

8.106 A patient receives 750 mL of a 10.% (w/v) aqueous glucose solution. (a) How many grams of glucose does the patient receive? (b) How many moles of glucose (molar mass 180.2 g/mol) does the patient receive?

8.107 Explain why a cucumber placed in a concentrated salt solution shrivels.

8.108 Explain why a raisin placed in water swells.

8.109 Explain why the solution contained in a dialyzer used in hemodialysis contains NaCl, KCl, and glucose dissolved in water.

8.110 Explain why pure water is not used in the solution contained in a dialyzer during hemodialysis.

8.111 A sports drink contains 15 g of soluble complex carbohydrates in 8.0 oz (1 fl oz = 29.6 mL). What weight/volume percent concentration does this represent?

8.112 A sports drink contains 25 mg of magnesium in an 8.0-oz portion (1 fl oz = 29.6 mL). How many parts per million does this represent? Assume that the mass of 1.0 mL of the solution is 1.0 g.

8.113 Each day, the stomach produces 2.0 L of gastric juice that contains 0.10 M HCl. How many grams of HCl does this correspond to?

8.114 Describe what happens when a red blood cell is placed in pure water.

8.115 An individual is legally intoxicated with a blood alcohol level of 0.08% (w/v) of ethanol. How many milligrams of ethanol are contained in 5.0 L of blood with this level?

8.116 A bottle of vodka labeled "80 proof" contains 40.% (v/v) ethanol in water. How many mL of ethanol are contained in 250 mL of vodka?

CHALLENGE PROBLEMS

8.117 The therapeutic concentration—the concentration needed to be effective—of acetaminophen ($C_8H_9NO_2$, molar mass 151.2 g/mol) is 10–20 μg/mL. Assume that the density of blood is 1.0 g/mL.

a. If the concentration of acetaminophen in the blood was measured at 15 ppm, is this concentration in the therapeutic range?

b. How many moles of acetaminophen are present at this concentration in 5.0 L of blood?

8.118 One individual was told that his total blood cholesterol concentration should be less than 200. mg/dL and another individual was told that his total cholesterol should be less than 5.2×10^{-3} M. Are these two values equivalent? If the values differ, which number represents the higher value?

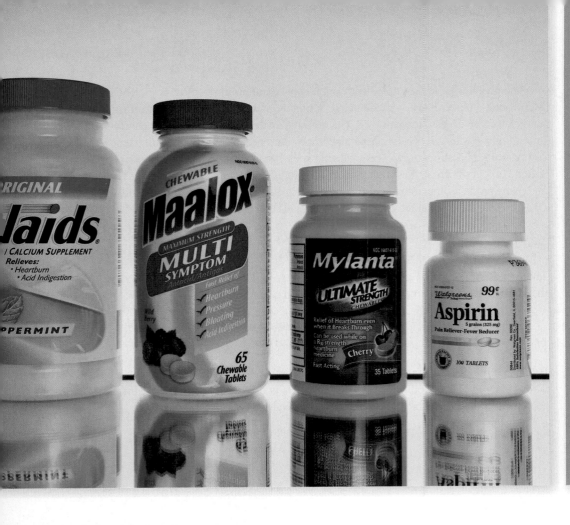

Many over-the-counter medications are acids or bases. The pain reliever aspirin—acetylsalicylic *acid*—is an acid, and the antacids Maalox, Mylanta, and Rolaids all contain a base as their active ingredient.

9

Acids and Bases

CHAPTER GOALS

In this chapter you will learn how to:

① Identify acids and bases and describe their characteristics

② Write equations for acid–base reactions

③ Relate acid strength to the direction of equilibrium of an acid–base reaction

④ Define the acid dissociation constant and relate its magnitude to acid strength

⑤ Define the ion–product of water and use it to calculate hydronium or hydroxide ion concentration

⑥ Calculate pH

⑦ Draw the products of common acid–base reactions

⑧ Determine whether a salt solution is acidic, basic, or neutral

⑨ Use a titration to determine the concentration of an acid or a base

⑩ Describe the fundamental features of a buffer

⑪ Understand the importance of buffers in maintaining pH in the body

Chemical terms such as *anion* and *cation* may be unfamiliar to most nonscientists, but **acid** has found a place in everyday language. Commercials advertise the latest remedy for the heartburn caused by excess stomach *acid*. The nightly news may report the latest environmental impact of *acid* rain. Wine lovers often know that wine sours because its alcohol has turned to *acid*. *Acid* comes from the Latin word *acidus,* meaning sour, because when tasting compounds was a routine method of identification, these compounds were found to be sour. Acids commonly react with **bases,** and many products, including antacid tablets, glass cleaners, and drain cleaners, all contain bases. In Chapter 9 we learn about the characteristics of acids and bases and the reactions they undergo.

9.1 Introduction to Acids and Bases

The earliest definition of acids and bases was suggested by Swedish chemist Svante Arrhenius in the late nineteenth century. According to Arrhenius,

- An *acid* contains a hydrogen atom and dissolves in water to form a hydrogen ion, H^+.
- A *base* contains hydroxide and dissolves in water to form OH^-.

By this definition, hydrogen chloride (HCl) is an acid because it forms aqueous H^+ and Cl^- when it dissolves in water. Sodium hydroxide (NaOH) is a base because it contains OH^- and forms solvated Na^+ and OH^- ions when it dissolves in water.

H^+ is formed from HCl.

$$HCl(g) \longrightarrow H^+(aq) + Cl^-(aq)$$
acid

$$NaOH(s) \longrightarrow Na^+(aq) + OH^-(aq)$$
base

OH^- is formed from NaOH.

$H^+(aq)$ and $H_3O^+(aq)$ are sometimes used interchangeably by chemists. Keep in mind, however, that $H^+(aq)$ does not really exist in aqueous solution.

While the Arrhenius definition correctly predicts the behavior of many acids and bases, this definition is limited and sometimes inaccurate. We now know, for example, that the hydrogen ion, H^+, does *not* exist in water. H^+ is a naked proton with no electrons, and this concentrated positive charge reacts rapidly with a molecule of H_2O to form the **hydronium ion, H_3O^+.** Although $H^+(aq)$ will sometimes be written in an equation for emphasis, $H_3O^+(aq)$ is actually the reacting species.

actually present in aqueous solution

$$H^+(aq) + H_2O(l) \longrightarrow H_3O^+(aq)$$
hydrogen ion   hydronium ion

does not really exist in aqueous solution

Moreover, several compounds contain no hydroxide anions, yet they still exhibit the characteristic properties of a base. Examples include the neutral molecule ammonia (NH_3) and the salt sodium carbonate (Na_2CO_3). As a result, a more general definition of acids and bases, proposed by Johannes **Brønsted** and Thomas **Lowry** in the early twentieth century, is widely used today.

In the Brønsted–Lowry definition, acids and bases are classified according to whether they can donate or accept a **proton**—a positively charged hydrogen ion, H^+.

- A Brønsted–Lowry acid is a *proton donor.*
- A Brønsted–Lowry base is a *proton acceptor.*

Consider what happens when HCl is dissolved in water.

This proton is donated. H_2O accepts a proton.

$$HCl(g) + H_2O(l) \longrightarrow H_3O^+(aq) + Cl^-(aq)$$
Brønsted–Lowry   **Brønsted–Lowry**
acid   **base**

- HCl is a Brønsted–Lowry *acid* because it *donates* a proton to the solvent water.
- H_2O is a Brønsted–Lowry *base* because it *accepts* a proton from HCl.

Before we learn more about the details of this process, we must first learn about the characteristics of Brønsted–Lowry acids and bases.

9.1A Brønsted–Lowry Acids

A Brønsted–Lowry acid must contain a hydrogen atom. HCl is a Brønsted–Lowry acid because it *donates* a proton (H^+) to water when it dissolves, forming the hydronium ion (H_3O^+) and chloride (Cl^-).

This proton is donated to H_2O.

$$HCl(g) \ + \ H_2O(l) \longrightarrow H_3O^+(aq) \ + \ Cl^-(aq)$$

Brønsted–Lowry acid

Although hydrogen chloride, HCl, is a covalent molecule and a gas at room temperature, when it dissolves in water it reacts to form two ions, H_3O^+ and Cl^-. An aqueous solution of hydrogen chloride is called **hydrochloric acid.**

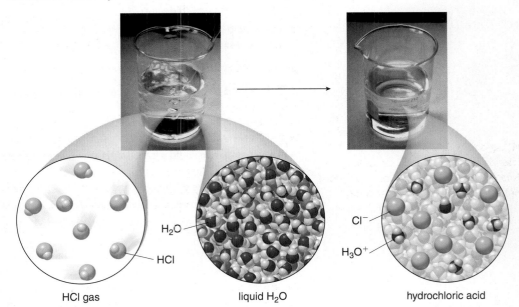

H_2O

HCl

HCl gas

liquid H_2O

Cl^-

H_3O^+

hydrochloric acid

Because a Brønsted–Lowry acid contains a hydrogen atom, a general Brønsted–Lowry acid is often written as **HA. A** can be a single atom such as Cl or Br. Thus, HCl and HBr are Brønsted–Lowry acids. **A** can also be a polyatomic ion. Sulfuric acid (H_2SO_4) and nitric acid (HNO_3) are Brønsted–Lowry acids, as well. **Carboxylic acids** are a group of Brønsted–Lowry acids that contain the atoms COOH arranged so that the carbon atom is doubly bonded to one O atom and singly bonded to another. Acetic acid, CH_3COOH, is a simple carboxylic acid. Although carboxylic acids may contain several hydrogen atoms, the **H atom of the OH group is the acidic proton that is donated.**

Common Brønsted–Lowry Acids		
HCl hydrochloric acid	H_2SO_4 sulfuric acid	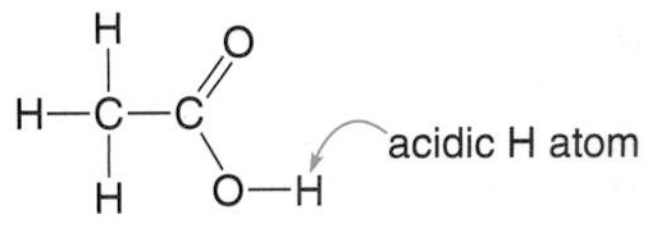 acidic H atom
HBr hydrobromic acid	HNO_3 nitric acid	acetic acid a carboxylic acid

Figure 9.1 Examples of Brønsted–Lowry Acids in Food Products

a.

b.

c.

acetic acid
CH_3COOH

citric acid
$C_6H_8O_7$

carbonic acid
H_2CO_3

a. Acetic acid is the sour-tasting component of vinegar. The air oxidation of ethanol to acetic acid is the process that makes "bad" wine taste sour.

b. Citric acid imparts a sour taste to oranges, lemons, and other citrus fruits.

c. Carbonated beverages contain carbonic acid, H_2CO_3.

A Brønsted–Lowry acid may contain one or more protons that can be donated.

- A monoprotic acid contains *one* acidic proton. HCl is a monoprotic acid.
- A diprotic acid contains *two* acidic protons. H_2SO_4 is a diprotic acid.
- A triprotic acid contains *three* acidic protons. H_3PO_4 is a triprotic acid.

Although a Brønsted–Lowry acid must contain a hydrogen atom, **it may be a neutral molecule or contain a net positive or negative charge.** Thus, H_3O^+, HCl, and HSO_4^- are all Brønsted–Lowry acids even though their net charges are +1, 0, and −1, respectively. Vinegar, citrus fruits, and carbonated soft drinks all contain Brønsted–Lowry acids, as shown in Figure 9.1.

SAMPLE PROBLEM 9.1

Which of the following species can be Brønsted–Lowry acids: (a) HF; (b) HSO_3^-; (c) Cl_2?

Analysis

A Brønsted–Lowry acid must contain a hydrogen atom, but it may be neutral or contain a net positive or negative charge.

Solution

a. HF is a Brønsted–Lowry acid since it contains a H.

b. HSO_3^- is a Brønsted–Lowry acid since it contains a H.

c. Cl_2 is not a Brønsted–Lowry acid because it does not contain a H.

PROBLEM 9.1

Which of the following species can be Brønsted–Lowry acids: (a) HI; (b) SO_4^{2-}; (c) $H_2PO_4^-$; (d) Cl^-?

9.1B Brønsted–Lowry Bases

A Brønsted–Lowry base is a proton acceptor and as such, it must be able to form a bond to a proton. Because a proton has no electrons, **a base must contain a lone pair of electrons** that can be donated to form a new bond. Thus, ammonia (NH_3) is a Brønsted–Lowry base because it contains a nitrogen atom with a lone pair of electrons. When NH_3 is dissolved in water, its N atom accepts a proton from H_2O, forming ammonium (NH_4^+) and hydroxide (OH^-).

This electron pair forms a new bond to a H from H_2O.

$$H-\overset{\displaystyle .\,.}{\underset{\displaystyle H}{N}}-H \;+\; H_2O(l) \;\longrightarrow\; \left[H-\overset{\displaystyle H}{\underset{\displaystyle H}{N}}-H\right]^+ \;+\; OH^-(aq)$$

Brønsted–Lowry base

A general Brønsted–Lowry base is often written as **B:** to emphasize that the base must contain a lone pair of electrons to bond to a proton. A base may be neutral or, more commonly, have a net negative charge. Hydroxide (OH^-), which contains an oxygen atom with three lone pairs of electrons, is the most common Brønsted–Lowry base. The source of hydroxide anions can be a variety of metal salts, including NaOH, KOH, $Mg(OH)_2$, and $Ca(OH)_2$. Ammonia (NH_3) and water (H_2O) are both Brønsted–Lowry bases because each contains an atom with a lone pair of electrons.

Common Brønsted–Lowry Bases	NaOH sodium hydroxide	$Mg(OH)_2$ magnesium hydroxide	$\overset{..}{N}H_3$ ammonia
	KOH potassium hydroxide	$Ca(OH)_2$ calcium hydroxide	$H_2\overset{..}{O}:$ water

OH^- is the base in each metal salt.   Lone pairs make these neutral compounds bases.

Many consumer products contain Brønsted–Lowry bases, as shown in Figure 9.2.

Figure 9.2   Examples of Brønsted–Lowry Bases in Consumer Products

a.

b.

c.

solid $CaCO_3$ — CO_3^{2-}, Ca^{2+}

OH^-, NH_4^+, NH_3, H_2O

solid NaOH — OH^-, Na^+, H_2O

a. Calcium carbonate ($CaCO_3$), a base, is the active ingredient in the antacid Rolaids.
b. Windex and other household cleaners contain ammonia (NH_3) dissolved in water, forming NH_4^+ cations and OH^- anions.
c. Drain cleaners contain pellets of solid sodium hydroxide (NaOH), which form Na^+ cations and OH^- anions when mixed with water.

SAMPLE PROBLEM 9.2

SAMPLE PROBLEM 9.2

Which of the following species can be Brønsted–Lowry bases: (a) LiOH; (b) Cl^-; (c) CH_4?

Analysis

A Brønsted–Lowry base must contain a lone pair of electrons, but it may be neutral or have a net negative charge.

Solution

a. LiOH is a base since it contains hydroxide, OH^-, which has three lone pairs on its O atom.

b. Cl^- is a base since it has four lone pairs.

c. CH_4 is not a base since it has no lone pairs.

PROBLEM 9.2

Which of the following species can be Brønsted–Lowry bases: (a) $Al(OH)_3$; (b) Br^-; (c) NH_4^+; (d) CN^-?

SAMPLE PROBLEM 9.3

Classify each reactant as a Brønsted–Lowry acid or base.

a. $HF(g) + H_2O(l) \longrightarrow F^-(aq) + H_3O^+(aq)$

b. $SO_4^{2-}(aq) + H_2O(l) \longrightarrow HSO_4^-(aq) + OH^-(aq)$

Analysis

In each equation, the Brønsted–Lowry acid is the species that loses a proton and the Brønsted–Lowry base is the species that gains a proton.

Solution

a. HF is the acid since it loses a proton (H^+) to form F^-, and H_2O is the base since it gains a proton to form H_3O^+.

$$
\begin{array}{ccccc}
\text{HF}(g) & + & \text{H}_2\text{O}(l) & \longrightarrow & \text{F}^-(aq) & + & \text{H}_3\text{O}^+(aq) \\
\text{acid} & & \text{base} & & &
\end{array}
$$

gain of H^+

loss of H^+

b. H_2O is the acid since it loses a proton (H^+) to form OH^-, and SO_4^{2-} is the base since it gains a proton to form HSO_4^-.

$$
\begin{array}{ccccc}
\text{SO}_4^{2-}(aq) & + & \text{H}_2\text{O}(l) & \longrightarrow & \text{HSO}_4^-(aq) & + & \text{OH}^-(aq) \\
\text{base} & & \text{acid} & & &
\end{array}
$$

gain of H^+

loss of H^+

PROBLEM 9.3

Classify each reactant as a Brønsted–Lowry acid or base.

a. $HCl(g) + NH_3(g) \longrightarrow Cl^-(aq) + NH_4^+(aq)$

b. $CH_3COOH(l) + H_2O(l) \longrightarrow CH_3COO^-(aq) + H_3O^+(aq)$

c. $OH^-(aq) + HSO_4^-(aq) \longrightarrow H_2O(l) + SO_4^{2-}(aq)$

9.2 The Reaction of a Brønsted–Lowry Acid with a Brønsted–Lowry Base

When a Brønsted–Lowry acid reacts with a Brønsted–Lowry base, a proton is *transferred* from the acid to the base. **The Brønsted–Lowry acid donates a proton to the Brønsted–Lowry base, which accepts it.**

Consider, for example, the reaction of the general acid H—A with the general base B:. **In an acid–base reaction, one bond is broken and one bond is formed.** The electron pair of the base B: forms a new bond to the proton of the acid, forming H—B$^+$. The acid H—A loses a proton, leaving the electron pair in the H—A bond on A, forming A:$^-$.

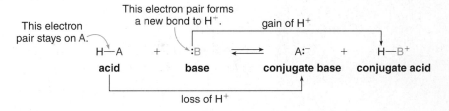

- The product formed by loss of a proton from an acid is called its *conjugate base.*
- The product formed by gain of a proton by a base is called its *conjugate acid.*

Thus, the conjugate base of the acid HA is A:$^-$. The conjugate acid of the base B: is HB$^+$.

- Two species that differ by the presence of a proton are called a conjugate acid–base pair.

Thus, in an acid–base reaction, the acid and the base on the left side of the equation (HA and B:) form two products that are also an acid and a base (HB$^+$ and A:$^-$). Equilibrium arrows ($\rightleftharpoons$) are often used to separate reactants and products because the reaction can proceed in either the forward or the reverse directions. In some reactions, the products are greatly favored, as discussed in Section 9.3.

When HBr is dissolved in water, for example, the acid HBr loses a proton to form its conjugate base Br$^-$, and the base H$_2$O gains a proton to form H$_3$O$^+$.

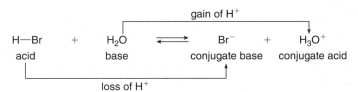

Thus, HBr and Br$^-$ are a conjugate acid–base pair since these two species differ by the presence of a proton (H$^+$). H$_2$O and H$_3$O$^+$ are also a conjugate acid–base pair because these two species differ by the presence of a proton as well.

The net charge must be the same on both sides of the equation. In this example, the two reactants are neutral (zero net charge), and the sum of the –1 and +1 charges in the products is also zero.

Take particular note of what happens to the charges in each conjugate acid–base pair. **When a species gains a proton (H$^+$), it gains a +1 charge.** Thus, if a reactant is neutral to begin with, it ends up with a +1 charge. **When a species loses a proton (H$^+$), it effectively gains a –1 charge** since the product has one fewer proton (+1 charge) than it started with. Thus, if a reactant is neutral to begin with, it ends up with a –1 charge.

0 charge   add H$^+$ +1 charge
H$_2$O   →   H$_3$O$^+$
base

0 charge   lose H$^+$ –1 charge
H—Br   →   Br$^-$
acid   Take away +1 charge.

The reaction of ammonia (NH_3) with HCl is also a Brønsted–Lowry acid–base reaction. In this example, NH_3 is the base since it gains a proton to form its conjugate acid, NH_4^+. HCl is the acid since it donates a proton, forming its conjugate base, Cl^-.

gain of H^+

H—N̈—H + HCl(*g*) ⇌ H—N—H + Cl^-(*aq*)

base   acid   conjugate acid   conjugate base

loss of H^+

- A Brønsted–Lowry acid–base reaction is a *proton transfer reaction* since it always results in the transfer of a proton from an acid to a base.

The ability to identify and draw a conjugate acid or base from a given starting material is a necessary skill, illustrated in Sample Problems 9.4 and 9.5.

SAMPLE PROBLEM 9.4

Determine the conjugate acid of each base: (a) F^-; (b) NO_3^-.

Analysis

Conjugate acid–base pairs differ by the presence of a proton. To draw a conjugate acid from a base, *add* a proton, H^+. This adds +1 to the charge of the base to give the charge on the conjugate acid.

Solution

a. $F^- + H^+$ gives HF as the conjugate acid. HF has no charge since a proton with a +1 charge is added to an anion with a –1 charge.
b. $NO_3^- + H^+$ gives HNO_3 (nitric acid) as the conjugate acid. HNO_3 has no charge since a proton with a +1 charge is added to an anion with a –1 charge.

PROBLEM 9.4

Determine the conjugate acid of each species: (a) H_2O; (b) I^-; (c) HCO_3^-.

SAMPLE PROBLEM 9.5

Determine the conjugate base of each acid: (a) H_2O; (b) HCO_3^-.

Analysis

Conjugate acid–base pairs differ by the presence of a proton. To draw a conjugate base from an acid, *remove* a proton, H^+. This adds –1 to the charge of the acid to give the charge on the conjugate base.

Solution

a. Remove H^+ from H_2O to form OH^-, the conjugate base. OH^- has a –1 charge since –1 is added to a molecule that was neutral to begin with.
b. Remove H^+ from HCO_3^- to form CO_3^{2-}, the conjugate base. CO_3^{2-} has a –2 charge since –1 is added to an anion that had a –1 charge to begin with.

PROBLEM 9.5

Determine the conjugate base of each species: (a) H_2S; (b) HCN; (c) HSO_4^-.

A compound that contains both a hydrogen atom and a lone pair of electrons can be either an acid or a base, depending on the particular reaction. Such a compound is said to be **amphoteric.** For example, when H_2O acts as a base it gains a proton, forming H_3O^+. Thus, H_2O and H_3O^+ are a conjugate acid–base pair. When H_2O acts as an acid it loses a proton, forming OH^-. H_2O and OH^- are also a conjugate acid–base pair.

When HCl donates a proton to NH_3 in the absence of water, NH_4^+ and Cl^- are formed, which combine to form solid ammonium chloride, NH_4Cl.

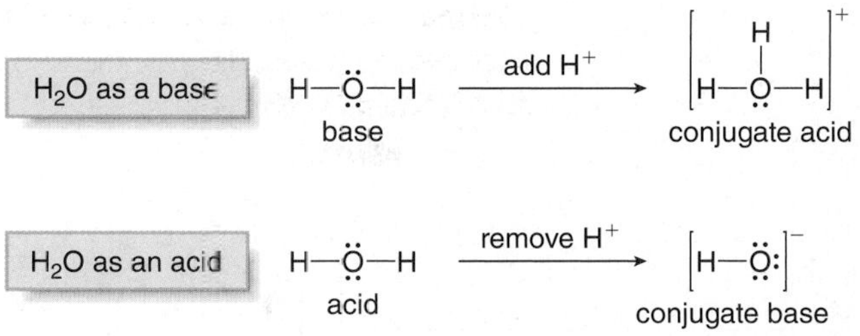

$$\text{H}_2\text{O as a base} \quad \text{H}-\ddot{\text{O}}-\text{H} \xrightarrow{\text{add } \text{H}^+} \left[\text{H}-\overset{\text{H}}{\underset{}{\text{O}}}-\text{H}\right]^+$$

base   conjugate acid

$$\text{H}_2\text{O as an acid} \quad \text{H}-\ddot{\text{O}}-\text{H} \xrightarrow{\text{remove } \text{H}^+} \left[\text{H}-\ddot{\text{O}}:\right]^-$$

acid   conjugate base

SAMPLE PROBLEM 9.6

Label the acid and the base and the conjugate acid and the conjugate base in the following reaction.

$$\text{NH}_4^+(aq) + \text{OH}^-(aq) \rightleftharpoons \text{NH}_3(g) + \text{H}_2\text{O}(l)$$

Analysis

The Brønsted–Lowry acid loses a proton to form its conjugate base. The Brønsted–Lowry base gains a proton to form its conjugate acid.

Solution

NH_4^+ is the acid since it loses a proton to form NH_3, its conjugate base. OH^- is the base since it gains a proton to form its conjugate acid, H_2O.

gain of H^+

$$\text{NH}_4^+(aq) \quad + \quad \text{OH}^-(aq) \rightleftharpoons \text{NH}_3(g) \quad + \quad \text{H}_2\text{O}(l)$$

acid   base   conjugate base   conjugate acid

loss of H^+

PROBLEM 9.6

Label the acid and the base and the conjugate acid and the conjugate base in each reaction.

a. $\text{H}_2\text{O}(l) + \text{HI}(g) \rightleftharpoons \text{I}^-(aq) + \text{H}_3\text{O}^+(aq)$
b. $\text{CH}_3\text{COOH}(l) + \text{NH}_3(g) \rightleftharpoons \text{CH}_3\text{COO}^-(aq) + \text{NH}_4^+(aq)$
c. $\text{Br}^-(aq) + \text{HNO}_3(aq) \rightleftharpoons \text{HBr}(aq) + \text{NO}_3^-(aq)$

PROBLEM 9.7

Ammonia, NH_3, is amphoteric. (a) Draw the conjugate acid of NH_3. (b) Draw the conjugate base of NH_3.

9.3 Acid and Base Strength

Although all Brønsted–Lowry acids contain protons, some acids readily donate protons while others do not. Similarly, some Brønsted–Lowry bases accept a proton much more readily than others. How readily proton transfer occurs is determined by the strength of the acid and base.

9.3A Relating Acid and Base Strength

When an acid dissolves in water, proton transfer forms H_3O^+ and an anion. The splitting apart of a covalent molecule (or an ionic compound) into individual ions is called **dissociation.** Acids differ in their tendency to donate a proton; that is, acids differ in the extent to which they *dissociate* in water.

- A strong acid readily donates a proton. When a strong acid dissolves in water, 100% of the acid dissociates into ions.
- A weak acid less readily donates a proton. When a weak acid dissolves in water, only a small fraction of the acid dissociates into ions.

Common strong acids include **HI, HBr, HCl, H$_2$SO$_4$,** and **HNO$_3$** (Table 9.1). When each acid is dissolved in water, 100% of the acid dissociates, forming H$_3$O$^+$ and the conjugate base, as shown for HCl and H$_2$SO$_4$.

> • Use a single reaction arrow.
> • The product is greatly favored at equilibrium.

$$HCl(g) \quad + \quad H_2O(l) \quad \longrightarrow \quad H_3O^+(aq) \quad + \quad Cl^-(aq)$$
  strong acid   conjugate base

$$H_2SO_4(l) \quad + \quad H_2O(l) \quad \longrightarrow \quad H_3O^+(aq) \quad + \quad HSO_4^-(aq)$$
  strong acid   conjugate base

HCl, hydrochloric acid, is secreted by the stomach to digest food (Figure 9.3), and **H$_2$SO$_4$,** sulfuric acid, is an important industrial starting material in the synthesis of phosphate fertilizers. A single reaction arrow ($\longrightarrow$) is drawn to show that essentially all of the reactants are converted to products.

Acetic acid, **CH$_3$COOH,** is a weak acid. When acetic acid dissolves in water, only a small fraction of acetic acid molecules donate a proton to water to form H$_3$O$^+$ and the conjugate base, CH$_3$COO$^-$. The major species at equilibrium is the undissociated acid, CH$_3$COOH. Equilibrium arrows that are unequal in length ($\rightleftharpoons$) are used to show that the equilibrium lies to the left. Other weak acids and their conjugate bases are listed in Table 9.1.

> • Use unequal reaction arrows.
> • The reactants are favored at equilibrium.

$$CH_3COOH(l) \quad + \quad H_2O(l) \quad \rightleftharpoons \quad H_3O^+(aq) \quad + \quad CH_3COO^-(aq)$$
  weak acid   conjugate base

Figure 9.4 illustrates the difference between an aqueous solution of a strong acid that is completely dissociated and a weak acid that contains much undissociated acid. Sample Problem 9.7 illustrates how the extent of dissociation and acid strength are related.

Figure 9.3   Focus on the Human Body: Hydrochloric Acid in the Stomach

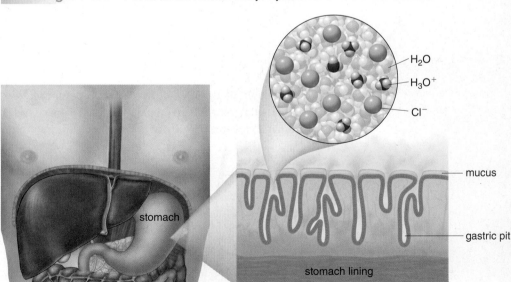

The thick mucous layer protects the stomach lining.

Although HCl is a corrosive acid secreted in the stomach, a thick layer of mucus covering the stomach wall protects it from damage by the strong acid. The strong acid HCl is completely dissociated to H$_3$O$^+$ and Cl$^-$.

Table 9.1 Relative Strength of Acids and Their Conjugate Bases

Acid		Conjugate Base	
Strong Acids			
Hydroiodic acid	HI	I^-	Iodide ion
Hydrobromic acid	HBr	Br^-	Bromide ion
Hydrochloric acid	HCl	Cl^-	Chloride ion
Sulfuric acid	H_2SO_4	HSO_4^-	Hydrogen sulfate ion
Nitric acid	HNO_3	NO_3^-	Nitrate ion
Hydronium ion	H_3O^+	H_2O	**Water**
Weak Acids			
Phosphoric acid	H_3PO_4	$H_2PO_4^-$	Dihydrogen phosphate ion
Hydrofluoric acid	HF	F^-	Fluoride ion
Acetic acid	CH_3COOH	CH_3COO^-	Acetate ion
Carbonic acid	H_2CO_3	HCO_3^-	Bicarbonate ion
Ammonium ion	NH_4^+	NH_3	Ammonia
Hydrocyanic acid	HCN	CN^-	Cyanide ion
Water	H_2O	OH^-	Hydroxide ion

Increasing acid strength →

Increasing base strength →

Figure 9.4   A Strong and Weak Acid Dissolved in Water

hydrochloric acid

Cl^-

H_3O^+

A strong acid is completely dissociated.

vinegar

CH_3COO^-

H_3O^+

CH_3COOH

A weak acid contains mostly undissociated acid, CH_3COOH.

- The strong acid HCl completely dissociates into H_3O^+ and Cl^- in water.

- Vinegar contains CH_3COOH dissolved in H_2O. The weak acid CH_3COOH is only slightly dissociated into H_3O^+ and CH_3COO^-, so mostly CH_3COOH is present at equilibrium.

SAMPLE PROBLEM 9.7

Diagrams **A–C** represent three acids (HA) dissolved in water. Which representation shows the strongest acid? Which representation shows the weakest acid?

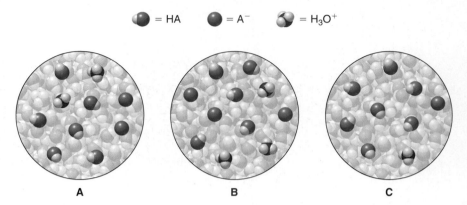

Analysis

The stronger the acid, the more readily it dissociates to form its conjugate base A^- and H_3O^+. In molecular art, the strongest acid has the most A^- and H_3O^+ ions, and the fewest molecules of undissociated HA.

Solution

B is the strongest acid since it contains the largest number of A^- and H_3O^+ ions (three each), and the smallest number (five) of undissociated HA molecules. **C** is the weakest acid since it contains the smallest number of A^- and H_3O^+ ions (one each), and the largest number (seven) of undissociated HA molecules.

PROBLEM 9.8

Diagrams **D–F** represent three acids (HA) dissolved in water. Rank the three acids (**D–F**) in order of increasing acidity.

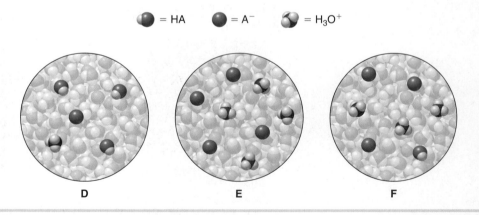

Bases also differ in their ability to accept a proton.

- A strong base readily accepts a proton. When a strong base dissolves in water, 100% of the base dissociates into ions.
- A weak base less readily accepts a proton. When a weak base dissolves in water, only a small fraction of the base forms ions.

The most common strong base is hydroxide, **OH⁻**, used as a variety of metal salts, including NaOH and KOH. Solid NaOH dissolves in water to form solvated Na^+ cations and OH^- anions. In contrast, when **NH₃**, a weak base, dissolves in water, only a small fraction of NH_3 molecules react to form NH_4^+ and OH^-. The major species at equilibrium is the undissociated molecule, NH_3.

Figure 9.5   A Strong and Weak Base Dissolved in Water

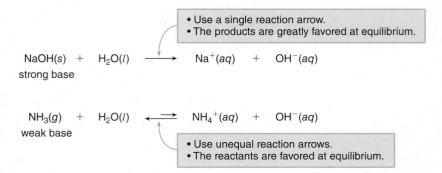

sodium hydroxide

Na⁺

OH⁻

A strong base is
completely dissociated.

ammonia

NH₃

NH₄⁺

OH⁻

A weak base contains mostly
undissociated base, NH₃.

- The strong base NaOH completely dissociates into Na⁺ and OH⁻ in water.

- The weak base NH₃ is only slightly dissociated into NH₄⁺ and OH⁻, so mostly NH₃ is present at equilibrium.

Figure 9.5 illustrates the difference between aqueous solutions of strong and weak bases. Table 9.1 lists common bases.

> - Use a single reaction arrow.
> - The products are greatly favored at equilibrium.

$$\text{NaOH}(s) + \text{H}_2\text{O}(l) \longrightarrow \text{Na}^+(aq) + \text{OH}^-(aq)$$
strong base

$$\text{NH}_3(g) + \text{H}_2\text{O}(l) \xrightleftharpoons{} \text{NH}_4^+(aq) + \text{OH}^-(aq)$$
weak base

> - Use unequal reaction arrows.
> - The reactants are favored at equilibrium.

An inverse relationship exists between acid and base strength.

- A strong acid readily donates a proton, forming a *weak* conjugate base.
- A strong base readily accepts a proton, forming a *weak* conjugate acid.

Why does this inverse relationship exist? Since a strong acid readily donates a proton, it forms a conjugate base that has little ability to accept a proton. Since a strong base readily accepts a proton, it forms a conjugate acid that tightly holds onto its proton, making it a weak acid.

Thus, a *strong* acid like HCl forms a *weak* conjugate base (Cl⁻), and a *strong* base like OH⁻ forms a *weak* conjugate acid (H₂O). The entries in Table 9.1 are arranged in order of *decreasing* acid strength. This means that Table 9.1 is also arranged in order of *increasing* strength of the resulting conjugate bases. Knowing the relative strength of two acids makes it possible to predict the relative strength of their conjugate bases.

SAMPLE PROBLEM 9.8

Using Table 9.1: (a) Is H_3PO_4 or HF the stronger acid? (b) Draw the conjugate base of each acid and predict which base is stronger.

Analysis

The stronger the acid, the weaker the conjugate base.

Solution

a. H_3PO_4 is located above HF in Table 9.1, making it the stronger acid.
b. To draw each conjugate base, remove a proton (H^+). Since each acid is neutral, both conjugate bases have a −1 charge. Since HF is the weaker acid, F^- is the stronger conjugate base.

$$H_3PO_4 \xrightarrow{\text{lose } H^+} H_2PO_4^- \quad \boxed{\text{weaker base}}$$
stronger acid

$$HF \xrightarrow{\text{lose } H^+} F^- \quad \boxed{\text{stronger base}}$$
weaker acid

PROBLEM 9.9

Label the stronger acid in each pair. Which acid has the stronger conjugate base?

a. H_2SO_4 or H_3PO_4 b. HF or HCl   c. H_2CO_3 or NH_4^+ d. HCN or HF

PROBLEM 9.10

(a) Draw the conjugate acids of NO_2^- and NO_3^-. (b) If NO_2^- is the stronger base, which acid is stronger?

9.3B Using Acid Strength to Predict the Direction of Equilibrium

A Brønsted–Lowry acid–base reaction represents an equilibrium. Since an acid donates a proton to a base, forming a conjugate acid and conjugate base, there are always two acids and two bases in the reaction mixture. Which pair of acids and bases is favored at equilibrium? **The position of the equilibrium depends upon the strength of the acids and bases.**

- **The stronger acid reacts with the stronger base to form the weaker acid and weaker base.**

Since a strong acid readily donates a proton and a strong base readily accepts one, these two species react to form a weaker conjugate acid and base that do not donate or accept a proton as readily. Thus, **when the stronger acid and base are the reactants on the left side, the reaction readily occurs and the reaction proceeds to the *right*.**

A larger forward arrow means that products are favored.

$$H{-}A + :B \rightleftharpoons A{:}^- + H{-}B^+$$
stronger acid   stronger base   weaker base   weaker acid

Products are favored.

On the other hand, **if an acid–base reaction would form the stronger acid and base, equilibrium favors the reactants and little product forms.**

A larger reverse arrow means that reactants are favored.

$$H{-}A + :B \rightleftharpoons A{:}^- + H{-}B^+$$
weaker acid   weaker base   stronger base   stronger acid

Reactants are favored.

Predicting the direction of equilibrium using the information in Table 9.1 is illustrated in the accompanying stepwise *How To* procedure.

How To **Predict the Direction of Equilibrium in an Acid–Base Reaction**

Example: Are the reactants or products favored in the following acid–base reaction?

$$HCN(g) + OH^-(aq) \rightleftharpoons CN^-(aq) + H_2O(l)$$

Step [1] Identify the acid in the reactants and the conjugate acid in the products.

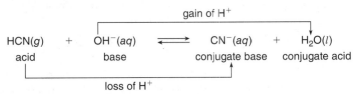

gain of H⁺

| $HCN(g)$ | + | $OH^-(aq)$ | $\rightleftharpoons$ | $CN^-(aq)$ | + | $H_2O(l)$ |
| acid | | base | | conjugate base | | conjugate acid |

loss of H⁺

- HCN is the acid since it donates a proton.
- H_2O is the conjugate acid formed from the hydroxide base.

Step [2] Determine the relative strength of the acid and the conjugate acid.
- According to Table 9.1, HCN is a stronger acid than H_2O.

Step [3] Equilibrium favors the formation of the weaker acid.
- Since the stronger acid HCN is a reactant, the reaction *proceeds to the right* as written, to form the weaker acid, H_2O. Unequal equilibrium arrows should be drawn with the larger arrow pointing towards the product side on the right.

| $HCN(g)$ | + | $OH^-(aq)$ | $\rightleftharpoons$ | $CN^-(aq)$ | + | $H_2O(l)$ |
| stronger acid | | | | | | weaker acid |

Products are favored.

HEALTH NOTE

Lactic acid accumulates in tissues during vigorous exercise, making muscles feel tired and sore. The formation of lactic acid is discussed in greater detail in Section 24.4.

PROBLEM 9.11

Are the reactants or products favored at equilibrium in each reaction?

a. $HF(g) + OH^-(aq) \rightleftharpoons F^-(aq) + H_2O(l)$
b. $NH_4^+(aq) + Cl^-(aq) \rightleftharpoons NH_3(g) + HCl(aq)$
c. $HCO_3^-(aq) + H_3O^+(aq) \rightleftharpoons H_2CO_3(aq) + H_2O(l)$

PROBLEM 9.12

If lactic acid is similar in strength to acetic acid (Table 9.1), predict whether reactants or products are favored in each reaction.

$$CH_3-\overset{\overset{\displaystyle H}{|}}{\underset{\underset{\displaystyle OH}{|}}{C}}-\overset{\overset{\displaystyle O}{\|}}{\underset{\underset{\displaystyle OH}{|}}{C}}$$

$C_3H_6O_3$
lactic acid

a. $C_3H_6O_3(aq)$ — $H_2O(l) \rightleftharpoons C_3H_5O_3^-(aq) + H_3O^+(aq)$
   lactic acid

b. $C_3H_6O_3(aq)$ — $HCO_3^-(aq) \rightleftharpoons C_3H_5O_3^-(aq) + H_2CO_3(aq)$
   lactic acid

9.4 Equilibrium and Acid Dissociation Constants

Like all equilibria, we can write an expression for the equilibrium constant for the acid–base reaction that takes place when an acid HA dissolves in water. The equilibrium constant (K) shows the ratio of the concentrations of the products to the concentrations of the reactants.

Reaction $HA(aq) + H_2O(l) \rightleftharpoons H_3O^+(aq) + A:^-$

Equilibrium constant $K = \dfrac{[H_3O^+][A:^-]}{[HA][H_2O]}$

concentrations of the products
concentrations of the reactants

Water serves as both the base and the solvent. Since water is a liquid and its concentration is essentially constant, the equation can be rearranged by multiplying both sides by $[H_2O]$. This forms a new constant called the **acid dissociation constant, K_a.**

$$K_a \quad = \quad K[H_2O] \quad = \quad \frac{[H_3O^+][A{:}^-]}{[HA]}$$

acid dissociation constant

How is K_a related to acid strength? The stronger the acid, the higher the concentration of the products of an acid–base reaction, and the larger the numerator in the expression for K_a. As a result:

- **The stronger the acid, the larger the value of K_a.**

The strong acids listed in Table 9.1 all have K_a values much greater than 1. Weak acids have K_a values less than 1. The K_a's for several weak acids are listed in Table 9.2.

Table 9.2 Acid Dissociation Constants (K_a) for Common Weak Acids

Acid	Structure	K_a
Hydrogen sulfate ion	HSO_4^-	1.2×10^{-2}
Phosphoric acid	H_3PO_4	7.5×10^{-3}
Hydrofluoric acid	HF	7.2×10^{-4}
Acetic acid	CH_3COOH	1.8×10^{-5}
Carbonic acid	H_2CO_3	4.3×10^{-7}
Dihydrogen phosphate ion	$H_2PO_4^-$	6.2×10^{-8}
Ammonium ion	NH_4^+	5.6×10^{-10}
Hydrocyanic acid	HCN	4.9×10^{-10}
Bicarbonate ion	HCO_3^-	5.6×10^{-11}
Hydrogen phosphate ion	HPO_4^{2-}	2.2×10^{-13}

(Increasing acidity, upward)

SAMPLE PROBLEM 9.9

Which acid in each pair is stronger: (a) HCN or HSO_4^-; (b) CH_3COOH or NH_4^+?

Analysis

Use Table 9.2 to find the K_a for each acid. The acid with the larger K_a is the stronger acid.

Solution

a. HCN HSO_4^- b. CH_3COOH NH_4^+
    $K_a = 4.9 \times 10^{-10}$ $K_a = 1.2 \times 10^{-2}$ 1.8×10^{-5} 5.6×10^{-10}
                                 larger K_a larger K_a
                                 stronger acid   **stronger acid**

PROBLEM 9.13

Rank the acids in each group in order of increasing acid strength.

a. H_3PO_4, $H_2PO_4^-$, HPO_4^{2-} b. HCN, HF, CH_3COOH

PROBLEM 9.14

(a) Which compound is the stronger acid, H_3PO_4 or CH_3COOH? (b) Draw the conjugate base of each compound and predict which base is stronger.

Because K_a values tell us the relative strength of two acids, we can use K_a's to predict the direction of equilibrium in an acid–base reaction, as shown in Sample Problem 9.10.

> • Equilibrium favors the formation of the weaker acid—that is, the acid with the *smaller* K_a value.

SAMPLE PROBLEM 9.10

HEALTH NOTE

Ascorbic acid, vitamin C, is needed for the formation of collagen, a common protein in connective tissues in muscles and blood vessels. If vitamin C has a K_a of 7.9×10^{-5}, are the reactants or products favored in the following acid–base reaction?

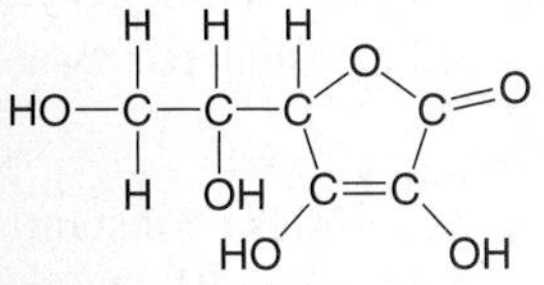

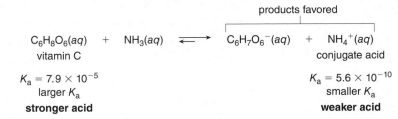

$$C_6H_8O_6(aq) \; + \; NH_3(aq) \; \rightleftharpoons \; C_6H_7O_6^-(aq) \; + \; NH_4^+(aq)$$

vitamin C   conjugate base of vitamin C

vitamin C
ascorbic acid
$C_6H_8O_6$

Citrus fruits (oranges, grapefruit, and lemons) are well known sources of vitamin C (ascorbic acid, Sample Problem 9.10), but guava, kiwifruit, and rose hips are excellent sources, too.

Analysis

To determine the direction of equilibrium, we must identify the acid in the reactants and the conjugate acid in the products. Then compare their K_a's. **Equilibrium favors the formation of the acid with the smaller K_a value.**

Solution

Vitamin C is the acid and NH_3 is the base on the reactant side. NH_3 gains a proton to form its conjugate acid, NH_4^+, which has a K_a of 5.6×10^{-10} (Table 9.2). The conjugate acid, therefore, has a *smaller K_a* than vitamin C (7.9×10^{-5}), making it the *weaker acid.* Thus, the products are favored at equilibrium.

products favored

$$C_6H_8O_6(aq) \; + \; NH_3(aq) \; \rightleftharpoons \; C_6H_7O_6^-(aq) \; + \; NH_4^+(aq)$$

vitamin C   conjugate acid

$K_a = 7.9 \times 10^{-5}$ $K_a = 5.6 \times 10^{-10}$
larger K_a smaller K_a
stronger acid   **weaker acid**

PROBLEM 9.15

Use the acid dissociation constants in Table 9.2 to determine whether the reactants or products are favored in the following reaction.

$$HCO_3^-(aq) \; + \; NH_3(aq) \; \rightleftharpoons \; CO_3^{2-}(aq) \; + \; NH_4^+(aq)$$

PROBLEM 9.16

Consider the weak acids, HCN and H_2CO_3.

  a. Which acid has the larger K_a?
  b. Which acid is stronger?
  c. Which acid has the stronger conjugate base?
  d. Which acid has the weaker conjugate base?
  e. When each acid is dissolved in water, for which acid does the equilibrium lie further to the right?

9.5 Dissociation of Water

In Section 9.2 we learned that water can behave as *both* a Brønsted–Lowry acid and a Brønsted–Lowry base. As a result, two molecules of water can react together in an acid–base reaction.

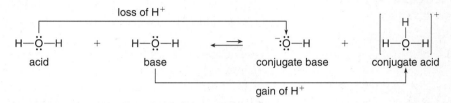

- One molecule of H_2O donates a proton (H^+), forming its conjugate base OH^-.
- One molecule of H_2O accepts a proton, forming its conjugate acid H_3O^+.

Equilibrium favors the starting materials in this reaction, since the reactant acid, H_2O, is much weaker than the conjugate acid, H_3O^+. Thus, pure water contains an exceedingly low concentration of ions, H_3O^+ and OH^-.

As usual, an expression for the equilibrium constant can be written that shows the ratio of the concentrations of the products, H_3O^+ and OH^-, to the concentration of the reactants, two molecules of H_2O. Since water is a liquid and its concentration is essentially constant, this equation can be rearranged by multiplying by $[H_2O]^2$ to afford a new equilibrium constant, K_w, **the ion–product constant** for water.

$$K = \frac{[H_3O^+][OH^-]}{[H_2O][H_2O]} = \frac{[H_3O^+][OH^-]}{[H_2O]^2}$$ —Multiply both sides by $[H_2O]^2$.

$$K_w = K[H_2O]^2 = [H_3O^+][OH^-]$$

ion–product constant

$$\boxed{K_w = [H_3O^+][OH^-]}$$

Since one H_3O^+ ion and one OH^- ion are formed in each reaction, the concentrations of H_3O^+ and OH^- are equal in pure water. Experimentally it can be shown that the $[H_3O^+] = [OH^-] = 1.0 \times 10^{-7}$ M at 25 °C. Thus,

$$K_w = [H_3O^+][OH^-]$$
$$K_w = (1.0 \times 10^{-7}) \times (1.0 \times 10^{-7})$$
$$K_w = 1.0 \times 10^{-14}$$

- The product, $[H_3O^+][OH^-]$, is a constant, 1.0×10^{-14}, for all aqueous solutions at 25 °C.

Thus, **the value of K_w applies to any aqueous solution,** not just pure water. If we know the concentration of one ion, H_3O^+ or OH^-, we can find the concentration of the other by rearranging the expression for K_w.

To calculate $[OH^-]$ when $[H_3O^+]$ is known:

$$K_w = [H_3O^+][OH^-]$$

$$[OH^-] = \frac{K_w}{[H_3O^+]}$$

$$[OH^-] = \frac{1.0 \times 10^{-14}}{[H_3O^+]}$$

To calculate $[H_3O^+]$ when $[OH^-]$ is known:

$$K_w = [H_3O^+][OH^-]$$

$$[H_3O^+] = \frac{K_w}{[OH^-]}$$

$$[H_3O^+] = \frac{1.0 \times 10^{-14}}{[OH^-]}$$

How to write numbers in scientific notation was presented in Section 1.6. Multiplying and dividing numbers written in scientific notation was described in Section 5.3.

Thus, if the concentration of H_3O^+ in a cup of coffee is 1.0×10^{-5} M, we can use this value to calculate $[OH^-]$.

$$[OH^-] = \frac{K_w}{[H_3O^+]} = \frac{1.0 \times 10^{-14}}{1.0 \times 10^{-5}}$$

$$[OH^-] = 1.0 \times 10^{-9}\ M$$

hydroxide ion concentration in a cup of coffee

Coffee is an *acidic* solution since the concentration of H_3O^+ is *greater* than the concentration of OH^-.

In a cup of coffee, therefore, the concentration of H_3O^+ ions is greater than the concentration of OH^- ions, but the product of these concentrations, 1.0×10^{-14}, is a constant, K_w.

Pure water and any solution that has an equal concentration of H_3O^+ and OH^- ions (1.0×10^{-7}) is said to be *neutral*. Other solutions are classified as **acidic** or **basic,** depending on which ion is present in a higher concentration.

- In an *acidic* solution, $[H_3O^+] > [OH^-]$; thus, $[H_3O^+] > 10^{-7}$ M.
- In a *basic* solution, $[OH^-] > [H_3O^+]$; thus, $[OH^-] > 10^{-7}$ M.

In an acidic solution, the concentration of the acid H_3O^+ is greater than the concentration of the base OH^-. In a basic solution, the concentration of the base OH^- is greater than the concentration of the acid H_3O^+. Table 9.3 summarizes information about neutral, acidic, and basic solutions.

Table 9.3 Neutral, Acidic, and Basic Solutions

Type	$[H_3O^+]$ and $[OH^-]$	$[H_3O^+]$	$[OH^-]$
Neutral	$[H_3O^+] = [OH^-]$	10^{-7} M	10^{-7} M
Acidic	$[H_3O^+] > [OH^-]$	$> 10^{-7}$ M	$< 10^{-7}$ M
Basic	$[H_3O^+] < [OH^-]$	$< 10^{-7}$ M	$> 10^{-7}$ M

SAMPLE PROBLEM 9.11

If $[H_3O^+]$ in blood is 4.0×10^{-8} M, what is the value of $[OH^-]$? Is blood acidic, basic, or neutral?

Analysis

Use the equation $[OH^-] = K_w/[H_3O^+]$ to calculate the hydroxide ion concentration.

Solution

Substitute the given value of $[H_3O^+]$ in the equation to find $[OH^-]$.

$$[OH^-] = \frac{K_w}{[H_3O^+]} = \frac{1.0 \times 10^{-14}}{4.0 \times 10^{-8}} = 2.5 \times 10^{-7}\ M$$

hydroxide ion concentration in the blood

Since $[OH^-] > [H_3O^+]$, blood is a basic solution.

PROBLEM 9.17

Calculate the value of $[OH^-]$ from the given $[H_3O^+]$ in each solution and label the solution as acidic or basic: (a) $[H_3O^+] = 10^{-3}$ M; (b) $[H_3O^+] = 10^{-11}$ M; (c) $[H_3O^+] = 2.8 \times 10^{-10}$ M; (d) $[H_3O^+] = 5.6 \times 10^{-4}$ M.

PROBLEM 9.18

Calculate the value of $[H_3O^+]$ from the given $[OH^-]$ in each solution and label the solution as acidic or basic: (a) $[OH^-] = 10^{-6}$ M; (b) $[OH^-] = 10^{-9}$ M; (c) $[OH^-] = 5.2 \times 10^{-11}$ M; (d) $[OH^-] = 7.3 \times 10^{-4}$ M.

Since a strong acid like HCl is completely dissociated in aqueous solution, the concentration of the acid tells us the concentration of hydronium ions present. Thus, a 0.1 M HCl solution completely dissociates, so the concentration of H_3O^+ is 0.1 M. This value can then be used to calculate the hydroxide ion concentration. Similarly, a strong base like NaOH completely dissociates, so the concentration of the base gives the concentration of hydroxide ions present. Thus, the concentration of OH^- in a 0.1 M NaOH solution is 0.1 M.

In 0.1 M HCl solution: $[H_3O^+] = 0.1\ M = 1 \times 10^{-1}\ M$
        strong acid

In 0.1 M NaOH solution: $[OH^-] = 0.1\ M = 1 \times 10^{-1}\ M$
        strong base

SAMPLE PROBLEM 9.12

Calculate the value of $[H_3O^+]$ and $[OH^-]$ in a 0.01 M NaOH solution.

Analysis

Since NaOH is a strong base that completely dissociates to form Na^+ and OH^-, the concentration of NaOH gives the concentration of OH^- ions. The $[OH^-]$ can then be used to calculate $[H_3O^+]$ from the expression for K_w.

Solution

The value of $[OH^-]$ in a 0.01 M NaOH solution is 0.01 M = 1×10^{-2} M.

$$[H_3O^+] = \frac{K_w}{[OH^-]} = \frac{1 \times 10^{-14}}{1 \times 10^{-2}} = 1 \times 10^{-12}\ M$$

concentration of OH^- concentration of H_3O^+

PROBLEM 9.19

Calculate the value of $[H_3O^+]$ and $[OH^-]$ in each solution: (a) 0.001 M NaOH; (b) 0.001 M HCl; (c) 1.5 M HCl; (d) 0.30 M NaOH.

9.6 The pH Scale

Knowing the hydronium ion concentration is necessary in many different instances. The blood must have an H_3O^+ concentration in a very narrow range for an individual's good health. Plants thrive in soil that is not too acidic or too basic. The H_3O^+ concentration in a swimming pool must be measured and adjusted to keep the water clean and free from bacteria and algae.

9.6A Calculating pH

Since values for the hydronium ion concentration are very small, with negative powers of ten, the **pH scale** is used to more conveniently report $[H_3O^+]$. The pH of a solution is a number generally between 0 and 14, defined in terms of the *logarithm* (log) of the H_3O^+ concentration.

$$pH = -\log\,[H_3O^+]$$

A logarithm is an exponent of a power of ten.

      The log is the exponent.

$\log(10^5) = 5 \qquad \log(10^{-10}) = -10 \qquad \log(0.001) = \log(10^{-3}) = -3$

              The log is the exponent.   Convert to scientific notation.

Apple juice has a pH of about 4, so it is an acidic solution.

In calculating pH, first consider an H_3O^+ concentration that has a coefficient of *one* when the number is written in scientific notation. For example, the value of $[H_3O^+]$ in apple juice is about 1×10^{-4}, or 10^{-4} written without the coefficient. The pH of this solution is calculated as follows:

$$pH = -\log [H_3O^+] = -\log(10^{-4})$$
$$= -(-4) \qquad = 4$$

pH of apple juice

Since pH is defined as the *negative* logarithm of $[H_3O^+]$ and these concentrations have *negative* exponents (10^{-x}), pH values are *positive* numbers.

Whether a solution is acidic, neutral, or basic can now be defined in terms of its pH.

- Acidic solution: pH < 7   ⟶ $[H_3O^+] > 1 \times 10^{-7}$
- Neutral solution: pH = 7   ⟶ $[H_3O^+] = 1 \times 10^{-7}$
- Basic solution: pH > 7   ⟶ $[H_3O^+] < 1 \times 10^{-7}$

Note the relationship between $[H_3O^+]$ and pH.

- The *lower* the pH, the *higher* the concentration of H_3O^+.

Since pH is measured on a *logarithmic* scale, **a small difference in pH translates to a large change in H_3O^+ concentration.** For example, a difference of one pH unit means a ten-fold difference in H_3O^+ concentration. A difference of three pH units means a thousand-fold difference in H_3O^+ concentration.

A difference of one pH unit...

pH = 2 $[H_3O^+] = 1 \times 10^{-2}$
pH = 3 $[H_3O^+] = 1 \times 10^{-3}$

...means the $[H_3O^+]$ differs by a factor of 10.

A difference of three pH units...

pH = 2 $[H_3O^+] = 1 \times 10^{-2}$
pH = 5 $[H_3O^+] = 1 \times 10^{-5}$

...means the $[H_3O^+]$ differs by a factor of 1,000.

The pH of a solution can be measured using a pH meter as shown in Figure 9.6. Approximate pH values are determined using pH paper or indicators that turn different colors depending on the pH of the solution. The pH of various substances is shown in Figure 9.7.

Figure 9.6   Measuring pH

a.

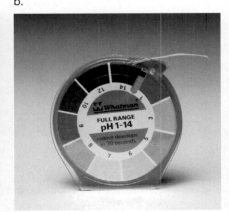

b.   c.

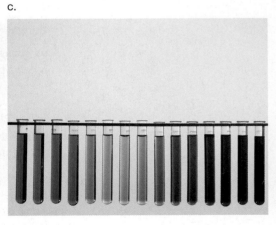

a. A pH meter is a small electronic device that measures pH when an electrode is dipped into a solution.

b. Paper strips called pH paper change color corresponding to a particular pH, when a drop of an aqueous solution is applied to them.

c. An acid–base indicator can be used to give an approximate pH. The indicator is a dye that changes color depending on the pH of the solution.

Figure 9.7   The pH of Some Common Substances

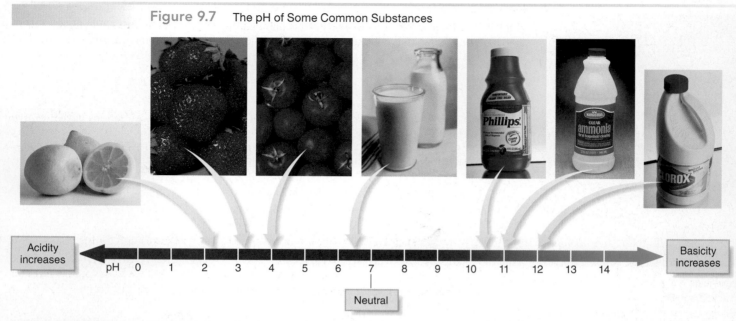

The pH of many fruits is less than 7, making them acidic. Many cleaning agents, such as household ammonia and bleach, are basic (pH > 7).

Converting a given H_3O^+ concentration to a pH value is shown in Sample Problem 9.13. The reverse process, converting a pH value to an H_3O^+ concentration, is shown in Sample Problem 9.14.

SAMPLE PROBLEM 9.13

What is the pH of a urine sample that has an H_3O^+ concentration of 1×10^{-5} M? Classify the solution as acidic, basic, or neutral.

Analysis

Use the formula pH = $-\log [H_3O^+]$. When the coefficient of a number written in scientific notation is one, the pH equals the value x in 10^{-x}.

Solution

$$pH = -\log [H_3O^+] = -\log(10^{-5})$$
$$= -(-5) = 5 \quad \text{pH of urine sample}$$
Answer

The urine sample is acidic since the pH < 7.

PROBLEM 9.20

Convert each H_3O^+ concentration to a pH value.

   a. 1×10^{-6} M   b. 1×10^{-12} M   c. 0.000 01 M   d. 0.000 000 000 01 M

SAMPLE PROBLEM 9.14

What is the H_3O^+ concentration in lemon juice that has a pH of about 2? Classify the solution as acidic, basic, or neutral.

Analysis

To find $[H_3O^+]$ from a pH, which is a logarithm, we must determine what number corresponds to the given logarithm. When the pH is a whole number x, the value of x becomes the exponent in the expression $1 \times 10^{-x} = [H_3O^+]$.

Solution

If the pH of lemon juice is 2, $[H_3O^+] = 1 \times 10^{-2}$ M. Since the pH is less than 7, the lemon juice is acidic.

Determining logarithms and anti-logarithms using an electronic calculator is shown in Appendix A.

PROBLEM 9.21

What H_3O^+ concentration corresponds to each pH value: (a) 13; (b) 7; (c) 3? Label each solution as acidic, basic, or neutral.

9.6B Calculating pH Using a Calculator

To calculate the pH of a solution in which the hydronium ion concentration has a coefficient in scientific notation that is *not* equal to one—as in 2.0×10^{-3}—you need a calculator that has a log function. How the keys are labeled and the order of the steps depend on your particular calculator.

Enter this number on your calculator.

$$pH = -\log [H_3O^+] \quad = \quad -\log(2.0 \times 10^{-3})$$
$$= \quad -(-2.70) \quad = \quad 2.70$$

Similarly, when a reported pH is *not* a whole number—as in the pH = 8.50 for a sample of seawater—you need a calculator to calculate an *antilogarithm*—that is, the number that has a logarithm of 8.50. To make sure your calculation is correct, note that since the pH of seawater is between 8 and 9, the H_3O^+ concentration must be between 10^{-8} and 10^{-9}.

$$[H_3O^+] = \text{antilog}(-pH) = \text{antilog}(-8.50)$$
$$= 3.2 \times 10^{-9} \, M$$

Care must be taken in keeping track of significant figures when using logarithms.

- A logarithm has the same number of digits to the right of the decimal point as are contained in the coefficient of the original number.

$$[H_3O^+] \quad = \quad 3.2 \times 10^{-9} \, M \qquad pH = 8.50 \quad \text{two digits after the decimal point}$$

two significant figures

Because seawater contains dissolved salts, its pH is 8.50, making it slightly basic, not neutral like pure water.

SAMPLE PROBLEM 9.15

What is the pH of wine that has an H_3O^+ concentration of 3.2×10^{-4} M?

Analysis

Use a calculator to determine the logarithm of a number that contains a coefficient in scientific notation that is not a whole number; $pH = -\log [H_3O^+]$.

Solution

The order of the steps in using an electronic calculator, as well as the labels on the calculator buttons, vary. In some cases it is possible to calculate the pH by following three steps: enter the number (H_3O^+ concentration); press the *log* button; and press the change sign key. Consult your calculator manual if these steps do not give the desired value. Because the coefficient in the original number had two significant figures, the pH must have two digits to the right of the decimal point.

two significant figures

$$pH = -\log [H_3O^+] \quad = \quad -\log(3.2 \times 10^{-4})$$
$$= \quad -(-3.49) \quad = \quad 3.49 \quad \text{two digits to the right of the decimal point}$$

PROBLEM 9.22

What H_3O^+ concentration corresponds to each pH value: (a) 10.2; (b) 7.8; (c) 4.3?

SAMPLE PROBLEM 9.16

What is the H_3O^+ concentration in sweat that has a pH of 5.8?

Analysis

Use a calculator to determine the antilogarithm of the negative of the pH; $[H_3O^+] = \text{antilog}(-pH)$.

Solution

The order of the steps in using an electronic calculator, as well as the labels on the calculator buttons, vary. In some cases it is possible to calculate $[H_3O^+]$ by the following steps: enter the pH value; press the change sign key; and press the *2nd + log* buttons. Since the pH has only one number to the right of the decimal point, the H_3O^+ concentration must have only one significant figure in its coefficient.

one digit to the right of the decimal point

$$[H_3O^+] \quad = \quad antilog(-pH) \quad = \quad antilog(-5.\overset{\frown}{8})$$

$$[H_3O^+] \quad = \quad 2 \times 10^{-6} \text{ M}$$

one significant figure

PROBLEM 9.23

Convert each H_3O^+ concentration to a pH value.

  a. 1.8×10^{-6} M   b. 9.21×10^{-12} M   c. 0.000 088 M   d. 0.000 000 000 076 2 M

9.6C FOCUS ON THE HUMAN BODY
The pH of Body Fluids

The human body contains fluids that vary in pH as shown in Figure 9.8. While saliva is slightly acidic, the gastric juice in the stomach has the lowest pH found in the body. The strongly acidic environment of the stomach aids in the digestion of food. It also kills many types of bacteria that might be inadvertently consumed along with food and drink. When food leaves the stomach, it passes to the basic environment of the small intestines. Bases in the small intestines react with acid from the stomach.

Figure 9.8   Variation in pH Values in the Human Body

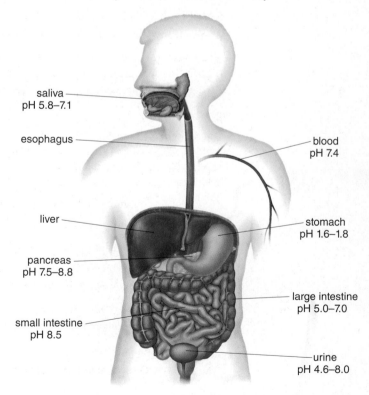

saliva
pH 5.8–7.1

esophagus

blood
pH 7.4

liver

stomach
pH 1.6–1.8

pancreas
pH 7.5–8.8

large intestine
pH 5.0–7.0

small intestine
pH 8.5

urine
pH 4.6–8.0

The pH of some body fluids must occupy a very narrow range. For example, a healthy individual has a blood pH in the range of 7.35–7.45. Maintaining this pH is accomplished by a complex mechanism described in Section 9.11. The pH of other fluids can be more variable. Urine has a pH anywhere from 4.6–8.0, depending on an individual's recent diet and exercise.

PROBLEM 9.24
Label each organ or fluid in Figure 9.8 as being acidic, basic, or neutral.

9.7 Common Acid–Base Reactions

Although we have already seen a variety of acid–base reactions in Sections 9.2–9.4, two common reactions deserve additional attention—reaction of acids with hydroxide bases (OH^-), and reaction of acids with bicarbonate (HCO_3^-) or carbonate (CO_3^{2-}).

9.7A Reaction of Acids with Hydroxide Bases

The reaction of a Brønsted–Lowry acid (HA) with the metal salt of a hydroxide base (MOH) is an example of a *neutralization* reaction—**an acid–base reaction that produces a salt and water as products.**

$$\underset{\text{acid}}{HA(aq)} + \underset{\text{base}}{MOH(aq)} \longrightarrow \underset{\text{water}}{H-OH(l)} + \underset{\text{salt}}{MA(aq)}$$

- The acid HA donates a proton (H^+) to the OH^- base to form H_2O.
- The anion A^- from the acid combines with the cation M^+ from the base to form the salt MA.

For example, hydrochloric acid, HCl, reacts with sodium hydroxide, NaOH, to form water and sodium chloride, NaCl. A single reaction arrow is drawn between reactants and products because equilibrium greatly favors the products.

$$\underset{\text{acid}}{HCl(aq)} + \underset{\text{base}}{NaOH(aq)} \longrightarrow \underset{\text{water}}{H-OH(l)} + \underset{\text{salt}}{NaCl(aq)}$$

The important reacting species in this reaction are H^+ from the acid HCl and OH^- from the base NaOH. To more clearly see the acid–base reaction, we can write an equation that contains only the species that are actually involved in the reaction. Such an equation is called a **net ionic equation.**

- A *net ionic equation* contains only the species involved in a reaction.

To write a net ionic equation for an acid–base reaction, we first write the acid, base, and salt as individual ions in solution. This process is simplified if we use H^+ (not H_3O^+) as the reacting species of the acid, since it is the H^+ ion that is transferred to the base. The reaction of HCl with NaOH using individual ions is then drawn as:

$$H^+(aq) + Cl^-(aq) + Na^+(aq) + OH^-(aq) \longrightarrow H-OH(l) + Na^+(aq) + Cl^-(aq)$$

Writing the equation in this manner shows that the Na^+ and Cl^- ions are unchanged in the reaction. Ions that appear on both sides of an equation but undergo no change in a reaction are called **spectator ions.** Removing the spectator ions from the equation gives the net ionic equation.

$$H^+(aq) + \underset{\text{Omit the spectator ions.}}{Cl^-(aq)} + \underset{\text{Omit the spectator ions.}}{Na^+(aq)} + OH^-(aq) \longrightarrow H-OH(l) + \underset{\text{Omit the spectator ions.}}{Na^+(aq)} + \underset{\text{Omit the spectator ions.}}{Cl^-(aq)}$$

Net ionic equation $\quad H^+(aq) + OH^-(aq) \longrightarrow H-OH(l)$

- Whenever a strong acid and strong base react, the net ionic equation is always the same—H^+ reacts with OH^- to form H_2O.

To draw the products of these neutralization reactions, keep in mind that **two products are always formed—water and a metal salt.** Balancing an acid–base equation can be done with the stepwise procedure for balancing a general reaction outlined in Section 5.2. The coefficients in a balanced chemical equation illustrate that one H^+ ion is always needed to react with each OH^- anion.

How To Draw a Balanced Equation for a Neutralization Reaction Between HA and MOH

Example: Write a balanced equation for the reaction of $Mg(OH)_2$, an active ingredient in the antacid product Maalox, with the hydrochloric acid (HCl) in the stomach.

Step [1] Identify the acid and base in the reactants and draw H_2O as one product.

- HCl is the acid and $Mg(OH)_2$ is the base. H^+ from the acid reacts with OH^- from the base to form H_2O.

$$HCl(aq) + Mg(OH)_2(aq) \longrightarrow H_2O(l) + salt$$
$$\text{acid} \text{base}$$

Step [2] Determine the structure of the salt formed as product.

- The salt is formed from the elements of the acid and base that are *not* used to form H_2O. The anion of the salt comes from the acid and the cation of the salt comes from the base.
- In this case, Cl^- (from HCl) and Mg^{2+} [from $Mg(OH)_2$] combine to form the salt $MgCl_2$.

Step [3] Balance the equation.

- Follow the procedure in Section 5.2 to balance an equation. The balanced equation shows that *two* moles of HCl are needed for *each* mole of $Mg(OH)_2$, since each mole of $Mg(OH)_2$ contains two moles of OH^-.

Place a 2 to balance H and O.

$$2\,HCl(aq) + Mg(OH)_2(aq) \longrightarrow 2\,H_2O(l) + MgCl_2$$

Place a 2 to balance Cl.

HEALTH NOTE

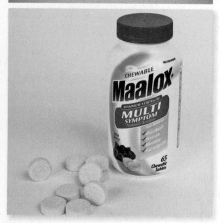

The antacid products Maalox and Mylanta both contain two bases—$Mg(OH)_2$ and $Al(OH)_3$—that react with excess stomach acid. A combination of bases is used so that the constipating effect of the aluminum salt is counteracted by the laxative effect of the magnesium salt.

PROBLEM 9.25

Write a balanced equation for each acid–base reaction.

a. $HNO_3(aq) + NaOH(aq) \longrightarrow$ b. $H_2SO_4(aq) + KOH(aq) \longrightarrow$

PROBLEM 9.26

Write the net ionic equation for each reaction in Problem 9.25.

9.7B   Reaction of Acids with Bicarbonate and Carbonate

Acids react with the bases bicarbonate (HCO_3^-) and carbonate (CO_3^{2-}). A bicarbonate base reacts with *one* proton to form carbonic acid, H_2CO_3. A carbonate base reacts with *two* protons. The carbonic acid formed in these reactions is unstable and decomposes to form CO_2 and H_2O. Thus, when an acid reacts with either base, bubbles of CO_2 gas are given off.

$$H^+(aq) + HCO_3^-(aq) \longrightarrow \left[H_2CO_3(aq)\right] \longrightarrow H_2O(l) + CO_2(g)$$
1 H^+ needed   bicarbonate   bubbles of CO_2

$$2\,H^+(aq) + CO_3^{2-}(aq) \longrightarrow \left[H_2CO_3(aq)\right] \longrightarrow H_2O(l) + CO_2(g)$$
2 H^+ needed   carbonate

Sodium bicarbonate ($NaHCO_3$), an ingredient in the over-the-counter antacid Alka-Seltzer, is the metal salt of a bicarbonate base that reacts with excess stomach acid, releasing CO_2. Like the

HEALTH NOTE

Like taking other over-the-counter medications, care must be exercised when using antacids. Ingestion of large amounts of $CaCO_3$ can increase the incidence of kidney stones.

neutralization reactions in Section 9.7A, a salt, NaCl, is formed in which the cation (Na^+) comes from the base and the anion (Cl^-) comes from the acid.

$$HCl(aq) \; + \; NaHCO_3(aq) \longrightarrow NaCl(aq) \; + \; H_2CO_3(aq)$$
$$\text{acid} \qquad\qquad \text{base} \qquad\qquad\qquad \text{salt} \qquad\qquad \searrow H_2O(l) \; + \; CO_2(g)$$

Calcium carbonate ($CaCO_3$), a calcium supplement and antacid in Tums, also reacts with excess stomach acid with release of CO_2. Since each carbonate ion reacts with two protons, the balanced equation shows a 2:1 ratio of HCl to $CaCO_3$.

$$2\,HCl(aq) \; + \; CaCO_3(aq) \longrightarrow CaCl_2(aq) \; + \; H_2CO_3(aq)$$
$$\text{acid} \qquad\qquad \text{base} \qquad\qquad\qquad \text{salt} \qquad\qquad \searrow H_2O(l) \; + \; CO_2(g)$$

SAMPLE PROBLEM 9.17

Write a balanced equation for the reaction of H_2SO_4 with $NaHCO_3$.

Analysis

The acid and base react to form a salt and carbonic acid (H_2CO_3), which decomposes to CO_2 and H_2O.

Solution

H_2SO_4 is the acid and $NaHCO_3$ is the base. H^+ from the acid reacts with HCO_3^- from the base to give H_2CO_3, which decomposes to H_2O and CO_2. A salt (Na_2SO_4) is also formed from the cation of the base (Na^+) and the anion of the acid (SO_4^{2-}).

Unbalanced equation: $\quad H_2SO_4(aq) \; + \; NaHCO_3(aq) \longrightarrow Na_2SO_4(aq) \; + \; H_2O(l) \; + \; CO_2(g)$
$$\text{acid} \qquad\qquad \text{base} \qquad\qquad\qquad \text{salt} \qquad\qquad\quad \text{from } H_2CO_3$$

To balance the equation, place coefficients so the number of atoms on both sides of the arrow is the same.

Place a 2 to balance Na...

$$H_2SO_4(aq) \; + \; 2\,NaHCO_3(aq) \longrightarrow Na_2SO_4(aq) \; + \; 2\,H_2O(l) \; + \; 2\,CO_2(g)$$
$$\text{acid} \qquad\qquad \text{base} \qquad\qquad\qquad \text{salt}$$

...then place 2's to balance C, H, and O.

PROBLEM 9.27

The acid in acid rain is generally sulfuric acid (H_2SO_4). When this rainwater falls on statues composed of marble ($CaCO_3$), the H_2SO_4 slowly dissolves the $CaCO_3$. Write a balanced equation for this acid–base reaction.

PROBLEM 9.28

Write a balanced equation for the reaction of nitric acid (HNO_3) with each base: (a) $NaHCO_3$; (b) $MgCO_3$.

9.8 The Acidity and Basicity of Salt Solutions

Thus far we have discussed what occurs when an acid or a base dissolves in water. What happens to the pH of water when a salt is dissolved? A salt is the product of a neutralization reaction (Section 9.7A). Does this mean that a salt dissolved in water forms a neutral solution with a pH of 7?

- A salt can form an acidic, basic, or neutral solution depending on whether its cation and anion are derived from a strong or weak acid and base.

Let's first examine what acid and base are used to form a salt M^+A^-.

- The cation M^+ comes from the base.
- The anion A^- comes from the acid HA.

Thus, we consider NaCl to be a salt formed when the strong base NaOH and the strong acid HCl react together. On the other hand, $NaHCO_3$ is formed from the strong base NaOH and the weak acid H_2CO_3, and NH_4Cl is formed from the weak base NH_3 and the strong acid HCl.

NaCl
Na$^+$ Cl$^-$
from NaOH   from HCl
strong base   strong acid

NaHCO$_3$
Na$^+$ HCO$_3^-$
from NaOH   from H$_2$CO$_3$
strong base   weak acid

NH$_4$Cl
NH$_4^+$ Cl$^-$
from NH$_3$ from HCl
weak base   strong acid

A salt derived from a strong base and a strong acid forms a neutral solution (pH = 7). When one ion of a salt is derived from a weak acid or base, one principle is followed: **the ion derived from the *stronger* acid or base determines whether the solution is acidic or basic.**

- A salt derived from a *strong base* and a weak acid forms a *basic* solution (pH > 7).
- A salt derived from a weak base and a *strong acid* forms an *acidic* solution (pH < 7).

For example, when $NaHCO_3$ dissolves in water, it forms $Na^+(aq)$ and $HCO_3^-(aq)$. Alkali metal cations like Na^+ do not react with H_2O, but HCO_3^- reacts with H_2O to form OH^-. Thus, **$NaHCO_3$, a salt derived from a *strong* base and a weak acid, forms a *basic* solution.**

$$HCO_3^-(aq) \;+\; H_2O(l) \rightleftharpoons H_2CO_3(aq) \;+\; \boxed{OH^-(aq)}$$

Hydroxide makes the solution basic,
so the pH > 7.

When NH_4Cl dissolves in water it forms $NH_4^+(aq)$ and $Cl^-(aq)$. Halide anions like Cl^- do not react with H_2O, but NH_4^+ reacts with H_2O to form H_3O^+. Thus, **NH_4Cl, a salt derived from a *strong* acid and a weak base, forms an *acidic* solution.**

$$NH_4^+(aq) \;+\; H_2O(l) \rightleftharpoons NH_3(aq) \;+\; \boxed{H_3O^+(aq)}$$

H_3O^+ makes the solution acidic,
so the pH < 7.

When NaCl dissolves in water it forms $Na^+(aq)$ and $Cl^-(aq)$. Neither ion reacts with water. Since no acid–base reaction occurs, the solution remains neutral. Thus, **NaCl, a salt derived from a strong acid and strong base, forms a neutral solution.** The acidity and basicity of salt solutions is summarized in Table 9.4.

Table 9.4 The Acidity and Basicity of Salt Solutions

Cation Derived from	Anion Derived from	Solution	pH	Examples
Strong base	Strong acid	neutral	7	NaCl, KBr, NaNO$_3$
Strong base	Weak acid	basic	> 7	NaHCO$_3$, KCN, CaF$_2$
Weak base	Strong acid	acidic	< 7	NH$_4$Cl, NH$_4$NO$_3$

SAMPLE PROBLEM 9.18

Determine whether each salt forms an acidic, basic, or neutral solution when dissolved in water:
(a) NaF; (b) KNO$_3$; (c) NH$_4$Br.

Analysis

Determine what type of acid and base (strong or weak) are used to form the salt. When the ions in the salt come from a strong acid and strong base, the solution is neutral. When the ions come from acids and bases of different strength, the ion derived from the stronger reactant determines the acidity.

Solution

a.
NaF

Na⁺   F⁻

from NaOH   from HF
strong base   weak acid
basic solution

b.
KNO₃

K⁺   NO₃⁻

from KOH   from HNO₃
strong base   **strong acid**
neutral solution

c.
NH₄Br

NH₄⁺   Br⁻

from NH₃   from HBr
weak base   **strong acid**
acidic solution

PROBLEM 9.29

Determine whether each salt forms an acidic, basic, or neutral solution when dissolved in w...
(a) KI; (b) K_2CO_3; (c) $Ca(NO_3)_2$; (d) NH_4I; (e) $BaCl_2$; (f) Na_3PO_4.

PROBLEM 9.30

Which of the following salts forms an aqueous solution that has a pH > 7: (a) LiCl; (b) K_2CO_3; (c) NH_4Br; (d) $MgCO_3$?

9.9   Titration

Sometimes it is necessary to know the exact concentration of acid or base in a solution. To determine the molarity of a solution, we carry out a **titration.** A titration uses a *buret,* a calibrated tube with a stopcock at the bottom that allows a solution of known molarity to be added in small quantities to a solution of unknown molarity. The procedure for determining the total acid concentration of a solution of HCl is illustrated in Figure 9.9.

Figure 9.9   Titration of an Acid with a Base of Known Concentration

b.

c.

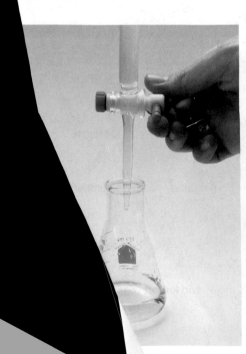
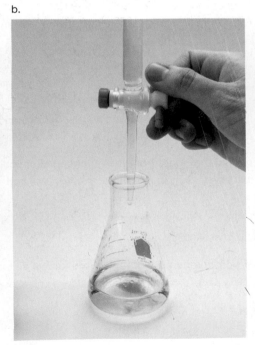

olarity of a solution of HCl:

f HCl solution to a flask. Add an acid–base indicator, often phenolphthalein, which is colorless in acid but turns

ution of known molarity and slowly add it to the HCl solution.

nd point is reached, the point at which the indicator changes color. At the end point, the **number of moles of**

ber of moles of HCl in the flask. In other words, all of the HCl has reacted with NaOH and the solution is no

f NaOH solution added from the buret. Using the known volume and molarity of the NaOH solution and the

molarity of the HCl solution can be calculated.

How does a titration tell us the concentration of an HCl solution? A titration is based on the acid–base reaction that occurs between the acid in the flask (HCl) and the base that is added (NaOH). **When the number of moles of base added equals the number of moles of acid in the flask, the acid is *neutralized*, forming a salt and water.**

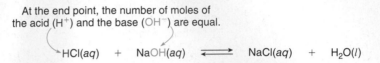

At the end point, the number of moles of the acid (H^+) and the base (OH^-) are equal.

$$HCl(aq) \quad + \quad NaOH(aq) \quad \rightleftarrows \quad NaCl(aq) \quad + \quad H_2O(l)$$

To determine an unknown molarity from titration data requires three operations.

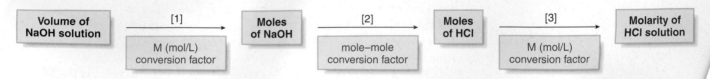

| Volume of NaOH solution | [1] M (mol/L) conversion factor | Moles of NaOH | [2] mole–mole conversion factor | Moles of HCl | [3] M (mol/L) conversion factor | Molarity of HCl solution |

First, we determine the number of moles of base added using its known molarity and volume. Then we use coefficients in the balanced acid–base equation to tell us the number of moles of acid that react with the base. Finally, we determine the molarity of the acid from the calculat number of moles and the known volume of the acid.

How To Determine the Molarity of an Acid Solution from a Titration

Example: What is the molarity of an HCl solution if 22.5 mL of a 0.100 M NaOH solution are needed to titrate a 25.0 mL sample the acid?

Step [1] Determine the number of moles of base used to neutralize the acid.

- Convert milliliters to liters of base using a mL–L conversion factor. Use the molarity (M) and volume (V) of the base to the number of moles (mol = MV).

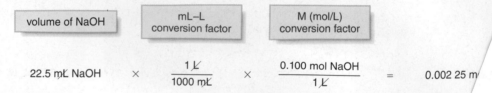

volume of NaOH | mL–L conversion factor | M (mol/L) conversion factor

$$22.5 \text{ mL NaOH} \quad \times \quad \frac{1 \text{ L}}{1000 \text{ mL}} \quad \times \quad \frac{0.100 \text{ mol NaOH}}{1 \text{ L}} \quad = \quad 0.002\ 25 \text{ m}$$

Step [2] Determine the number of moles of acid that react from the balanced chemical equation.

- In this reaction, one mole of HCl reacts with one mole of NaOH, so the number of moles of NaOH equals of HCl at the end point.

$$HCl(aq) \quad + \quad NaOH(aq) \quad \longrightarrow \quad NaCl(aq) \quad + \quad H_2O(l)$$
$$0.002\ 25 \text{ mol} \quad 0.002\ 25 \text{ mol}$$

Step [3] Determine the molarity of the acid from the number of moles and known volume.

- Convert milliliters to liters of acid using a mL–L conversion factor. Use the number of moles ar calculate the molarity (M = mol/L).

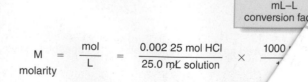

mL–L conversion fac

$$M = \frac{\text{mol}}{\text{L}} = \frac{0.002\ 25 \text{ mol HCl}}{25.0 \text{ mL solution}} \quad \times \quad \frac{1000}{}$$

molarity

Sample Problem 9.19 illustrates a calculation for a titration in which the ra~~ of~~ ~~acid to~~
the balanced acid–base equation is something other than 1:1.

SAMPLE PROBLEM 9.19

Acid rain is rainwater with a lower-than-normal pH, caused by the presence of di~~ssolved~~ ~~acids such~~
as H_2SO_4. What is the molarity of H_2SO_4 in rainwater if 5.22 mL of a 0.20 M NaO~~H is~~
needed to titrate 125 mL of the sample? The balanced equation for this acid–bas~~e is given.~~

$$H_2SO_4(aq) + 2\ NaOH(aq) \longrightarrow Na_2SO_4(aq) + 2\ H_2O(l)$$

Analysis and Solution

[1] Determine the number of moles of base used to neutralize the acid.

- Use the molarity (M) and volume (V) of the base to calculate the number of m~~oles~~ (mol = MV).

$$5.22\ \cancel{mL}\ NaOH \times \frac{1\ \cancel{L}}{1000\ \cancel{mL}} \times \frac{0.20\ mol\ NaOH}{1\ \cancel{L}} = 0.0010\ mol\ NaO\text{H}$$

[2] Determine the number of moles of acid that react from the balanced chemic~~al equation.~~

- Since each H_2SO_4 molecule contains two protons, *one* mole of the acid H_2SO_4
  two moles of the base NaOH in the neutralization reaction. The coefficients in t~~he balanced~~
  equation form a mole ratio to calculate the number of moles of acid that react.

$$0.0010\ mol\ NaOH \times \frac{1\ mol\ H_2SO_4}{2\ mol\ NaOH} = 0.000\ 50\ mol\ H_2SO_4$$

[3] Determine the molarity of the acid from the number of moles and known volume.

$$M = \frac{mol}{L} = \frac{0.000\ 50\ mol\ H_2SO_4}{125\ \cancel{mL}\ solution} \times \frac{1000\ \cancel{mL}}{1\ L} = 0.0040\ M\ H_2SO_4$$

molarity   **Answer**

PROBLEM 9.31

What is the molarity of an HCl solution if 25.5 mL of a 0.24 M NaOH solution are needed to neutralize 15.0 mL of the sample?

PROBLEM 9.32

How many milliliters of 2.0 M NaOH are needed to neutralize 5.0 mL of a 6.0 M H_2SO_4 solution?

ENVIRONMENTAL NOTE

The sulfur oxides formed when sulfur-containing fuel is burned form H_2SO_4, which acidifies rainwater. This acid rain destroys forest vegetation and makes lakes and streams too acidic for fish and shellfish to survive.

9.10 Buffers

A *buffer* is a solution whose pH changes very little when acid or base is added. Most buffers are solutions composed of approximately equal amounts of a weak acid and the salt of its conjugate base.

- The weak acid of the buffer reacts with added base, OH⁻.
- The conjugate base of the buffer reacts with added acid, H_3O^+.

9.10A General Characteristics of a Buffer

The effect of a buffer can be illustrated by comparing the pH change that occurs when a small amount of strong acid or strong base is added to water, compared to the pH change that occurs when the same amount of strong acid or strong base is added to a buffer, as shown in Figure 9.10. When 0.020 mol of HCl is added to 1.0 L of water, the pH changes from 7 to 1.7, and when 0.020 mol of NaOH is added to 1.0 L of water, the pH changes from 7 to 12.3. In this example, addition of a small quantity of a strong acid or strong base to neutral water changes the pH by over 5 pH units.

Figure 9.10   The Effect of a Buffer on pH Changes

a.

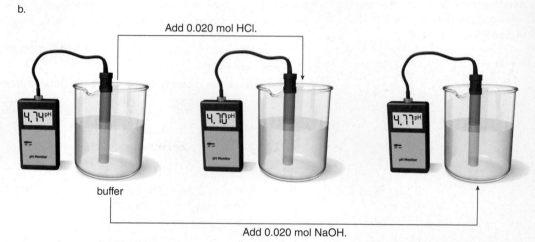

a. The pH of pure water changes drastically when a small amount of strong acid or strong base is added.

b. The pH of a buffer changes very little when the same amount of strong acid or strong base is added.

In contrast, a buffer prepared from 0.50 M acetic acid (CH_3COOH) and 0.50 M sodium acetate ($NaCH_3COO$) has a pH of 4.74. Addition of the same quantity of acid, 0.020 mol HCl, changes the pH to 4.70, and addition of the same quantity of base, 0.020 mol of NaOH, changes the pH to 4.77. In this example, the change of pH in the presence of the buffer is no more than 0.04 pH units!

Why is a buffer able to absorb acid or base with very little pH change? Let's use as an example a buffer that contains equal concentrations of acetic acid (CH_3COOH), and the sodium salt of its conjugate base, sodium acetate ($NaCH_3COO$). CH_3COOH is a weak acid, so when it dissolves in water, only a small fraction dissociates to form its conjugate base CH_3COO^-. In the buffer solution, however, the sodium acetate provides an equal amount of the conjugate base.

$$CH_3COOH(aq) \; + \; H_2O(l) \; \rightleftharpoons \; H_3O^+(aq) \; + \; CH_3COO^-(aq)$$

approximately equal amounts

Solution

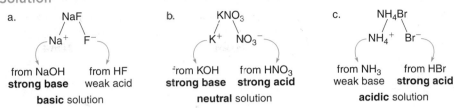

a.
NaF
Na⁺ F⁻
from NaOH — **strong base** | from HF — weak acid
basic solution

b.
KNO₃
K⁺ NO₃⁻
From KOH — **strong base** | from HNO₃ — **strong acid**
neutral solution

c.
NH₄Br
NH₄⁺ Br⁻
from NH₃ — weak base | from HBr — **strong acid**
acidic solution

PROBLEM 9.29

Determine whether each salt forms an acidic, basic, or neutral solution when dissolved in water:
(a) KI; (b) K_2CO_3; (c) $Ca(NO_3)_2$; (d) NH_4I; (e) $BaCl_2$; (f) Na_3PO_4.

PROBLEM 9.30

Which of the following salts forms an aqueous solution that has a pH > 7: (a) LiCl; (b) K_2CO_3;
(c) NH_4Br; (d) $MgCO_3$?

9.9 Titration

Sometimes it is necessary to know the exact concentration of acid or base in a solution. To determine the molarity of a solution, we carry out a **titration.** A titration uses a *buret,* a calibrated tube with a stopcock at the bottom that allows a solution of known molarity to be added in small quantities to a solution of unknown molarity. The procedure for determining the total acid concentration of a solution of HCl is illustrated in Figure 9.9.

Figure 9.9 Titration of an Acid with a Base of Known Concentration

a.
b.
c.

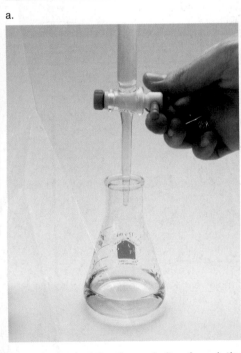

Steps in determining the molarity of a solution of HCl:

a. Add a measured volume of HCl solution to a flask. Add an acid–base indicator, often phenolphthalein, which is colorless in acid but turns bright pink in base.

b. Fill a buret with an NaOH solution of known molarity and slowly add it to the HCl solution.

c. Add NaOH solution until the *end point* is reached, the point at which the indicator changes color. At the end point, the **number of moles of NaOH added equals the number of moles of HCl** in the flask. In other words, all of the HCl has reacted with NaOH and the solution is no longer acidic. Read the volume of NaOH solution added from the buret. Using the known volume and molarity of the NaOH solution and the known volume of HCl solution, the molarity of the HCl solution can be calculated.

How does a titration tell us the concentration of an HCl solution? A titration is based on the acid–base reaction that occurs between the acid in the flask (HCl) and the base that is added (NaOH). **When the number of moles of base added equals the number of moles of acid in the flask, the acid is** *neutralized,* **forming a salt and water.**

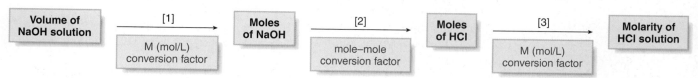

At the end point, the number of moles of
the acid (H^+) and the base (OH^-) are equal.

$$HCl(aq) \quad + \quad NaOH(aq) \quad \rightleftharpoons \quad NaCl(aq) \quad + \quad H_2O(l)$$

To determine an unknown molarity from titration data requires three operations.

Volume of NaOH solution	$\xrightarrow{[1]}$	Moles of NaOH	$\xrightarrow{[2]}$	Moles of HCl	$\xrightarrow{[3]}$	Molarity of HCl solution
	M (mol/L) conversion factor		mole–mole conversion factor		M (mol/L) conversion factor	

First, we determine the number of moles of base added using its known molarity and volume. Then we use coefficients in the balanced acid–base equation to tell us the number of moles of acid that react with the base. Finally, we determine the molarity of the acid from the calculated number of moles and the known volume of the acid.

How To Determine the Molarity of an Acid Solution from a Titration

Example: What is the molarity of an HCl solution if 22.5 mL of a 0.100 M NaOH solution are needed to titrate a 25.0 mL sample of the acid?

Step [1] Determine the number of moles of base used to neutralize the acid.

- Convert milliliters to liters of base using a mL–L conversion factor. Use the molarity (M) and volume (V) of the base to calculate the number of moles (mol = MV).

$$22.5 \text{ mL NaOH} \quad \times \quad \frac{1 \text{ L}}{1000 \text{ mL}} \quad \times \quad \frac{0.100 \text{ mol NaOH}}{1 \text{ L}} \quad = \quad 0.002\,25 \text{ mol NaOH}$$

Step [2] Determine the number of moles of acid that react from the balanced chemical equation.

- In this reaction, one mole of HCl reacts with one mole of NaOH, so the number of moles of NaOH equals the number of moles of HCl at the end point.

$$HCl(aq) \quad + \quad NaOH(aq) \quad \longrightarrow \quad NaCl(aq) \quad + \quad H_2O(l)$$

0.002 25 mol   0.002 25 mol

Step [3] Determine the molarity of the acid from the number of moles and known volume.

- Convert milliliters to liters of acid using a mL–L conversion factor. Use the number of moles and known volume of the acid to calculate the molarity (M = mol/L).

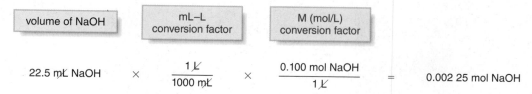

$$M = \frac{\text{mol}}{\text{L}} = \frac{0.002\,25 \text{ mol HCl}}{25.0 \text{ mL solution}} \quad \times \quad \frac{1000 \text{ mL}}{1 \text{ L}} \quad = \quad 0.0900 \text{ M HCl}$$

molarity

Sample Problem 9.19 illustrates a calculation for a titration in which the ratio of acid to base in the balanced acid–base equation is something other than 1:1.

SAMPLE PROBLEM 9.19

Acid rain is rainwater with a lower-than-normal pH, caused by the presence of dissolved acids such as H_2SO_4. What is the molarity of H_2SO_4 in rainwater if 5.22 mL of a 0.20 M NaOH solution are needed to titrate 125 mL of the sample? The balanced equation for this acid–base reaction is given.

$$H_2SO_4(aq) + 2\ NaOH(aq) \longrightarrow Na_2SO_4(aq) + 2\ H_2O(l)$$

Analysis and Solution

[1] Determine the number of moles of base used to neutralize the acid.

- Use the molarity (M) and volume (V) of the base to calculate the number of moles (mol = MV).

$$5.22\ \cancel{mL}\ NaOH \times \frac{1\ \cancel{L}}{1000\ \cancel{mL}} \times \frac{0.20\ mol\ NaOH}{1\ \cancel{L}} = 0.0010\ mol\ NaOH$$

[2] Determine the number of moles of acid that react from the balanced chemical equation.

- Since each H_2SO_4 molecule contains two protons, *one* mole of the acid H_2SO_4 reacts with *two* moles of the base NaOH in the neutralization reaction. The coefficients in the balanced equation form a mole ratio to calculate the number of moles of acid that react.

$$0.0010\ mol\ NaOH \times \frac{1\ mol\ H_2SO_4}{2\ mol\ NaOH} = 0.000\ 50\ mol\ H_2SO_4$$

[3] Determine the molarity of the acid from the number of moles and known volume.

$$M = \frac{mol}{L} = \frac{0.000\ 50\ mol\ H_2SO_4}{125\ \cancel{mL}\ solution} \times \frac{1000\ \cancel{mL}}{1\ L} = 0.0040\ M\ H_2SO_4$$

molarity   **Answer**

PROBLEM 9.31

What is the molarity of an HCl solution if 25.5 mL of a 0.24 M NaOH solution are needed to neutralize 15.0 mL of the sample?

PROBLEM 9.32

How many milliliters of 2.0 M NaOH are needed to neutralize 5.0 mL of a 6.0 M H_2SO_4 solution?

9.10 Buffers

A *buffer* is a solution whose pH changes very little when acid or base is added. Most buffers are solutions composed of approximately equal amounts of a weak acid and the salt of its conjugate base.

- The weak acid of the buffer reacts with added base, OH^-.
- The conjugate base of the buffer reacts with added acid, H_3O^+.

9.10A General Characteristics of a Buffer

The effect of a buffer can be illustrated by comparing the pH change that occurs when a small amount of strong acid or strong base is added to water, compared to the pH change that occurs when the same amount of strong acid or strong base is added to a buffer, as shown in Figure 9.10. When 0.020 mol of HCl is added to 1.0 L of water, the pH changes from 7 to 1.7, and when 0.020 mol of NaOH is added to 1.0 L of water, the pH changes from 7 to 12.3. In this example, addition of a small quantity of a strong acid or strong base to neutral water changes the pH by over 5 pH units.

ENVIRONMENTAL NOTE

The sulfur oxides formed when sulfur-containing fuel is burned form H_2SO_4, which acidifies rainwater. This acid rain destroys forest vegetation and makes lakes and streams too acidic for fish and shellfish to survive.

Figure 9.10   The Effect of a Buffer on pH Changes

a.

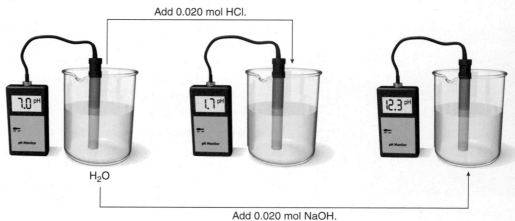

b.

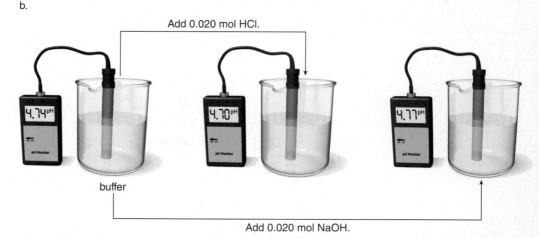

a. The pH of pure water changes drastically when a small amount of strong acid or strong base
   is added.

b. The pH of a buffer changes very little when the same amount of strong acid or strong base
   is added.

In contrast, a buffer prepared from 0.50 M acetic acid (CH_3COOH) and 0.50 M sodium acetate
($NaCH_3COO$) has a pH of 4.74. Addition of the same quantity of acid, 0.020 mol HCl, changes
the pH to 4.70, and addition of the same quantity of base, 0.020 mol of NaOH, changes the pH to
4.77. In this example, the change of pH in the presence of the buffer is no more than 0.04 pH units!

Why is a buffer able to absorb acid or base with very little pH change? Let's use as an example
a buffer that contains equal concentrations of acetic acid (CH_3COOH), and the sodium salt of its
conjugate base, sodium acetate ($NaCH_3COO$). CH_3COOH is a weak acid, so when it dissolves in
water, only a small fraction dissociates to form its conjugate base CH_3COO^-. In the buffer solution, however, the sodium acetate provides an equal amount of the conjugate base.

$$CH_3COOH(aq) \quad + \quad H_2O(l) \quad \rightleftharpoons \quad H_3O^+(aq) \quad + \quad CH_3COO^-(aq)$$

approximately equal amounts

In Section 9.4, we learned how to write the expression for the acid dissociation constant K_a for this reaction. Rearranging this expression to solve for $[H_3O^+]$ then illustrates why a buffer does not change pH much when acid or base is added.

Expression for K_a: $K_a = \dfrac{[H_3O^+][CH_3COO^-]}{[CH_3COOH]}$

Rearranging the expression: $[H_3O^+] = K_a \times \dfrac{[CH_3COOH]}{[CH_3COO^-]}$

If this ratio does not change much, then $[H_3O^+]$ does not change much.

The H_3O^+ concentration depends on two terms—K_a, which is a constant, and the ratio of the concentrations of the weak acid and its conjugate base. If these concentrations do not change much, then the concentration of H_3O^+ and therefore the pH do not change much.

Suppose a small amount of strong acid is added to the buffer. Added H_3O^+ reacts with CH_3COO^- to form CH_3COOH, so that $[CH_3COO^-]$ decreases slightly and $[CH_3COOH]$ increases slightly. However, the ratio of these two concentrations is not altered significantly, so the $[H_3O^+]$ and therefore the pH change only slightly.

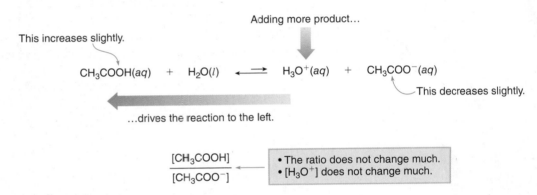

On the other hand, if a small amount of strong base is added to the buffer, OH^- reacts with CH_3COOH to form CH_3COO^-, so that $[CH_3COOH]$ decreases slightly and $[CH_3COO^-]$ increases slightly. However, the ratio of these two concentrations is not altered significantly, so the $[H_3O^+]$ and therefore the pH change only slightly.

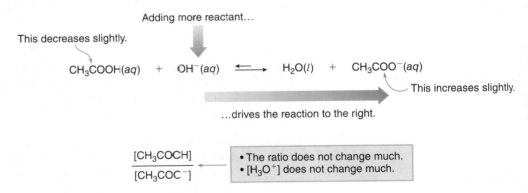

For a buffer to be effective, the amount of added acid or base must be small compared to the amount of buffer present. When a large amount of acid or base is added to a buffer, the concentrations of the weak acid and its conjugate base change a great deal, so the H_3O^+ concentration changes a great deal as well. Some common buffers are listed in Table 9.5.

Table 9.5 Common Buffers

Buffer	Weak Acid	Conjugate Base	K_a
Acetic acid/acetate	CH_3COOH	CH_3COO^-	1.8×10^{-5}
Bicarbonate/carbonate	HCO_3^-	CO_3^{2-}	5.6×10^{-11}
Dihydrogen phosphate/ hydrogen phosphate	$H_2PO_4^-$	HPO_4^{2-}	6.2×10^{-8}
Hydrogen phosphate/ phosphate	HPO_4^{2-}	PO_4^{3-}	2.2×10^{-13}

PROBLEM 9.33

Determine whether a solution containing each of the following substances is a buffer. Explain your reasoning.

a. HBr and NaBr   b. HF and KF   c. CH_3COOH alone

PROBLEM 9.34

Consider a buffer prepared from the weak acid HCO_3^- and its conjugate base CO_3^{2-}.

$$HCO_3^-(aq) + H_2O(l) \rightleftharpoons CO_3^{2-}(aq) + H_3O^+(aq)$$

a. Explain why both HCO_3^- and CO_3^{2-} are needed to prepare the buffer.
b. What happens to the concentrations of HCO_3^- and CO_3^{2-} when a small amount of acid is added to the buffer?
c. What happens to the concentrations of HCO_3^- and CO_3^{2-} when a small amount of base is added to the buffer?

9.10B Calculating the pH of a Buffer

The effective pH range of a buffer depends on its K_a. The pH of a buffer can be calculated from the K_a of the weak acid (HA), and the concentrations of the weak acid (HA) and conjugate base (A:$^-$) used to prepare it, as shown in Sample Problem 9.20.

Acid dissociation constant K_a for the general acid HA:

$$K_a = \frac{[H_3O^+][A:^-]}{[HA]}$$

Rearranging the expression to solve for $[H_3O^+]$:

$$[H_3O^+] = K_a \times \frac{[HA]}{[A:^-]}$$

determines the buffer pH

SAMPLE PROBLEM 9.20

What is the pH of a buffer that contains 0.20 M CH_3COOH and 0.20 M $NaCH_3COO$?

Analysis

Use the K_a of the weak acid of the buffer in Table 9.5 and the expression $[H_3O^+] = K_a([HA]/[A:^-])$ to calculate $[H_3O^+]$. Calculate the pH using the expression, pH = $-\log [H_3O^+]$.

Solution

[1] Substitute the given concentrations of CH_3COOH and CH_3COO^- for [HA] and [A:$^-$], respectively. K_a for CH_3COOH is 1.8×10^{-5}.

$$[H_3O^+] = K_a \times \frac{[CH_3COOH]}{[CH_3COO^-]} = (1.8 \times 10^{-5}) \times \frac{[0.20\ M]}{[0.20\ M]}$$

$$[H_3O^+] = 1.8 \times 10^{-5}\ M$$

[2] Use an electronic calculator to convert the H_3O^+ concentration to pH, as in Sample Problem 9.15.

$$pH = -\log [H_3O^+] = -\log(1.8 \times 10^{-5})$$
$$pH = 4.74$$

PROBLEM 9.35

Calculate the pH of a dihydrogen phosphate/hydrogen phosphate buffer prepared with each of the following concentrations. What cc you conclude about the pH of a buffer when equal concentrations of the weak acid and conjugate base are used to prepare it?

a. 0.10 M NaH_2PO_4 and 0.10 M Na_2HPO_4
b. 1.0 M NaH_2PO_4 and 1.0 M Na_2HPO_4
c. 0.50 M NaH_2PO_4 and 0.50 M Na_2HPO_4

PROBLEM 9.36

What is the pH of a buffer that contains 0.20 M CH_3COOH and 0.15 M $NaCH_3COO$?

9.10C FOCUS ON THE ENVIRONMENT
Acid Rain and a Naturally Buffered Lake

Unpolluted rainwater is not a neutral solution with a pH of 7; rather, because it contains dissolved carbon dioxide, it is slightly acidic with a pH of about 5.6.

$$CO_2(g) \;+\; 2\,H_2O(l) \;\rightleftharpoons\; H_3O^+(aq) \;+\; HCO_3^-(aq)$$

carbon dioxide
from the air

A low concentration of H_3O^+ gives rainwater a pH < 7.

Rainwater that contains dissolved H_2SO_4 (or HNO_3) from burning fossil fuels has a pH lower than 5.6. In some parts of the United States, rainwater often has a pH range of 4–5, and readings as low as pH = 1.8 have been recorded. When the rain in a region consistently has a lower-than-normal pH, this acid rain can have a devastating effect on plant and animal life.

The pH of some lakes changes drastically as the result of acid rain, whereas the pH of other lakes does not. In fact, the ability of some lakes to absorb acid rain without much pH change is entirely due to buffers (Figure 9.11). Lakes that are surrounded by limestone-rich soil are in contact with

Figure 9.11 Acid Rain and a Naturally Buffered Lake

CO_3^{2-}

HCO_3^-

lake surrounded by limestone ($CaCO_3$)

lake with no natural buffer

Acid rain adds H_3O^+ to the water, decreasing the pH.

The lake contains a natural buffer of CO_3^{2-} and HCO_3^-. H_3O^+ from rain reacts with dissolved CO_3^{2-}, forming more HCO_3^-. Since the concentrations of CO_3^{2-} and HCO_3^- do not change by much, the pH changes only slightly.

Acid precipitation contains H_2SO_4 and HNO_3 dissolved in rain and snow.

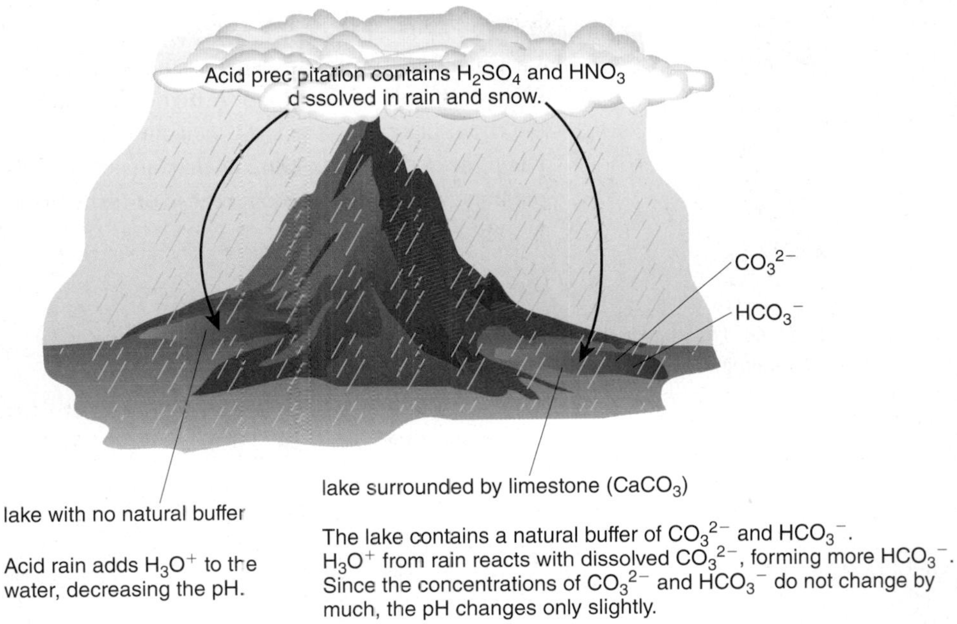

solid calcium carbonate, $CaCO_3$. As a result, the lake contains a natural carbonate/bicarbonate buffer. When acid precipitation falls on the lake, the dissolved carbonate (CO_3^{2-}) reacts with the acid to form bicarbonate (HCO_3^-).

The buffer reacts with added acid from rain.

$$CO_3^{2-}(aq) + H_3O^+(aq) \rightleftharpoons HCO_3^-(aq) + H_2O(l)$$

A lake surrounded by limestone contains a natural CO_3^{2-}/HCO_3^- buffer.

The carbonate/bicarbonate buffer thus allows the lake to resist large pH changes when acid is added. In some areas acidic lakes have been treated with limestone, thus adding calcium carbonate to neutralize the acid and restore the natural pH. This procedure is expensive and temporary because with time and more acid rain, the pH of the lakes decreases again.

9.11 FOCUS ON THE HUMAN BODY
Buffers in the Blood

The normal blood pH of a healthy individual is in the range of 7.35 to 7.45. A pH above or below this range is generally indicative of an imbalance in respiratory or metabolic processes. The body is able to maintain a very stable pH because the blood and other tissues are buffered. The principal buffer in the blood is carbonic acid/bicarbonate (H_2CO_3/HCO_3^-).

In examining the carbonic acid/bicarbonate buffer system in the blood, two equilibria are important. First of all, carbonic acid (H_2CO_3) is in equilibrium with CO_2 dissolved in the bloodstream (Section 9.7). Second, since carbonic acid is a weak acid, it is also dissociated in water to form its conjugate base, bicarbonate (HCO_3^-). Bicarbonate is also generated in the kidneys.

$$CO_2(g) + H_2O(l) \rightleftharpoons \underset{\text{carbonic acid}}{H_2CO_3(aq)} \overset{H_2O}{\rightleftharpoons} H_3O^+(aq) + \underset{\text{bicarbonate}}{HCO_3^-(aq)}$$

principal buffer in the blood

CO_2 is constantly produced by metabolic processes in the body and then transported to the lungs to be eliminated. Thus, the amount of CO_2 dissolved in the blood is directly related to the H_3O^+ concentration and therefore the pH of the blood. If the pH of the blood is lower than 7.35, the blood is more acidic than normal, and the condition is called **acidosis.** If the pH of the blood is higher than 7.45, the blood is more basic than normal, and the condition is called **alkalosis.**

Le Châtelier's principle explains the effect of increasing or decreasing the level of dissolved CO_2 on the pH of the blood. A higher-than-normal CO_2 concentration shifts the equilibrium to the right, increasing the H_3O^+ concentration and lowering the pH. **Respiratory acidosis** results when the body fails to eliminate adequate amounts of CO_2 through the lungs. This may occur in patients with advanced lung disease or respiratory failure.

A lower respiratory rate increases $[CO_2]$.

$$CO_2(g) + 2 H_2O(g) \rightleftharpoons H_3O^+(aq) + HCO_3^-(aq)$$

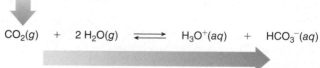

This drives the reaction to the right, increasing $[H_3O^+]$.
Blood has a higher $[H_3O^+]$ ⟶ lower pH

HEALTH NOTE

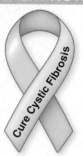

Individuals with cystic fibrosis, the most common genetic disease in Caucasians, produce thick mucus in the lungs, resulting in a higher-than-normal level of CO_2 and respiratory acidosis.

HEALTH NOTE

A lower-than-normal CO_2 concentration shifts the equilibria to the left, decreasing the H_3O^+ concentration and raising the pH. **Respiratory alkalosis** is caused by hyperventilation, very rapid breathing that occurs when an individual experiences excitement or panic.

$$CO_2(g) \quad + \quad 2\,H_2O(g) \;\rightleftharpoons\; H_3O^+(aq) \quad + \quad HCO_3^-(aq)$$

A faster respiratory rate decreases $[CO_2]$.

This drives the reaction to the left, decreasing $[H_3O^+]$.
Blood has a lower $[H_3O^+] \longrightarrow$ higher pH

The pH of the blood may also be altered when the metabolic processes of the body are not in balance. **Metabolic acidosis** results when excessive amounts of acid are produced and the blood pH falls. This may be observed in patients with severe infections (sepsis) when a large amount of lactic acid accumulates. It may also occur in poorly controlled diabetes when keto acid levels rise (Chapter 24). **Metabolic alkalosis** may occur when recurrent vomiting decreases the amount of acid in the stomach, thus causing a rise in pH.

During strenuous exercise, the lungs expel more CO_2 than usual and the pH of the blood increases.

CHAPTER HIGHLIGHTS

KEY TERMS

Acid (9.1)
Acid dissociation constant (K_a, 9.4)
Acidic solution (9.5)
Amphoteric (9.2)
Base (9.1)
Basic solution (9.5)
Brønsted–Lowry acid (9.1)
Brønsted–Lowry base (9.1)

Buffer (9.10)
Conjugate acid (9.2)
Conjugate acid–base pair (9.2)
Conjugate base (9.2)
Diprotic acid (9.1)
Dissociation (9.3)
Ion–product constant (K_w, 9.5)
Monoprotic acid (9.1)

Net ionic equation (9.7)
Neutral solution (9.5)
Neutralization reaction (9.7)
pH scale (9.6)
Proton transfer reaction (9.2)
Spectator ion (9.7)
Titration (9.9)
Triprotic acid (9.1)

KEY CONCEPTS

① Describe the principal features of acids and bases. (9.1)

- A Brønsted–Lowry acid is a proton donor, often symbolized by HA. A Brønsted–Lowry acid must contain one or more hydrogen atoms.
- A Brønsted–Lowry base is a proton acceptor, often symbolized by B:. To form a bond to a proton, a Brønsted–Lowry base must contain a lone pair of electrons.

② What are the principal features of an acid–base reaction? (9.2)

- In a Brønsted–Lowry acid–base reaction, a proton is transferred from the acid (HA) to the base (B:). In this reaction, the acid loses a proton to form its conjugate base (A:⁻) and the base gains a proton to form its conjugate acid (HB⁺).

③ How is acid strength related to the direction of equilibrium in an acid–base reaction? (9.3)

- A strong acid readily donates a proton, and when dissolved in water, 100% of the acid dissociates into ions. A strong base readily accepts a proton, and when dissolved in water, 100% of the base dissociates into ions.
- An inverse relationship exists between acid and base strength. A strong acid forms a weak conjugate base, whereas a weak acid forms a strong conjugate base.
- In an acid–base reaction, the stronger acid reacts with the stronger base to form the weaker acid and the weaker base.

4 **What is the acid dissociation constant and how is it related to acid strength? (9.4)**

- For a general acid HA, the acid dissociation constant K_a is defined by the equation:

$$K_a = \frac{[H_3O^+][A:^-]}{[HA]}$$

- The stronger the acid, the larger the K_a. Equilibrium in an acid–base reaction favors formation of the acid with the smaller K_a value.

5 **What is the ion–product of water and how is it used to calculate hydronium or hydroxide ion concentration? (9.5)**

- The ion–product of water, K_w, is a constant for all aqueous solutions; $K_w = [H_3O^+][OH^-] = 1.0 \times 10^{-14}$ at 25 °C. If either $[H_3O^+]$ or $[OH^-]$ is known, the other value can be calculated from K_w.

6 **What is pH? (9.6)**

- The pH of a solution measures the concentration of H_3O^+; $pH = -\log[H_3O^+]$.
- A pH = 7 means $[H_3O^+] = [OH^-]$ and the solution is neutral.
- A pH < 7 means $[H_3O^+] > [OH^-]$ and the solution is acidic.
- A pH > 7 means $[H_3O^+] < [OH^-]$ and the solution is basic.

7 **Draw the products of some common acid–base reactions. (9.7)**

- In a Brønsted–Lowry acid–base reaction with hydroxide bases (MOH), the acid HA donates a proton to OH^- to form H_2O. The anion from the acid HA combines with the cation M^+ of the base to form the salt MA. This reaction is called a neutralization reaction.
- In acid–base reactions with bicarbonate (HCO_3^-) or carbonate (CO_3^{2-}) bases, carbonic acid (H_2CO_3) is formed, which decomposes to form H_2O and CO_2.

8 **What happens to the pH of an aqueous solution when a salt is dissolved? (9.8)**

- A salt can form an acidic, basic, or neutral solution depending on whether its cation and anion are derived from strong or weak acids and bases. A salt derived from a strong acid and strong base forms a neutral solution with pH = 7. When one ion of a salt is derived from a weak acid or base, the ion derived from the stronger acid or base determines whether the solution is acidic or basic.

9 **How is a titration used to determine the concentration of an acid or base? (9.9)**

- A titration is a procedure that uses a base (or acid) of known volume and molarity to react with a known volume of acid (or base) of unknown molarity. The volume and molarity of the base are used to calculate the number of moles of base that react, and from this value, the molarity of the acid can be determined.

10 **What is a buffer? (9.10)**

- A buffer is a solution whose pH changes very little when acid or base is added. Most buffers are composed of approximately equal amounts of a weak acid and the salt of its conjugate base.

11 **What is the principal buffer present in the blood? (9.11)**

- The principal buffer in the blood is carbonic acid/bicarbonate. Since carbonic acid (H_2CO_3) is in equilibrium with dissolved CO_2, the amount of CO_2 in the blood affects its pH, which is normally maintained in the range of 7.35–7.45. When the CO_2 concentration in the blood is higher than normal, the acid–base equilibrium shifts to form more H_3O^+ and the pH decreases. When the CO_2 concentration in the blood is lower than normal, the acid–base equilibrium shifts to consume $[H_3O^+]$, so $[H_3O^+]$ decreases, and the pH increases.

PROBLEMS

Selected in-chapter and odd-numbered end-of-chapter problems have brief answers in Appendix B. The *Student Study Guide and Solutions Manual* contains detailed solutions to all in-chapter and odd-numbered end-of-chapter problems, as well as additional worked examples and a chapter self-test.

Acids and Bases

9.37 Which of the following species can be Brønsted–Lowry acids?
- a. HBr
- b. Br_2
- c. $AlCl_3$
- d. HCOOH
- e. NO_2^-
- f. HNO_2

9.38 Which of the following species can be Brønsted–Lowry acids?
- a. H_2O
- b. I^-
- c. HOCl
- d. $FeBr_3$
- e. CH_3CH_2COOH
- f. CO_2

9.39 Which of the following species can be Brønsted–Lowry bases?
- a. OH^-
- b. Ca^{2+}
- c. C_2H_6
- d. PO_4^{3-}
- e. OCl^-
- f. $MgCO_3$

9.40 Which of the following species can be Brønsted–Lowry bases?
- a. Cl^-
- b. BH_3
- c. H_2O
- d. Na^+
- e. $Ca(OH)_2$
- f. $HCOO^-$

9.41 Draw the conjugate acid of each base.
- a. HS^-
- b. CO_3^{2-}
- c. NO_2^-
- d. $H-\overset{\overset{\displaystyle H}{|}}{\underset{\underset{\displaystyle H}{|}}{C}}-\overset{\overset{\displaystyle \cdot\cdot}{}}{\underset{\underset{\displaystyle H}{|}}{N}}-H$

9.42 Draw the conjugate acid of each base.
- a. Br^-
- b. HPO_4^{2-}
- c. CH_3COO^-
- d. $H-\overset{\overset{\displaystyle H}{|}}{\underset{\underset{\displaystyle H}{|}}{C}}-\overset{\cdot\cdot}{\underset{}{O}}-H$

9.43 Draw the conjugate base of each acid.
- a. HNO_2
- b. NH_4^+
- c. H_2O_2

9.44 Draw the conjugate base of each acid.
- a. H_3O^+
- b. H_2Se
- c. HSO_4^-

9.45 Identify the acid, base, conjugate acid, and conjugate base in each diagram. Gray spheres correspond to H atoms.

a.

b. (diagram)

9.46 Use the given representations for H_2Z, HZ^-, and Z^{2-}, as well as the space-filling structures of H_2O, H_3O^+, and OH^- that appear in Chapter 9, to depict each equation. Label the acid, base, conjugate acid, and conjugate base in each equation.

$\bullet\!\!\bullet$ = H_2Z $\bullet\!\!\bullet$ = HZ^- $\bullet$ = Z^{2-}

a. $H_2Z + H_2O \longrightarrow HZ^- + H_3O^+$

b. $HZ^- + OH^- \longrightarrow Z^{2-} + H_2O$

9.47 Label the conjugate acid–base pairs in each equation.

a. $HI(g) + NH_3(g) \rightleftharpoons NH_4^+(aq) + I^-(aq)$

b. $HCOOH(l) + H_2O(l) \rightleftharpoons H_3O^+(aq) + HCOO^-(aq)$

c. $HSO_4^-(aq) + H_2O(l) \rightleftharpoons H_2SO_4(aq) + OH^-(aq)$

9.48 Label the conjugate acid–base pairs in each equation.

a. $Cl^-(aq) + HSO_4^-(aq) \rightleftharpoons HCl(aq) + SO_4^{2-}(aq)$

b. $HPO_4^{2-}(aq) + OH^-(aq) \rightleftharpoons PO_4^{3-}(aq) + H_2O(l)$

c. $NH_3(g) + HF(g) \rightleftharpoons NH_4^+(aq) + F^-(aq)$

9.49 Like H_2O, HCO_3^- is amphoteric. (a) Draw the conjugate acid of HCO_3^-. (b) Draw the conjugate base of HCO_3^-.

9.50 Like H_2O, $H_2PO_4^-$ is amphoteric. (a) Draw the conjugate acid of $H_2PO_4^-$. (b) Draw the conjugate base of $H_2PO_4^-$.

9.51 Write the equation for the acid–base reaction that takes place when nitric acid (HNO_3) dissolves in H_2O.

9.52 Write the equation for the acid–base reaction that takes place when formic acid ($HCOOH$) dissolves in H_2O.

Acid and Base Strength

9.53 Which diagram represents an aqueous solution of HF and which represents HCl? Explain your choice.

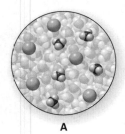 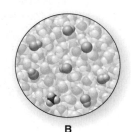

A   B

9.54 Which diagram represents what happens when HCN dissolves in water? Explain your choice.

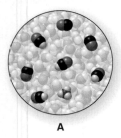 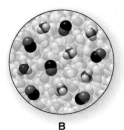

A   B

9.55 (a) Which of the following represents a strong acid HZ dissolved in water? (b) Which represents a weak acid HZ dissolved in water?

$\bullet\!\!\bullet$ = HZ $\bullet$ = Z^-

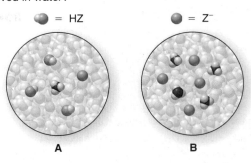

A   B

9.56 (a) Using molecular art, draw a diagram that represents an aqueous solution of a strong acid H_2Z. (b) Using molecular art, draw a diagram that represents an aqueous solution of a weak acid H_2Z.

$\bullet\!\!\bullet$ = H_2Z $\bullet\!\!\bullet$ = HZ^-

9.57 Use the data in Tables 9.1 and 9.2 to label the stronger acid in each pair.

a. H_2O or CH_3COOH

b. H_3PO_4 or HCO_3^-

c. H_2SO_4 or HSO_4^-

9.58 Use the data in Tables 9.1 and 9.2 to label the stronger acid in each pair.

a. HPO_4^{2-} or HCN

b. HSO_4^- or NH_4^+

c. H_2O or HF

9.59 Which acid in each pair in Problem 9.57 has the stronger conjugate base?

9.60 Which acid in each pair in Problem 9.58 has the stronger conjugate base?

9.61 Which acid, **A** or **B,** is stronger in each part?

a. **A** dissociates to a greater extent in water.

b. **A** has a smaller K_a.

c. The conjugate base of **A** is stronger than the conjugate base of **B.**

9.62 Which acid, **A** or **B,** is stronger in each part?

a. **B** dissociates to a greater extent in water.

b. **A** has a larger K_a.

c. The conjugate base of **B** is stronger than the conjugate base of **A.**

Equilibrium and Acid Dissociation Constants

9.63 For each pair of acids: [1] Label the stronger acid. [2] Draw the conjugate bases. [3] Label the stronger conjugate base.

a. HSO_4^- or $H_2PO_4^-$
      bisulfate   dihydrogen phosphate
      $K_a = 1.2 \times 10^{-2}$ $K_a = 6.2 \times 10^{-8}$

b. CH_3CH_2COOH or CH_3COOH
      propanoic acid   acetic acid
      $K_a = 1.3 \times 10^{-5}$ $K_a = 1.8 \times 10^{-5}$

9.64 For each pair of acids: [1] Label the stronger acid. [2] Draw the conjugate bases. [3] Label the stronger conjugate base.

a. H_3PO_4 or   HCOOH

phosphoric acid   formic acid

$K_a = 7.5 \times 10^{-3}$ $K_a = 1.8 \times 10^{-4}$

b.   HCOOH   or C_6H_5COOH

formic acid   benzoic acid

$K_a = 1.8 \times 10^{-4}$ $K_a = 6.5 \times 10^{-5}$

9.65 (a) Which diagram illustrates the stronger acid? (b) Which diagram represents the acid with the larger K_a?

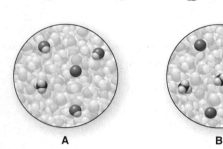

● = HA   ● = A⁻   ◔ = H_3O^+

A   B

9.66 Which diagram in Problem 9.65 contains the stronger conjugate base? Explain your choice.

9.67 Label the acid in the reactants and the conjugate acid in the products in each reaction. Use the data in Tables 9.1 and 9.2 to determine whether the reactants or products are favored at equilibrium. Explain your reasoning.

a. $H_3PO_4(aq) + CN^-(aq) \rightleftharpoons H_2PO_4^-(aq) + HCN(aq)$

b. $Br^-(aq) + HSO_4^-(aq) \rightleftharpoons SO_4^{2-}(aq) + HBr(aq)$

c. $CH_3COO^-(aq) + H_2CO_3(aq) \rightleftharpoons$

$CH_3COOH(aq) + HCO_3^-(aq)$

9.68 Label the acid in the reactants and the conjugate acid in the products in each reaction. Use the data in Tables 9.1 and 9.2 to determine whether the reactants or products are favored at equilibrium. Explain your reasoning.

a. $HF(g) + NH_3(g) \rightleftharpoons NH_4^+(aq) + F^-(aq)$

b. $Br^-(aq) + H_2O(l) \rightleftharpoons HBr(aq) + OH^-(aq)$

c. $HCN(aq) + HCO_3^-(aq) \rightleftharpoons H_2CO_3(aq) + CN^-(aq)$

Water and the pH Scale

9.69 Calculate the value of $[OH^-]$ from the given $[H_3O^+]$ and label the solution as acidic or basic.

a. 10^{-8} M   c. 3.0×10^{-4} M

b. 10^{-10} M   d. 2.5×10^{-11} M

9.70 Calculate the value of $[OH^-]$ from the given $[H_3O^+]$ and label the solution as acidic or basic.

a. 10^{-1} M   c. 2.6×10^{-7} M

b. 10^{-13} M   d. 1.2×10^{-12} M

9.71 Calculate the value of $[H_3O^+]$ from the given $[OH^-]$ and label the solution as acidic or basic.

a. 10^{-2} M   c. 6.2×10^{-7} M

b. 4.0×10^{-8} M   d. 8.5×10^{-13} M

9.72 Calculate the value of $[H_3O^+]$ from the given $[OH^-]$ and label the solution as acidic or basic.

a. 10^{-12} M   c. 6.0×10^{-4} M

b. 5.0×10^{-10} M   d. 8.9×10^{-11} M

9.73 Calculate the pH from each H_3O^+ concentration determined in Problem 9.71.

9.74 Calculate the pH from each H_3O^+ concentration determined in Problem 9.72.

9.75 Complete the following table with the needed $[H_3O^+]$, $[OH^-]$, and pH, and classify the solution as acidic, basic, or neutral.

$[H_3O^+]$	$[OH^-]$	pH	Classification
5.3×10^{-3}			
	2.0×10^{-8}		
		4.4	
	6.8×10^{-10}		

9.76 Complete the following table with the needed $[H_3O^+]$, $[OH^-]$, and pH, and classify the solution as acidic, basic, or neutral.

$[H_3O^+]$	$[OH^-]$	pH	Classification
6.3×10^{-4}			
	2.5×10^{-9}		
		9.4	
	6.8×10^{-4}		

9.77 Calculate the H_3O^+ concentration from each pH: (a) 12; (b) 1; (c) 1.80; (d) 8.90.

9.78 Calculate the H_3O^+ concentration from each pH: (a) 4; (b) 8; (c) 2.60; (d) 11.30.

9.79 If a urine sample has a pH of 5.90, calculate the concentrations of H_3O^+ and OH^- in the sample.

9.80 If pancreatic fluids have a pH of 8.2, calculate the concentrations of H_3O^+ and OH^- in the pancreas.

9.81 What are the concentrations of H_3O^+ and OH^- in tomatoes that have a pH of 4.10?

9.82 What are the concentrations of H_3O^+ and OH^- in a cola beverage that has a pH of 3.15?

9.83 Calculate the pH of each aqueous solution: (a) 0.0025 M HCl; (b) 0.015 M KOH.

9.84 Calculate the pH of each aqueous solution: (a) 0.015 M HNO_3; (b) 0.0025 M NaOH.

9.85 Why is the pH of 0.10 M HCl lower than the pH of 0.10 M CH_3COOH solution (1.0 vs. 2.88)?

9.86 Why is the pH of 0.0050 M CH_3COOH solution higher than the pH of 0.0050 M HCl solution (3.5 vs. 2.3)?

Acid–Base Reactions

9.87 Write a balanced equation for each reaction.
 a. $HBr(aq) + KOH(aq) \longrightarrow$
 b. $HNO_3(aq) + Ca(OH)_2(aq) \longrightarrow$
 c. $HCl(aq) + NaHCO_3(aq) \longrightarrow$
 d. $H_2SO_4(aq) + Mg(OH)_2(aq) \longrightarrow$

9.88 Write a balanced equation for each reaction.
 a. $HNO_3(aq) + LiOH(aq) \longrightarrow$
 b. $H_2SO_4(aq) + NaOH(aq) \longrightarrow$
 c. $K_2CO_3(aq) + HCl(aq) \longrightarrow$
 d. $HI(aq) + NaHCO_3(aq) \longrightarrow$

9.89 Marble statues, which are composed of calcium carbonate ($CaCO_3$), are slowly eaten away by the nitric acid (HNO_3) in acid rain. Write a balanced equation for the reaction of $CaCO_3$ with HNO_3.

9.90 Some liquid antacids contain suspensions of aluminum hydroxide [$Al(OH)_3$]. Write a balanced equation for the reaction of $Al(OH)_3$ with the HCl in stomach acid.

Salt Solutions

9.91 Determine whether each salt forms an acidic, basic, or neutral solution when it dissolves in water.
 a. NaI   c. NH_4NO_3 e. $MgBr_2$
 b. LiF   d. $KHCO_3$ f. NaH_2PO_4

9.92 Determine whether each salt forms an acidic, basic, or neutral solution when it dissolves in water.
 a. NaBr   c. KCH_3COO e. $CaBr_2$
 b. NaCN   d. CsF   f. K_3PO_4

Titration

9.93 What is the molarity of an HCl solution if 35.5 mL of 0.10 M NaOH are needed to neutralize 25.0 mL of the sample?

9.94 What is the molarity of an HCl solution if 17.2 mL of 0.15 M NaOH are needed to neutralize 5.00 mL of the sample?

9.95 What is the molarity of an acetic acid (CH_3COOH) solution if 15.5 mL of 0.20 M NaOH are needed to neutralize 25.0 mL of the sample?

9.96 What is the molarity of an H_2SO_4 solution if 18.5 mL of 0.18 M NaOH are needed to neutralize 25.0 mL of the sample?

9.97 How many milliliters of 1.0 M NaOH solution are needed to neutralize 10.0 mL of 2.5 M CH_3COOH solution?

9.98 How many milliliters of 2.0 M NaOH solution are needed to neutralize 8.0 mL of 3.5 M H_2SO_4 solution?

Buffers

9.99 Consider a weak acid H_2A and its conjugate base HA^-. Which diagram represents a buffer? Explain your choice.

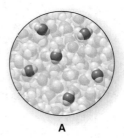   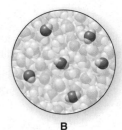

 A   B

9.100 Consider a weak acid H_2A and its conjugate base HA^-. Which diagram represents a buffer? Explain your choice.

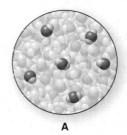   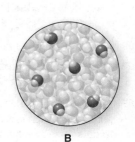

 A   B

9.101 Why is a buffer most effective at minimizing pH changes when the concentrations of the weak acid and its conjugate base are equal?

9.102 Although most buffers are prepared from a weak acid and its conjugate base, explain why a buffer can also be prepared from a weak base such as NH_3 and its conjugate acid NH_4^+.

9.103 Can a buffer be prepared from equal amounts of NaCN and HCN? Explain why or why not.

9.104 Can a buffer be prepared from equal amounts of HNO_3 and KNO_3? Explain why or why not.

9.105 Consider a buffer prepared from the weak acid HNO_2 and its conjugate base NO_2^-.

$$HNO_2(aq) + H_2O(l) \rightleftharpoons NO_2^-(aq) + H_3O^+(aq)$$

 a. Explain why both HNO_2 and NO_2^- are needed to prepare the buffer.
 b. What happens to the concentrations of HNO_2 and NO_2^- when a small amount of acid is added to the buffer?
 c. What happens to the concentrations of HNO_2 and NO_2^- when a small amount of base is added to the buffer?

9.106 Consider a buffer prepared from the weak acid HF and its conjugate base F⁻.

$$HF(aq) + H_2O(l) \rightleftharpoons F^-(aq) + H_3O^+(aq)$$

 a. Explain why both HF and F⁻ are needed to prepare the buffer.
 b. What happens to the concentrations of HF and F⁻ when a small amount of acid is added to the buffer?
 c. What happens to the concentrations of HF and F⁻ when a small amount of base is added to the buffer?

9.107 Using the K_a values in Table 9.5, calculate the pH of a buffer that contains the given concentrations of a weak acid and its conjugate base.
 a. 0.10 M Na_2HPO_4 and 0.10 M Na_3PO_4
 b. 0.22 M $NaHCO_3$ and 0.22 M Na_2CO_3

9.108 Using the K_a values in Table 9.5, calculate the pH of a buffer that contains the given concentrations of a weak acid and its conjugate base.
 a. 0.55 M CH_3COOH and 0.55 M $NaCH_3COO$
 b. 0.15 M NaH_2PO_4 and 0.15 M Na_2HPO_4

9.109 Calculate the pH of an acetic acid/acetate buffer in which the concentration of acetic acid is always 0.20 M, but the concentration of sodium acetate ($NaCH_3COO$) corresponds to each of the following values: (a) 0.20 M; (b) 0.40 M; (c) 0.10 M.

9.110 Calculate the pH of a bicarbonate/carbonate buffer in which the concentration of sodium bicarbonate ($NaHCO_3$) is always 0.20 M, but the concentration of sodium carbonate (Na_2CO_3) corresponds to each of the following values: (a) 0.20 M; (b) 0.40 M; (c) 0.10 M.

Applications

9.111 Why is the pH of unpolluted rainwater lower than the pH of pure water?

9.112 Why is the pH of acid rain lower than the pH of rainwater?

9.113 The optimum pH of a swimming pool is 7.50. Calculate the value of $[H_3O^+]$ and $[OH^-]$ at this pH.

9.114 A sample of rainwater has a pH of 4.18. (a) Calculate the H_3O^+ concentration in the sample. (b) Suggest a reason why this pH differs from the pH of unpolluted rainwater (5.6).

9.115 When an individual hyperventilates, he is told to blow into a paper bag held over his mouth. What effect should this process have on the CO_2 concentration and pH of the blood?

9.116 What is the difference between respiratory acidosis and respiratory alkalosis?

9.117 How is CO_2 concentration related to the pH of the blood?

9.118 Explain why a lake on a bed of limestone is naturally buffered against the effects of acid rain.

CHALLENGE PROBLEMS

9.119 Calcium hypochlorite [$Ca(OCl)_2$] is used to chlorinate swimming pools. $Ca(OCl)_2$ acts as a source of the weak acid hypochlorous acid, HOCl, a disinfectant that kills bacteria. Write the acid–base reaction that occurs when OCl⁻ dissolves in water and explain why this reaction makes a swimming pool more basic.

9.120 Most buffer solutions are prepared using a weak acid and a salt of its conjugate base. Explain how the following combination can also form a buffer solution: 0.20 M H_3PO_4 and 0.10 M NaOH.

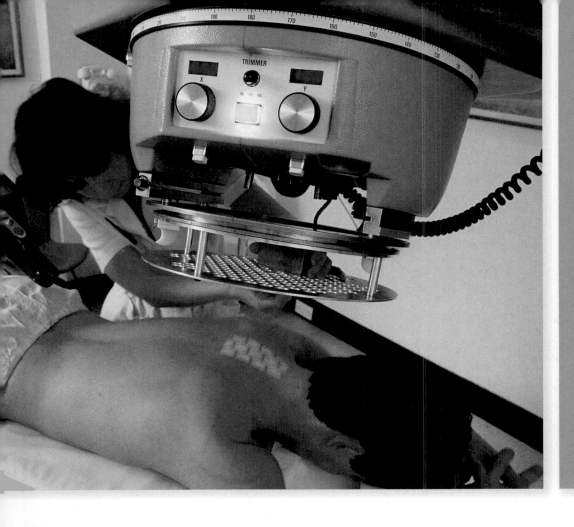

Radiation produced by cobalt-60 and other radioactive isotopes is used to treat many different forms of cancer.

10

Nuclear Chemistry

CHAPTER OUTLINE

CHAPTER GOALS

In this chapter you will learn how to:

1. Describe the different types of radiation emitted by a radioactive nucleus

2. Write equations for nuclear reactions

3. Define half-life

4. Recognize the units used for measuring radioactivity

5. Give examples of common radioisotopes used in medical diagnosis and treatment

6. Describe the general features of nuclear fission and nuclear fusion

7. Describe the features of medical imaging techniques that do not use radioactivity

Thus far our study of reactions has concentrated on processes that involve the valence electrons of atoms. In these reactions, bonds that join atoms are broken and new bonds between atoms are formed, but the identity of the atoms does not change. In Chapter 10, we turn our attention to **nuclear reactions,** processes that involve changes in the nucleus of atoms. While certainly much less common than chemical reactions that occur with electrons, nuclear reactions form a useful group of processes with a wide range of applications. Nuclear medicine labs in hospitals use radioactive isotopes to diagnose disease, visualize organs, and treat tumors. Generating energy in nuclear power plants, dating archaeological objects using the isotope carbon-14, and designing a simple and reliable smoke detector all utilize the concepts of nuclear chemistry discussed here in Chapter 10.

10.1   Introduction

Although most reactions involve valence electrons, a small but significant group of reactions, **nuclear reactions,** involves the subatomic particles of the nucleus. To understand nuclear reactions we must first review facts presented in Chapter 2 regarding isotopes and the characteristics of the nucleus.

10.1A   Isotopes

The nucleus of an atom is composed of protons and neutrons.

- The atomic number (Z) = the number of protons in the nucleus.
- The mass number (A) = the number of protons and neutrons in the nucleus.

Atoms of the same type of element have the same atomic number, but the number of neutrons may vary.

- Isotopes are atoms of the same element having a different number of neutrons.

As a result, isotopes have the same atomic number (Z) but different mass numbers (A). Carbon, for example, has three naturally occurring isotopes. Each isotope has six protons in the nucleus (i.e., $Z = 6$), but the number of neutrons may be six, seven, or eight. Thus, the mass numbers (A) of these isotopes are 12, 13, and 14, respectively. As we learned in Chapter 2, we can refer to these isotopes as carbon-12, carbon-13, and carbon-14. Isotopes are also written with the mass number to the upper left of the element symbol and the atomic number to the lower left.

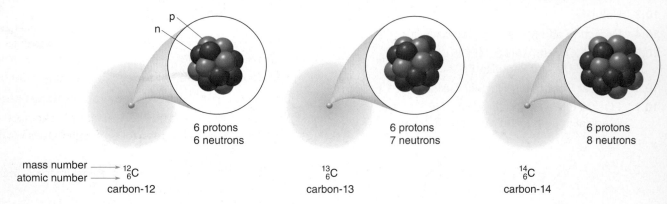

Many isotopes are stable, but a larger number are not.

- A *radioactive isotope,* called a *radioisotope,* is unstable and spontaneously emits energy to form a more stable nucleus.

Radioactivity **is the nuclear radiation emitted spontaneously by an unstable radioactive isotope.** Of the known isotopes of all the elements, 264 are stable and 300 are naturally occurring but unstable. An even larger number of radioactive isotopes, called **artificial isotopes,** have been produced in the laboratory. Both carbon-12 and carbon-13 are stable isotopes and occur in higher natural abundance than carbon-14, a radioactive isotope.

SAMPLE PROBLEM 10.1

Iodine-123 and iodine-131 are radioactive isotopes used for the diagnosis or treatment of thyroid disease. Complete the following table for both isotopes.

	Atomic Number	Mass Number	Number of Protons	Number of Neutrons	Isotope Symbol
Iodine-123		123			
Iodine-131		131			

Analysis

- The atomic number = the number of protons.
- The mass number = the number of protons + the number of neutrons.
- Isotopes are written with the mass number to the upper left of the element symbol and the atomic number to the lower left.

Solution

	Atomic Number	Mass Number	Number of Protons	Number of Neutrons	Isotope Symbol
Iodine-123	53	123	53	$123 - 53 = 70$	$^{123}_{53}\text{I}$
Iodine-131	53	131	53	$131 - 53 = 78$	$^{131}_{53}\text{I}$

PROBLEM 10.1

Complete the following table for two isotopes of cobalt. Cobalt-60 is commonly used in cancer therapy.

	Atomic Number	Mass Number	Number of Protons	Number of Neutrons	Isotope Symbol
Cobalt-59					
Cobalt-60					

PROBLEM 10.2

Each of the following radioisotopes is used in medicine. For each isotope give its: [1] atomic number; [2] mass number; [3] number of protons; [4] number of neutrons.

a. $^{85}_{38}\text{Sr}$
    used in bone scans

b. $^{67}_{31}\text{Ga}$
    used in abdominal scans

c. selenium-75
    used in pancreas scans

10.1B Types of Radiation

Different forms of radiation are emitted when a radioactive nucleus is converted to a more stable nucleus, including **alpha particles, beta particles, positrons,** and **gamma radiation.**

- An *alpha particle* is a high-energy particle that contains two protons and two neutrons.

$$\text{alpha particle:} \quad \alpha \quad \text{or} \quad ^{4}_{2}\text{He}$$

An alpha particle, symbolized by the Greek letter **alpha (α)** or the element symbol for helium, has a +2 charge and a mass number of 4.

- A *beta particle* is a high-energy electron.

$$\text{beta particle:} \quad \beta \quad \text{or} \quad {}_{-1}^{0}e$$

An electron has a −1 charge and a negligible mass compared to a proton. A beta particle, symbolized by the Greek letter **beta (β),** is also drawn with the symbol for an electron, **e,** with a mass number of 0 in the upper left corner and a charge of −1 in the lower left corner. A β particle is formed when a neutron (n) is converted to a proton (p) and an electron.

$$\overset{\text{mass} = 1 \text{ amu}}{{}_{0}^{1}n \longrightarrow {}_{1}^{1}p + {}_{-1}^{0}e}$$

neutron   proton   β particle

- A *positron* is called an *antiparticle* of a β particle, since their charges are different but their masses are the same.

Thus, a **positron** has a negligible mass like a β particle, but is opposite in charge, +1. A positron, symbolized as β⁺, is also drawn with the symbol for an electron, **e,** with a mass number of 0 in the upper left corner and a charge of +1 in the lower left corner. A positron, which can be thought of as a "positive electron," is formed when a proton is converted to a neutron.

Symbol: ${}_{+1}^{0}e$ or β^{+} **Formation:** ${}_{1}^{1}p \longrightarrow {}_{0}^{1}n + {}_{+1}^{0}e$

positron   proton   neutron positron

- *Gamma rays* are high-energy radiation released from a radioactive nucleus.

Gamma rays, symbolized by the Greek letter **gamma (γ),** are a form of energy and thus they have no mass or charge. Table 10.1 summarizes the properties of some of the different types of radiation.

$$\text{gamma ray:} \quad \gamma$$

Table 10.1 Types of Radiation

Type of Radiation	Symbol	Charge	Mass
Alpha particle	α or ${}_{2}^{4}He$	+2	4
Beta particle	β or ${}_{-1}^{0}e$	−1	0
Positron	β^{+} or ${}_{+1}^{0}e$	+1	0
Gamma ray	γ	0	0

PROBLEM 10.3

What is the difference between an α particle and a helium atom?

PROBLEM 10.4

Identify Q in each of the following symbols.

a. ${}_{-1}^{0}Q$ b. ${}_{2}^{4}Q$ c. ${}_{+1}^{0}Q$

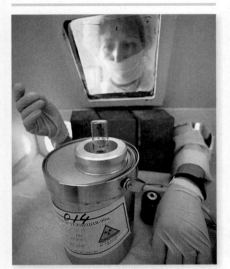

A lab worker must use protective equipment when working with radioactive substances.

CONSUMER NOTE

Strawberries that have been irradiated (on left) show no mold growth after two weeks, compared to strawberries that have not been irradiated (on right), which are moldy.

10.1C FOCUS ON HEALTH & MEDICINE
The Effects of Radioactivity

Radioactivity cannot be seen, smelled, tasted, heard, or felt, and yet it can have powerful effects. Because it is high in energy, nuclear radiation penetrates the surface of an object or living organism, where it can damage or kill cells. The cells that are most sensitive to radiation are those that undergo rapid cell division, such as those in bone marrow, reproductive organs, skin, and the intestinal tract. Since cancer cells also rapidly divide, they are also particularly sensitive to radiation, a fact that makes radiation an effective method of cancer treatment (Section 10.5).

Alpha (α) particles, β particles, and γ rays differ in the extent to which they can penetrate a surface. Alpha particles are the heaviest of the radioactive particles, and as a result they move the slowest and penetrate the least. Individuals who work with radioisotopes that emit α particles wear lab coats and gloves that provide a layer of sufficient protection. Beta particles move much faster since they have negligible mass, and they can penetrate into body tissue. Lab workers and health professionals must wear heavy lab coats and gloves when working with substances that give off β particles. Gamma rays travel the fastest and readily penetrate body tissue. Working with substances that emit γ rays is extremely hazardous, and a thick lead shield is required to halt their penetration.

That γ rays kill cells is used to an advantage in the food industry. To decrease the incidence of harmful bacteria in foods, certain fruits and vegetables are irradiated with γ rays that kill any bacteria contained in them. **Foods do not come into contact with radioisotopes and the food is not radioactive after irradiation.** Gamma rays merely penetrate the food and destroy any live organism, and often as a result, the food product has a considerably longer shelf life.

10.2 Nuclear Reactions

Radioactive decay **is the process by which an unstable radioactive nucleus emits radiation, forming a nucleus of new composition.** A nuclear equation can be written for this process, which contains the original nucleus, the new nucleus, and the radiation emitted. Unlike a chemical equation that balances atoms, in a nuclear equation the mass numbers and the atomic numbers of the nuclei must be balanced.

- The sum of the mass numbers (A) must be equal on both sides of a nuclear equation.
- The sum of the atomic numbers (Z) must be equal on both sides of a nuclear equation.

10.2A Alpha Emission

Alpha emission **is the decay of a nucleus by emitting an α particle.** For example, uranium-238 decays to thorium-234 by loss of an α particle.

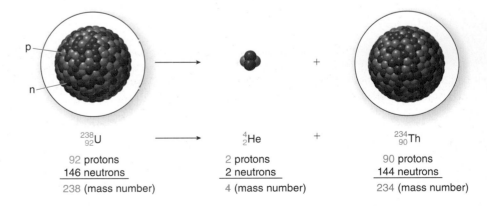

$^{238}_{92}\text{U}$	$\longrightarrow$	$^{4}_{2}\text{He}$	+	$^{234}_{90}\text{Th}$
92 protons		2 protons		90 protons
146 neutrons		2 neutrons		144 neutrons
238 (mass number)		4 (mass number)		234 (mass number)

Since an α particle has two protons, **the new nucleus has *two fewer protons* than the original nucleus.** Because it has a *different* number of protons, **the new nucleus represents a *different* element.** Uranium-238 has 92 protons, so loss of two protons forms the element thorium with 90 protons. The thorium nucleus has a mass number that is four fewer than the original—234— because it has been formed by loss of an α particle with a mass number of four.

As a result, the sum of the mass numbers is equal on both sides of the equation—238 = 4 + 234. The sum of the atomic numbers is also equal on both sides of the equation—92 = 2 + 90.

How To   Balance an Equation for a Nuclear Reaction

Example: Write a balanced nuclear equation showing how americium-241, a radioactive element used in smoke detectors, decays to form an α particle.

Step [1] **Write an incomplete equation with the original nucleus on the left and the particle emitted on the right.**
   • Include the mass number and atomic number (from the periodic table) in the equation.

$$^{241}_{95}\text{Am} \longrightarrow {}^{4}_{2}\text{He} + ?$$

Step [2] **Calculate the mass number and atomic number of the newly formed nucleus on the right.**
   • Mass number: Subtract the mass of an α particle (4) to obtain the mass of the new nucleus; 241 − 4 = 237.
   • Atomic number: Subtract the two protons of an α particle to obtain the atomic number of the new nucleus; 95 − 2 = 93.

Step [3] **Use the atomic number to identify the new nucleus and complete the equation.**
   • From the periodic table, the element with an atomic number of 93 is neptunium, Np.
   • Write the mass number and the atomic number with the element symbol to complete the equation.

$$\begin{array}{c} 241 = 4 + 237 \\ 95 = 2 + 93 \end{array} \quad ^{241}_{95}\text{Am} \longrightarrow {}^{4}_{2}\text{He} + {}^{237}_{93}\text{Np}$$

HEALTH NOTE

Americium-241 is a radioactive element contained in smoke detectors. The decay of α particles creates an electric current that is interrupted when smoke enters the detector, sounding an alarm.

PROBLEM 10.5

Radon, a radioactive gas formed in the soil, can cause lung cancers when inhaled in high concentrations for a long period of time. Write a balanced nuclear equation for the decay of radon-222, which emits an α particle.

PROBLEM 10.6

Radon (Problem 10.5) is formed in the soil as a product of radioactive decay that produces an α particle. Write a balanced nuclear equation for the formation of radon-222 and an α particle.

PROBLEM 10.7

Write a balanced equation showing how each nucleus decays to form a new element after releasing an α particle: (a) polonium-218; (b) thorium-230; (c) Es-252.

10.2B   Beta Emission

***Beta emission* is the decay of a nucleus by emitting a β particle.** For example, carbon-14 decays to nitrogen-14 by loss of a β particle. The decay of carbon-14 is used to date archaeological specimens (Section 10.3).

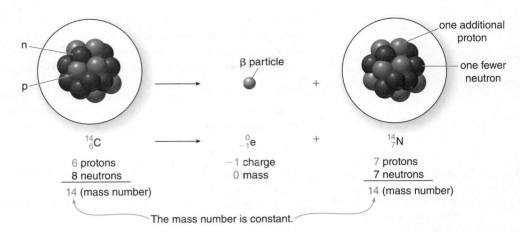

$$^{14}_{6}\text{C} \longrightarrow \ ^{\ 0}_{-1}e \ + \ ^{14}_{7}\text{N}$$

6 protons
8 neutrons
14 (mass number)

−1 charge
0 mass

7 protons
7 neutrons
14 (mass number)

The mass number is constant.

In β emission, one neutron of the original nucleus decays to a β particle and a proton. As a result, the **new nucleus has *one more proton* and *one fewer neutron* than the original nucleus.** In this example, a carbon atom with six protons decays to a nitrogen atom with seven protons. Since the total number of particles in the nucleus does not change, the **mass number is constant.**

The subscripts that represent the atomic numbers are balanced because the β particle has a charge of −1. Seven protons on the right side plus a −1 charge for the β particle gives a total "charge" of +6, the atomic number of carbon on the left. The mass numbers are also balanced since a β particle has zero mass, and both the original nucleus and the new nucleus contain 14 subatomic particles (protons + neutrons).

Radioactive elements that emit β radiation are widely used in medicine. Since β radiation is composed of high-energy, rapidly moving electrons that penetrate tissue in a small, localized region, radioactive elements situated in close contact with tumor cells kill them. Although both healthy and diseased cells are destroyed by this internal radiation therapy, rapidly dividing tumor cells are more sensitive to its effects and therefore their growth and replication are affected the most.

Iodine-131, a radioactive element that emits β radiation, is used to treat hyperthyroidism, a condition resulting from an overactive thyroid gland (Figure 10.1). When iodine-131 is administered, it is incorporated into thyroxine, an iodine-containing hormone that is concentrated in the thyroid gland. The β radiation emitted by the iodine-131 kills some of the thyroid tissue, so that the gland is no longer overactive.

Figure 10.1   The Use of Iodine-131 to Treat Hyperthyroidism

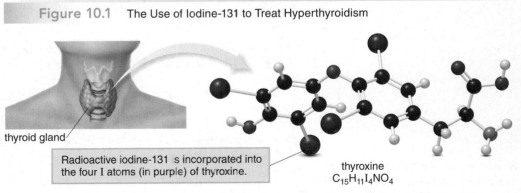

thyroid gland

Radioactive iodine-131 is incorporated into the four I atoms (in purple) of thyroxine.

thyroxine
$C_{15}H_{11}I_4NO_4$

Iodine-131 is incorporated into the thyroid hormone thyroxine. Beta radiation emitted by the radioactive isotope destroys nearby thyroid cells, thus decreasing the activity of the thyroid gland and bringing the disease under control.

SAMPLE PROBLEM 10.2

Write a balanced nuclear equation for the β emission of phosphorus-32, a radioisotope used to treat leukemia and other blood disorders.

Analysis

Balance the atomic numbers and mass numbers on both sides of a nuclear equation. With β emission, treat the β particle as an electron with zero mass in balancing mass numbers, and a –1 charge when balancing the atomic numbers.

Solution

[1] Write an incomplete equation with the original nucleus on the left and the particle emitted on the right.

- Use the identity of the element to determine the atomic number; phosphorus has an atomic number of 15.

$$^{32}_{15}\text{P} \longrightarrow {}^{0}_{-1}\text{e} + \text{?}$$

[2] Calculate the mass number and the atomic number of the newly formed nucleus on the right.

- Mass number: Since a β particle has no mass, the masses of the new particle and the original particle are the same, 32.
- Atomic number: Since β emission converts a neutron into a proton, the new nucleus has one more proton than the original nucleus; $15 = -1 + ?$. Thus the new nucleus has an atomic number of 16.

[3] Use the atomic number to identify the new nucleus and complete the equation.

- From the periodic table, the element with an atomic number of 16 is sulfur, S.
- Write the mass number and the atomic number with the element symbol to complete the equation.

$$^{32}_{15}\text{P} \longrightarrow {}^{0}_{-1}\text{e} + {}^{32}_{16}\text{S}$$

PROBLEM 10.8

Write a balanced nuclear equation for the β emission of iodine-131.

PROBLEM 10.9

Write a balanced nuclear equation for the β emission of each of the following isotopes.

a. $^{20}_{9}\text{F}$ b. $^{92}_{38}\text{Sr}$ c. chromium-55

10.2C Positron Emission

***Positron emission* is the decay of a nucleus by emitting a positron (β⁺).** For example, carbon-11, an artificial radioactive isotope of carbon, decays to boron-11 by loss of a β⁺ particle. Positron emitters are used in a relatively new diagnostic technique, positron emission tomography (PET), described in Section 10.5.

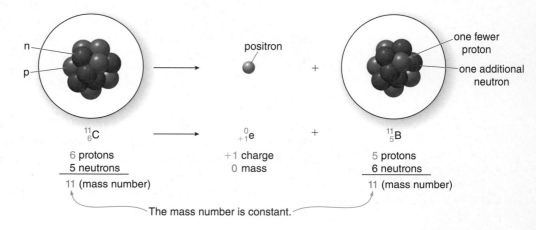

$^{11}_{6}\text{C}$		$^{0}_{+1}\text{e}$		$^{11}_{5}\text{B}$
6 protons		+1 charge		5 protons
5 neutrons		0 mass		6 neutrons
11 (mass number)				11 (mass number)

The mass number is constant.

In positron emission, one proton of the original nucleus decays to a β^+ particle and a neutron. As a result, the **new nucleus has** *one fewer proton* **and** *one more neutron* **than the original nucleus.** In this example, a carbon atom with six protons decays to a boron atom with five protons. Since the total number of particles in the nucleus does not change, the **mass number is constant.**

SAMPLE PROBLEM 10.3

Write a balanced nuclear equation for the positron emission of fluorine-18, a radioisotope used for imaging in PET scans.

Analysis

Balance the atomic numbers and mass numbers on both sides of a nuclear equation. With β^+ emission, treat the positron as a particle with zero mass when balancing mass numbers, and a +1 charge when balancing the atomic numbers.

Solution

[1] **Write an incomplete equation with the original nucleus on the left and the particle emitted on the right.**

- Use the identity of the element to determine the atomic number; fluorine has an atomic number of 9.

$$^{18}_{9}\text{F} \longrightarrow ^{\ 0}_{+1}\text{e} + \ ?$$

[2] **Calculate the mass number and the atomic number of the newly formed nucleus on the right.**

- Mass number: Since a β^+ particle has no mass, the masses of the new particle and the original particle are the same, 18.
- Atomic number: Since β^+ emission converts a proton into a neutron, the new nucleus has one fewer proton than the original nucleus; $9 - 1 = 8$. Thus, the new nucleus has an atomic number of 8.

[3] **Use the atomic number to identify the new nucleus and complete the equation.**

- From the periodic table, the element with an atomic number of 8 is oxygen, O.
- Write the mass number and the atomic number with the element symbol to complete the equation.

$$^{18}_{9}\text{F} \longrightarrow ^{\ 0}_{+1}\text{e} + ^{18}_{8}\text{O}$$

PROBLEM 10.10

Write a balanced nuclear equation for the positron emission of each of the following nuclei:
(a) arsenic-74; (b) oxygen-15.

10.2D Gamma Emission

Gamma emission **is the decay of a nucleus by emitting γ radiation.** Since γ rays are simply a form of energy, their emission causes **no change in the atomic number or mass number** of a radioactive nucleus. Gamma emission sometimes occurs alone. For example, one form of technetium-99, written as technetium-99m, is an energetic form of the technetium nucleus that decays with emission of γ rays to technetium-99, a more stable but still radioactive element.

$$^{99m}_{43}\text{Tc} \longrightarrow ^{99}_{43}\text{Tc} + \gamma$$

The mass number and atomic number are the same.

The *m* in technetium-99m stands for *metastable*. This designation is meant to indicate that the isotope decays to a more stable form of the same isotope.

Technetium-99m is a widely used radioisotope in medical imaging. Because it emits high-energy γ rays but decays in a short period of time, it is used to image the brain, thyroid, lungs, liver, skeleton, and many other organs. It has also been used to detect ulcers in the gastrointestinal system, and combined with other compounds, it is used to map the circulatory system and gauge damage after a heart attack.

More commonly, γ emission accompanies α or β emission. For example, cobalt-60 decays with both β and γ emission. Because a β particle is formed, decay generates an element with the *same* mass but a *different* number of protons, and thus a new element, nickel-60.

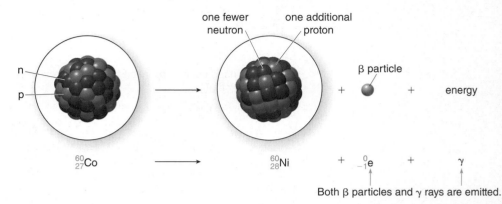

$$^{60}_{27}\text{Co} \longrightarrow \ ^{60}_{28}\text{Ni} \ + \ ^{0}_{-1}\text{e} \ + \ \gamma$$

Both β particles and γ rays are emitted.

Cobalt-60 is used in external radiation treatment for cancer. Radiation generated by cobalt-60 decay is focused on a specific site in the body that contains cancerous cells (Figure 10.2). By directing the radiation on the tumor, damage to surrounding healthy tissues is minimized.

PROBLEM 10.11

Write a nuclear equation for the decay of iridium-192 with β and γ emission. Iridium implants have been used to treat breast cancer. After the correct dose is administered, the iridium source is removed.

PROBLEM 10.12

Complete each nuclear equation.

a. $^{11}_{5}\text{B} \longrightarrow \ ? \ + \ \gamma$ b. $^{40}_{19}\text{K} \longrightarrow \ ? \ + \ ^{0}_{-1}\text{e} \ + \ \gamma$

Figure 10.2   Focus on Health & Medicine: External Radiation Treatment for Tumors

a.   b.   c.

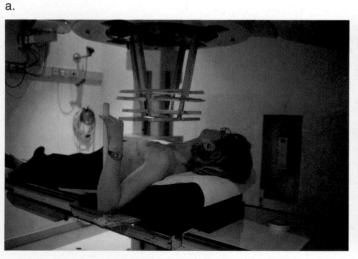
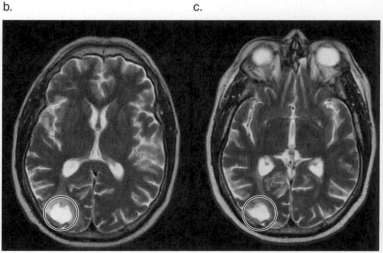

a. Gamma radiation from the decay of cobalt-60 is used to treat a variety of tumors, especially those that cannot be surgically removed.

b. A tumor (bright area in circle) before radiation treatment

c. A tumor (bright area in circle) that has decreased in size after six months of radiation treatment

10.3   Half-Life

How fast do radioactive isotopes decay? It depends on the isotope.

- The *half-life* ($t_{1/2}$) of a radioactive isotope is the time it takes for one-half of the sample to decay.

10.3A   General Features

Suppose we have a sample that contains 16 g of phosphorus-32, a radioactive isotope that decays to sulfur-32 by β emission (Sample Problem 10.2). Phosphorus-32 has a half-life of approximately 14 days. Thus, after 14 days, the sample contains only half the amount of P-32—8.0 g. After another 14 days (a total of two half-lives), the 8.0 g of P-32 is again halved to 4.0 g. After another 14 days (a total of three half-lives), the 4.0 g of P-32 is halved to 2.0 g, and so on. Every 14 days, half of the P-32 decays.

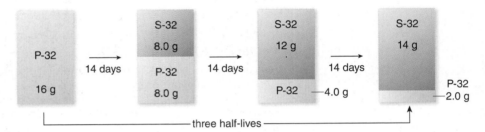

Many naturally occurring isotopes have long half-lives. Examples include carbon-14 (5,730 years) and uranium-235 (7.0×10^8 years). Radioisotopes that are used for diagnosis and imaging in medicine have short half-lives so they do not linger in the body. Examples include technetium-99m (6.0 hours) and iodine-131 (8.0 days). The half-lives of several elements are given in Table 10.2.

The half-life of a radioactive isotope is a property of a given isotope and is independent of the amount of sample, temperature, and pressure. Thus, if the half-life and amount of a sample are known, it is possible to predict how much of the radioactive isotope will remain after a period of time.

Table 10.2 Half-Lives of Some Common Radioisotopes

Radioisotope	Symbol	Half-Life	Use
Carbon-14	$^{14}_{6}C$	5,730 years	Archaeological dating
Cobalt-60	$^{60}_{27}Co$	5.3 years	Cancer therapy
Iodine-131	$^{131}_{53}I$	8.0 days	Thyroid therapy
Potassium-40	$^{40}_{19}K$	1.3×10^9 years	Geological dating
Phosphorus-32	$^{32}_{15}P$	14.3 days	Leukemia treatment
Technetium-99m	$^{99m}_{43}Tc$	6.0 hours	Organ imaging
Uranium-235	$^{235}_{92}U$	7.0×10^8 years	Nuclear reactors

How To Use a Half-Life to Determine the Amount of Radioisotope Present

Example: If the half-life of iodine-131 is 8.0 days, how much of a 100. mg sample of iodine-131 remains after 32 days?

Step [1] **Determine how many half-lives occur in the given amount of time.**
- Use the half-life of iodine-131 as a conversion factor to convert the number of days to the number of half-lives.

$$32 \text{ days} \times \frac{1 \text{ half-life}}{8.0 \text{ days}} = 4.0 \text{ half-lives}$$

Step [2] **For each half-life, multiply the initial mass by one-half to obtain the final mass.**
- Since 32 days corresponds to *four* half-lives, multiply the initial mass by ½ *four* times to obtain the final mass. After four half-lives, 6.25 mg of iodine-131 remains.

$$\underbrace{100. \text{ mg}}_{\text{initial mass}} \times \underbrace{\frac{1}{2} \times \frac{1}{2} \times \frac{1}{2} \times \frac{1}{2}}_{\text{The mass is halved four times.}} = 6.25 \text{ mg of iodine-131 remains.}$$

PROBLEM 10.13

How much phosphorus-32 remains from a 1.00 g sample after each of the following number of half-lives: (a) 2; (b) 4; (c) 8; (d) 20?

PROBLEM 10.14

If a 160. mg sample of technetium-99m is used for a diagnostic procedure, how much Tc-99m remains after each interval: (a) 6.0 h; (b) 18.0 h; (c) 24.0 h; (d) 2 days?

10.3B   Archaeological Dating

Archaeologists use the half-life of carbon-14 to determine the age of carbon-containing material derived from plants or animals. The technique, **radiocarbon dating,** is based on the fact that the ratio of radioactive carbon-14 to stable carbon-12 is a constant value in a living organism that is constantly taking in CO_2 and other carbon-containing nutrients from its surroundings. Once the organism dies, however, the radioactive isotope (C-14) decays (Section 10.2B) without being replenished, thus decreasing its concentration, while the stable isotope of carbon (C-12) remains at a constant value. By comparing the ratio of C-14 to C-12 in an artifact to the ratio of C-14 to C-12 in organisms today, the age of the artifact can be determined. Radiocarbon dating can be used to give the approximate age of wood, cloth, bone, charcoal, and many other substances that contain carbon.

The half-life of carbon-14 is 5,730 years, so half of the C-14 has decayed after about 6,000 years. Thus, a 6,000-year-old object has a ratio of C-14 to C-12 that has decreased by a factor of two, a 12,000-year-old object has a ratio of C-14 to C-12 that has decreased by a factor of four, and so forth.

This isotope decays, so its concentration decreases. $\frac{1}{2}$ (original amount) $\frac{1}{4}$ (original amount)

$$\frac{\text{carbon-14}}{\text{carbon-12}} \xrightarrow[\text{5,730 years}]{\text{1}^{\text{st}}\text{ half-life}} \frac{\text{carbon-14}}{\text{carbon-12}} \xrightarrow[\text{5,730 years}]{\text{2}^{\text{nd}}\text{ half-life}} \frac{\text{carbon-14}}{\text{carbon-12}}$$

This isotope does not decay, so its concentration remains the same.

Using this technique, archaeologists have determined the age of the paintings on cave walls in Algeria to be about 8,000 years old (Figure 10.3). Because the amount of carbon-14 decreases with time, artifacts older than about 20,000 years have too little carbon-14 to accurately estimate their age.

Figure 10.3   Radiocarbon Dating

Radiocarbon dating has been used to estimate the age of this Algerian cave painting at about 8,000 years.

A Geiger counter is a device used to detect radiation.

Individuals who work with radioactivity wear badges to monitor radiation levels.

PROBLEM 10.15

Estimate the age of an artifact that has 1/8 of the amount of C-14 (relative to C-12) compared to living organisms.

10.4   Detecting and Measuring Radioactivity

We all receive a miniscule daily dose of radiation from cosmic rays and radioactive substances in the soil. Additional radiation exposure comes from television sets, dental X-rays, and other man-made sources. Moreover, we are still exposed to nuclear fallout, residual radiation resulting from the testing of nuclear weapons in the atmosphere decades ago.

Although this background radiation is unavoidable and minute, higher levels can be harmful and life-threatening because radiation is composed of high-energy particles and waves that damage cells and disrupt key biological processes, often causing cell death. How can radiation be detected and measured when it can't be directly observed by any of the senses?

A **Geiger counter** is a small portable device used for measuring radioactivity. It consists of a tube filled with argon gas that is ionized when it comes into contact with nuclear radiation. This in turn generates an electric current that produces a clicking sound or registers on a meter. Geiger counters are used to locate a radiation source or a site that has become contaminated by radioactivity.

Individuals who work with radioactivity wear protective clothing (Section 10.1) as well as radiation badges. A radiation badge contains photographic film that fogs when it comes into contact with radioactivity. These badges are regularly monitored to assure that these individuals are not exposed to unhealthy levels of harmful radiation.

10.4A Measuring the Radioactivity in a Sample

The amount of radioactivity in a sample is measured by the number of nuclei that decay per unit time—disintegrations per second. The most common unit is the **curie** (Ci), and smaller units derived from it, the **millicurie** (mCi) and the **microcurie** (μCi). One curie equals 3.7×10^{10} disintegrations/second, which corresponds to the decay rate of 1 g of the element radium.

$$1 \text{ Ci} = 3.7 \times 10^{10} \text{ disintegrations/second}$$
$$1 \text{ Ci} = 1{,}000 \text{ mCi}$$
$$1 \text{ Ci} = 1{,}000{,}000 \text{ } \mu\text{Ci}$$

The **becquerel** (Bq), an SI unit, is also used to measure radioactivity; 1 Bq = 1 disintegration/second. Since each nuclear decay corresponds to one becquerel, 1 Ci = 3.7×10^{10} Bq. Radioactivity units are summarized in Table 10.3.

Often a dose of radiation is measured in the number of millicuries that must be administered. For example, a diagnostic test for thyroid activity uses sodium iodide that contains iodine-131—that is, $Na^{131}I$. The radioisotope is purchased with a known amount of radioactivity per milliliter, such as 3.5 mCi/mL. By knowing the amount of radioactivity a patient must be given, as well as the concentration of radioactivity in the sample, one can calculate the volume of radioactive isotope that must be administered (Sample Problem 10.4).

SAMPLE PROBLEM 10.4

A patient must be given a 4.5-mCi dose of iodine-131, which is available as a solution that contains 3.5 mCi/mL. What volume of solution must be administered?

Analysis

Use the amount of radioactivity (mCi/mL) as a conversion factor to convert the dose of radioactivity from millicuries to a volume in milliliters.

Solution

The dose of radioactivity is known in millicuries, and the amount of radioactivity per unit volume (3.5 mCi/mL) is also known. Use 3.5 mCi/mL as a millicurie–milliliter conversion factor.

$$\underset{\text{Millicuries cancel.}}{4.5 \text{ mCi dose}} \times \underset{\substack{\text{mCi–mL} \\ \text{conversion factor}}}{\frac{1 \text{ mL}}{3.5 \text{ mCi}}} = \mathbf{1.3 \text{ mL dose}}$$

Answer

PROBLEM 10.16

To treat a thyroid tumor, a patient must be given a 110-mCi dose of iodine-131, supplied in a vial containing 25 mCi/mL. What volume of solution must be administered?

10.4B Measuring Human Exposure to Radioactivity

Several units are used to measure the amount of radiation *absorbed* by an organism.

- The **rad**—radiation absorbed dose—is the amount of radiation absorbed by one gram of a substance. The amount of energy absorbed varies with both the nature of the substance and the type of radiation.
- The **rem**—radiation equivalent for man—is the amount of radiation that also factors in its energy and potential to damage tissue. Using rem as a measure of radiation, 1 rem of any type of radiation produces the same amount of tissue damage.

Other units to measure absorbed radiation include the **gray** (1 Gy = 100 rad) and the **sievert** (1 Sv = 100 rem).

Table 10.3 Units Used to Measure Radioactivity

1 Ci = 3.7×10^{10} disintegrations/s
1 Ci = 3.7×10^{10} Bq
1 Ci = 1,000 mCi
1 Ci = 1,000,000 μCi

The curie is named for Polish chemist Marie Skłodowska Curie who discovered the radioactive elements polonium and radium, and received Nobel Prizes for both Chemistry and Physics in the early twentieth century.

Although background radiation varies with location, the average radiation dose per year for an individual is estimated at 0.27 rem. Generally, no detectable biological effects are noticed when the dose of radiation is less than 25 rem. A single dose of 25–100 rem causes a temporary decrease in white blood cell count. The symptoms of radiation sickness—nausea, vomiting, fatigue, and prolonged decrease in white blood cell count—are visible at a dose of more than 100 rem.

Death results at still higher doses of radiation. The **LD$_{50}$—the lethal dose that kills 50% of a population**—is 500 rem in humans, and exposure to 600 rem of radiation is fatal for an entire population.

PROBLEM 10.17

The unit millirem (1 rem = 1,000 mrem) is often used to measure the amount of radiation absorbed. (a) The average yearly dose of radiation from radon gas is 200 mrem. How many rem does this correspond to? (b) If a thyroid scan exposes a patient to 0.014 rem of radiation, how many mrem does this correspond to? (c) Which represents the larger dose?

10.5 FOCUS ON HEALTH & MEDICINE
Medical Uses of Radioisotopes

Radioactive isotopes are used for both diagnostic and therapeutic procedures in medicine. In a diagnostic test to measure the function of an organ or to locate a tumor, low doses of radioactivity are generally given. When the purpose of using radiation is therapeutic, such as to kill diseased cells or cancerous tissue, a much higher dose of radiation is required.

10.5A Radioisotopes Used in Diagnosis

Radioisotopes are routinely used to determine if an organ is functioning properly or to detect the presence of a tumor. The isotope is ingested or injected and the radiation it emits can be used to produce a scan. Sometimes the isotope is an atom or ion that is not part of a larger molecule. Examples include iodine-131, which is administered as the salt sodium iodide (Na^{131}I), and xenon-133, which is a gas containing radioactive xenon atoms. At other times the radioactive atom is bonded to a larger molecule that targets a specific organ. An organ that has increased or decreased uptake of the radioactive element can indicate disease, the presence of a tumor, or other conditions.

A HIDA scan (hepatobiliary iminodiacetic acid scan) uses a technetium-99m-labeled molecule to evaluate the functioning of the gall bladder and bile ducts (Figure 10.4). After injection, the technetium-99m travels through the bloodstream and into the liver, gall bladder, and bile ducts, where, in a healthy individual, the organs are all clearly visible on a scan. When the gall bladder is inflamed or the bile ducts are obstructed by gallstones, uptake of the radioisotope does not occur and these organs are not visualized because they do not contain the radioisotope.

Red blood cells tagged with technetium-99m are used to identify the site of internal bleeding in an individual. Bone scans performed with technetium-99m can show the location of metastatic cancer, so that specific sites can be targeted for radiation therapy (Figure 10.5).

Thallium-201 is used in stress tests to diagnose coronary artery disease. Thallium injected into a vein crosses cell membranes into normal heart muscle. Little radioactive thallium is found in areas of the heart that have a poor blood supply. This technique is used to identify individuals who may need bypass surgery or other interventions because of blocked coronary arteries.

PROBLEM 10.18

The half-life of thallium-201 is three days. What fraction of thallium-201 is still present in an individual after nine days?

Figure 10.4   HIDA Scan Using Technetium-99m

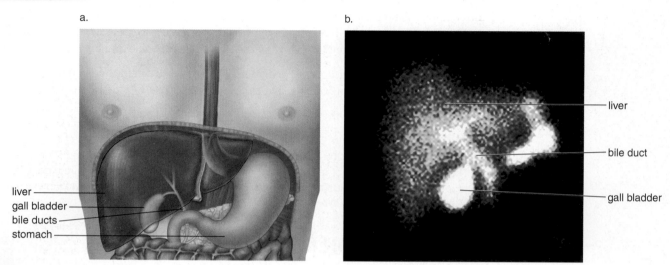

a.

b.

liver

bile duct

gall bladder

liver
gall bladder
bile ducts
stomach

a. Schematic showing the location of the liver, gall bladder, and bile ducts

b. A scan using technetium-99m showing bright areas for the liver, gall bladder, and bile ducts, indicating normal function

Figure 10.5   Bone Scan Using Technetium-99m

a.

b.

kidneys

bladder

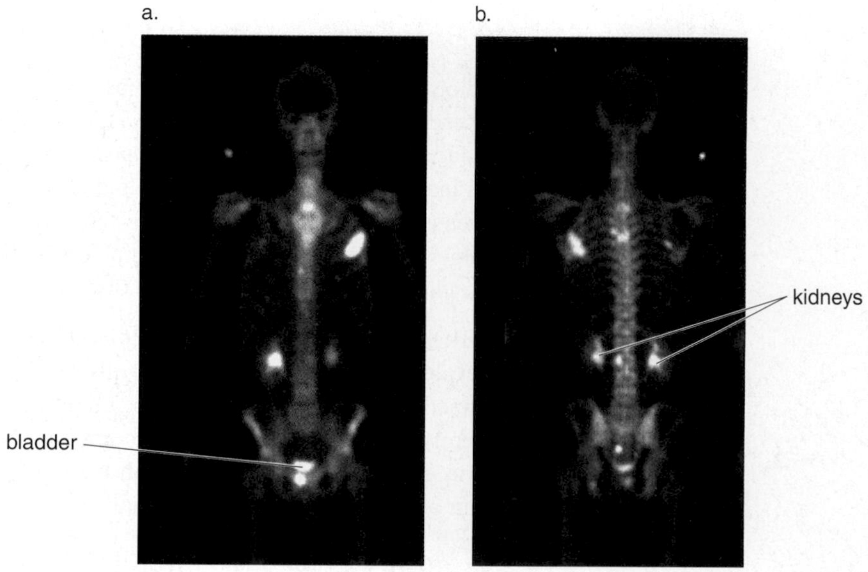

The bone scan of a patient whose lung cancer has spread to other organs. The anterior view [from the front in (a)] shows the spread of disease to the ribs, while the posterior view [from the back in (b)] shows spread of disease to the ribs and spine. The bright areas in the mid-torso and lower pelvis are due to a collection of radioisotope in the kidneys and bladder, before it is eliminated in the urine.

10.5B   Radioisotopes Used in Treatment

The high-energy radiation emitted by radioisotopes can be used to kill rapidly dividing tumor cells. Two techniques are used. Sometimes the radiation source is external to the body. For example, a beam of radiation produced by decaying cobalt-60 can be focused at a tumor. Such a radiation source must have a much longer half-life—5.3 years in this case—than radioisotopes that are ingested for diagnostic purposes. With this method some destruction of healthy tissue often occurs, and a patient may experience some signs of radiation sickness, including vomiting, fatigue, and hair loss.

Figure 10.6   Common Radioisotopes Used in Medicine

Xenon-133
lung function

Iodine-131
hyperthyroidism
and thyroid tumors

Technetium-99m
bone scan

Phosphorus-32
treating leukemia
and lymphomas

Technetium-99m
gall bladder function

Iridium-192
cancers of
the breast

Technetium-99m
visualizing gastrointestinal
bleeding

Thallium-201
heart function

A more selective approach to cancer treatment involves using a radioactive isotope internally at the site of the tumor within the body. Using iodine-131 to treat hyperthyroidism has already been discussed (Section 10.1). Other examples include using radioactive "seeds" or wire that can be implanted close to a tumor. Iodine-125 seeds are used to treat prostate cancer and iridium-192 wire is used to treat some cancers of the breast.

Figure 10.6 illustrates radioisotopes that are used for diagnosis or treatment.

10.5C   Positron Emission Tomography—PET Scans

Positron emission tomography (PET) scans use radioisotopes that emit positrons when the nucleus decays. Once formed, a positron combines with an electron to form two γ rays, which create a scan of an organ.

Carbon-11, oxygen-15, nitrogen-13, and fluorine-18 are common radioactive isotopes used in PET scans. For example, a carbon-11 or fluorine-18 isotope can be incorporated in a glucose molecule. When this radioactive molecule is taken internally, its concentration becomes highest in areas in the body that continually use glucose. A healthy brain shows a high level of radioactivity from labeled glucose. When an individual suffers a stroke or has Alzheimer's disease, brain activity is significantly decreased and radioactivity levels are decreased.

PET scans are also used to detect tumors and coronary artery disease, and determine whether cancer has spread to other organs of the body. A PET scan is also a noninvasive method of monitoring whether cancer treatment has been successful (Figure 10.7).

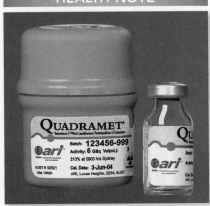

HEALTH NOTE

Quadramet is the trade name of a medication that contains radioactive samarium-153. Quadramet is administered to relieve pain in patients whose cancer has spread to the bone.

PROBLEM 10.19

Samarium-153, a radioactive isotope with a half-life of approximately 48 hours, is used to treat cancers lodged in the bone. (a) How many protons, neutrons, and electrons does samarium-153 contain? (b) Write a balanced nuclear equation for the emission of a β particle from samarium-153. (c) If a vial with an activity of 150 mCi is purchased, what is the activity of the solution after eight days?

Figure 10.7   PET Scans

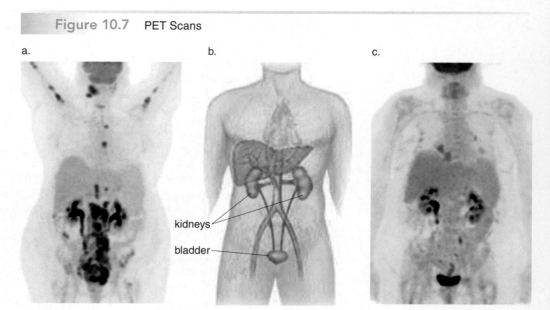

a. The PET scan shows cancer of the lymph nodes in the neck and abdomen, as well as scattered areas of tumor in the bone marrow of the arms and spine before treatment.

b. The schematic of selected organs in the torso and pelvis

c. The PET scan shows significant clearing of disease after chemotherapy by the decrease in intensity of the radioisotope. The dark regions in the kidneys (in the torso) and bladder (in the lower pelvis) are due to the concentration of the radioisotope before elimination in the urine.

PROBLEM 10.20

Write a nuclear equation for the emission of a positron from nitrogen-13.

10.6   Nuclear Fission and Nuclear Fusion

The nuclear reactions used in nuclear power plants occur by a process called *nuclear fission,* whereas the nuclear reactions that take place in the sun occur by a process called *nuclear fusion.*

- *Nuclear fission* is the splitting apart of a heavy nucleus into lighter nuclei and neutrons.
- *Nuclear fusion* is the joining together of two light nuclei to form a larger nucleus.

10.6A   Nuclear Fission

When uranium-235 is bombarded by a neutron, it undergoes **nuclear fission** and splits apart into two lighter nuclei. Several different fission products have been identified. One common nuclear reaction is the fission of uranium-235 into krypton-91 and barium-142.

$$^{235}_{92}\text{U} \quad + \quad ^{1}_{0}\text{n} \quad \longrightarrow \quad ^{91}_{36}\text{Kr} \quad + \quad ^{142}_{56}\text{Ba} \quad + \quad 3\,^{1}_{0}\text{n}$$

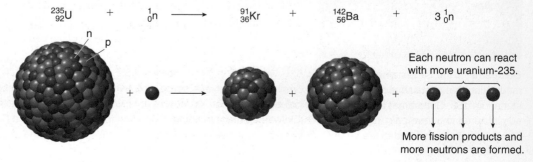

Each neutron can react with more uranium-235.

More fission products and more neutrons are formed.

Three high-energy neutrons are also produced in the reaction as well as a great deal of energy. Whereas burning 1 g of methane in natural gas releases 13 kcal of energy, fission of 1 g of uranium-235 releases 3.4×10^8 kcal. Each neutron produced during fission can go on to bombard three other uranium-235 nuclei to produce more nuclei and more neutrons. Such a process is called a **chain reaction.**

In order to sustain a chain reaction there must be a sufficient amount of uranium-235. When that amount—the **critical mass**—is present, the chain reaction occurs over and over again and an atomic explosion occurs. When less than the critical mass of uranium-235 is present, there is a more controlled production of energy, as is the case in a nuclear power plant.

A nuclear power plant utilizes the tremendous amount of energy produced by fission of the uranium-235 nucleus to heat water to steam, which powers a generator to produce electricity (Figure 10.8). While nuclear energy accounts for a small but significant fraction of the electricity needs in the United States, most of the electricity generated in some European countries comes from nuclear power.

Two problems that surround nuclear power generation are the possibility of radiation leaks and the disposal of nuclear waste. Plants are designed and monitored to contain the radioactive materials within the nuclear reactor. The reactor core itself is located in a containment facility with thick walls, so that should a leak occur, the radiation should in principle be kept within the building. The nuclear reactor in Chernobyl, Russia, was built without a containment facility and in 1986 it exploded, releasing high levels of radioactivity to the immediate environment and sending a cloud of radioactivity over much of Europe.

The products of nuclear fission are radioactive nuclei with long half-lives, often hundreds or even thousands of years. As a result, nuclear fission generates radioactive waste that must be stored in a secure facility so that it does not pose a hazard to the immediate surroundings. Burying waste far underground is currently considered the best option, but this issue is still unresolved.

Figure 10.8   A Nuclear Power Plant

a.

b.

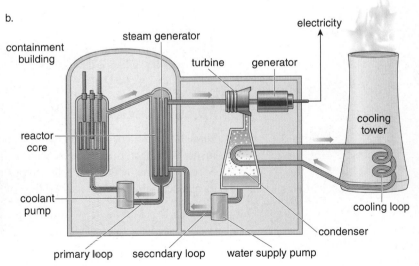

a. Nuclear power plant with steam rising from a cooling tower

b. Fission occurs in a nuclear reactor core that is housed in a containment facility. Water surrounding the reactor is heated by the energy released during fission, and this energy drives a turbine, which produces electricity. Once the steam has been used to drive the turbine, it is cooled and re-circulated around the core of the reactor. To prevent the loss of any radioactive material to the environment, the water that surrounds the reactor core never leaves the containment building.

SAMPLE PROBLEM 10.5

Write a nuclear equation for the fission of uranium-235 by neutron bombardment to form strontium-90, an isotope of xenon, and three neutrons.

Analysis

Balance the atomic numbers and mass numbers on both sides of the nuclear equation. In fission reactions, include the neutron used for bombardment on the left and the high-energy neutrons produced on the right. Each neutron has a mass of one and zero charge.

Solution

[1] Write an incomplete equation with the original nucleus and neutron used for bombardment on the left, and the particles formed on the right.

- Use the identity of each element to determine its atomic number. Uranium has an atomic number of 92, and xenon has an atomic number of 54.
- Include one neutron on the left side. In this reaction, three high-energy neutrons are formed, so include three neutrons on the right side.

$$^{235}_{92}\text{U} \; + \; ^{1}_{0}\text{n} \; \longrightarrow \; ^{90}_{38}\text{Sr} \; + \; ^{?}_{54}\text{Xe} \; + \; 3\,^{1}_{0}\text{n}$$

[2] Calculate the mass numbers and atomic numbers of all newly formed nuclei on the right.

- Atomic number: In this problem all atomic numbers are known from the identity of the elements.
- Mass number: Balance mass numbers by taking into account the mass of the neutrons used or produced in the reaction. On the left side, the total mass of the particles (the uranium nucleus and one neutron) is 236 (235 + 1). On the right side, the sum of the masses of Sr-90, xenon, and three neutrons (total mass of three) must also equal 236.

$$236 = 90 + ? + 3(1)$$ three neutrons
$$236 = 93 + ?$$ one mass unit from each neutron
$$143 = ?$$

The mass number of xenon is 143.

[3] Write the complete equation.

$$^{235}_{92}\text{U} \; + \; ^{1}_{0}\text{n} \; \longrightarrow \; ^{90}_{38}\text{Sr} \; + \; ^{143}_{54}\text{Xe} \; + \; 3\,^{1}_{0}\text{n}$$

PROBLEM 10.21

Write a nuclear equation for the fission of uranium-235 by neutron bombardment to form antimony-133, three neutrons, and one other isotope.

10.6B   Nuclear Fusion

Nuclear fusion occurs when two light nuclei join together to form a larger nucleus. For example, fusion of a deuterium nucleus with a tritium nucleus forms helium and a neutron. Recall from Section 2.3 that deuterium is an isotope of hydrogen that contains one proton and one neutron in its nucleus, while tritium is an isotope of hydrogen that contains one proton and two neutrons in its nucleus.

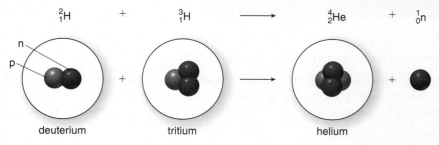

deuterium   tritium   helium

Like fission, fusion also releases a great deal of energy—namely, 5.3×10^8 kcal/mol of helium produced. The light and heat of the sun and other stars result from nuclear fusion.

One limitation of using fusion to provide energy for mankind is the extreme ⟨ ⟩ tions needed to produce it. Because it takes a considerable amount of energy to ⟨ ⟩ sive forces of the like charges of two nuclei, fusion can only be accomplished a ⟨ ⟩ (greater than 100,000,000 °C) and pressures (greater than 100,000 atm). Since t ⟨ ⟩ not easily achieved, using controlled nuclear fusion as an energy source has yet ⟨ ⟩

Controlled nuclear fusion has the potential of providing cheap and clean power. It is not plagued by the nuclear waste issues of fission reactors, and the needed reactants are readily available.

PROBLEM 10.22

Nuclear fusion in the stars occurs by a series of reactions. Identify **X**, **Y**, and **Z** in the following nuclear reactions that ultimately convert hydrogen into helium.

a. $^1_1\text{H} + \textbf{X} \longrightarrow {}^2_1\text{H} + {}^0_{+1}\text{e}$

b. $^1_1\text{H} + {}^2_1\text{H} \longrightarrow \textbf{Y}$

c. $^1_1\text{H} + {}^3_2\text{He} \longrightarrow {}^4_2\text{He} + \textbf{Z}$

10.7 FOCUS ON HEALTH & MEDICINE
Medical Imaging Without Radioactivity

X-rays, CT scans, and **MRIs** are also techniques that provide an image of an organ or extremity that is used for diagnosis of a medical condition. Unlike PET scans and other procedures discussed thus far, however, **these procedures are *not* based on nuclear reactions and they do *not* utilize radioactivity.** In each technique, an energy source is directed towards a specific region in the body, and a scan is produced that is analyzed by a trained medical professional.

X-rays are a high-energy type of radiation called electromagnetic radiation. Tissues of different density interact differently with an X-ray beam, and so a map of bone and internal organs is created on an X-ray film. Dense bone is clearly visible in an X-ray, making it a good diagnostic

Figure 10.9 Imaging the Human Body

a.

b.

c.

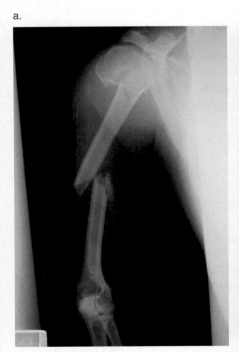

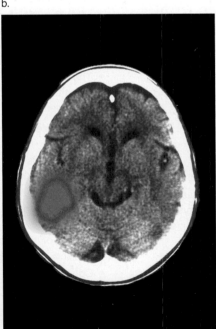

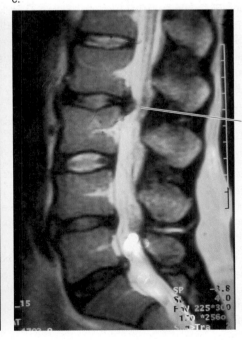

herniated disc

a. X-ray of a broken humerus in a patient's arm

b. A color-enhanced CT scan of the head showing the site of a stroke

c. MRI of the spinal cord showing spinal compression from a herniated disc

technique for finding fractures (Figure 10.9a). Although X-rays are a form of high-energy radiation, they are lower in energy than the γ rays produced in nuclear reactions. Nonetheless, X-rays still cause adverse biological effects on the cells with which they come in contact, and the exposure of both the patient and X-ray technician must be limited.

CT (computed tomography) scans, which also use X-rays, provide high resolution images of "slices" of the body. Historically, CT images have shown a slice of tissue perpendicular to the long axis of the body. Modern CT scanners can now provide a three-dimensional view of the body's organs. CT scans of the head are used to diagnose bleeding and tumors in the brain (Figure 10.9b).

MRI (magnetic resonance imaging) uses low-energy radio waves to visualize internal organs. Unlike methods that use high-energy radiation, MRIs do not damage cells. An MRI is a good diagnostic method for visualizing soft tissue (Figure 10.9c), and thus it complements X-ray techniques.

CHAPTER HIGHLIGHTS

KEY TERMS

Alpha (α) particle (10.1)

Becquerel (10.4)

Beta (β) particle (10.1)

Chain reaction (10.6)

Critical mass (10.6)

Curie (10.4)

Gamma (γ) ray (10.1)

Geiger counter (10.4)

Gray (10.4)

Half-life (10.3)

LD_{50} (10.4)

Nuclear fission (10.6)

Nuclear fusion (10.6)

Nuclear reaction (10.1)

Positron (10.1)

Rad (10.4)

Radioactive decay (10.2)

Radioactive isotope (10.1)

Radioactivity (10.1)

Radiocarbon dating (10.3)

Rem (10.4)

Sievert (10.4)

X-ray (10.7)

KEY CONCEPTS

❶ Describe the different types of radiation emitted by a radioactive nucleus. (10.1)

- A radioactive nucleus can emit α particles, β particles, positrons, or γ rays.
- An α particle is a high-energy nucleus that contains two protons and two neutrons.
- A β particle is a high-energy electron that has a −1 charge and negligible mass.
- A positron is an antiparticle of a β particle. A positron has a +1 charge and negligible mass.
- A γ ray is high-energy radiation with no mass or charge.

❷ How are equations for nuclear reactions written? (10.2)

- In an equation for a nuclear reaction, the sum of the mass numbers (A) must be equal on both sides of the equation. The sum of the atomic numbers (Z) must be equal on both sides of the equation as well.

❸ What is the half-life of a radioactive isotope? (10.3)

- The half-life ($t_{1/2}$) is the time it takes for one-half of a radioactive sample to decay. Knowing the half-life and the amount of a radioactive substance, one can calculate how much sample remains after a period of time.

❹ What units are used to measure radioactivity? (10.4)

- Radiation in a sample is measured by the number of disintegrations per second, most often using the curie (Ci); 1 Ci = 3.7×10^{10} disintegrations/s. The becquerel (Bq) is also used; 1 Bq = 1 disintegration/s; 1 Ci = 3.7×10^{10} Bq.
- The exposure of a substance to radioactivity is measured with the rad (radiation absorbed dose) or the rem (radiation equivalent for man).

❺ Give examples of common radioisotopes used in medicine. (10.5)

- Iodine-131 is used to diagnose and treat thyroid disease.
- Technetium-99m is used to evaluate the functioning of the gall bladder and bile ducts, and in bone scans to evaluate the spread of cancer.
- Red blood cells tagged with technetium-99m are used to find the site of a gastrointestinal bleed.
- Thallium-201 is used to diagnose coronary artery disease.
- Cobalt-60 is used as an external source of radiation for cancer treatment.
- Iodine-125 and iridium-192 are used in internal radiation treatment of prostate cancer and breast cancer, respectively.
- Carbon-11, oxygen-15, nitrogen-13, and fluorine-18 are used in positron emission tomography.

6 **What are nuclear fission and nuclear fusion? (10.6)**

- Nuclear fission is the splitting apart of a heavy nucleus into lighter nuclei and neutrons.
- Nuclear fusion is the joining together of two light nuclei to form a larger nucleus.
- Both nuclear fission and nuclear fusion release a great deal of energy. Nuclear fission is used in nuclear power plants to generate electricity. Nuclear fusion occurs in stars.

7 **What medical imaging techniques do not use radioactivity? (10.7)**

- X-rays and CT scans both use X-rays, a high-energy form of electromagnetic radiation.
- MRIs use low-energy radio waves to image soft tissue.

PROBLEMS

Selected in-chapter and odd-numbered end-of-chapter problems have brief answers in Appendix B. The *Student Study Guide and Solutions Manual* contains detailed solutions to all in-chapter and odd-numbered end-of-chapter problems, as well as additional worked examples and a chapter self-test.

Isotopes and Radiation

10.23 Compare fluorine-18 and fluorine-19 with regard to each of the following: (a) atomic number; (b) number of protons; (c) number of neutrons; (d) mass number. Give the isotope symbol for each isotope. F-19 is a stable nucleus and F-18 is used in PET scans.

10.24 Compare nitrogen-13 and nitrogen-14 with regard to each of the following: (a) atomic number; (b) number of protons; (c) number of neutrons; (d) mass number. Give the isotope symbol for each isotope. N-14 is a stable nucleus and N-13 is used in PET scans.

10.25 Complete the table of isotopes, each of which has found use in medicine.

	Atomic Number	Mass Number	Number of Protons	Number of Neutrons	Isotope Symbol
a. Chromium-51					
b.	46	103			
c.			19	23	
d.		133	54		

10.26 Complete the table of isotopes, each of which has found use in medicine.

	Atomic Number	Mass Number	Number of Protons	Number of Neutrons	Isotope Symbol
a. Sodium-24					
b.		89		51	
c.		59	26		
d. Samarium-153					

10.27 How much does the mass and charge of a nucleus change when each type of radiation is emitted: (a) α particle; (b) β particle; (c) γ ray; (d) positron?

10.28 Compare α particles, β particles, and γ rays with regard to each of the following: (a) speed the radiation travels; (b) penetrating power; (c) protective equipment that must be worn when handling.

10.29 What is the mass and charge of radiation that has each of the following symbols: (a) α; (b) n; (c) γ; (d) β?

10.30 What is the mass and charge of radiation that has each of the following symbols?

 a. $^0_{-1}e$ b. $^0_{+1}e$ c. ^4_2He d. β^+

Nuclear Reactions

10.31 Complete the nuclear equation by drawing the nucleus of the missing atom. Give the symbol for each atom and type of radiation. (The blue spheres represent protons and the red spheres represent neutrons.)

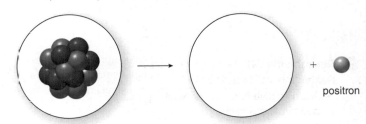

positron

10.32 Complete the nuclear equation by drawing the nucleus of the missing atom. Give the symbol for each atom and type of radiation. (The blue spheres represent protons and the red spheres represent neutrons.)

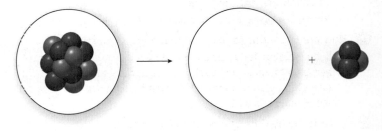

10.33 Complete each nuclear equation.

 a. $^{59}_{26}Fe \longrightarrow$? $+ \, ^0_{-1}e$ c. $^{178}_{80}Hg \longrightarrow$? $+ \, ^0_{+1}e$

 b. $^{190}_{78}Pt \longrightarrow$? $+ \, ^4_2He$

10.34 Complete each nuclear equation.

a. $^{77}_{37}\text{Rb} \longrightarrow \text{?} + ^{0}_{+1}e$ c. $^{66}_{29}\text{Cu} \longrightarrow \text{?} + ^{0}_{-1}e$

b. $^{251}_{102}\text{No} \longrightarrow \text{?} + ^{4}_{2}\text{He}$

10.35 Complete each nuclear equation.

a. $^{90}_{39}\text{Y} \longrightarrow ^{90}_{40}\text{Zr} + \text{?}$ c. $^{210}_{83}\text{Bi} \longrightarrow \text{?} + ^{4}_{2}\text{He}$

b. $\text{?} \longrightarrow ^{135}_{59}\text{Pr} + ^{0}_{+1}e$

10.36 Complete each nuclear equation.

a. $\text{?} \longrightarrow ^{90}_{39}\text{Y} + ^{0}_{-1}e$ c. $^{214}_{84}\text{Po} \longrightarrow \text{?} + ^{4}_{2}\text{He}$

b. $^{29}_{15}\text{P} \longrightarrow ^{29}_{14}\text{Si} + \text{?}$

10.37 Bismuth-214 can decay to form either polonium-214 or thallium-210, depending on what type of radiation is emitted. Write a balanced nuclear equation for each process.

10.38 Lead-210 can be formed by the decay of either thallium-210 or polonium-214, depending on what type of radiation is emitted. Write a balanced nuclear equation for each process.

10.39 Write a balanced nuclear equation for each reaction.
a. decay of thorium-232 by α emission
b. decay of sodium-25 by β emission
c. decay of xenon-118 by positron emission
d. decay of curium-243 by α emission

10.40 Write a balanced nuclear equation for each reaction.
a. decay of sulfur-35 by β emission
b. decay of thorium-225 by α emission
c. decay of rhodium-93 by positron emission
d. decay of silver-114 by β emission

Half-Life

10.41 A radioactive element (shown with blue spheres) forms a decay product (shown with green spheres) with a half-life of three days. How many half-lives have elapsed in diagram **A**?

initial sample   A

10.42 A radioactive element (shown with blue spheres) forms a decay product (shown with green spheres) with a half-life of 10 min. How many minutes have elapsed to form the sample in diagram **B**?

 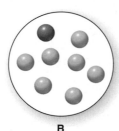

initial sample   B

10.43 If the amount of a radioactive element decreases from 2.4 g to 0.30 g in 12 days, what is its half-life?

10.44 If the amount of a radioactive element decreases from 0.36 g to 90. mg in 22 min, what is its half-life?

10.45 Radioactive iodine-131 ($t_{1/2}$ = 8.0 days) decays to form xenon-131 by emission of a β particle. How much of each isotope is present after each time interval if 64 mg of iodine-131 was present initially: (a) 8.0 days; (b) 16 days; (c) 24 days; (d) 32 days?

10.46 Radioactive phosphorus-32 decays to form sulfur-32 by emission of a β particle. Estimating the half-life to be 14 days, how much of each isotope is present after each time interval if 124 mg of phosphorus-32 was present initially: (a) 14 days; (b) 28 days; (c) 42 days; (d) 56 days?

10.47 If the half-life of an isotope is 24 hours, has all the isotope decayed in 48 hours?

10.48 Explain how the half-life of carbon-14 is used to date objects.

10.49 Why can't radiocarbon dating be used to determine the age of an artifact that is over 50,000 years old?

10.50 Why can't radiocarbon dating be used to estimate the age of rocks?

10.51 A patient is injected with a sample of technetium-99m ($t_{1/2}$ = 6.0 h), which has an activity of 20 mCi. What activity is observed after each interval: (a) 6 h; (b) 12 h; (c) 24 h?

10.52 A sample of iodine-131 ($t_{1/2}$ = 8.0 days) has an activity of 200. mCi. What activity is observed after each interval: (a) 8.0 days; (b) 24 days; (c) 48 days?

Measuring Radioactivity

10.53 If a radioactive sample had an activity of 5.0 mCi, how many disintegrations per second does this correspond to?

10.54 Why is the average amount of background radiation generally higher at higher elevations?

10.55 A patient must be administered a 28-mCi dose of technetium-99m, which is supplied in a vial containing a solution with an activity of 12 mCi/mL. What volume of solution must be given?

10.56 A radioactive isotope used for imaging is supplied in an 8.0-mL vial containing a solution with an activity of 108 mCi. What volume must be given to a patient who needs a 12-mCi dose?

10.57 Radioactive sodium-24, administered as $^{24}\text{NaCl}$, is given to treat leukemia. If a patient must receive 190 μCi/kg and the isotope is supplied as a solution that contains 5.0 mCi/mL, what volume is needed for a 68-kg patient?

10.58 Radioactive phosphorus-32, administered as sodium phosphate ($\text{Na}_3{}^{32}\text{PO}_4$), is used to treat chronic leukemia. The activity of an intravenous solution is 670 μCi/mL. What volume of solution must be used to supply a dose of 15 mCi?

10.59 The units chosen to report radiation amounts give us different information. What is measured using the curie compared to the rad?

10.60 The units chosen to report radiation amounts give us different information. What is measured using the millicurie compared to the rem?

10.61 The initial responders to the Chernobyl nuclear disaster were exposed to 20 Sv of radiation. Convert this value to rem. Did these individuals receive a fatal dose of radiation?

10.62 Many individuals who fought fires at the Chernobyl nuclear disaster site were exposed to 0.25 Sv of radiation. Convert this value to rem. Did these individuals receive a fatal dose of radiation? Would you expect any of these individuals to have shown ill health effects?

Nuclear Fission and Nuclear Fusion

10.63 What is the difference between nuclear fission and nuclear fusion?

10.64 What is the difference between the nuclear fission process that takes place in a nuclear reactor and the nuclear fission that occurs in an atomic bomb?

10.65 For which process does each statement apply—nuclear fission, nuclear fusion, both fission and fusion?
 a. The reaction occurs in the sun.
 b. A neutron is used to bombard a nucleus.
 c. A large amount of energy is released.
 d. Very high temperatures are required.

10.66 For which process does each statement apply—nuclear fission, nuclear fusion, both fission and fusion?
 a. The reaction splits a nucleus into lighter nuclei.
 b. The reaction joins two lighter nuclei into a heavier nucleus.
 c. The reaction is used to generate energy in a nuclear power plant.
 d. The reaction generates radioactive waste with a long half-life.

10.67 Complete each nuclear fission equation.
 a. $^{235}_{92}\text{U} + ^{1}_{0}\text{n} \longrightarrow ? + ^{97}_{42}\text{Mo} + 2\,^{1}_{0}\text{n}$
 b. $^{235}_{92}\text{U} + ^{1}_{0}\text{n} \longrightarrow ? + ^{140}_{56}\text{Ba} + 3\,^{1}_{0}\text{n}$

10.68 Complete each nuclear fission equation.
 a. $^{235}_{92}\text{U} + ^{1}_{0}\text{n} \longrightarrow ? + ^{139}_{57}\text{La} + 2\,^{1}_{0}\text{n}$
 b. $^{235}_{92}\text{U} + ^{1}_{0}\text{n} \longrightarrow ? + ^{140}_{58}\text{Ce} + 2\,^{1}_{0}\text{n} + 6\,^{0}_{-1}\text{e}$

10.69 Complete the nuclear fusion equation by drawing in the nucleus of the missing atom. Blue spheres represent protons and red spheres represent neutrons.

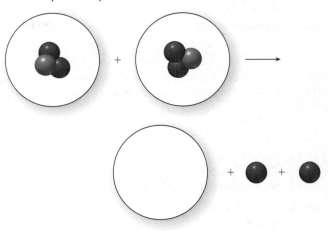

10.70 Complete the nuclear fusion equation by drawing in the nucleus of the missing atom. Blue spheres represent protons and red spheres represent neutrons.

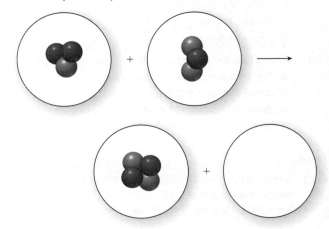

10.71 The fusion of two deuterium nuclei (hydrogen-2) forms a hydrogen nucleus (hydrogen-1) as one product. What other product is formed?

10.72 Fill in the missing product in the following nuclear fusion reaction.

$$^{3}_{2}\text{He} + ^{3}_{2}\text{He} \longrightarrow ? + 2\,^{1}_{1}\text{H}$$

10.73 Discuss two problems that surround the generation of electricity from a nuclear power plant.

10.74 Why are there as yet no nuclear power plants that use nuclear fusion to generate electricity?

10.75 All nuclei with atomic numbers around 100 or larger do not exist naturally; rather they have been synthesized by fusing two lighter-weight nuclei together. Complete the following nuclear equation by giving the name, atomic number, and mass number of the element made by this reaction.

$$^{209}_{83}Bi + {}^{58}_{26}Fe \longrightarrow ? + {}^{1}_{0}n$$

10.76 Complete the following nuclear equation, and give the name, atomic number, and mass number of the element made by this reaction.

$$^{235}_{92}U + {}^{14}_{7}N \longrightarrow ? + 5\,{}^{1}_{0}n$$

General Questions

10.77 Arsenic-74 is a radioisotope used for locating brain tumors.
   a. Write a balanced nuclear equation for the positron emission of arsenic-74.
   b. If $t_{1/2}$ for As-74 is 18 days, how much of a 120-mg sample remains after 90 days?
   c. If the radioactivity of a 2.0-mL vial of arsenic-74 is 10.0 mCi, what volume must be administered to give a 7.5-mCi dose?

10.78 Sodium-24 is a radioisotope used for examining circulation.
   a. Write a balanced nuclear equation for the β decay of sodium-24.
   b. If $t_{1/2}$ for Na-24 is 15 h, how much of an 84-mg sample remains after 2.5 days?
   c. If the radioactivity of a 5.0-mL vial of sodium-24 is 10.0 mCi, what volume must be administered to give a 6.5-mCi dose?

10.79 Strontium-89 is a radioactive isotope ($t_{1/2}$ = 50. days) used to reduce the pain of prostate and bone cancer. (a) How many protons, neutrons, and electrons does strontium-89 contain? (b) Write a balanced nuclear equation for the emission of a β particle from strontium-89. (c) If a vial contains 10.0 μg of strontium-89, how much of the radioisotope remains after 200. days?

10.80 Rhenium-186 is a radioactive isotope ($t_{1/2}$ = 4.0 days) used for pain relief in bone cancer. (a) How many protons, neutrons, and electrons does rhenium-186 contain? (b) Write a balanced nuclear equation for the emission of a β particle from rhenium-186. (c) If a vial contains 200. μg of rhenium-186, how much of the radioisotope remains after 16 days?

Applications

10.81 Explain how each isotope is used in medicine.
   a. iodine-131
   b. iridium-192
   c. thallium-201

10.82 Explain how each isotope is used in medicine.
   a. iodine-125
   b. technetium-99m
   c. cobalt-60

10.83 How does the half-life of each of the following isotopes of iodine affect the manner in which it is administered to a patient: (a) iodine-125, $t_{1/2}$ = 60 days; (b) iodine-131, $t_{1/2}$ = 8 days?

10.84 Explain why food is irradiated with γ rays.

10.85 A mammogram is an X-ray of the breast. Why does an X-ray technician leave the room or go behind a shield when a mammogram is performed on a patient?

10.86 Why is a lead apron placed over a patient's body when dental X-rays are taken?

10.87 One of the radioactive isotopes that contaminated the area around Chernobyl after the nuclear accident in 1986 was iodine-131. Suggest a reason why individuals in the affected region were given doses of NaI that contained the stable iodine-127 isotope.

10.88 The element strontium has similar properties to calcium. Suggest a reason why exposure to strontium-90, a product of nuclear testing in the atmosphere, is especially hazardous for children.

CHALLENGE PROBLEMS

10.89 An article states that the fission of 1.0 g of uranium-235 releases 3.4×10^8 kcal, the same amount of energy as burning one ton (2,000 lb) of coal. If this report is accurate, how much energy is released when 1.0 g of coal is burned?

10.90 Radioactive isotopes with high atomic numbers often decay to form isotopes that are themselves radioactive, and once formed, decay to form new isotopes. Sometimes a series of such decays occurs over many steps until a stable nucleus is formed. The following series of decays occurs: Polonium-218 decays with emission of an α particle to form **X**, which emits a β particle to form **Y**, which emits an α particle to form **Z**. Identify **X**, **Y**, and **Z**.

Useful Mathematical Concepts

Three common mathematical concepts are needed to solve many problems in chemistry:

- Using scientific notation
- Determining the number of significant figures
- Using a scientific calculator

Scientific Notation

To write numbers that contain many leading zeros (at the beginning) or trailing zeros (at the end), scientists use **scientific notation.**

- In scientific notation, a number is written as $y \times 10^x$, where y (the coefficient) is a number between 1 and 10, and x is an exponent, which can be any positive or negative whole number.

To convert a standard number to scientific notation:

1. Move the decimal point to give a number between 1 and 10.
2. Multiply the result by 10^x, where x is the number of places the decimal point was moved.
   - If the decimal point is moved to the **left,** x is **positive.**
   - If the decimal point is moved to the **right,** x is **negative.**

$$2822. \quad = \quad 2.822 \times 10^3 \qquad \text{the number of places the decimal point was moved to the left}$$

Move the decimal point three places to the left.

$$0.000\ 004\ 5 \quad = \quad 4.5 \times 10^{-6} \qquad \text{the number of places the decimal point was moved to the right}$$

Move the decimal point six places to the right.

To convert a number in scientific notation to a standard number, use the value of x in 10^x to indicate the number of places to move the decimal point in the coefficient.

- Move the decimal point to the **right** when x is **positive.**
- Move the decimal point to the **left** when x is **negative.**

$$2.521 \times 10^2 \qquad\qquad 2.521 \quad ------\rightarrow \quad 252.1$$

Move the decimal point to the right two places.

$$2.68 \times 10^{-2} \qquad\qquad 002.68 \quad ------\rightarrow \quad 0.0268$$

Move the decimal point to the left two places.

Table A.1 shows how several numbers are written in scientific notation.

Table A.1 Numbers in Standard Form and Scientific Notation

Number	Scientific Notation
26,200	2.62×10^4
0.006 40	6.40×10^{-3}
3,000,000	3×10^6
0.000 000 139	1.39×10^{-7}
2,000.20	2.00020×10^3

Often, numbers written in scientific notation must be multiplied or divided.

- **To multiply two numbers in scientific notation, *multiply* the coefficients together and *add* the exponents in the powers of 10.**

Add exponents.
(8 + 3)

$$(3.0 \times 10^8) \quad \times \quad (2.0 \times 10^3) \quad = \quad 6.0 \times 10^{11}$$

Multiply coefficients.
(3.0 × 2.0)

- **To divide two numbers in scientific notation, *divide* the coefficients and *subtract* the exponents in the powers of 10.**

Divide coefficients. $\quad \dfrac{6.0 \times 10^6}{2.0 \times 10^{10}} \quad$ Subtract exponents. $\quad = \quad 3.0 \times 10^{-4}$
(6.0 ÷ 2.0) $\qquad\qquad\qquad\qquad$ (6 − 10)

Table A.2 shows the result of multiplying or dividing several numbers written in scientific notation.

Table A.2 Calculations Using Numbers Written in Scientific Notation

Calculation	Answer
$(3.5 \times 10^3) \times (2.2 \times 10^{22}) =$	7.7×10^{25}
$(3.5 \times 10^3) \div (2.2 \times 10^{22}) =$	1.6×10^{-19}
$(3.5 \times 10^3) \times (2.2 \times 10^{-10}) =$	7.7×10^{-7}
$(3.5 \times 10^3) \div (2.2 \times 10^{-10}) =$	1.6×10^{13}

Significant Figures

Whenever we measure a number, there is a degree of uncertainty associated with the result. The last number (furthest to the right) is an estimate. **Significant figures** are all of the digits in a measured number including one estimated digit. How many significant figures are contained in a number?

- All nonzero digits are always significant.
- A zero *counts* as a significant figure when it occurs between two nonzero digits, or at the end of a number with a decimal point.
- A zero does *not* count as a significant figure when it occurs at the beginning of a number, or at the end of a number that does not have a decimal point.

Table A.3 lists the number of significant figures in several quantities.

Table A.3 Examples Illustrating Significant Figures

Quantity	Number of Significant Figures	Quantity	Number of Significant Figures
1,267 g	Four	203 L	Three
24,345 km	Five	6.10 atm	Three
1.200 mg	Four	0.3040 g	Four
0.000 001 mL	One	1,200 m	Two

The number of significant figures must also be taken into account in calculations. To avoid reporting a value with too many digits, we must often **round off the number** to give the correct number of significant figures. Two rules are used in rounding off numbers.

- If the first number that must be dropped is 4 or less, drop it and all remaining numbers.
- If the first number that must be dropped is 5 or greater, *round the number up* by adding one to the last digit that will be retained.

To round 63.854 to two significant figures:

These digits must be retained.

$$\overline{63}.854 \qquad \text{first digit to be dropped}$$

These digits must be dropped.

- Since the first digit to be dropped is 8 (5 or greater), add 1 to the first digit to its left.
- The number 63.854 rounded to two digits is **64**.

Table A.4 gives other examples of rounding off numbers.

Table A.4 Rounding Off Numbers

Original Number	Rounded to	Rounded Number
15.2538	Two places	15
15.2538	Three places	15.3
15.2538	Four places	15.25
15.2538	Five places	15.254

The first number to be dropped is indicated in red in each original number.

The number of significant figures in the answer of a problem depends on the type of mathematical calculation—multiplication (and division) or addition (and subtraction).

> • In multiplication and division, the answer has the same number of significant figures as the original number with the *fewest* significant figures.

five significant figures

first digit to be dropped

$$5.5067 \quad \times \quad 2.6 \quad = \quad 14.31742 \text{ rounded to } \mathbf{14}$$

two significant figures

The answer must contain only **two** significant figures.

> • In addition and subtraction, the answer has the same number of decimal places as the original number with the *fewest* decimal places.

two digits after the decimal point

$$10.17 \quad + \quad 3.5 \quad = \quad 13.67 \text{ rounded to } \mathbf{13.7}$$

one digit after the decimal point

last significant digit   The answer can have only **one** digit after the decimal point.

Table A.5 lists other examples of calculations that take into account the number of significant figures.

Table A.5 Calculations Using Significant Figures

Calculation	Answer
$3.2 \times 699 =$	2,236.8 rounded to **2,200**
$4.66892 \div 2.13 =$	2.191981221 rounded to **2.19**
$25.3 + 3.668 + 29.1004 =$	58.0684 rounded to **58.1**
$95.1 - 26.335 =$	68.765 rounded to **68.8**

Using a Scientific Calculator

A scientific calculator is capable of carrying out more complicated mathematical functions than simple addition, subtraction, multiplication, and division. For example, these calculators allow the user to convert a standard number to scientific notation, as well as readily determine the logarithm (log) or antilogarithm (antilog) of a value. Carrying out these operations is especially important in determining pH or hydronium ion concentration in Chapter 9.

Described in this section are the steps that can be followed in calculations with some types of calculators. Consult your manual if these steps do not produce the stated result.

Converting a Number to Scientific Notation

To convert a number, such as 1,200, from its standard form to scientific notation:

- Enter 1200.
- Press 2nd and then SCI.
- The number will appear as 1.2^{03}, indicating that $1,200 = 1.2 \times 10^3$.

Entering a Number Written in Scientific Notation

To enter a number written in scientific notation with a positive exponent, such as 1.5×10^8:

- Enter 1.5.
- Press EE.
- Enter 8.
- The number will appear as 1.5^{08}, indicating that it is equal to 1.5×10^8.

To enter a number written in scientific notation with a negative exponent, such as 3.5×10^{-4}:

- Enter 3.5.
- Press EE.
- Enter 4.
- Press CHANGE SIGN ($+ \rightarrow -$).
- The number will appear as 3.5^{-04}, indicating that it is equal to 3.5×10^{-4}.

Taking the Logarithm of a Number: Calculating pH from a Known [H_3O^+]

Since pH = $-\log$ [H_3O^+], we must learn how to calculate logarithms on a calculator in order to determine pH values. To determine the pH from a known hydronium ion concentration, say [H_3O^+] = 1.8×10^{-5}, carry out the following steps:

- Enter 1.8×10^{-5} (Enter 1.8; press EE; enter 5; press CHANGE SIGN). The number 1.8^{-05} will appear.
- Press LOG.
- Press CHANGE SIGN ($+ \rightarrow -$).
- The number 4.744 727 495 will appear. Since the coefficient, 1.8, contains two significant figures, round the logarithm to 4.74, which has two digits to the right of the decimal point. Thus, the pH of the solution is 4.74.

Taking the Antilogarithm of a Number: Calculating [H_3O^+] from a Known pH

Since [H_3O^+] = antilog($-$pH), we must learn how to calculate an antilogarithm—that is, the number that has a given logarithm value—using a calculator. To determine the hydronium ion concentration from a given pH, say 3.91, carry out the following steps:

- Enter 3.91.
- Press CHANGE SIGN ($+ \rightarrow -$).
- Press 2nd and then LOG.
- The number 0.000 123 027 will appear. To convert this number to scientific notation, press 2nd and SCI.
- The number $1.230\ 268\ 771^{-04}$ will appear, indicating that [H_3O^+] = $1.230\ 268\ 771 \times 10^{-4}$. Since the original pH (a logarithm) had two digits to the right of the decimal point, the answer must have two significant figures in the coefficient in scientific notation. As a result, [H_3O^+] = 1.2×10^{-4}.

Table A.6 lists pH values that correspond to given $[H_3O^+]$ values. You can practice using a calculator to determine pH or $[H_3O^+]$ by entering a value in one column, following the listed steps, and then checking to see if you obtain the corresponding value in the other column.

Table A.6 The pH of a Solution from a Given Hydronium Ion Concentration $[H_3O^+]$

$[H_3O^+]$	pH	$[H_3O^+]$	pH
1.8×10^{-10}	9.74	4.0×10^{-13}	12.40
3.8×10^{-2}	1.42	6.6×10^{-4}	3.18
5.0×10^{-12}	11.30	2.6×10^{-9}	8.59
4.2×10^{-7}	6.38	7.3×10^{-8}	7.14

Selected Answers to In-Chapter and End-of-Chapter Problems

CHAPTER 1

1.1 water, rock, tree: natural
tennis ball, CD, plastic bag: synthetic

1.3 b, c, e: chemical   a, d: physical

1.5 a. pure substance   b. mixture

1.7 a. element   b, c, d: compound

1.9 1,000,000,000

1.11 a. 3 cL   b. 1 μg   c. 5 km   d. 2 mL

1.12 a. 4   b. 5   c. 2   d. 4   e. 3   f. 3   g. 7   h. 2

1.13 a. 4   b. 5   c. 6   d. 4   e. 5   f. 4   g. 4   h. 6

1.15 a. 1.3   b. 0.0025   c. 3,800

1.16 a. 37   b. 0.000 007 93   c. 32   d. 3,100

1.17 a. 28.0 cm   b. 127.5 mL   c. 30. mg   d. 2.08 s

1.18 9.8×10^{-5} g/dL

1.19 a. 9.32×10^{4} c. 6.78×10^{6} e. 4.52×10^{12}
b. 7.25×10^{-4} d. 3.0×10^{-5} f. 2.8×10^{-11}

1.20 6,020,000,000,000,000,000,000 molecules

1.21 a. 6,500   c. 0.037 80   e. 2,221,000
b. 0.000 032 6   d. 104,000,000   f. 0.000 000 000 45

1.22 a. $\dfrac{0.621\ \text{mi}}{1\ \text{km}}$ $\dfrac{1\ \text{km}}{0.621\ \text{mi}}$ c. $\dfrac{454\ \text{g}}{1\ \text{lb}}$ $\dfrac{1\ \text{lb}}{454\ \text{g}}$
b. $\dfrac{1000\ \text{mm}}{1\ \text{m}}$ $\dfrac{1\ \text{m}}{1000\ \text{mm}}$ d. $\dfrac{1000\ \mu\text{g}}{1\ \text{mg}}$ $\dfrac{1\ \text{mg}}{1000\ \mu\text{g}}$

1.23 2,560 mi

1.25 a. 1.91 km   b. 0.7 L   c. 140 cm

1.26 1.5 tsp

1.27 4 tablets

1.29 83.3 °F or 302 K

1.31 7.13 g

1.33 a. **A**   b. **B**

1.35 a. element   b. compound   c, d: mixture

1.37 An element is a pure substance that cannot be broken down into simpler substances by a chemical reaction. A compound is a pure substance formed by combining two or more elements.

1.39

Phase	a. Volume	b. Shape	c. Organization	d. Particle Proximity
Solid	Definite	Definite	Very organized	Very close
Liquid	Definite	Assumes shape of container	Less organized	Close
Gas	Not fixed	None	Disorganized	Far apart

1.41 a. physical   b. chemical   c. physical

1.43 This is a physical change since the compound CO_2 is unchanged in this transition. The same "particles" exist at the beginning and end of the process.

1.45 a. 76.5 °F   b. three   c. 24.7 °C

1.47 An exact number results from counting objects or is part of a definition, such as having 20 people in a class. An inexact number results from a measurement or observation and contains some uncertainty, such as the distance from the earth to the sun, 9.3×10^{7} miles.

1.49 a. 5 dL   b. 10 mg   c. 5 cm   d. 10 Ms

1.51 a. 4   b. 2   c. 3   d. 2   e. 3   f. 4   g. 4   h. 2

1.53 a. 25,400   c. 0.001 27   e. 195
b. 1,250,000   d. 0.123   f. 197

1.55 a. 22   b. 21.97   c. 5.4   d. 50.1   e. 100   f. 1,044

1.57 a. 1.234×10^{3} g   c. 5.244×10^{6} L   e. 4.4×10^{4} km
b. 1.62×10^{-5} m   d. 5.62×10^{-3} g

1.59 a. 340,000,000   c. 300
b. 0.000 058 22   d. 0.000 000 068 6

1.61 a. 4.44×10^{3} c. 1.3×10^{8}
b. 5.6×10^{-5} d. 9.8×10^{-4}

1.63 a. 4.00×10^{-4} g   c. 8.0×10^{-5} g
b. 2×10^{-3} g   d. 3.4×10^{3} mg

1.65 a. 1,500 g   b. 3.3 lb   c. 53 oz

1.67 a. 300,000 mg   d. 10 oz
b. 2,000,000 μL   e. 0.6 m
c. 0.050 m   f. 3.2 m

1.69 a. 106 kg   b. 130 cm   c. 1.4 L   d. 99.9 °F

1.71 a. 946 mL   b. 33.9 fl oz

1.73 a. 127 °F or 326 K   b. 177 °C or 450. K

1.75 a. −10 °C   b. −50 °F

1.77 Density is the mass per unit volume, usually reported in g/mL or g/cc. Specific gravity is the ratio of the density of a substance to the density of water and has no units.

1.79 1.01 g/mL

1.81 0.974 kg

1.83 a. heptane   b. olive oil   c. water   d. water

1.85 a. 13.6   b. 0.789 g/mL

1.87 a. 0.186 g/dL   b. 1,860 mg/L

1.89 three

1.91 7.8 (or 8)

1.93 a. $0.67   b. $1.00

1.95 784.6 doses, so 784 full doses

1.97 16 tablets

1.99 1.0×10^{2} mg

1.101 2 tablets (2.4)

1.103 0.15 g

CHAPTER 2

2.1   a. Ca   b. Rn   c. N   d. Au

2.3   a. neon   c. iodine   e. boron
      b. sulfur   d. silicon   f. mercury

2.5   As, B, Si: metalloids
      Cr, Co, Cu, Fe, Mn, Mo, Ni, Zn: metals
      F, I, Se: nonmetals

2.6   a. 4 hydrogens, 1 carbon
      b. 3 hydrogens, 1 nitrogen
      c. 6 hydrogens, 2 carbons, 1 oxygen

2.7   a. 1 sodium, 1 carbon, 1 nitrogen
      b. 2 hydrogens, 1 sulfur
      c. 2 carbons, 6 hydrogens
      d. 1 tin, 2 fluorines
      e. 1 carbon, 1 oxygen
      f. 3 carbons, 8 hydrogens, 3 oxygens

2.9   a. 9   b. 9   c. fluorine

2.10

Atomic Number	Element	Protons	Electrons
a. 2	Helium	2	2
b. 11	Sodium	11	11
c. 20	Calcium	20	20
d. 47	Silver	47	47
e. 78	Platinum	78	78

2.11 a. 4 protons and 5 neutrons
      b. atomic number 4, mass number 9
      c. beryllium

2.12

	Protons	Neutrons	Electrons
a.	17	18	17
b.	14	14	14
c.	92	146	92

2.13 a. 95   b. 52

2.14

	Atomic Number	Mass Number	Protons	Neutrons	Electrons
a.	6	13	6	7	6
b.	51	121	51	70	51

2.15

	Protons	Electrons	Atomic Number	Mass Number
$^{24}_{12}$Mg	12	12	12	24
$^{25}_{12}$Mg	12	12	12	25
$^{26}_{12}$Mg	12	12	12	26

2.16 a. 24.31 amu   b. 50.94 amu

2.17

Element	Period	Group
a. Oxygen	2	6A (or 16)
b. Calcium	4	2A (or 2)
c. Phosphorus	3	5A (or 15)
d. Platinum	6	8B (or 10)
e. Iodine	5	7A (or 17)

2.19 a. titanium, Ti, group 4B (or 4), period 4, transition metal
      b. phosphorus, P, group 5A (or 15), period 3, main group element
      c. dysprosium, Dy, no group number, period 6, inner transition element

2.21 a. silicon   b. sulfur   c. scandium   d. zinc

2.23 a. magnesium

$$\uparrow\downarrow \quad \uparrow\downarrow \quad \uparrow\downarrow \; \uparrow\downarrow \; \uparrow\downarrow \quad \uparrow\downarrow$$
$$1s \qquad 2s \qquad 2p \qquad 3s$$

      b. aluminum

$$\uparrow\downarrow \quad \uparrow\downarrow \quad \uparrow\downarrow \; \uparrow\downarrow \; \uparrow\downarrow \quad \uparrow\downarrow \quad \uparrow \; \_ \; \_$$
$$1s \qquad 2s \qquad 2p \qquad 3s \qquad 3p$$

      c. bromine

$$\uparrow\downarrow \quad \uparrow\downarrow \quad \uparrow\downarrow \; \uparrow\downarrow \; \uparrow\downarrow \quad \uparrow\downarrow \quad \uparrow\downarrow \; \uparrow\downarrow \; \uparrow\downarrow$$
$$1s \qquad 2s \qquad 2p \qquad 3s \qquad 3p$$

$$\uparrow\downarrow \quad \uparrow\downarrow \; \uparrow\downarrow \; \uparrow\downarrow \; \uparrow\downarrow \; \uparrow\downarrow \quad \uparrow\downarrow \; \uparrow\downarrow \; \uparrow$$
$$4s \qquad 3d \qquad 4p$$

2.25 a. 12 electrons, 2 valence electrons, magnesium
      b. 15 electrons, 5 valence electrons, phosphorus
      c. 40 electrons, 2 valence electrons, zirconium
      d. 26 electrons, 2 valence electrons, iron

2.26 a. 7 valence electrons: $2s^2 2p^5$
      b. 8 valence electrons: $4s^2 4p^6$
      c. 2 valence electrons: $3s^2$
      d. 4 valence electrons: $4s^2 4p^2$

2.27 Se, selenium: $4s^2 4p^4$
      Te, tellurium: $5s^2 5p^4$
      Po, polonium: $6s^2 6p^4$

2.28 a. :B̈r·   b. Li·   c. Äl·   d. :S̈·   e. :N̈e:

2.29 a. neon, carbon, boron
      b. beryllium, magnesium, calcium
      c. sulfur, silicon, magnesium
      d. neon, krypton, xenon
      e. oxygen, sulfur, silicon
      f. fluorine, sulfur, aluminum

2.31 a. carbon (black), oxygen (red)
      b. carbon (black), hydrogen (gray), chlorine (green)

2.33 a. gold, astatine, silver
      b. nitrogen, sodium, nickel
      c. sulfur, silicon, tin
      d. calcium, chromium, chlorine
      e. phosphorus, lead, platinum
      f. titanium, tantalum, thallium

2.35 a, c, e: element   b, d: compound

2.37 a. cesium   d. beryllium
      b. ruthenium   e. fluorine
      c. chlorine   f. cerium

2.39 a. sodium: metal, alkali metal, main group element
      b. silver: metal, transition metal
      c. xenon: nonmetal, noble gas, main group element
      d. platinum: metal, transition metal
      e. uranium: metal, inner transition metal
      f. tellurium: metalloid, main group element

2.41 a. 5 protons and 6 neutrons   b. 5   c. 11   d. 5   e. B

2.43

	Element Symbol	Atomic Number	Mass Number	Number of Protons	Number of Neutrons	Number of Electrons
a.	C	6	12	6	6	6
b.	P	15	31	15	16	15
c.	Zn	30	65	30	35	30
d.	Mg	12	24	12	12	12
e.	I	53	127	53	74	53
f.	Be	4	9	4	5	4
g.	Zr	40	91	40	51	40
h.	S	16	32	16	16	16

2.45

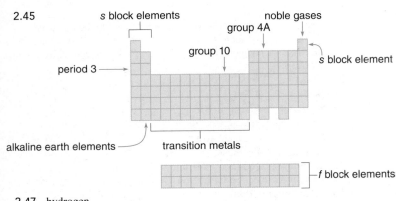

2.47 hydrogen

2.49 K, Ca, Sc, Ti, V, Cr, Mn, Fe, Co, Ni, Cu, Zn, Ga: metals
Ge, As: metalloids
Se, Br, Kr: nonmetals

2.51 8A

2.53

Mass	Protons	Neutrons	Electrons	Group	Symbol
16	8	8	8	6A	$^{16}_{8}O$
17	8	9	8	6A	$^{17}_{8}O$
18	8	10	8	6A	$^{18}_{8}O$

2.55

	Protons	Neutrons	Electrons
a.	13	14	13
b.	17	18	17
c.	16	18	16

2.57 a. $^{127}_{53}I$ b. $^{79}_{35}Br$ c. $^{107}_{47}Ag$

2.59 107.9 amu

2.61 No, two different elements must have a different number of protons and so, in the neutral atom, they must have a different number of electrons.

2.63 a. 1   b. 4   c. 9   d. 16

2.65 a. B
1s   2s   2p

b. K
1s   2s   2p   3s   3p   4s

c. Se
1s   2s   2p   3s   3p
4s   3d   4p

d. Ar
1s   2s   2p   3s   3p

e. Zn
1s   2s   2p   3s   3p
4s   3d

2.67 a. B: $1s^2 2s^2 2p^1$ [He]$2s^2 2p^1$
b. K: $1s^2 2s^2 2p^6 3s^2 3p^6 4s^1$ [Ar]$4s^1$
c. Se: $1s^2 2s^2 2p^6 3s^2 3p^6 4s^2 3d^{10} 4p^4$ [Ar]$4s^2 3d^{10} 4p^4$
d. Ar: $1s^2 2s^2 2p^6 3s^2 3p^6$ [Ar]
e. Zn: $1s^2 2s^2 2p^6 3s^2 3p^6 4s^2 3d^{10}$ [Ar]$4s^2 3d^{10}$

2.69 a. 1   b. 3   c. 1

2.71 a. 38 electrons, 2 valence electrons, strontium
b. 16 electrons, 6 valence electrons, sulfur
c. 11 electrons, 1 valence electron, sodium
d. 17 electrons, 7 valence electrons, chlorine

2.73 An alkali metal has one valence electron and an alkaline earth element has two valence electrons.

2.75

	Electrons	Group Number	Valence Electrons	Period	Valence Shell
a. Carbon	6	4A	4	2	2
b. Calcium	20	2A	2	4	4
c. Krypton	36	8A	8	4	4

2.77 a. carbon: $1s^2 2s^2 2p^2$; $2s^2 2p^2$
b. calcium: $1s^2 2s^2 2p^6 3s^2 3p^6 4s^2$; $4s^2$
c. krypton: $1s^2 2s^2 2p^6 3s^2 3p^6 4s^2 3d^{10} 4p^6$; $4s^2 4p^6$

2.79 a. 2   b. 4   c. 7

2.81 a. sulfur: 6, $3s^2 3p^4$
b. chlorine: 7, $3s^2 3p^5$
c. barium: 2, $6s^2$
d. titanium: 2, $4s^2$
e. tin: 4, $5s^2 5p^2$

2.83 a. Be·   b. ·$\overset{\cdot}{\underset{\cdot}{\text{Si}}}$·   c. ·$\overset{\cdot\cdot}{\underset{\cdot\cdot}{\text{I}}}$:   d. ·Mg·   e. :$\overset{\cdot\cdot}{\underset{\cdot\cdot}{\text{Ar}}}$:

2.85 a. iodine   b. carbon   c. potassium   d. selenium

2.87 a. bromine   b. nitrogen   c. silicon   d. chlorine

2.89 fluorine, oxygen, sulfur, silicon, magnesium

2.91 sodium, magnesium, phosphorus, nitrogen, fluorine

2.93

	a. Type	b. Block	c, d: Radius	e, f: Ionization E	g. Valence Electrons
Sodium	Metal	s			1
Potassium	Metal	s	Largest	Lowest	1
Chlorine	Nonmetal	p	Smallest	Highest	7

2.95 Carbon-11 has the same number of protons and electrons as carbon-12—that is, six. Carbon-11 has only five neutrons, whereas carbon-12 has six neutrons. The symbol for carbon-11 is $^{11}_{6}\text{C}$.

2.97 There is only one $4s$ electron.

CHAPTER 3

3.1 a, d, e, f: covalent   b, c: ionic

3.3 covalent

3.4 a. K^+ b. N^{3-} c. Br^- d. V^{2+}

3.5 a. 28 protons, 26 electrons   c. 30 protons, 28 electrons
     b. 34 protons, 36 electrons   d. 26 protons, 23 electrons

3.6 a. +2   b. −1   c. −2   d. +1

3.7 a. Ne   b. Xe   c. Kr   d. Kr

3.9 a. 25 protons, 25 electrons
     b. 25 protons, 23 electrons
     c. $1s^2 2s^2 2p^6 3s^2 3p^6 4s^2 3d^5$ The two $4s^2$ valence electrons would be lost to form Mn^{2+}.

3.11 a. NaBr   b. BaO   c. MgI_2 d. Li_2O

3.12 a.

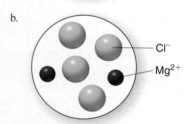

b.

3.13 ZnO

3.15 a. Sn^{4+} b. I^- c. Mn^{2+} d. Pb^{2+} e. Se^{2-}

3.16 a. sodium fluoride   d. lithium oxide
      b. magnesium oxide   e. titanium oxide
      c. strontium bromide   f. aluminum chloride

3.17 a. chromium(III) chloride, chromic chloride
      b. lead(II) sulfide
      c. tin(IV) fluoride, stannic fluoride
      d. lead(IV) oxide
      e. iron(II) bromide, ferrous bromide
      f. gold(III) chloride

3.19 iron(III) oxide, ferric oxide

3.20 a. $CaBr_2$ c. $FeBr_3$ e. $CrCl_2$
      b. CuI   d. MgS   f. Na_2O

3.21 Ionic compounds have high melting points and high boiling points. They usually dissolve in water. Their solutions conduct electricity and they form crystalline solids.

3.22 a. $MgSO_4$ c. $NiSO_4$ e. Li_2SO_4
      b. Na_2SO_4 d. $Al_2(SO_4)_3$

3.23 a. $NaHCO_3$ c. $(NH_4)_2SO_4$ e. $Ca(HSO_4)_2$
      b. KNO_3 d. $Mg_3(PO_4)_2$ f. $Ba(OH)_2$

3.25 a. sodium carbonate   d. manganese acetate
      b. calcium hydroxide   e. iron(III) hydrogen sulfite, ferric bisulfite
      c. magnesium nitrate   f. magnesium phosphate

3.27 a, b, d: covalent   c. ionic

3.29 a. ionic   b, c, d: covalent

3.31 There is a transfer of electrons from the metal to the nonmetal. A metal gains a noble gas configuration of electrons by giving up electrons. A nonmetal can gain a noble gas configuration by gaining electrons.

3.33 a. Be^{2+} c. S^{2-} e. Cl^-
      b. Ti^{2+} d. Al^{3+} f. Ca^{2+}

3.35 a. Be   b. Cl^- c. Rb^+

3.37 By gaining two electrons they have a filled valence shell.

3.39 a. Na^+ b. Se^{2-} c. Mn^{2+} d. Au^{3+} e. Sn^{4+} f. Hg_2^{2+}

3.41 a, b, c, e: Ne   d. Ar   f. He

3.43 a. lose one electron   c. gain two electrons
      b. gain one electron   d. lose two electrons

3.45 b, d: likely to form
      a, e: only seven electrons in outer shell
      c: one electron in outer shell
      f: two electrons in outer shell

3.47

	Number of Valence Electrons	Group Number	Number of Electrons Gained or Lost	Charge	Example
a.	1	1A	Lose 1	1+	Li
b.	2	2A	Lose 2	2+	Mg
c.	6	6A	Gain 2	2−	S
d.	7	7A	Gain 1	1−	Cl

3.49 a. sulfate, SO_4^{2-} b. nitrite, NO_2^- c. sulfide, S^{2-}

3.51 a. SO_4^{2-} b. NH_4^+ c. HCO_3^- d. CN^-

3.53 a. 9 protons, 10 electrons
      b. 11 protons, 10 electrons
      c. 47 protons, 50 electrons

3.55 Transition metals have one or more d electrons. All of these electrons would have to be lost to follow the octet rule, and most transition metals do not lose that many electrons.

3.57 Na donates an electron to F; then each atom has eight electrons in its outer shell.

3.59 a. CaS   b. $AlBr_3$ c. LiI   d. $NiCl_2$ e. Na_2Se

3.61 a. $LiNO_2$ c. $NaHSO_3$ e. $Mg(HSO_3)_2$
      b. $Ca(CH_3COO)_2$ d. $Mn_3(PO_4)_2$

3.63

	Y^-	Y^{2-}	Y^{3-}
X^+	XY	X_2Y	X_3Y
X^{2+}	XY_2	XY	X_3Y_2
X^{3+}	XY_3	X_2Y_3	XY

3.65

	Br^-	OH^-	HCO_3^-	SO_3^{2-}	PO_4^{3-}
Na^+	NaBr	NaOH	$NaHCO_3$	Na_2SO_3	Na_3PO_4
Co^{2+}	$CoBr_2$	$Co(OH)_2$	$Co(HCO_3)_2$	$CoSO_3$	$Co_3(PO_4)_2$
Al^{3+}	$AlBr_3$	$Al(OH)_3$	$Al(HCO_3)_3$	$Al_2(SO_3)_3$	$AlPO_4$

3.67 a. $KHSO_4$ c. $Al(HSO_4)_3$
     b. $Ba(HSO_4)_2$ d. $Zn(HSO_4)_2$

3.69 a. $Ba(CN)_2$ c. $BaHPO_4$
     b. $Ba_3(PO_4)_2$ d. $Ba(H_2PO_4)_2$

3.71 a. sodium oxide   e. cobalt(II) bromide
     b. barium sulfide   f. rubidium bromide
     c. lead(IV) sulfide   g. lead(II) bromide
     d. silver chloride

3.73 a. iron(II) chloride, ferrous chloride
     b. iron(III) bromide, ferric bromide
     c. iron(II) sulfide, ferrous sulfide
     d. iron(III) sulfide, ferric sulfide

3.75 Copper cations can be 1+ or 2+, so the Roman numeral designation is required. Ca only exists as 2+.
     $CuBr_2$: copper(II) bromide or cupric bromide
     $CaBr_2$: calcium bromide

3.77 a. Na_2S Na_2SO_4
     b. MgO $Mg(OH)_2$
     c. $MgSO_4$ $Mg(HSO_4)_2$

3.79 a. ammonium chloride
     b. lead(II) sulfate
     c. copper(II) nitrate, cupric nitrate
     d. calcium bicarbonate, calcium hydrogen carbonate
     e. iron(II) nitrate, ferrous nitrate

3.81 a. $MgCO_3$ e. $Au(NO_3)_3$
     b. $NiSO_4$ f. Li_3PO_4
     c. $Cu(OH)_2$ g. $Al(HCO_3)_3$
     d. K_2HPO_4 h. $Cr(CN)_2$

3.83 a. $Pb(OH)_4$ lead(IV) hydroxide
     b. $Pb(SO_4)_2$ lead(IV) sulfate
     c. $Pb(HCO_3)_4$ lead(IV) bicarbonate
     d. $Pb(NO_3)_4$ lead(IV) nitrate
     e. $Pb_3(PO_4)_4$ lead(IV) phosphate
     f. $Pb(CH_3CO_2)_4$ lead(IV) acetate

3.85 a. True.
     b. False—ionic compounds are solids at room temperature.
     c. False—most ionic compounds are soluble in water.
     d. False—ionic solids exist as crystalline lattices with the ions arranged to maximize the electrostatic interactions of anions and cations.

3.87 NaCl

3.89 a. 30 protons, 30 electrons
     b. 30 protons, 28 electrons
     c. $1s^2 2s^2 2p^6 3s^2 3p^6 4s^2 3d^{10}$ The $4s^2$ electrons are lost to form Zn^{2+}.

3.91

Cation	a. Number of Protons	b. Number of Electrons	c. Noble Gas	d. Role
Na^+	11	10	Ne	Major cation in extracellular fluids and blood; maintains blood volume and blood pressure
K^+	19	18	Ar	Major intracellular cation
Ca^{2+}	20	18	Ar	Major cation in solid tissues like bone and teeth; required for normal muscle contraction and nerve function
Mg^{2+}	12	10	Ne	Required for normal muscle contraction and nerve function

3.93 $AgNO_3$
3.95 calcium sulfite
3.97 NH_4NO_3
3.99 a. MgO, KI
     b. calcium hydrogen phosphate
     c. iron(III) phosphate, ferric phosphate
     d. Na_2SeO_3
     e. The name chromium chloride is ambiguous. Without a designation as chromium(II) or chromium(III), one does not know the ratio of chromium cations to chloride anions.

CHAPTER 4

4.1 $H\cdot + \cdot \ddot{\underset{\cdot\cdot}{Cl}}: \longrightarrow H:\ddot{\underset{\cdot\cdot}{Cl}}:$

     H is surrounded by two electrons, giving it the noble gas configuration of He. Cl is surrounded by eight valence electrons, giving it the noble gas configuration of Ar.

4.3 a. 1   b. 4   c. 1   d. 2   e. 3   f. 2

4.5 Ionic bonding is observed in CaO since Ca is a metal and readily transfers electrons to a nonmetal. Covalent bonding is observed in CO_2 since carbon is a nonmetal and does not readily transfer electrons.

4.6

4.7

4.8

4.9

4.11

     Boron has only six electrons around it, so it does not follow the octet rule.

4.13 a. [Lewis structure] b. [Lewis structure]

4.15 :Ö—S̈=Ö: ⟷ Ö=S̈—Ö:

4.17 a. carbon disulfide c. phosphorus pentachloride
b. sulfur dioxide d. boron trifluoride

4.18 a. SiO_2 b. PCl_3 c. SO_3 d. N_2O_3

4.19 trigonal planar

4.21 [H—N̈—H]⁻ The ion has a bent geometry (b), because the N is surrounded by four groups.

4.23 a. polar c. nonpolar e. polar
b. ionic d. polar f. polar

4.25 a. $\overset{\delta^+}{H}$—$\overset{\delta^-}{Cl}$ →, polar
c. [Lewis structure] polar
e. [Lewis structure] nonpolar
b. [Lewis structure] nonpolar
d. H—C≡N $\overset{\delta^+\ \ \delta^-}{}$ → polar

4.26 a. [Lewis structure] polar C–O, O–H, All C's are tetrahedral.
b. [Lewis structure] trigonal planar, tetrahedral

4.27 a. LiCl: ionic; the metal Li donates electrons to chlorine.
HCl: covalent; H and Cl share electrons since both are nonmetals and the electronegativity difference is not large enough for electron transfer to occur.
b. KBr: ionic; the metal K donates electrons to bromine.
HBr: covalent; H and Br share electrons since the electronegativity difference is not large enough for electron transfer to occur.

4.29 a. 4 bonds, 0 lone pairs c. 1 bond, 3 lone pairs
b. 2 bonds, 2 lone pairs d. 3 bonds, 1 lone pair

4.31 a. [Lewis structure] b. [Lewis structure]

4.33 [Lewis structure] H—Ö—C—C—Ö—H

4.35 a. H—Ï: c. H—S̈e—H e. [Lewis structure]
b. [Lewis structure] d. C≡Ö

4.37 a. [Lewis structure] b. H—Ö—N̈=Ö c. [Lewis structure]

4.39 [Lewis structure]

4.41 a. [H—Ö:]⁻ b. [Lewis structure]⁺

4.43 a. :Cl̈—B—Cl̈: b. [Lewis structure]

4.45 A resonance structure is one representation of an electron arrangement with a given placement of atoms. A resonance hybrid is a composite of two or more resonance structures.

4.47 [Lewis structure]⁻

4.49 a. resonance structures b. not resonance structures

4.51 [Lewis structure]²⁻ ⟷ [Lewis structure]²⁻ ⟷ [Lewis structure]²⁻

4.53 a. phosphorus tribromide c. nitrogen trichloride
b. sulfur trioxide d. diphosphorus pentasulfide

4.55 a. SeO_2 b. CCl_4 c. N_2O_5

4.57 water

4.59 a. [Lewis structure] tetrahedral, bent
c. [Lewis structure] tetrahedral, trigonal planar
b. N̈F₃ trigonal pyramid

4.61 a. H—N̈—Ö—H trigonal pyramid, bent
c. [Lewis structure]⁺ tetrahedral
b. [Lewis structure] tetrahedral, trigonal planar

4.63 a. [1] A linear geometry means two groups, so no lone pairs. [2] $BeCl_2$
b. [1] A bent geometry generally means four groups, so two lone pairs. [2] H_2O

4.65 BCl_3 is trigonal planar because it has three chlorines bonded to B but no lone pairs. NCl_3 is trigonal pyramidal because it has three Cl's around N as well as a lone pair.

4.67 a. [Lewis structure] both 109.5°
b. H—C≡C—C—Ö—H 180°, 109.5°, 109.5°
c. H—C=C=Ö 120° 180°, 120°

4.69 $:\overset{..}{\underset{..}{Cl}}-\overset{\overset{..}{\underset{..}{Cl}}}{\underset{\overset{..}{\underset{..}{Cl}}}{C}}-\overset{..}{\underset{..}{Cl}}:$ $\overset{:\overset{..}{Cl}:}{\underset{:\overset{..}{Cl}:}{C}}=\overset{:\overset{..}{Cl}:}{\underset{:\overset{..}{Cl}:}{C}}$

CCl_4 is tetrahedral since carbon has four substituents. Each C in C_2Cl_4 has trigonal planar geometry since each carbon has three substituents.

4.71 a. Se, S, O   b. Na, P, Cl   c. S, Cl, F   d. P, N, O

4.73 a, b, c: covalent   d. ionic

4.75 a. nonpolar   b. polar   c. polar   d. polar   e. nonpolar

4.77 a. C—O   b. C—F   c. Si—C

4.79 $\overset{\delta^+ \; \delta^-}{C-O}$ $\overset{\delta^+ \; \delta^-}{C-N}$ $\overset{\delta^+ \; \delta^-}{C-F}$ $\overset{\delta^+ \; \delta^-}{C-Cl}$ $\overset{\delta^+ \; \delta^-}{Si-C}$ $P-H$

$\longmapsto$ $\longmapsto$ $\longmapsto$ $\longmapsto$ $\longmapsto$ no dipole

4.81 In CH_3NH_2 carbon bears a partial positive charge since nitrogen is more electronegative than carbon. In CH_3MgBr carbon bears a partial negative charge since carbon is more electronegative than magnesium.

4.83 No, a compound with only one polar bond must be polar. The single bond dipole is not cancelled by another bond dipole.

4.85 a.

$\overset{H}{\underset{H}{}}C=C\overset{Cl}{\underset{H}{}}$

polar bond, polar compound

b.

$\overset{Cl}{\underset{Cl}{}}C=C\overset{Cl}{\underset{Cl}{}}$

polar bonds, nonpolar compound

c.

$H-\overset{H}{\underset{H}{C}}-C\overset{O}{\underset{Cl}{}}$

polar bonds, polar compound

4.87 $CHCl_3$ has a net dipole, making it polar. CCl_4 has four polar bonds but no net dipole because the four bonds have dipoles that cancel one another.

4.89 a. 20 valence electrons

b, c: $:\overset{..}{\underset{..}{Cl}}\overset{\overset{..}{O}}{}\overset{..}{\underset{..}{Cl}}:$

d. bent

e. The compound is polar since the two bond dipoles do not cancel.

4.91 a.–c.

trigonal pyramid ⟷   bent

$H-\overset{\overset{|}{N}}{\underset{\overset{|}{H}}{|}}-\overset{\overset{:\overset{..}{O}:}{|}}{\underset{H}{C}}-\overset{..}{\underset{..}{O}}-H$

tetrahedral ⟷   trigonal planar

d. Glycine is a polar molecule since the many bond dipoles do not cancel.

4.93 One possibility:

(structural formula of an indole-containing molecule with OH, CH₂, CH₂, NH₂ substituents)

4.95 a. The predicted shape around each carbon is tetrahedral.
b. 60°
c. The 60° bond angle deviates greatly from the theoretical tetrahedral bond angle, making the molecule unstable.

CHAPTER 5

5.1 The process is a chemical reaction because the reactants contain two gray spheres joined (indicating H_2) and two red spheres joined (indicating O_2), while the product (H_2O) contains a red sphere joined to two gray spheres (indicating O–H bonds).

5.3

reactants   products

a. $2 H_2O_2(aq) \longrightarrow 2 H_2O(l) + O_2(g)$ (4 H, 4 O)

b. $2 C_8H_{18} + 25 O_2 \longrightarrow 16 CO_2 + 18 H_2O$
(16 C, 50 O, 36 H)

c. $2 Na_3PO_4(aq) + 3 MgCl_2(aq) \longrightarrow Mg_3(PO_4)_2(s)$
$+ 6 NaCl(aq)$ (3 Mg, 2 P, 8 O, 6 Na, 6 Cl)

5.5 $CH_4(g) + 4 Cl_2(g) \overset{\Delta}{\longrightarrow} CCl_4(l) + 4 HCl(g)$

5.6 a. $2 H_2 + O_2 \longrightarrow 2 H_2O$
b. $2 NO + O_2 \longrightarrow 2 NO_2$
c. $CH_4 + 2 Cl_2 \longrightarrow CH_2Cl_2 + 2 HCl$

5.7 $2 CO + O_2 \longrightarrow 2 CO_2$

5.8 $2 C_2H_6 + 7 O_2 \longrightarrow 4 CO_2 + 6 H_2O$

5.9 $N_2 + 3 H_2 \longrightarrow 2 NH_3$

5.10 a. $2 Al + 3 H_2SO_4 \longrightarrow Al_2(SO_4)_3 + 3 H_2$
b. $3 Na_2SO_3 + 2 H_3PO_4 \longrightarrow 3 H_2SO_3 + 2 Na_3PO_4$

5.11 a, b, c, d: 6.02×10^{23}

5.12 a. 1.20×10^{24} C atoms   c. 3.01×10^{23} C atoms
b. 3.61×10^{24} C atoms   d. 1.51×10^{25} C atoms

5.13 a. 1.5×10^{24} molecules   c. 2.4×10^{23} molecules
b. 1.5×10^{23} molecules   d. 3.33×10^{25} molecules

5.14 a. 100. mol   b. 0.0500 mol   c. 15 mol

5.15 a. 100.09 amu   b. 166.0 amu

5.17 424.4 g/mol

5.18 a. 29.2 g   b. 332 g   c. 101 g   d. 26.3 g

5.19 a. 1.71 mol   c. 1.39×10^{-3} mol
b. 1.59 mol   d. 1.39 mol

5.20 1.80×10^{21} molecules

5.21 a. 6.6 mol   b. 1.0 mol   c. 1.2 mol

5.23 a. 51 g   b. 22 g   c. 90. g

5.25 a. 72.4 g   b. 24.1 g   c. 7.24 g

5.27 a. 154 g   b. 34.7%

5.29 a. 111 g   b. 59.0%

5.31 a. 35%   b. 11%   c. 19%   d. 1.0%

5.32 H_2 is the limiting reactant.

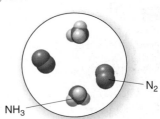

5.33 a, b, d: H_2 c. O_2

5.34 a. 1.0 mol   b. 0.67 mol   c. 1.3 mol   d. 4.0 mol

5.35 a. N_2 b. O_2

5.36 a. 26.8 g   b. 24.4 g

5.37 11.3 g

5.38 (oxidized) (reduced)

a. $Zn(s) + 2 H^+(aq) \longrightarrow Zn^{2+}(aq) + H_2(g)$

$Zn \longrightarrow Zn^{2+} + 2 e^-$

$2 H^+ + 2 e^- \longrightarrow H_2$

(reduced) (oxidized)

b. $Fe^{3+}(aq) + Al(s) \longrightarrow Al^{3+}(aq) + Fe(s)$

$Al \longrightarrow Al^{3+} + 3 e^-$

$Fe^{3+} + 3 e^- \longrightarrow Fe$

(oxidized) (reduced)

c. $2 I^- + Br_2 \longrightarrow I_2 + 2 Br^-$

$2 I^- \longrightarrow I_2 + 2 e^-$

$Br_2 + 2 e^- \longrightarrow 2 Br^-$

d. $2 AgBr \longrightarrow 2 Ag + Br_2$

$2 Br^-$ (oxidized) $2 Ag^+$ (reduced)

$2 Br^- \longrightarrow Br_2 + 2 e^-$

$2 Ag^+ + 2 e^- \longrightarrow 2 Ag$

5.39 a. Zn reducing agent, H^+ oxidizing agent

b. Fe^{3+} oxidizing agent, Al reducing agent

c. I^- reducing agent, Br_2 oxidizing agent

d. Br^- reducing agent, Ag^+ oxidizing agent

5.41 H_2 is oxidized since it gains an O atom and $C_2H_4O_2$ is reduced since it gains hydrogen.

5.43 $2 CO + 2 O_3 \longrightarrow 2 CO_2 + 2 O_2$ (not balanced)

5.45 The coefficient indicates the number of molecules or moles undergoing reaction, whereas the subscript indicates the number of atoms of each element in a chemical formula.

5.47 a. 2 H, 2 Cl, 1 Ca on both sides; therefore balanced

b. 1 Ti, 4 Cl, 4 H, 2 O on left side, and 1 Ti, 1 Cl, 1 H, 2 O on right side; therefore NOT balanced

c. 1 Al, 1 P, 7 O, 6 H on both sides; therefore balanced

5.49 $H_2 + Cl_2 \longrightarrow 2 HCl$

5.51 a. $Ni(s) + 2 HCl(aq) \longrightarrow NiCl_2(aq) + H_2(g)$

b. $CH_4(g) + 4 Cl_2(g) \longrightarrow CCl_4(g) + 4 HCl(g)$

c. $2 KClO_3 \longrightarrow 2 KCl + 3 O_2$

d. $Al_2O_3 + 6 HCl \longrightarrow 2 AlCl_3 + 3 H_2O$

e. $2 Al(OH)_3 + 3 H_2SO_4 \longrightarrow Al_2(SO_4)_3 + 6 H_2O$

5.53 a. $2 C_6H_6 + 15 O_2 \longrightarrow 12 CO_2 + 6 H_2O$

b. $C_7H_8 + 9 O_2 \longrightarrow 7 CO_2 + 4 H_2O$

c. $2 C_8H_{18} + 25 O_2 \longrightarrow 16 CO_2 + 18 H_2O$

5.55 $2 S(s) + 3 O_2(g) + 2 H_2O(l) \longrightarrow 2 H_2SO_4(l)$

5.57

5.59 a. 69.00 amu, 69.00 g/mol

b. 342.2 amu, 342.2 g/mol

c. 176.12 amu, 176.12 g/mol

5.61 a. $C_9H_{11}NO_4$ b. 197.2 amu   c. 197.2 g/mol

5.63 a. 1 mol Sn

b. 6.02×10^{23} N atoms

c. 1 mol N_2 molecules

d. 1 mol CO_2

5.65 a. 182 g   b. 710. g   c. 130. g   d. 390. g

5.67 a. 1.46×10^{-3} mol   c. 0.0730 mol

b. 0.0146 mol   d. 7.30×10^{-5} mol

5.69 a. 1.20×10^{24} c. 1.60×10^{25} e. 3.01×10^{29}

b. 1.51×10^{23} d. 1.34×10^{26}

5.71 a. 324 g   b. 52.2 g   c. 1.1×10^3 g   d. 9.82 g

5.73 a. 12.5 mol   b. 12 mol   c. 0.50 mol   d. 0.40 mol

5.75 a. 220 g   b. 44 g   c. 4.5 g   d. 240 g

5.77 75%

5.79 a. 23.9 g   b. 62.8%

5.81 a. **B** limiting reactant   **A** in excess

b. **A** limiting reactant   **B** in excess

c. **B** limiting reactant   **A** in excess

5.83 a. NO   b. O_2 c. NO   d. NO

5.85 a. 1.0 mol, 46 g   c. 0.333 mol, 15.3 g

b. 1.0 mol, 46 g   d. 0.933 mol, 42.9 g

5.87 a. 0.285 mol ethylene and 0.329 mol HCl

b. ethylene

c. 0.285 mol

d. 18.4 g

e. 57.6%

5.89 A substance that is oxidized loses electrons. A substance that gains electrons acts as an oxidizing agent.

5.91 a. Fe (oxidized) Cu^{2+} (reduced)

$Fe \longrightarrow Fe^{2+} + 2 e^-$

$Cu^{2+} + 2 e^- \longrightarrow Cu$

b. Cl_2 (reduced) $2 I^-$ (oxidized)

$2 I^- \longrightarrow I_2 + 2 e^-$

$Cl_2 + 2 e^- \longrightarrow 2 Cl^-$

c. 2 Na (oxidized) Cl_2 (reduced)

$2 Na \longrightarrow 2 Na^+ + 2 e^-$

$Cl_2 + 2 e^- \longrightarrow 2 Cl^-$

5.93   Zn Ag^+

oxidized   reduced

reducing agent   oxidizing agent

5.95 Acetylene is reduced because it gains hydrogen atoms.

5.97 $2 Mg + O_2 \longrightarrow 2 MgO$

$2 Mg \longrightarrow 2 Mg^{2+} + 4 e^-$ $O_2 + 4 e^- \longrightarrow 2 O^{2-}$

5.99 a. 342.3 g/mol

b. $C_{12}H_{22}O_{11}(s) + H_2O(l) \longrightarrow 4 C_2H_6O(l) + 4 CO_2(g)$

c. 8 mol   e. 101 g   g. 9.21 g

d. 10 mol   f. 18.4 g   h. 13.6%

5.101 a. 0.485 mol   b. 2.92×10^{23}

5.103 a. 2.38×10^{-4} mol   b. 1.43×10^{20} molecules

5.105 6.3×10^{22} ions

5.107 a. 354.5 g/mol   b. 18 g   c. 17.8 g   d. 84.3%

5.109 a. 2.1×10^{-3} g   b. 3.9×10^{18} molecules

CHAPTER 6

6.1 a. 10. cal   b. 55,600 cal   c. 1,360 kJ   d. 107,000 J

6.3 126 Cal, rounded to 100 Cal

6.5 a. +88 kcal/mol; endothermic

b. −136 kcal/mol; exothermic

c. +119 kcal/mol; endothermic

6.6 The indicated bond has the higher bond dissociation energy, making it the stronger bond.

a. $H-\overset{\overset{H}{|}}{\underset{\underset{H}{|}}{C}}-\ddot{\ddot{Br}}:$ b. $H-OH$

6.7 a. absorbed   c. reactants

b. reactants   d. endothermic

6.8 106 kcal

6.9 a. 96 kcal   b. 8.0 kcal   c. 1.8 kcal

6.10

Energy (y-axis) vs Reaction coordinate (x-axis). Curve showing transition state at peak with E_a indicated, reactants at lower level, products at higher level, $\Delta H = +20$ kcal/mol.

6.11

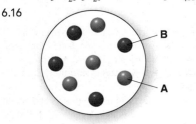

6.13 Yes, H_2SO_4 is a catalyst because it speeds up the rate of the reaction. It does not affect the relative energies of reactants and products.

6.15 a. $\dfrac{[PCl_5]}{[PCl_3][Cl_2]}$ c. $\dfrac{[HBr]^2}{[Br_2][H_2]}$

     b. $\dfrac{[SO_3]^2}{[SO_2]^2[O_2]}$ d. $\dfrac{[HCl]^3[CHCl_3]}{[CH_4][Cl_2]^3}$

6.16

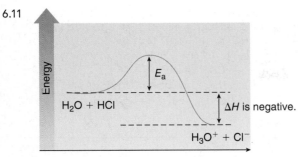

6.17 a. reactants favored   c. products favored
     b. products favored   d. reactants and products present

6.19 a. $\dfrac{[H_2S]^2}{[H_2]^2[S_2]}$

     b. products favored
     c. ΔH negative
     d. products lower in energy
     e. One cannot predict the rate of reaction without knowing the energy of activation.

6.20 a. 4.75   b. 218
6.21 a, d: right   b, c: left
6.22 a. right   b. left
6.23 a. left   b. right
6.24 a. right   b. left
6.25 Potential energy is stored energy, while kinetic energy is the energy of motion. A stationary object on a hill has potential energy, but as it moves down the hill this potential energy is converted to kinetic energy.
6.27 a. 563,000 cal/h   c. 2.36×10^6 J/h
     b. 563 kcal/h   d. 2,360 kJ/h
6.29 a. 0.05 kcal   b. 0.23 kJ   c. 230 cal   d. 1.01×10^6 cal
6.31 236 Calories, rounded to 200 Calories
6.33 30 g
6.35 salmon, 113 Calories vs. chicken, 107 Calories
6.37 When energy is absorbed, the reaction is endothermic and ΔH is positive (+). When energy is released, the reaction is exothermic and ΔH is negative (−).
6.39 a. Cl_2 b. Cl_2 c. HF
6.41 a, d: exothermic   b, c: endothermic
6.43 a. 240 kcal   b. 280 kcal   c. 2.0×10^2 kcal
6.45 a. stronger bonds in products   c. 339 kcal
     b. 2,710 kcal   d. 37.6 kcal

6.47 The transition state is the unstable intermediate located at the top of the energy hill that separates reactants from products. The difference in energy between the reactants and the transition state is the energy of activation, symbolized by E_a.
6.49 a. X   b. Z   c. Y   d. X,Y   e. X,Z   f. Y   g. Z
6.51 a.

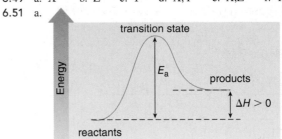

     b.

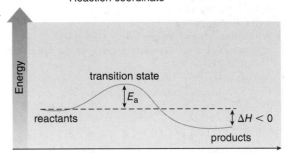

     c.

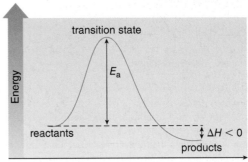

6.53 The reaction is exothermic.

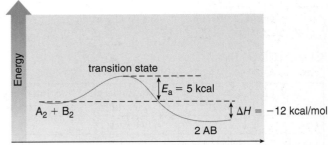

6.55 Reacting molecules must have the proper orientation for new bonds to form.
6.57 Increasing temperature increases the number of collisions. Since the average kinetic energy of the colliding molecules is larger, more collisions are effective at causing reaction.
6.59 a. The reaction with $E_a = 1$ kcal will proceed faster because the energy of activation is lower.
     b. K doesn't affect the reaction rate, so we cannot predict which reaction is faster.
     c. One cannot predict which reaction will proceed faster from the ΔH.

6.61 b. and c.

6.63 A catalyst increases the reaction rate (a) and lowers the E_a (c). It has no effect on ΔH (b), K (d), or the relative energies of the reactants and products (e).

6.65 The forward reaction proceeds from left to right as drawn and the reverse reaction proceeds from right to left as drawn.

6.67 a, b: products favored   c, d: reactants favored

6.69 $K > 1$ is associated with a negative value of ΔH. A $K < 1$ means ΔH has a positive value.

6.71 a. [1]   b. [3]   c. [2]

6.73 a. $\dfrac{[NO_2]^2}{[NO]^2[O_2]}$ b. $\dfrac{[HBr]^2[CH_2Br_2]}{[CH_4][Br_2]^2}$

6.75 a. $2\,A \rightleftharpoons A_2$ b. $A_2 + 3\,B_2 \rightleftharpoons 2\,AB_3$

6.77 a. $\dfrac{[Br_2][H_2]}{[HBr]^2}$

    b. reactants favored

    c. ΔH positive

    d. reactants lower in energy

    e. You can't predict the reaction rate from the value of K.

6.79 a. $\dfrac{[CO_2][H_2]}{[CO][H_2O]}$ b. $K = 4.2$

6.81 a. increases NO and O_2, decreases N_2

    b. increases N_2, NO, and O_2

6.83 a, f: favor shift to right

    b, c, d: favor shift to left

    e. no change

6.85 a, c, f: favor shift to right

    b, d, e: favor shift to left

6.87 a. $\dfrac{[C_2H_6]}{[H_2][C_2H_4]}$

    b. reactants higher in energy

    c. $K > 1$

    d. 20. kcal

    e. increase in rate

    f. 1, 2, 4: favor shift to right; 3: favors shift to left; 5: no change, but reduces rate of reaction

6.89 Lactase is an enzyme that converts lactose, a naturally occurring sugar in dairy products, into the two simple sugars, glucose and galactose.

6.91 400 Calories

6.93 1.9 h, rounded to 2 h

6.95 propane 12.0 kcal/g   butane 11.8 kcal/g

6.97 30,200 kcal

CHAPTER 7

7.1

	a. Density	b. Intermolecular Spacing	c. Intermolecular Attraction
Gas	Lowest	Greatest	Lowest
Liquid	Higher	Smaller	Higher
Solid	Highest	Smallest	Highest

7.2 a. 0.83 atm   b. 12 psi

7.3 a. 2,300 mm Hg   b. 14 psi   c. 0.558 atm

7.5 a. 1.6 L   b. 3.2 L   c. 0.80 L   d. 16 L

7.7 0.44 L

7.9 392 K or 119 °C

7.11 As a sealed container is heated, the gases inside expand and increase the container's internal pressure, eventually popping the lid off.

7.12 290 mm Hg

7.13 a. 1.8 L   b. 2.6 L   c. 15 L

7.14 a. 1.0×10^2 L   b. 7.8 L   c. 12.6 L

7.15 a. 0.067 mol   b. 0.38 mol   c. 1.1×10^{-3} mol

7.16 36 mol

7.17 a. 1.1 atm   b. 1.7 atm

7.18 O_2: 2.5 atm CO_2: 1.5 atm

7.19 methane: 640 mm Hg   ethane: 75 mm Hg
propane: 38 mm Hg

7.21 all: a–d

7.23

	London Dispersion	Dipole–Dipole	Hydrogen Bonding
a. Cl_2	+		
b. HCN	+	+	
c. HF	+	+	+
d. CH_3Cl	+	+	
e. H_2	+		

7.25 For both boiling point and melting point:
    a. C_2H_6 b. CH_3OH c. HBr   d. CH_3Br

7.27 a. CH_4 b. CH_4 c. C_2H_6

7.29 Benzene cannot hydrogen bond, whereas water can, so benzene has much weaker intermolecular forces than water and is thus less viscous. Ethylene glycol, on the other hand, has two OH groups capable of hydrogen bonding, so it has stronger intermolecular forces than water and is thus more viscous.

7.31 a. ionic   b. metallic   c. molecular   d. molecular

7.32 a. 3,990 cal   b. 2,790 cal   c. 2.79 kcal   d. 1,430 cal

7.33 a. 23,000 cal   b. 23,000 cal   c. 9.7 kcal   d. 34 kcal

7.34 exothermic

7.35 a. heating curve   c. 77 °C   e. liquid
    b. 40 °C   d. solid and liquid

7.37 1.071 atm

7.39 a. 41 psi   b. 0.68 atm   c. 15,200 torr   d. 13,300 Pa

7.41 a. increases   b. decreases   c. increases

7.43 a, b, c: Volume increases.

7.45 a. Volume increases as outside atmospheric pressure decreases.
    b. Volume decreases at the lower temperature.
    c. Volume decreases as external pressure increases.
    d. Volume increases as temperature increases.

7.47 a. 0.75 L   b. 1.1 L   c. 99.7 mm Hg

7.49 35 mL

7.51 a. 4.0 L   b. 1.1 L   c. 820 K

7.53 1.4 L

7.55 a. 4.34 atm   b. 350 mm Hg   c. 1,300 K

7.57 1.1 atm

7.59 a. 1.4 atm   b. 110 L   c. 740 K

7.61 1,200 L

7.63 STP is "standard temperature and pressure," or 0 °C at 760 mm Hg. The standard molar volume is the volume that one mole of a gas occupies at STP, or 22.4 liters.

7.65 a. 0.22 mol   b. 0.500 mol   c. 0.002 23 mol

7.67 a. 94 L   b. 1.8 L   c. 1.7 L

7.69 0.017 mol

7.71 0.19 mol or 1.1×10^{23} molecules

7.73 O_2 has more moles and more mass.

7.75 **A:** 210 mm Hg   **B:** 420 mm Hg

7.77 97 mm Hg for O_2 360 mm Hg for N_2

7.79 1,780 mm Hg

7.81 Water is capable of hydrogen bonding and these strong intermolecular attractive forces give it a higher boiling point than H_2S.

7.83 a. London forces, dipole–dipole   b. London forces only

7.85 d.

7.87 No, $H_2C{=}O$ has no H on the O atom.

7.89 a. Ethylene has London forces only, whereas methanol has London forces, dipole–dipole forces, and hydrogen bonding.
b. Methanol has a higher boiling point.
c. Ethylene has a higher vapor pressure at any given temperature.

7.91 butane, acetaldehyde, Freon-113

7.93 Glycerol is more viscous than water since it has three OH groups and has many opportunities for hydrogen bonding. Acetone cannot hydrogen bond so its intermolecular forces are weaker and thus it has low viscosity.

7.95 a. ionic   c. metallic   e. amorphous
b. molecular   d. network

7.97 Evaporation is an endothermic process by which a liquid enters the gas phase. Condensation is an exothermic process that occurs when a gas enters the liquid phase.

7.99 vaporization; energy absorbed

7.101 a, d: absorbed   b, c: released

7.103 Vaporizing 50.0 g of water takes more energy; 27,000 cal vs. 20,000 cal.

7.105 a. [1] **W $\longrightarrow$ X; [2] Y $\longrightarrow$ Z**   b. 10 °C   c. 85 °C

7.107

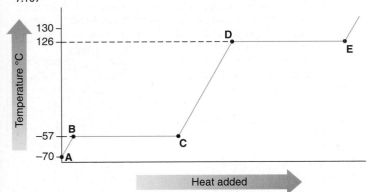

7.109 290 mL
The gases inside the bag had a volume of 250 mL at 760 mm Hg and take up a greater volume at the reduced pressure of 650 mm Hg.

7.111 Water is one of the few substances that expands as it enters the solid phase. This causes the bottle to crack as the water occupies a larger volume as it freezes.

7.113 a. As a person breathes faster, he eliminates more CO_2 from the lungs; therefore, the measured value of CO_2 is lower than the normal value of 40 mm Hg.
b. Many people with advanced lung disease have lost lung tissue over time and therefore cannot exchange adequate amounts of oxygen through the lungs and into the blood, leading to a lower-than-normal partial pressure of oxygen. In addition, they often breathe more slowly and with lower volumes than normal, so they cannot eliminate enough CO_2 and therefore the partial pressure of CO_2 climbs.

7.115 The molar mass is 4 g/mol and the gas is helium.

CHAPTER 8

8.1 a. heterogeneous mixture   b. colloid   c, d, e: solution

8.3 a, c, d, e: water soluble

8.5 a, c, e, f: water soluble   b, d: water insoluble

8.7 A soft drink becomes "flat" when CO_2 escapes from the solution. CO_2 comes out of solution faster at room temperature than at the cooler temperature of the refrigerator because the solubility of gases in liquids decreases as the temperature increases.

8.9 3.5%

8.11 8.4% (v/v)

8.12 2.4 mL

8.13 2.0×10^2 mL

8.15 a. 0.030 ppm   b. 0.5 ppm   c. 2.0 ppm   d. 0.23 ppm

8.16 a. 2.0 M   c. 10. M   e. 1.2 M
b. 8.0 M   d. 0.10 M   f. 1.4 M

8.17 10.0 g NaOH in 150 mL gives a concentration of 1.7 M vs. only 1.5 M for 15.0 g in 250 mL.

8.18 a. 1.0×10^2 mL   c. 2.0 mL
b. 13 mL   d. 2.0×10^3 mL

8.19 a. 4.0 moles   c. 0.050 moles
b. 0.63 moles   d. 0.063 moles

8.20 a. 7.3 g   b. 150 g   c. 40. g   d. 3.7 g

8.21 a. 5.8 mL   b. 23 mL   c. 15 mL   d. 0.58 mL

8.22 0.35 M

8.23 a. 220 mL   b. 5.0×10^2 mL   c. 7.5 mL   d. 15 mL

8.25 a. 101.0 °C   b. 102.0 °C   c. 103.1 °C   d. 100.4 °C

8.26 a. –3.7 °C   b. –7.4 °C   c. –11 °C   d. –1.27 °C

8.27 –7.4 °C

8.28 a. 5.0% sugar solution   b. 4.0 M NaCl   c. 0.75 M NaCl

8.29 a. Water flows across the membrane.
b. More water initially flows from the 1.0 M side to the more concentrated 1.5 M side. When equilibrium is reached there is equal flow of water in both directions.
c. The height of the 1.5 M side will be higher and the height of the 1.0 M NaCl will be lower.

8.31 **A.** The K^+ and I^- ions are separated when KI is dissolved in water. The solution contains ions so it conducts an electric current.

8.33 a, b, d, e: solution   c. heterogeneous mixture   f. colloid

8.35 a. unsaturated   b, c: saturated   d. supersaturated

8.37 a, c, d

8.39

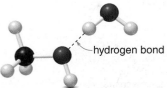

hydrogen bond

8.41 Water-soluble compounds are ionic or are small polar molecules that can hydrogen bond with the water solvent, but nonpolar compounds, such as oil, are soluble in nonpolar solvents.

8.43 Iodine would not be soluble in water but is soluble in CCl_4 since I_2 is nonpolar and CCl_4 is a nonpolar solvent.

8.45 Cholesterol is not water soluble because it is a large nonpolar molecule with a single OH group.

8.47 a.   b.

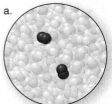 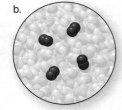

8.49 a. increased   b. decreased   c, d: no change

8.51 A decrease in temperature (a) increases the solubility of a gas and (b) decreases the solubility of a solid.

8.53 The ion–dipole interactions between ions and water provide the energy needed to break apart the ions from the crystal lattice. The water molecules form a loose shell of solvent around each ion.

8.55 a, b, d, e, g: water soluble

8.57 5% (w/v) $\dfrac{5\text{ g}}{100\text{ mL}}$ $\dfrac{100\text{ mL}}{5\text{ g}}$

 6.0 M $\dfrac{6.0\text{ mol}}{1.0\text{ L}}$ $\dfrac{1.0\text{ L}}{6.0\text{ mol}}$

 10 ppm $\dfrac{10\text{ g}}{10^6\text{ g}}$ $\dfrac{10^6\text{ g}}{10\text{ g}}$

8.59 a. 1.3% (w/v)   b. 17% (w/v)   c. 8.00% (w/v)

8.61 17% (v/v)

8.63 a. 2.3 M   b. 0.51 M   c. 0.66 M   d. 0.036 M

8.65 a. Add 12 g of acetic acid to the flask and then water to bring the volume to 250 mL.
 b. Add 55 mL of ethyl acetate to the flask and then water to bring the volume to 250 mL.
 c. Add 37 g of NaCl to the flask and then water to bring the volume to 250 mL.

8.67 a. 0.038 mol   b. 0.090 mol   c. 3.8 mol

8.69 a. 3.2 g   b. 5.7 g   c. 140 g

8.71 83 mL

8.73 a. 95 g   b. 1.6 mol   c. 0.85 M

8.75 a. 0.08 ppm   b. 0.7 ppm

8.77 **B**

8.79 a. 0.05 M   b. 50.0 mL

8.81 Concentration is the amount of solute per unit volume in a solution. Dilution is the addition of solvent to decrease the concentration of solute.

8.83 a. 15.0% (w/v)   c. 5.0% (w/v)
 b. 6.00% (w/v)   d. 14% (w/v)

8.85 1.8 M

8.87 a. 10. mL   b. 450 mL   c. 1.5 mL   d. 2.5 mL

8.89 Ocean water contains nonvolatile dissolved salts, increasing the boiling point.

8.91 a. 101.5 °C   b. 101.2 °C   c. 103.1 °C

8.93 −4.5 °C

8.95 a. NaCl   b. glucose   c. NaCl   d. glucose

8.97 a. 0.10 M glucose   c. 0.10 M Na_2SO_4
 b. 0.20 M NaCl   d. 0.10 M glucose

8.99 a. **A > B**   c. no change   e. no change
 b. **B > A**   d. **A > B**

8.101 At warmer temperatures, CO_2 is less soluble in water and more is in the gas phase and escapes as the can is opened and pressure is reduced.

8.103 0.09% (w/v)   0.005 M

8.105 a. 280 mL would have to be given.
 b. The hypertonic mannitol draws water out of swollen brain cells and thus reduces the pressure on the brain.

8.107 Water moves out of the cells of the cucumber to the hypertonic salt solution, so the cucumber shrinks and loses its crispness.

8.109 NaCl, KCl, and glucose are found in the bloodstream. If they weren't in the dialyzer fluid, they would move out of the bloodstream into the dialyzer, and their concentrations in the bloodstream would fall.

8.111 6.3% (w/v)

8.113 7.3 g

8.115 4,000 mg

8.119 a. yes   b. 0.000 50 mol

CHAPTER 9

9.1 a, c

9.2 a, b, d

9.3 acid base base acid
 a. HCl(g) + NH_3(g)   c. OH^-(aq) + HSO_4^-(aq)
  acid base
 b. CH_3COOH(l) + H_2O(l)

9.4 a. H_3O^+ b. HI   c. H_2CO_3

9.5 a. HS^- b. CN^- c. SO_4^{2-}

9.6 conjugate conjugate
  base acid base acid
 a. H_2O(l) + HI(g) $\rightleftharpoons$ I^-(aq) + H_3O^+(aq)

  conjugate conjugate
  acid base base acid
 b. CH_3COOH(l) + NH_3(g) $\rightleftharpoons$ CH_3COO^-(aq) + NH_4^+(aq)

  conjugate conjugate
  base acid acid base
 c. Br^-(aq) + HNO_3(aq) $\rightleftharpoons$ HBr(aq) + NO_3^-(aq)

9.7 a. NH_4^+ b. NH_2^-

9.8 **D < F < E**

9.9 a. H_2SO_4 is the stronger acid; H_3PO_4 has the stronger conjugate base.
 b. HCl is the stronger acid; HF has the stronger conjugate base.
 c. H_2CO_3 is the stronger acid; NH_4^+ has the stronger conjugate base.
 d. HF is the stronger acid; HCN has the stronger conjugate base.

9.11 a, c: products   b. reactants

9.13 a. HPO_4^{2-}, $H_2PO_4^-$, H_3PO_4 b. HCN, CH_3COOH, HF

9.15 reactants favored

9.17 a. 10^{-11} M acidic   c. 3.6×10^{-5} M basic
 b. 10^{-3} M basic   d. 1.8×10^{-11} M acidic

9.19

	$[H_3O^+]$	$[OH^-]$
a.	10^{-11} M	10^{-3} M
b.	10^{-3} M	10^{-11} M
c.	1.5 M	6.7×10^{-15} M
d.	3.3×10^{-14} M	3.0×10^{-1} M

9.20 a. 6   b. 12   c. 5   d. 11

9.21 a. 1×10^{-13} M   basic
 b. 1×10^{-7} M   neutral
 c. 1×10^{-3} M   acidic

9.22 a. 6×10^{-11} M   b. 2×10^{-8} M   c. 5×10^{-5} M

9.23 a. 5.74   b. 11.036   c. 4.06   d. 10.118

9.25 a. HNO_3(aq) + NaOH(aq) $\longrightarrow$ H_2O(l) + $NaNO_3$(aq)
 b. H_2SO_4(aq) + 2 KOH(aq) $\longrightarrow$ 2 H_2O(l) + K_2SO_4(aq)

9.27 H_2SO_4(aq) + $CaCO_3$(s) $\longrightarrow$ $CaSO_4$(aq) + $\underline{H_2O(l) + CO_2(g)}$
  from H_2CO_3

9.29 a, c, e: neutral   b, f: basic   d. acidic

9.31 0.41 M

9.33 a. Not a buffer since it contains a strong acid, HBr.
 b. A buffer since HF is a weak acid and F^- is its conjugate base.
 c. Not a buffer since it contains a weak acid only.

9.35 a, b, c: pH 7.21
 The pH remains the same if equal amounts of the weak acid and conjugate base are present.

9.37 a, d, f

9.39 a, d, e, f

9.41 a. H_2S b. HCO_3^- c. HNO_2 d. $\left[\begin{array}{c} H\ \ H \\ H-C-N-H \\ H\ \ H \end{array}\right]^+$

9.43 a. NO_2^- b. NH_3 c. HO_2^-

9.45 a. ⬤ + ⬤ ⟶ ⬤ + ⬤
  acid base conjugate base conjugate acid

 b. ⬤ + ⬤ ⟶ ⬤ + ⬤
  base acid conjugate acid conjugate base

9.47 a. HI(g) acid — $I^-(aq)$ conjugate base
  $NH_3(g)$ base — $NH_4^+(aq)$ conjugate acid
 b. HCOOH(l) acid — $HCOO^-(aq)$ conjugate base
  $H_2O(l)$ base — $H_3O^+(aq)$ conjugate acid
 c. $HSO_4^-(aq)$ base — $H_2SO_4(aq)$ conjugate acid
  $H_2O(l)$ acid — $OH^-(aq)$ conjugate base

9.49 a. H_2CO_3 b. CO_3^{2-}

9.51 $HNO_3(aq) + H_2O(l) \longrightarrow H_3O^+(aq) + NO_3^-(aq)$

9.53 **A** represents HCl because it shows a fully dissociated acid. **B** represents HF because it is only partially dissociated.

9.55 a. **B** b. **A**

9.57 a. CH_3COOH b. H_3PO_4 c. H_2SO_4

9.59 a. H_2O b. HCO_3^- c. HSO_4^-

9.61 a. **A** b. **B** c. **B**

9.63 a. HSO_4^- stronger acid
  SO_4^{2-} conjugate base
  $H_2PO_4^-$
  HPO_4^{2-} conjugate base, stronger base
 b. CH_3COOH stronger acid
  CH_3COO^- conjugate base
  CH_3CH_2COOH
  $CH_3CH_2COO^-$ conjugate base, stronger base

9.65 a. **B** b. **B**

9.67
 a. acid — conjugate acid
  $H_3PO_4(aq) + CN^-(aq) \rightleftharpoons H_2PO_4^-(aq) + HCN(aq)$
  products favored
 b. acid — conjugate acid
  $Br^-(aq) + HSO_4^-(aq) \rightleftharpoons SO_4^{2-}(aq) + HBr(g)$
  reactants favored
 c. acid
  $CH_3COO^-(aq) + H_2CO_3(aq)$
  reactants favored — conjugate acid
  $\rightleftharpoons CH_3COOH(aq) + HCO_3^-(aq)$

9.69 a. 10^{-6} M basic c. 3.3×10^{-11} M acidic
 b. 10^{-4} M basic d. 4.0×10^{-4} M basic

9.71 a. 10^{-12} M basic c. 1.6×10^{-8} M basic
 b. 2.5×10^{-7} M acidic d. 1.2×10^{-2} M acidic

9.73 a. 12 b. 6.60 c. 7.80 d. 1.92

9.75

$[H_3O^+]$	$[OH^-]$	pH	Classification
5.3×10^{-3}	1.9×10^{-12}	2.28	acidic
5.0×10^{-7}	2.0×10^{-8}	6.30	acidic
4×10^{-5}	2.5×10^{-10}	4.4	acidic
1.5×10^{-5}	6.8×10^{-10}	4.82	acidic

9.77 a. 1×10^{-12} M c. 1.6×10^{-2} M
 b. 1×10^{-1} M d. 1.3×10^{-9} M

9.79 $[H_3O^+] = 1.3 \times 10^{-6}$ M $[OH^-] = 7.7 \times 10^{-9}$ M

9.81 $[H_3O^+] = 7.9 \times 10^{-5}$ M $[OH^-] = 1.3 \times 10^{-10}$ M

9.83 a. 2.60 b. 12.17

9.85 HCl is fully dissociated to H_3O^+ and Cl^- and CH_3COOH is not fully dissociated.

9.87 a. $HBr(aq) + KOH(aq) \longrightarrow KBr(aq) + H_2O(l)$
 b. $2 HNO_3(aq) + Ca(OH)_2(aq) \longrightarrow 2 H_2O(l) + Ca(NO_3)_2(aq)$
 c. $HCl(aq) + NaHCO_3(aq) \longrightarrow NaCl(aq) + H_2O(l) + CO_2(g)$
 d. $H_2SO_4(aq) + Mg(OH)_2(aq) \longrightarrow 2 H_2O(l) + MgSO_4(aq)$

9.89 $2 HNO_3(aq) + CaCO_3(s)$
  $\longrightarrow Ca(NO_3)_2(aq) + CO_2(g) + H_2O(l)$

9.91 a, e: neutral b, d, f: basic c. acidic

9.93 0.14 M

9.95 0.12 M

9.97 25 mL

9.99 **B** is a buffer because it contains equal amounts of the acid and its conjugate base.

9.101 If the concentrations of the weak acid and its conjugate base are equal, then a proton donor and a proton acceptor are available and the H_3O^+ concentration will change very little when acid or base is added to a buffer.

9.103 Yes. HCN is a weak acid and CN^- is its conjugate base, so in equal amounts they form a buffer.

9.105 a. HNO_2 is a proton donor that will react with added base and NO_2^- is a proton acceptor that will react with added acid.
 b. The concentration of HNO_2 increases and that of NO_2^- decreases when a small amount of acid is added to the buffer.
 c. The concentration of HNO_2 decreases and that of NO_2^- increases when a small amount of base is added to the buffer.

9.107 a. 12.66 b. 10.25

9.109 a. 4.74 b. 5.05 c. 4.44

9.111 CO_2 combines with rainwater to form H_2CO_3, which is acidic, lowering the pH.

9.113 $[H_3O^+] = 3.2 \times 10^{-8}$ M $[OH^-] = 3.1 \times 10^{-7}$ M

9.115 By breathing into a bag, the individual breathes in air with a higher CO_2 concentration. Thus, the CO_2 concentration in the lungs and the blood increases, thereby lowering the pH.

9.117 A rise in CO_2 concentration leads to an increase in $H^+(aq)$ concentration by the following equilibria:
  $CO_2(g) + H_2O(l) \rightleftharpoons H_2CO_3(aq) \rightleftharpoons HCO_3^-(aq) + H^+(aq)$

9.119 $OCl^-(aq) + H_2O(l) \longrightarrow HOCl(aq) + OH^-(aq)$
  OH^- is formed by this reaction, so the water is basic.

CHAPTER 10

10.1

	Atomic Number	Mass Number	Number of Protons	Number of Neutrons	Isotope Symbol
Cobalt-59	27	59	27	32	$^{59}_{27}Co$
Cobalt-60	27	60	27	33	$^{60}_{27}Co$

10.3 An α particle has no electrons around the nucleus.

10.5 $^{222}_{86}Rn \longrightarrow {}^4_2He + {}^{218}_{84}Po$

10.7 a. $^{218}_{84}Po \longrightarrow {}^4_2He + {}^{214}_{82}Pb$
 b. $^{230}_{90}Th \longrightarrow {}^4_2He + {}^{226}_{88}Ra$
 c. $^{252}_{99}Es \longrightarrow {}^4_2He + {}^{248}_{97}Bk$

10.8 $^{131}_{53}I \longrightarrow {}^0_{-1}e + {}^{131}_{54}Xe$

10.9 a. $^{20}_{9}F \longrightarrow {}^0_{-1}e + {}^{20}_{10}Ne$
 b. $^{92}_{38}Sr \longrightarrow {}^0_{-1}e + {}^{92}_{39}Y$
 c. $^{55}_{24}Cr \longrightarrow {}^0_{-1}e + {}^{55}_{25}Mn$

10.10 a. $^{74}_{33}As \longrightarrow {}^0_{+1}e + {}^{74}_{32}Ge$
 b. $^{15}_{8}O \longrightarrow {}^0_{+1}e + {}^{15}_{7}N$

10.11 $^{192}_{77}Ir \longrightarrow {}^{192}_{78}Pt + {}^0_{-1}e + \gamma$

10.13 a. 0.250 g b. 0.0625 g c. 0.003 91 g d. 9.54×10^{-7} g

10.15 17,200 years

10.16 4.4 mL

10.17 a. 0.2 rem b. 14 mrem c. "a" is the higher dose.

10.19 a. 62 protons, 91 neutrons, 62 electrons c. 9.4 mCi
 b. $^{153}_{62}Sm \longrightarrow {}^{153}_{63}Eu + {}^0_{-1}e$

10.21 $^{235}_{92}U + {}^1_0n \longrightarrow {}^{133}_{51}Sb + {}^{100}_{41}Nb + 3 {}^1_0n$

10.23

	a. Atomic Number	b. Number of Protons	c. Number of Neutrons	d. Mass Number	Isotope Symbol
Fluorine-18	9	9	9	18	$^{18}_{9}F$
Fluorine-19	9	9	10	19	$^{19}_{9}F$

10.25

	Atomic Number	Mass Number	Number of Protons	Number of Neutrons	Isotope Symbol
a. Chromium-51	24	51	24	27	$_{24}^{51}Cr$
b. Palladium-103	46	103	46	57	$_{46}^{103}Pd$
c. Potassium-42	19	42	19	23	$_{19}^{42}K$
d. Xenon-133	54	133	54	79	$_{54}^{133}Xe$

10.27

	Change in Mass	Change in Charge
a. α particle	−4	−2
b. β particle	0	+1
c. γ ray	0	0
d. Positron	0	−1

10.29

	Mass	Charge
a. α	4	+2
b. n	1	0
c. γ	0	0
d. β	0	−1

10.31

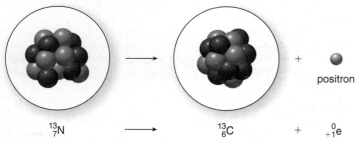

$_{7}^{13}N \longrightarrow {}_{6}^{13}C + {}_{+1}^{0}e$

10.33 a. $_{26}^{59}Fe \longrightarrow {}_{27}^{59}Co + {}_{-1}^{0}e$

b. $_{78}^{190}Pt \longrightarrow {}_{76}^{186}Os + {}_{2}^{4}He$

c. $_{80}^{178}Hg \longrightarrow {}_{79}^{178}Au + {}_{+1}^{0}e$

10.35 a. $_{39}^{90}Y \longrightarrow {}_{40}^{90}Zr + {}_{-1}^{0}e$

b. $_{60}^{135}Nd \longrightarrow {}_{59}^{135}Pr + {}_{+1}^{0}e$

c. $_{83}^{210}Bi \longrightarrow {}_{81}^{206}Tl + {}_{2}^{4}He$

10.37 $_{83}^{214}Bi \longrightarrow {}_{84}^{214}Po + {}_{-1}^{0}e$

$_{83}^{214}Bi \longrightarrow {}_{81}^{210}Tl + {}_{2}^{4}He$

10.39 a. $_{90}^{232}Th \longrightarrow {}_{2}^{4}He + {}_{88}^{228}Ra$

b. $_{11}^{25}Na \longrightarrow {}_{12}^{25}Mg + {}_{-1}^{0}e$

c. $_{54}^{118}Xe \longrightarrow {}_{53}^{118}I + {}_{+1}^{0}e$

d. $_{96}^{243}Cm \longrightarrow {}_{2}^{4}He + {}_{94}^{239}Pu$

10.41 two

10.43 4.0 days

10.45

	Iodine-131	Xenon-131
a.	32 mg	32 mg
b.	16 mg	48 mg
c.	8.0 mg	56 mg
d.	4.0 mg	60. mg

10.47 No, 25% remains.

10.49 In artifacts over 50,000 years old, the percentage of carbon-14 is too small to accurately measure.

10.51 a. 10 mCi   b. 5 mCi   c. 1 mCi

10.53 1.9×10^8 disintegrations/s

10.55 2.3 mL

10.57 2.6 mL

10.59 Curie refers to the number of disintegrations per second and the number of rads indicates the radiation absorbed by one gram of a substance.

10.61 20 Sv = 2,000 rem
This represents a fatal dose because 600 rem is uniformly fatal.

10.63 Nuclear fission refers to the splitting of nuclei and fusion refers to the joining of small nuclei to form larger ones.

10.65 a. fusion   b. fission   c. both   d. fusion

10.67 a. $_{92}^{235}U + {}_{0}^{1}n \longrightarrow {}_{50}^{137}Sn + {}_{42}^{97}Mo + 2\,{}_{0}^{1}n$

b. $_{92}^{235}U + {}_{0}^{1}n \longrightarrow {}_{36}^{93}Kr + {}_{56}^{140}Ba + 3\,{}_{0}^{1}n$

10.69

10.71 tritium; $_{1}^{3}H$

10.73 The containment of radiation leaks and disposal of radioactive waste are two problems that are associated with nuclear power production.

10.75 $_{83}^{209}Bi + {}_{26}^{58}Fe \longrightarrow {}_{109}^{266}Mt + {}_{0}^{1}n$
meitnerium-266

10.77 a. $_{33}^{74}As \longrightarrow {}_{+1}^{0}e + {}_{32}^{74}Ge$ b. 4 mg   c. 1.5 mL

10.79 a. 38 protons, 51 neutrons, 38 electrons   c. 0.625 μg

b. $_{38}^{89}Sr \longrightarrow {}_{39}^{89}Y + {}_{-1}^{0}e$

10.81 a. used for the treatment and diagnosis of thyroid diseases
b. used for the treatment of breast cancer
c. used for the diagnosis of heart disease

10.83 a. Iodine-125, with its longer half-life, is used for the treatment of prostate cancers using implanted radioactive seeds.
b. Iodine-131, with its shorter half-life, is used for the diagnostic and therapeutic treatment of thyroid diseases and tumors. A patient is administered radioactive iodine-131, which is then incorporated into the thyroid hormone, thyroxine. Since its half-life is short, the radioactive iodine isotope decays so that little remains after a month or so.

10.85 Radiology technicians must be shielded to avoid exposure to excessive and dangerous doses of radiation.

10.87 High doses of stable iodine will prevent the absorption and uptake of the radioactive iodine-131.

10.89 370 kcal

CHAPTER 11

11.1 organic (a), (e)
inorganic (b), (c), (d), (f)

11.2 a.

```
    H   H H   H
    |   | |   |
H — C — C=C — C — H
    |   |     |
    H   H H   H
```

b.

```
    H  :O:  H
    |   ‖   |
H — C — C — C — H
    |       |
    H       H
```

c.

```
    H  :O:  H
    |   ‖   |
H — C — C — C — H
    |       |
    H       H
```

d.

```
    H  :O:  H   H
    |   ‖   |   |
H — C — C — N — C — H
    |       ..  |
    H           H
```

e.

```
   H   H
    \ /
     C
    / \ ..
   C — O:
  / \   ..
 H   H
```

11.3 a. (1), (2) both trigonal planar
b. (1) linear; (2) tetrahedral; (3) bent
c. (1) trigonal planar; (2) bent
d. (1) trigonal planar; (2) linear

11.5 a. 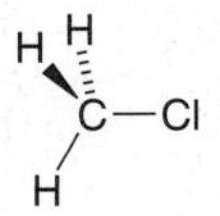 [structure: CH_3–Cl] b. 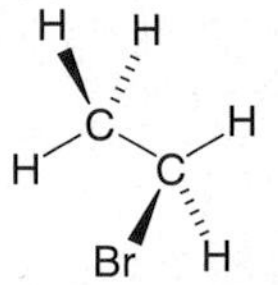 [structure: CH_3–$CHBr$–H]

11.6 (1) bent; (2) linear; (3),(4) trigonal planar; (5) bent; (6) tetrahedral

11.7 a. $CH_3(CH_2)_3CH_3$
b. $Br(CH_2)_2Br$
c. $CH_3CH_2O(CH_2)_2OH$
d. $CH_3CH_2C(CH_3)_3$

11.9 a. 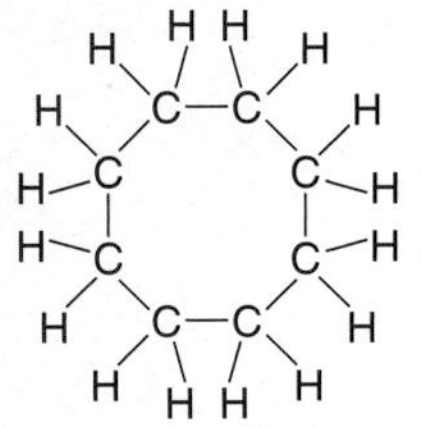 [ring structure] c. 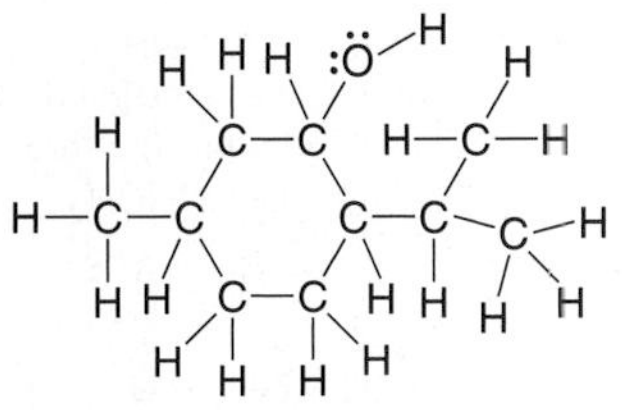 [chain structure with OH]
b. 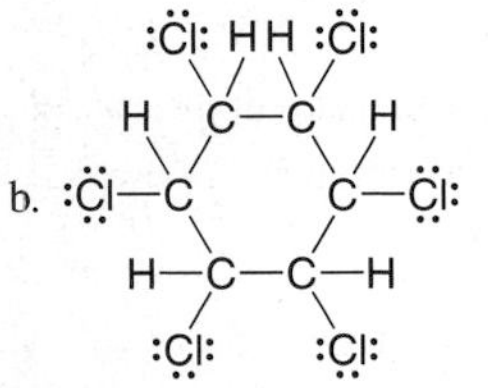 [ring structure with Cl substituents]

11.10 C1: no H; C2: 1 H; C3: 2 H; C4: 1 H; C5: 1 H

11.11 a. hydroxyl   b. alkene; aromatic ring   c. two amine groups

11.12 a. 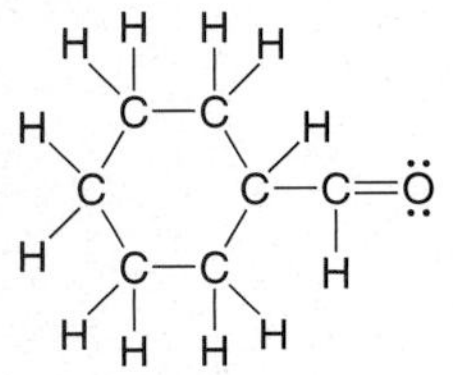 [structure] aldehyde
b. 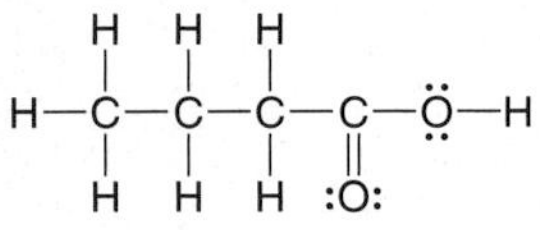 [structure] carboxylic acid
c. 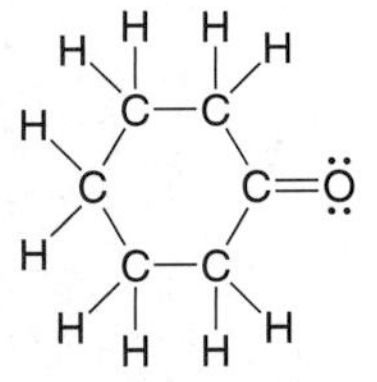 [structure] ketone
d. 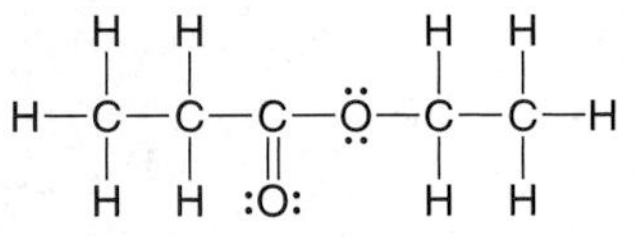 [structure] ester
e. 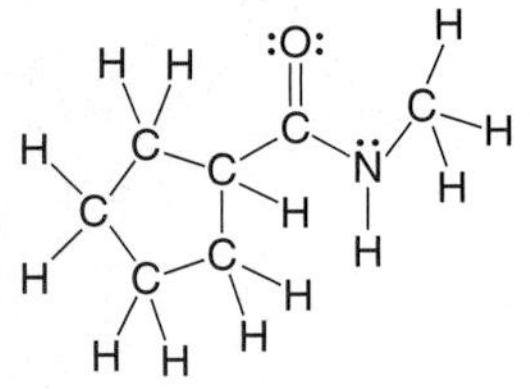 [structure] amide

11.13 amide, aromatic ring, ether, hydroxyl, amine

11.14 a. $CH_3CH_2OCH_2CH_3$, ether
b. $CH_3CH_2CH{=}CHCH_2CHO$, alkene, aldehyde

11.15 three ethers, aromatic ring, alkene

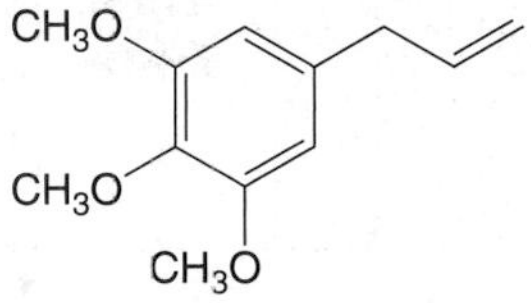

[structure with CH_3O groups]

11.17 a. nonpolar; all nonpolar bonds
b. polar; one polar C=O bond
c. nonpolar; the four bond dipoles cancel
d. polar; the polar C—N and N—H bond dipoles don't cancel

11.19 a. insoluble   b. soluble   c. insoluble

11.21 Niacin is soluble in water.

11.23 inorganic: (a), (b)   organic: (c)

11.25 a. 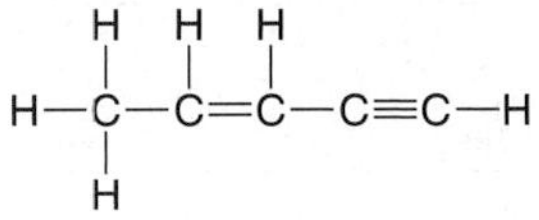 [structure]   c. 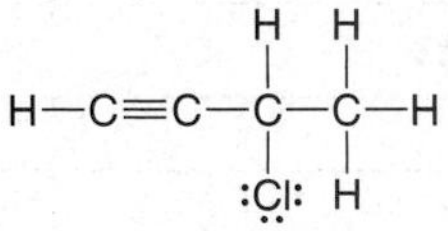 [structure]
b. 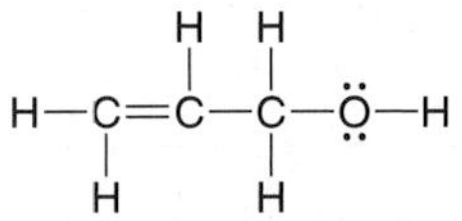 [structure]   d. 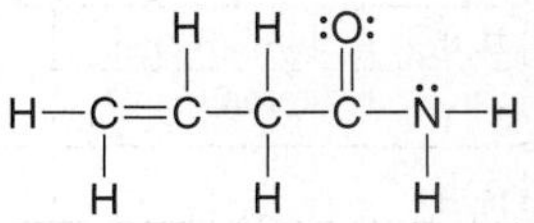 [structure]

11.27 a. (1) trigonal planar; (2) linear
b. (1) tetrahedral; (2) bent; (3) tetrahedral

11.29 a. (1) and (2) 180°
b. (1) and (2) 120°
c. (1) and (2) 109.5°

11.31 (1) bent; (2) trigonal planar; (3) tetrahedral; (4) trigonal pyramidal

11.33 Each C is surrounded by three groups, so each carbon is trigonal planar giving 120° bond angles.

11.35 a. $CH_3(CH_2)_2C(CH_3)_3$ c. $(CH_3)_2CHCH_2O(CH_2)_2CH_3$
b. $BrCH_2CH_2CHCH_2CH_3$ d. $CH_3(CH_2)_2CHO$
      (with Cl substituent)

11.37 a. 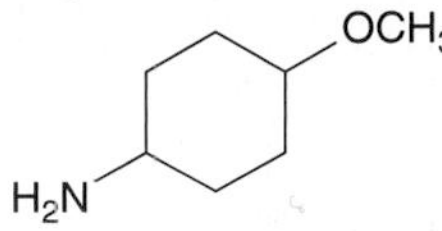 [structure with OCH_3, H_2N]   b. 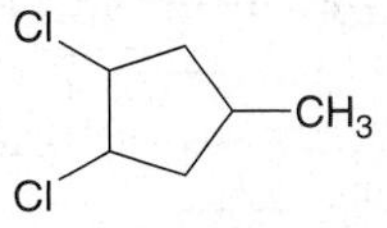 [structure with Cl, CH_3]

11.39 a. 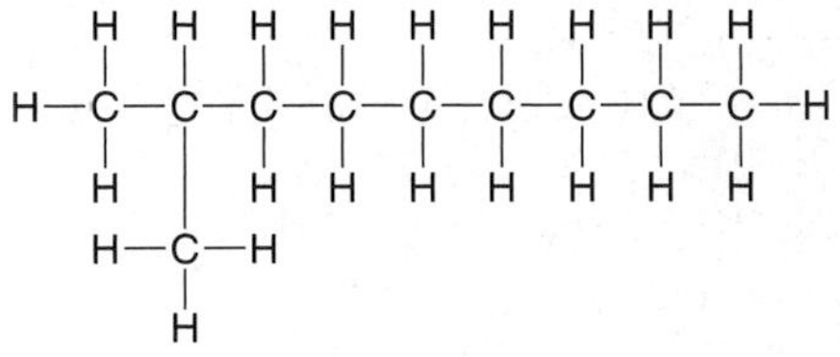 [structure]
b. 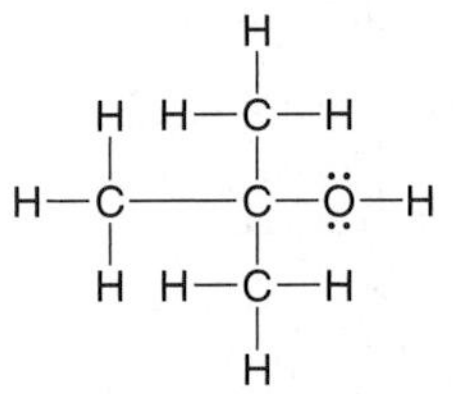 [structure]
c. 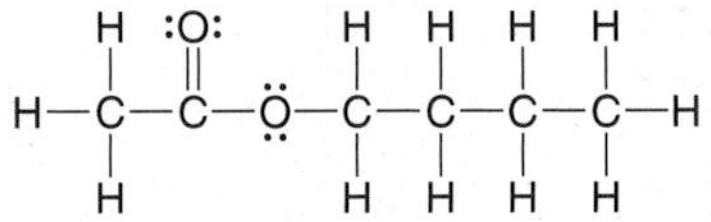 [structure]
d. 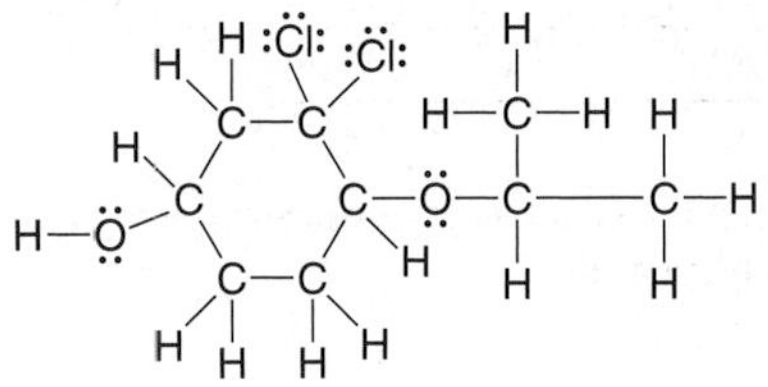 [structure]

11.41   a.   (CH$_3$)$_3$CHCH$_2$CH$_3$ ↰ Five bonds to C

     b.   CH$_3$(CH$_2$)$_4$CH$_3$OH   ↰ Five bonds to C

     c.   (CH$_3$)$_2$C=CH$_3$ ↰ Five bonds to C

     d.   [cyclohexene ring with CH$_3$ and CH$_3$]   ↱ Five bonds to C

     e.   [cyclopentane ring with CH$_3$, CH$_3$, CH$_3$]   ↱ Five bonds to C

11.43   [structural formula with H—Ö—C ring, C=C alkenes, CH groups, C=O, O—H, N—H]

11.45   a.   two alkenes
     b.   ketone
     c.   ester

11.47   a.   ester
     b.   two alkenes, two alkynes, one hydroxyl
     c.   hydroxyl, ether, aldehyde, aromatic ring

11.49   two hydroxyl groups, aromatic ring, amine

11.51   (CH$_3$)$_2$C=CHCH$_2$CH$_2$C(CH$_3$)=CHCHO, two alkenes, aldehyde

11.53   In a carboxylic acid, the C=O is bonded to a hydroxyl group. In an ester, the C=O is bonded to an OR group.
     Examples: CH$_3$CH$_2$COOH (carboxylic acid) and CH$_3$CO$_2$CH$_3$ (ester)

11.55   a.   HC≡C—CH$_3$ c.   CH$_3$CH$_2$CHO

     b.   CH$_3$CH$_2$CH$_2$OH   d.   CH$_3$CH$_2$CCH$_3$ (with O double bond)

11.57   alkane   CH$_3$CH$_2$CH$_2$CH$_2$CH$_3$ C$_5$H$_{12}$

     alkene   CH$_3$—C—C=C—CH$_3$ C$_5$H$_{10}$ [with H's shown]

     alkyne   CH$_3$—C—C≡C—CH$_3$ C$_5$H$_8$ [with H's shown]

11.59   NaCl dissolves in water but not in dichloromethane and cholesterol dissolves in dichloromethane but not in water.

11.61   Net dipoles and molecular geometry will determine whether a molecule is polar or nonpolar. When a molecule has polar bonds, we must determine whether the bond dipoles cancel or reinforce.

11.63
     a.   [F—C—Cl structure with δ$^-$, δ$^+$, and three Cl with δ$^-$]

     b.   [H—O—CH$_2$CHCH$_2$—O—H structure with OH and δ charges]

11.65   a.   nonpolar
     b.   polar
     c.   polar

11.67   Ethylene glycol is more water soluble because it contains two polar hydroxyl groups capable of hydrogen bonding.

11.69   Sucrose has multiple OH groups and this makes it water soluble. 1-Dodecanol has a long hydrocarbon chain and a single OH group so it is not water soluble.

11.71   a.   Spermaceti wax is an ester.
     b.   The very long hydrocarbon chains would make it insoluble in water and soluble in organic solvents.

11.73   Fat-soluble vitamins will persist in tissues and accumulate, whereas any excess of water-soluble vitamins will be excreted in the urine.

11.75   Vitamin E is a fat-soluble vitamin, making it soluble in organic solvents and insoluble in water.

11.77   a.   Yes, there are just enough H's to give each C four bonds.
     b.   No, there are too many H's.
     c.   Yes, if you put the three C's in a ring, each C gets two H's.

11.79   a.   CH$_3$CH$_2$CH$_2$NHCH$_3$

     b.   CH$_3$CH$_2$CH$_2$—N—CH$_3$ [with δ$^+$ on H and CH$_3$, δ$^-$ on N]

     c.   trigonal pyramid around N
     d.   This is a polar molecule. The bond dipoles don't cancel.

11.81   a.   C$_9$H$_{11}$NO$_2$ c.   seven   d.   water soluble
     b, e: Polar bonds are in **bold.**

     [structure: aromatic ring with C=O, O—CH$_2$CH$_3$ ester, and H—N—H amine]

11.83   [steroid structure with labeled positions 1–6, 1'–6', and functional groups (a)–(f)]

     a.   functional groups:
         (a) ketone
         (b) alkene
         (c) hydroxyl
         (d) aldehyde
         (e) ketone
         (f) hydroxyl
     b.   Each O needs two lone pairs.
     c.   21 C's
     d.   number of H's at carbon:
         1'- 0 H's
         2'- 0 H's
         3'- 1 H
         4'- 2 H's
         5'- 1 H
         6'- 1 H
     e.   shape at each carbon:
         1- tetrahedral
         2- tetrahedral
         3- bent
         4- trigonal planar
         5- tetrahedral

f.

11.85 The waxy coating will prevent loss of water from leaves and will keep leaves crisp.

11.87 THC is not water soluble. THC is fat soluble and will therefore persist in tissues for an extended period of time. Ethanol is water soluble and will be quickly excreted in the urine.

CHAPTER 12

12.1   a. 8   b. 8   c. 18   d. 16

12.3   a. not isomers   b. isomers   c. isomers

12.4 $CH_3CHCHCH_3$ with CH_3 and CH_3 substituents; $CH_3CCH_2CH_3$ with CH_3 and CH_3 substituents

12.5   d.

12.6   a. $CH_3CH_2CH_2CH_3$ (1°, 2°)

   b. $(CH_3)_3CH$ (1°, 3°)

   c. $CH_3-C-CH_2CH_3$ with CH_3 (1°), H (3°), and CH_2CH_3 (2°)

   d. CH_3-C-CH_3 with CH_3 substituents (1°, 4°)

12.7   a. $CH_3CH_2CH_3$ b. $CH_3CHCH_2CH_3$ with CH_3 c. $CH_3CCH_2CCH_3$ with CH_3, CH_3, CH_3, CH_3

12.9   a. H–C–C–C–C–C–H (pentane, all H)

   b. H–C–C–C–C–C–H with H–C–H branch

   c. cyclopentane ring with –C–C–C–H chain

12.10   a. 3-methylpentane
   b. 4-methyl-5-propylnonane
   c. 2,4-dimethylhexane

12.11   a. 2,3-dimethylbutane
   b. 4-ethyldecane
   c. 4-ethyl-3,4-dimethyloctane

12.12   a. $CH_3CH_2CHCH_2CH_2CH_3$ with CH_3

   b. $CH_3CH_2CCH_2CH_3$ with CH_3 and CH_3

   c. $CH_3CH_2CHCH_2CCH_2CH_2CH_3$ with CH_3, CH_3, CH_3

   d. $CH_3CH_2CHCHCH_2CH_3$ with CH_3, CH_2, CH_3

12.13   a. $CH_3CCH_2CH_3$ with CH_3 and CH_3

   b. $CH_3CH_2CHCH_2CH_2CHCH_2CH_2CH_3$ with $CH_2CH_2CH_2CH_3$ and CH_3

   c. $CH_3CH_2CH_2C-CCH_2CH_2CH_2CH_3$ with CH_3, CH_3, CH_3, CH_3

   d. $CH_3CH_2CHCH_2CHCH_2CH_2CH_3$ with CH_2CH_3 and $CH_2CH_2CH_3$

12.15   Vitamin D_3 has many nonpolar C—C and C—H bonds, which make it water insoluble but fat soluble.

12.16   a. methylcyclobutane
   b. 1,1-dimethylcyclohexane
   c. 1-ethyl-3-propylcyclopentane
   d. 1-ethyl-4-methylcyclohexane

12.17   a. cyclopentane with $-CH_2CH_2CH_3$

   b. cyclobutane with CH_3 and CH_3

   c. cyclopropane with CH_3, CH_3, CH_3

   d. cyclohexane with CH_3, CH_3, CH_2CH_3

12.19 Vaseline is nonpolar, so it is insoluble in a polar solvent like water and soluble in a weakly polar solvent like dichloromethane.

12.21 a. $CH_3CH_2CH_3 + 5\ O_2 \longrightarrow 3\ CO_2 + 4\ H_2O$
b. $2\ CH_3CH_2CH_2CH_3 + 13\ O_2 \longrightarrow 8\ CO_2 + 10\ H_2O$

12.23 64

12.25 26 C has 54 H's
27 C has 56 H's
28 C has 58 H's
29 C has 60 H's
30 C has 62 H's

12.27 To form a cycloalkane, you need to form a C—C bond between 2 C's in a chain. To do this, 1 H from each C must be removed. This means a cycloalkane always has two fewer H's than an acyclic alkane of the same number of C's.

12.29 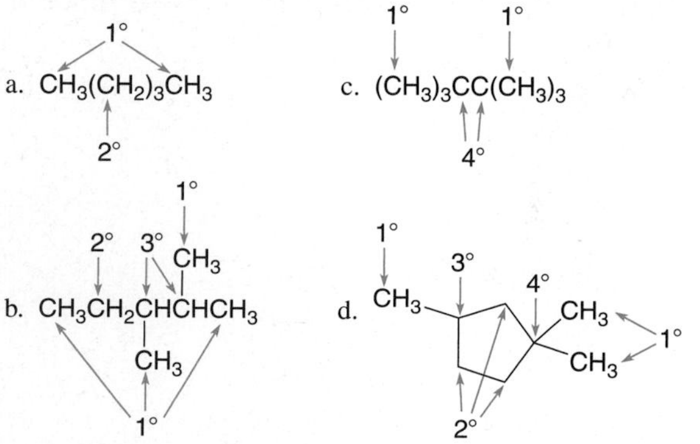

12.31 a. 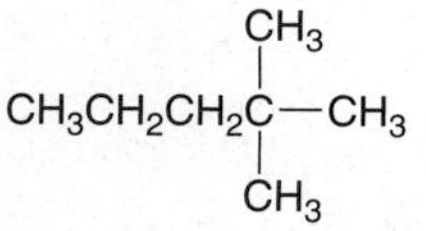
b. $CH_3CH_2CH_2CH_2CH_2CH_2CH_3$

12.33 a, c, d: constitutional isomers
b. identical

12.35 a, d: constitutional isomers
b, c, e: identical

12.37 a. 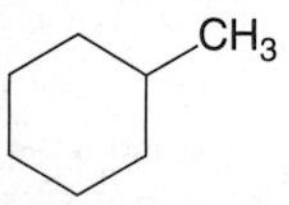 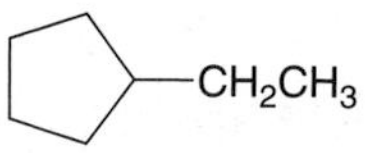
b. $CH_3CH_2CH_2CH_2CH_2OH$ $CH_3OCH_2CH_2CH_2CH_3$
c. $CH_3CH_2CH_2Cl$ 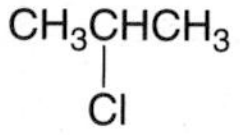

12.39 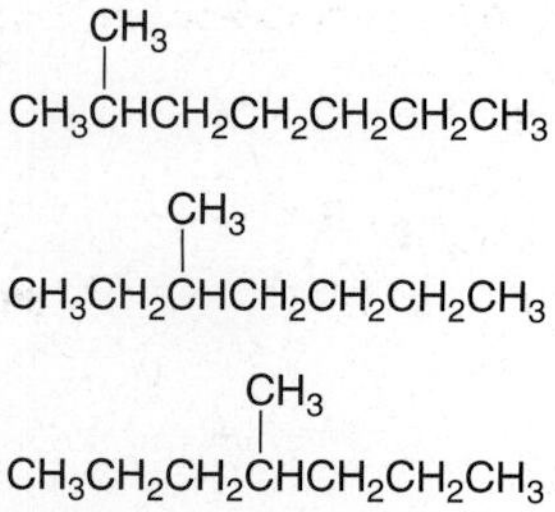

12.41 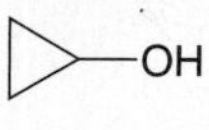

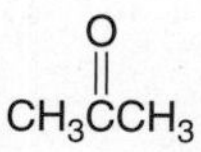

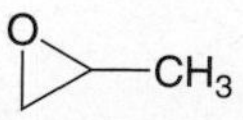

12.43 hexane; 2-methylpentane; 3-methylpentane; 2,2-dimethylbutane; 2,3-dimethylbutane

12.45 a. 4-methylheptane b. ethylcyclopentane

12.47 a. 3-methylheptane
b. 3,5-dimethyloctane
c. 3,3-diethylhexane
d. 4-ethyl-2,6-dimethyloctane
e. 6-ethyl-2-methyloctane
f. 2,2,8,8-tetramethyldecane

12.49 a. cyclooctane
b. methylcyclopropane
c. 1,1,2,2-tetramethylcyclobutane
d. 1,3-diethylcyclohexane

12.51 a. 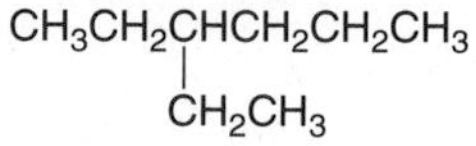
b. 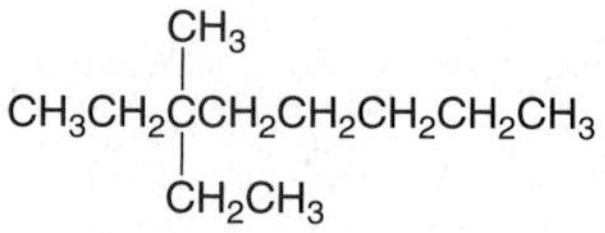
c. 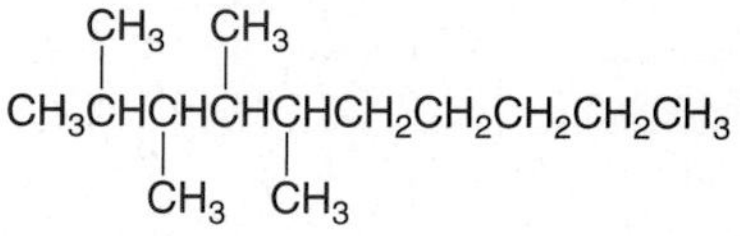
d. 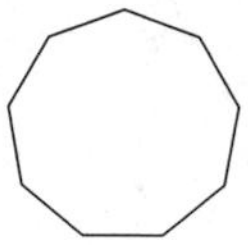
e. 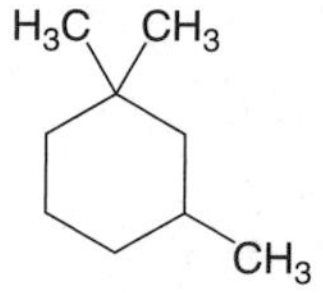
f. 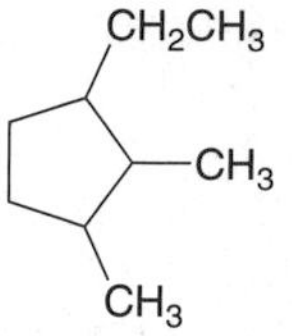

12.53 a. 2-methylbutane: Number to give CH_3 the lower number, 2 not 3.
b. methylcyclopentane: no number assigned if only one substituent
c. 2-methylpentane: five-carbon chain
d. 2,5-dimethylheptane: longest chain not chosen
e. 1,3-dimethylcyclohexane: Number to give the second substituent the lower number.
f. 1-ethyl-2-propylcyclopentane: lower number assigned alphabetically

12.55 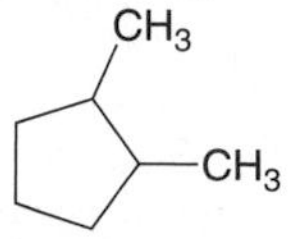

1,2-dimethylcyclopentane

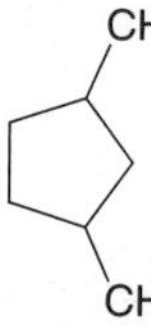

1,3-dimethylcyclopentane

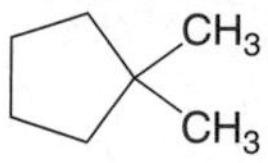

1,1-dimethylcyclopentane

12.57 a. 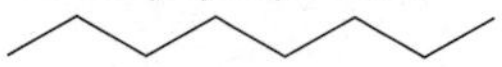
b. 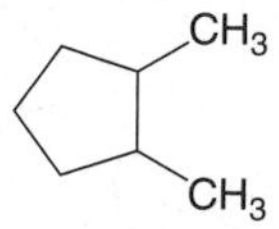
c. 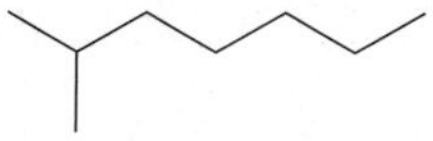

12.59 a. 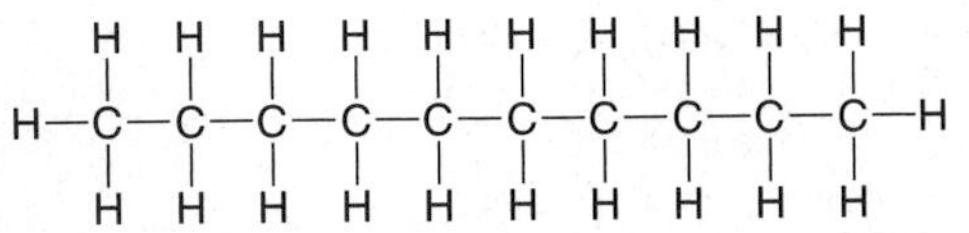

b. 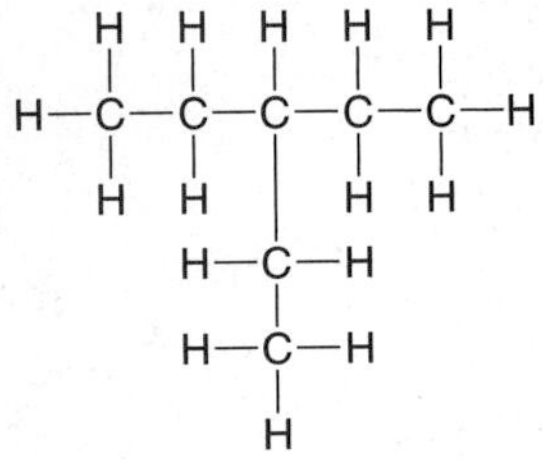

c. 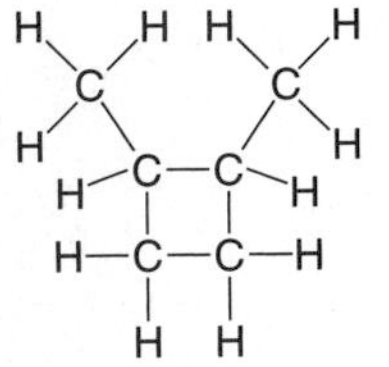

12.61 a. 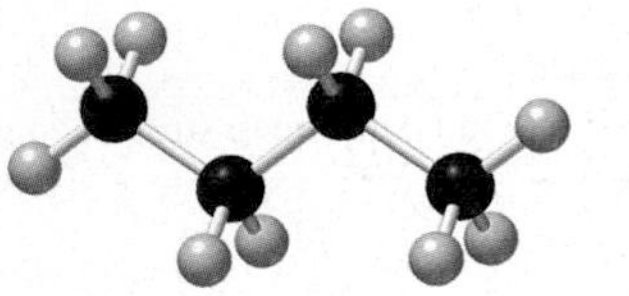

b. 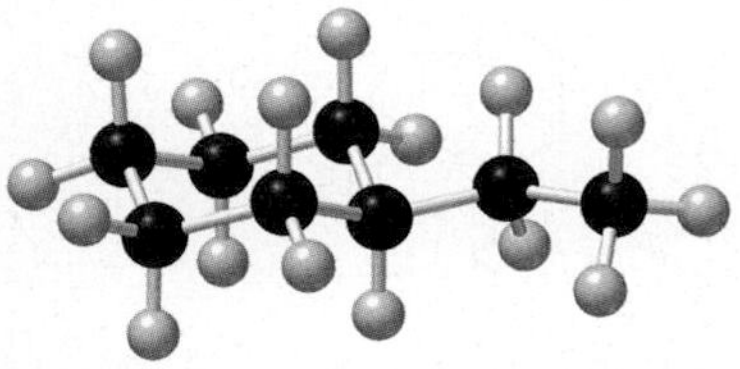

12.63 a. $(CH_3)_4C$, $(CH_3)_2CHCH_2CH_3$, $CH_3CH_2CH_2CH_2CH_3$
b. $(CH_3)_2CHCH(CH_3)_2$, $CH_3CH_2CH_2CH(CH_3)_2$, $CH_3(CH_2)_4CH_3$

12.65 Hexane is a nonpolar hydrocarbon and is soluble in organic solvents but not in water.

12.67 a. $2\ CH_3CH_3 + 7\ O_2 \longrightarrow 4\ CO_2 + 6\ H_2O$
b. $(CH_3)_2CHCH_2CH_3 + 8\ O_2 \longrightarrow 5\ CO_2 + 6\ H_2O$

12.69 a. $2\ CH_3CH_2CH_3 + 7\ O_2 \longrightarrow 6\ CO + 8\ H_2O$
b. $2\ CH_3CH_2CH_2CH_3 + 9\ O_2 \longrightarrow 8\ CO + 10\ H_2O$

12.71 $C_6H_{12}O_6 + 6\ O_2 \longrightarrow 6\ CO_2 + 6\ H_2O$

12.73 Higher molecular weight alkanes in warmer weather means less evaporation. Lower molecular weight alkanes in colder weather means the gasoline won't freeze.

12.75 The mineral oil can prevent the body's absorption of important fat-soluble vitamins, which are expelled with the mineral oil.

12.77 c. The nonpolar asphalt will be most soluble in the paint thinner because "like dissolves like."

12.79 a. 3-ethyl-4,4-dimethylheptane

b. 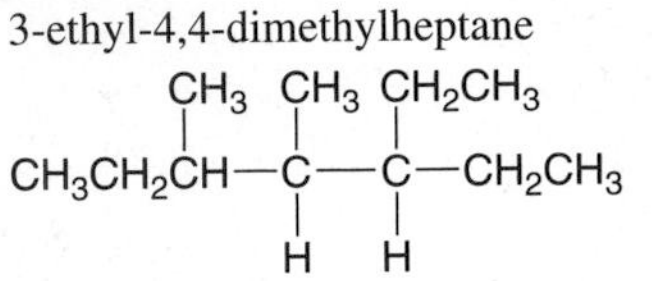

c. not water soluble
d. soluble in organic solvents
e. $C_{11}H_{24} + 17\ O_2 \longrightarrow 11\ CO_2 + 12\ H_2O$

f. 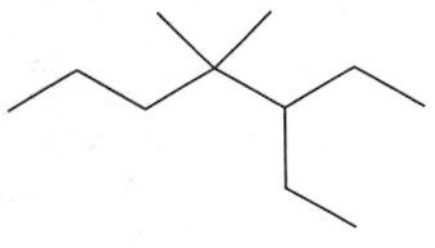

12.81 a. propylcyclopentane

b. 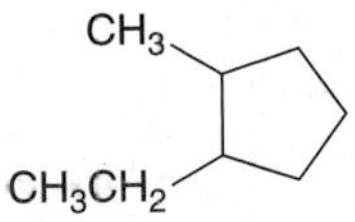

c. not water soluble
d. soluble in organic solvents
e. $C_8H_{16} + 12\ O_2 \longrightarrow 8\ CO_2 + 8\ H_2O$

f. 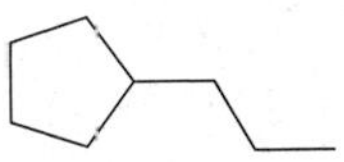

12.83 $C_{10}H_{18}$

12.85 Cyclopentane has a more rigid structure. The rings can get closer together since they are not floppy, resulting in an increased force of attraction.

CHAPTER 13

13.1 a. 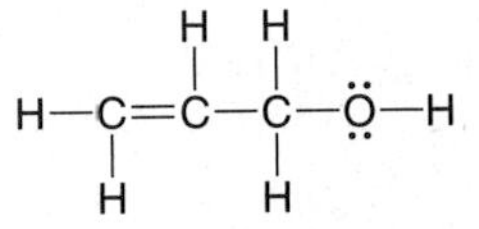

b. 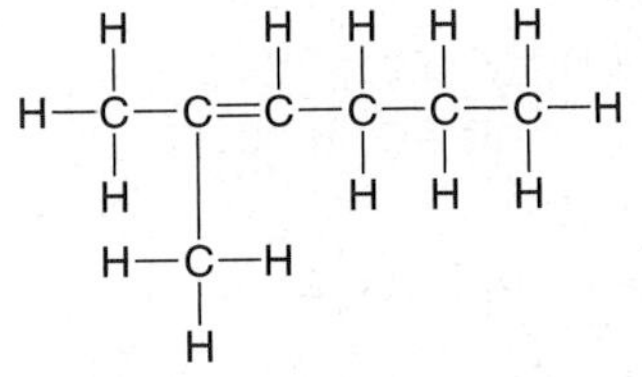

c. 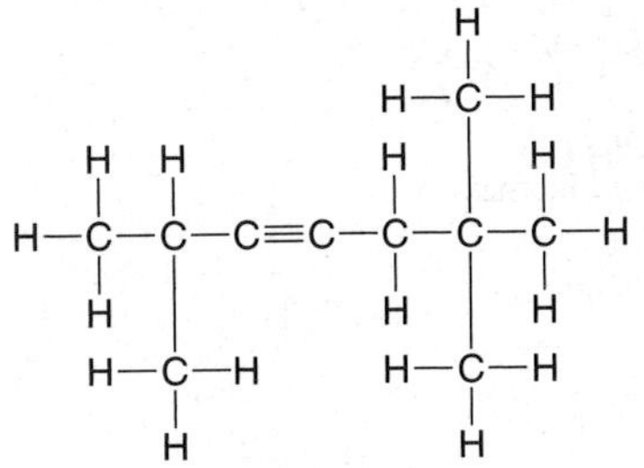

13.3 a. C_4H_8 b. C_6H_{14} c. C_7H_{12} d. C_5H_{10}

13.4 a. 3-methyl-1-pentene
b. 3-ethyl-3-heptene
c. 2,4-heptadiene
d. 3-ethylcyclopentene

13.5 a. 2-methyl-3-nonyne b. 6,6-dimethyl-3-octyne

13.6 a. 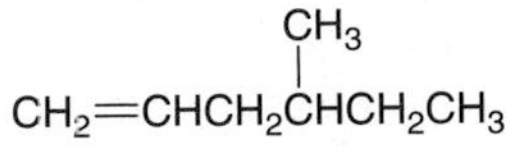

b. 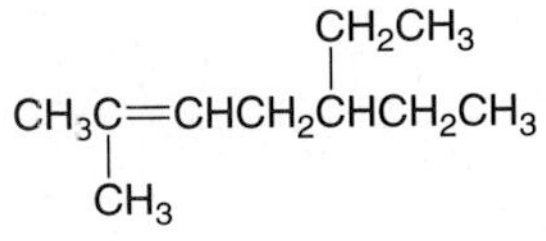

c. 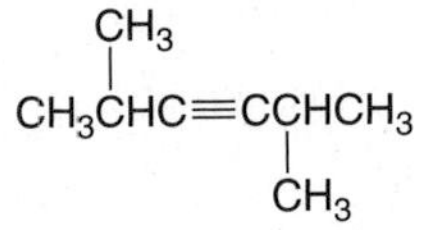

d. 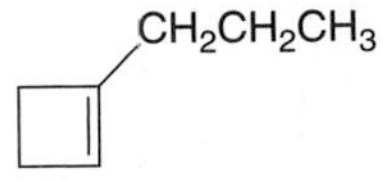

e. 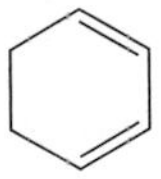

f. 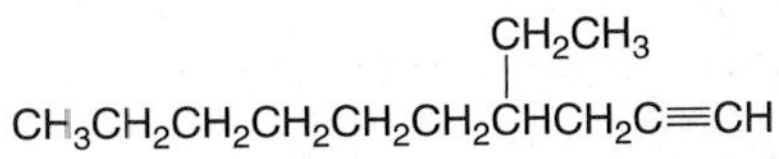

13.7　a.

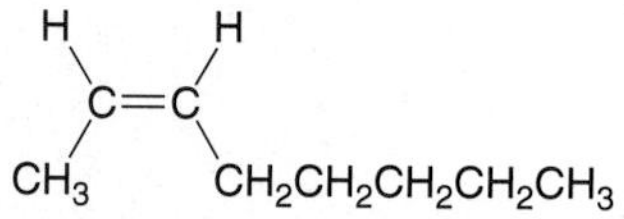

b.

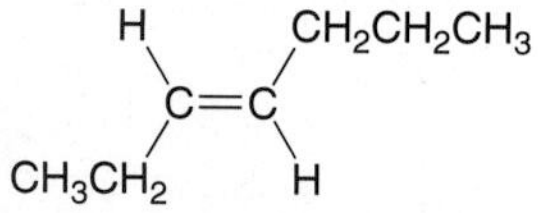

c.

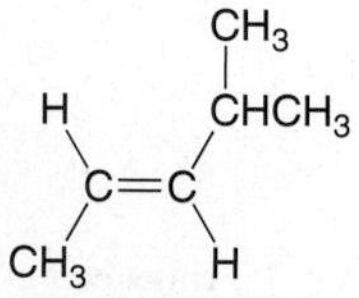

13.9

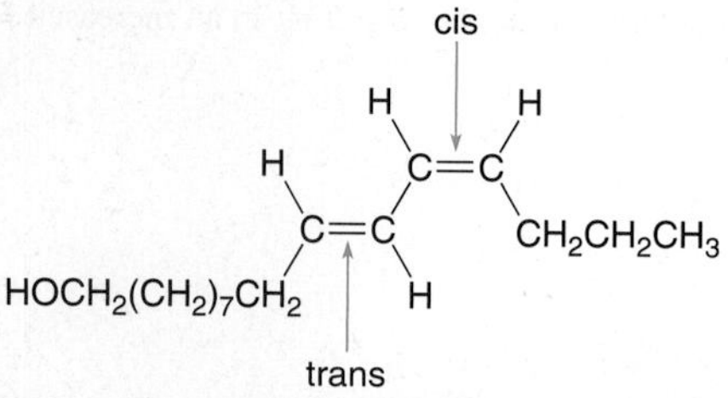

cis

trans

13.11

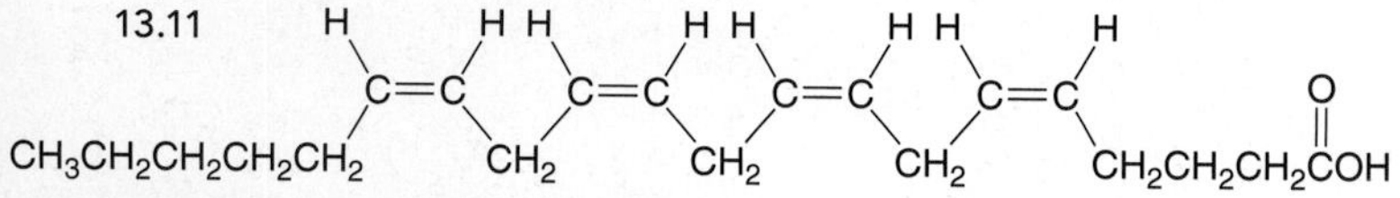

13.13　three aromatic rings, alkene, ether, amine

13.15　a. $CH_3CH_2CH_2CH_2CH_2CH_3$

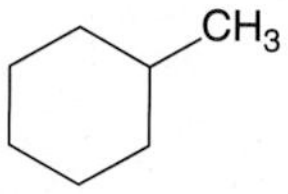

　　　b. 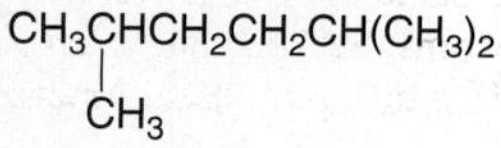 $CH_3CHCH_2CH_2CH(CH_3)_2$
　　　　　　CH_3

　　　c.

13.17　a.

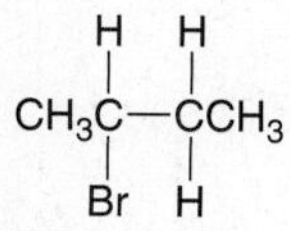

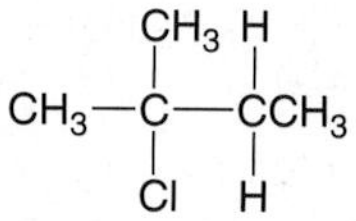

　　　b.

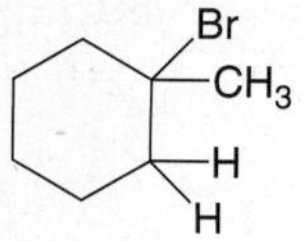

　　　c.

　　　d.

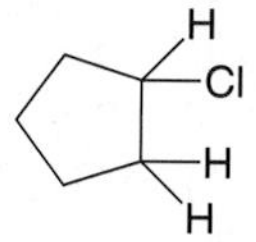

13.19　a. 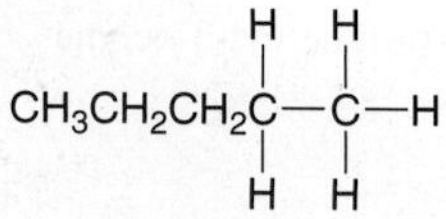 $CH_3CH_2CH_2C{-}C{-}H$

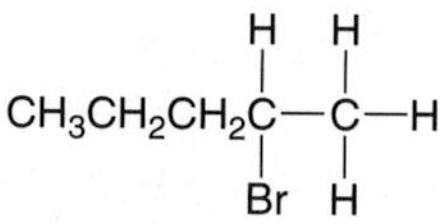

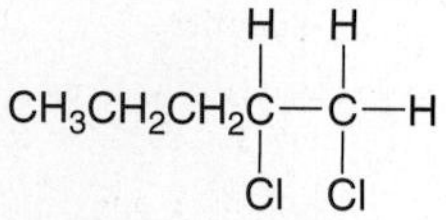

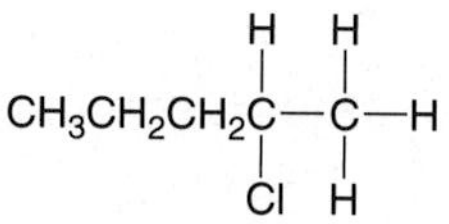

　　　b. $CH_3CH_2CH_2C{-}C{-}H$

　　　c. $CH_3CH_2CH_2C{-}C{-}H$

　　　d. $CH_3CH_2CH_2C{-}C{-}H$

　　　e. $CH_3CH_2CH_2C{-}C{-}H$

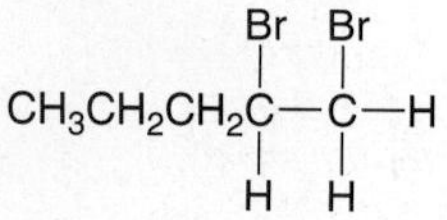

　　　f. 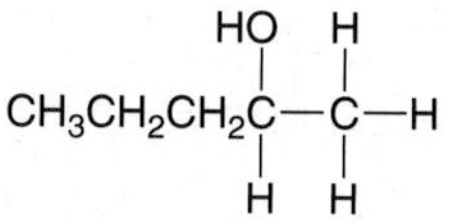 $CH_3CH_2CH_2C{-}C{-}H$

13.21　a.

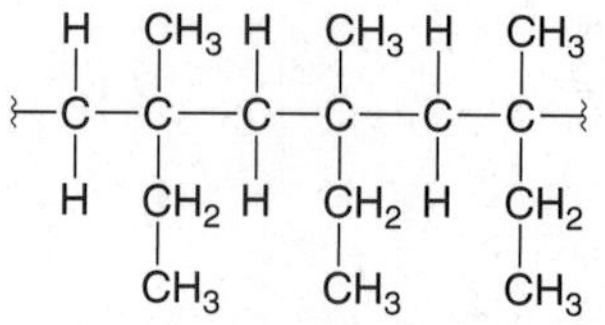

　　　b.

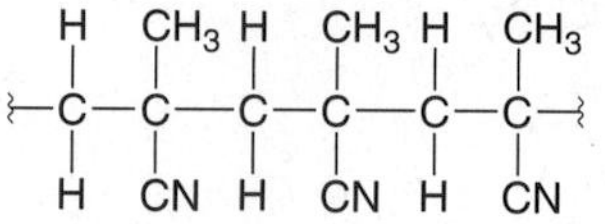

　　　c.

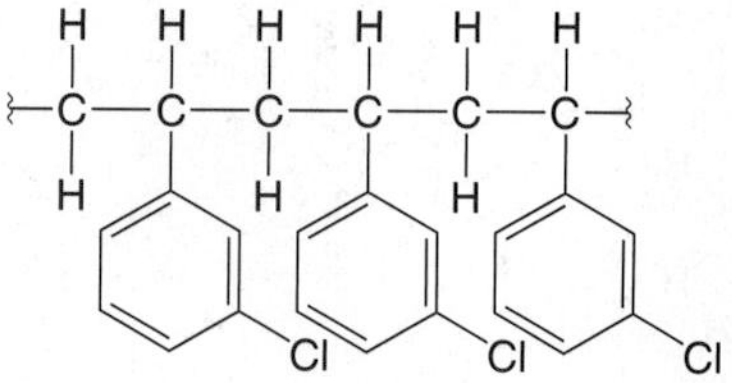

13.23　a. propylbenzene
　　　b. *p*-ethyliodobenzene
　　　c. *m*-butylphenol
　　　d. 2-bromo-5-chlorotoluene

13.25　Compound (a) might be found in a sunscreen since it contains two aromatic rings.

13.27　a.

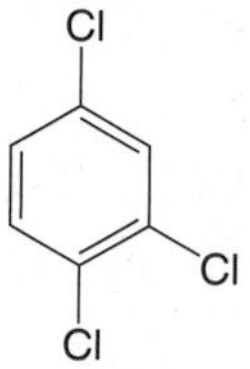

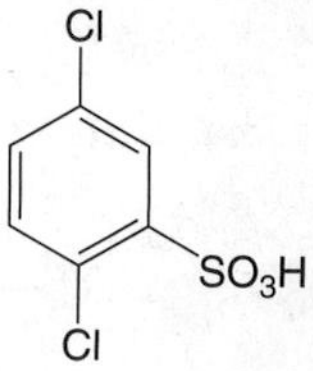

　　　b.

　　　c.

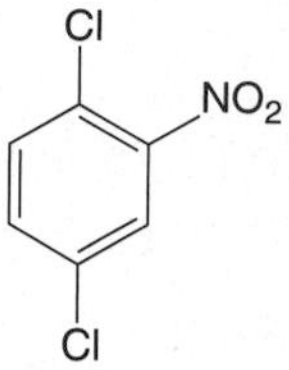

13.29　a. $C_{10}H_{12}O$
　　　b. aromatic ring, alkene, ether
　　　c. trans
　　　d.

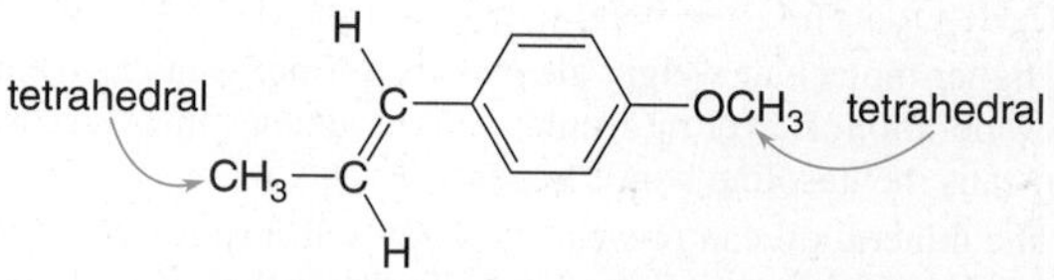

tetrahedral　　　　　　　　　　　　tetrahedral

All other C's are trigonal planar.

13.31　a. $C_{10}H_{22}$
　　　b. $C_{10}H_{20}$
　　　c. $C_{10}H_{18}$

13.33　$HC{\equiv}CCH_2CH_2CH_3$

　　　$CH_3C{\equiv}CCH_2CH_3$

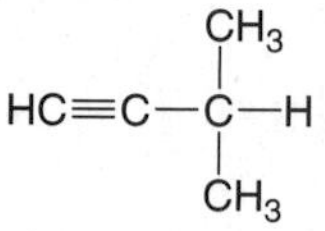

13.35 a.

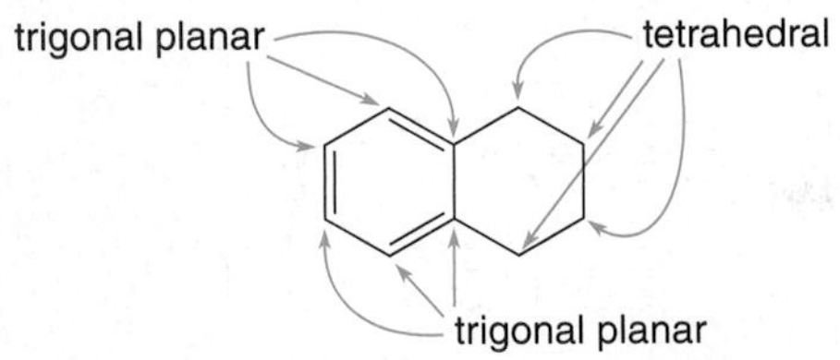

trigonal planar — tetrahedral — trigonal planar

b. linear

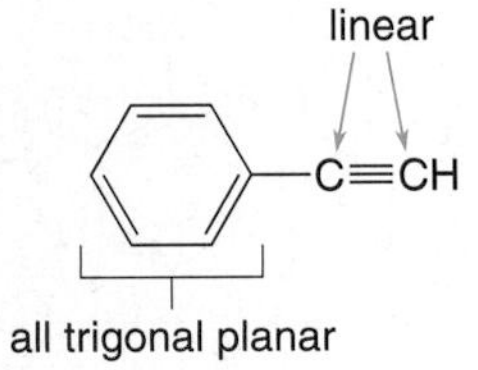

$-C\equiv CH$

all trigonal planar

c. tetrahedral — trigonal planar

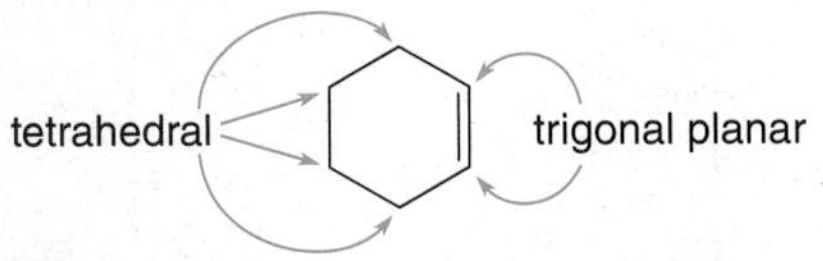

13.37 a. 2-ethyl-1-butene   b. 2-hexyne

13.39 a. 5,5-dimethyl-1-hexene
b. 3-ethyl-5,7-dimethyl-3-octene
c. 2-ethyl-1-heptene
d. 5,5-dimethyl-2-hexyne
e. 6-ethyl-5,6-dimethyl-2-octyne
f. 3,3-dimethyl-1,5-hexadiene

13.41 a. 4-methylcyclohexene
b. 3,3-diethylcyclobutene

13.43 a. $CH_2=CHCH(CH_3)CH_2CH_2CH_2CH_2CH_3$

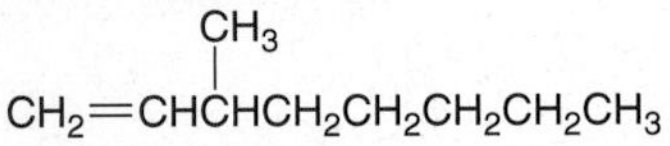

b. (cyclobutene with CH_2CH_3 substituent)

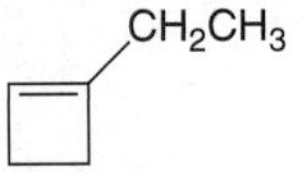

c. $CH_3CH_2C\equiv CC(CH_3)(H)CH_3$

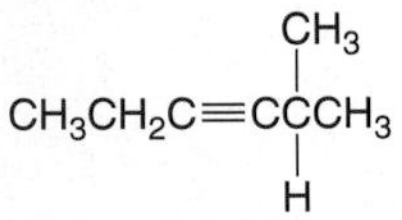

d. $CH_3CH_2CH(CH_2CH_3)C=C(CH_3)(CH_2CH_3)CHCH_3$

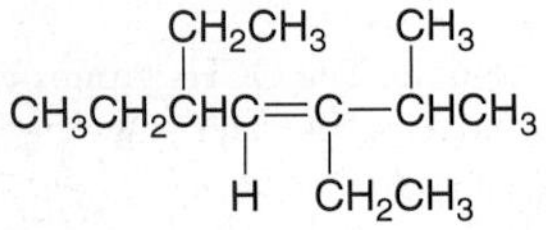

e. $CH_2=CH-CH=CHCH_2CH_2CH_3$

f. CH_3 and $CH_2CH_2CH_2CH(CH_3)CH_3$ on $C=C$ with H, H

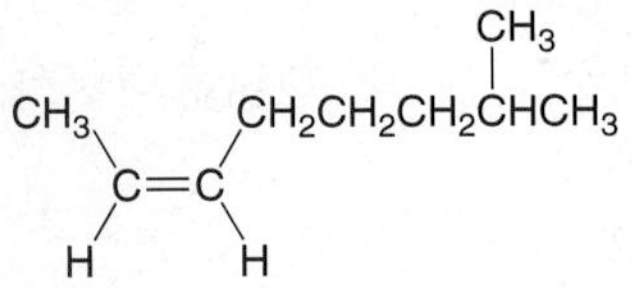

13.45 a. Assign lower number to alkene: 2-methyl-2-hexene.
b. five-carbon chain: 2-pentene
c. Number to put the C=C between C1 and C2, and then give the first substituent the lower number: 1,6-dimethylcyclohexene.
d. seven-carbon chain: 3-methyl-1-heptyne

13.47

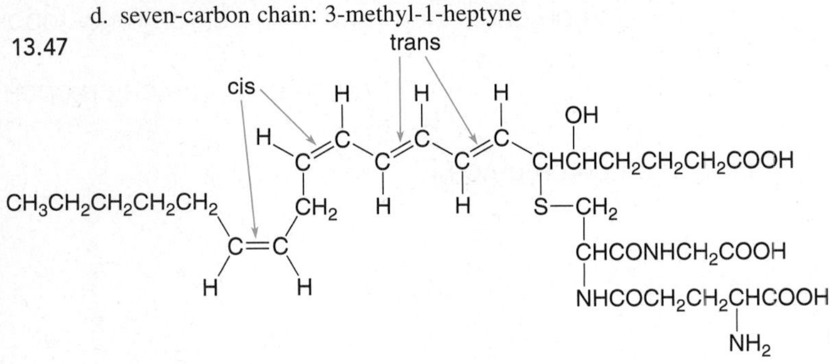

cis — trans

$CH_3CH_2CH_2CH_2CH_2$ ... $C=C$ ... chain with OH, $CHCHCH_2CH_2CH_2COOH$, $S-CH_2$, $CHCONHCH_2COOH$, $NHCOCH_2CH_2CHCOOH$, NH_2

13.49 cis alkene, *cis*-4-methyl-2-pentene

13.51 a.

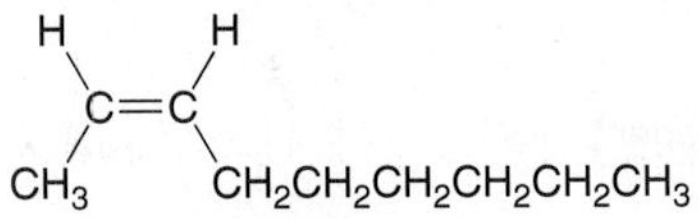

H, H on $C=C$; CH_3 and $CH_2CH_2CH_2CH_2CH_2CH_3$

cis-2-nonene

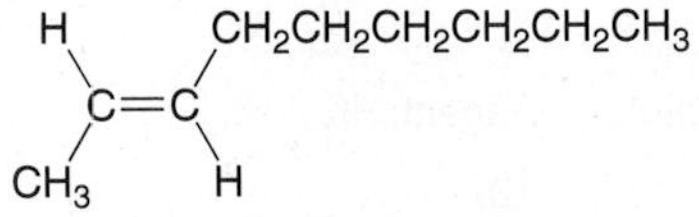

H and $CH_2CH_2CH_2CH_2CH_2CH_3$; CH_3 and H on $C=C$

trans-2-nonene

b.

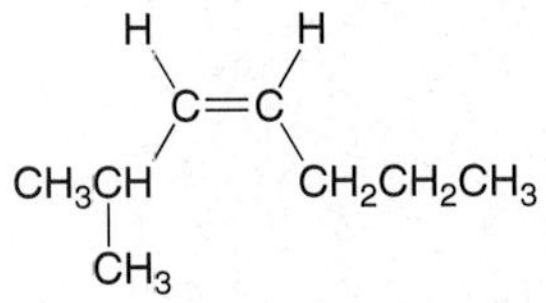

H, H on $C=C$; $CH_3CH(CH_3)$ and $CH_2CH_2CH_3$

cis-2-methyl-3-heptene

H and $CH_2CH_2CH_3$; $CH_3CH(CH_3)$ and H on $C=C$

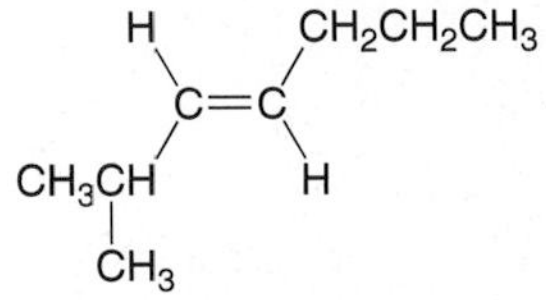

trans-2-methyl-3-heptene

13.53 Constitutional isomers have the same molecular formula but have the atoms bonded to different atoms. Stereoisomers have atoms bonded to the same atoms but in a different three-dimensional arrangement.

13.55 a. identical   b. constitutional isomers

13.57 a. $CH_3CH_2CH_2CH_2CH_2CH_3$

b. $(CH_3)_2CHCH_2CH_2CH_2CH_3$

c. (methylcyclohexane, CH_3)

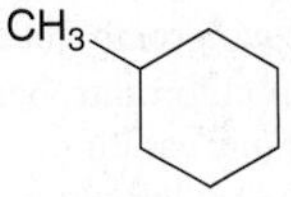

d. (methylcyclohexane, H and CH_3)

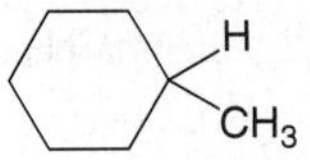

13.59 a. (cyclobutane with Cl)

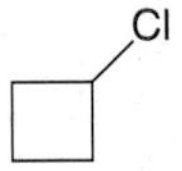

b. $(CH_3)_2C-C(CH_3)_2$ with Cl and H

c. $CH_3CHCH_2CH(CH_3)_2$ with Cl

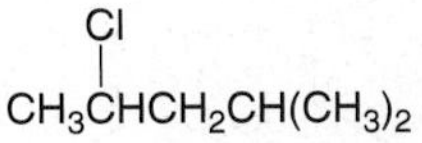

d. (cyclohexane with CH_3 and Cl)

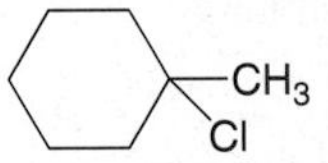

13.61 a. (cyclohexane: CH_2CH_3, H, H)

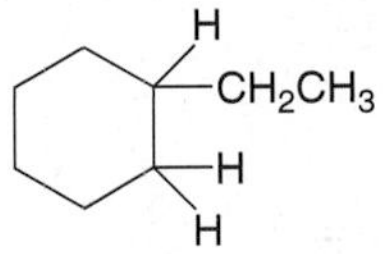

b. (cyclohexane: Cl, CH_2CH_3, Cl, H)

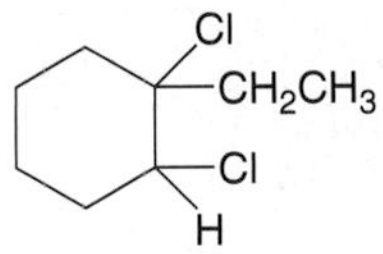

c. (cyclohexane: Br, CH_2CH_3, Br, H)

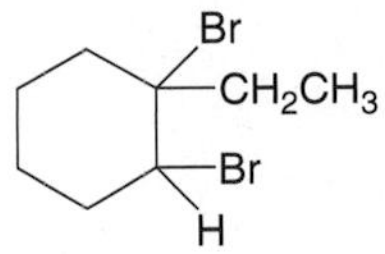

d. (cyclohexane: Cl, CH_2CH_3, H, H)

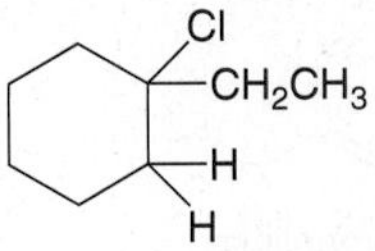

e. (cyclohexane: Br, CH_2CH_3, H, H)

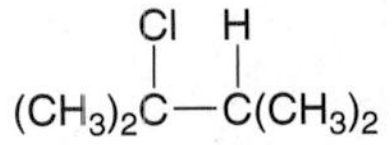

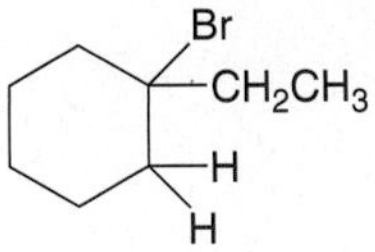

f. (cyclohexane: OH, CH_2CH_3, H, H)

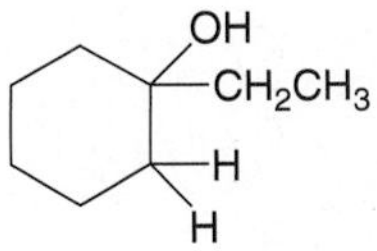

13.63 $CH_2{=}CH_2$ reagent: HBr

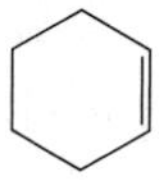

reagent: HCl

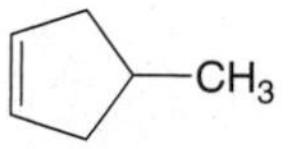

$—CH_3$ reagent: Cl_2

$CH_2{=}CHCH_2CH(CH_3)_2$ reagent: Br_2

13.65 a. HCl   d. HBr
b. H_2, Pd   e. Br_2
c. H_2O, H_2SO_4 f. Cl_2

13.67

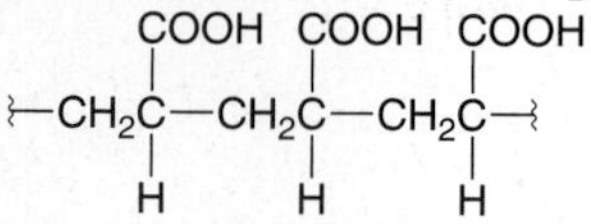

13.69 a.

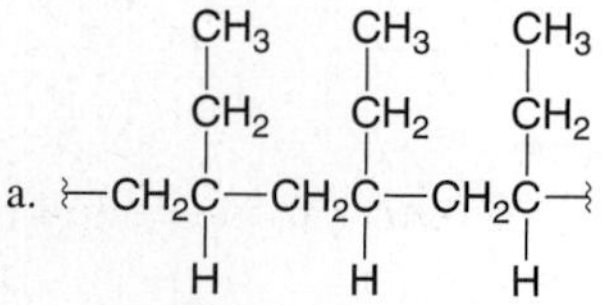

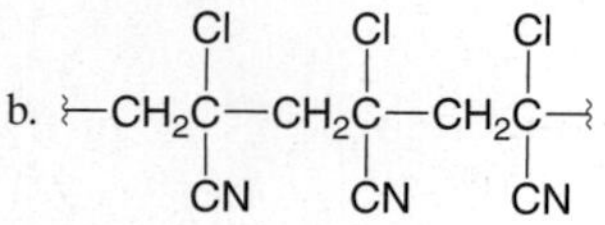

c.

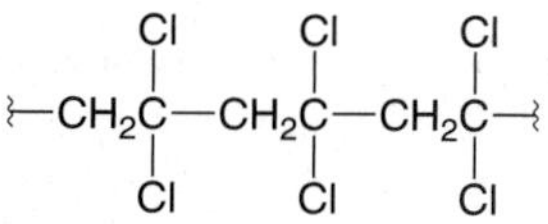

b.

13.71 $CH_2{=}C$

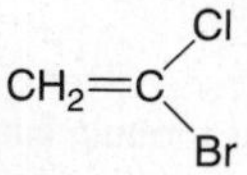

13.73

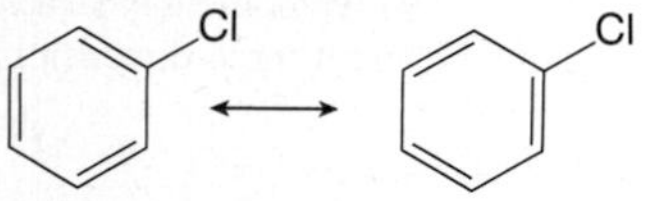

13.75 a. *p*-chloroethylbenzene   b. *o*-bromofluorobenzene
13.77 a. *m*-chloronitrobenzene
b. *p*-nitroaniline
c. *o*-butylethylbenzene
d. 2,5-dichlorophenol

13.79 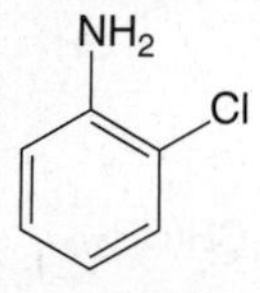
o-chloroaniline

p-chloroaniline

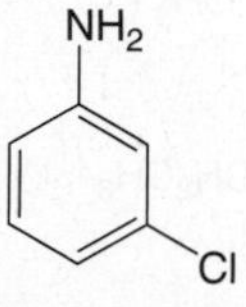

m-chloroaniline

13.81 a.

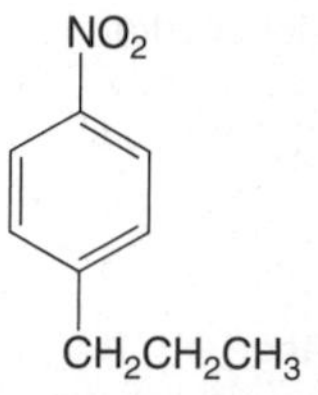

b.

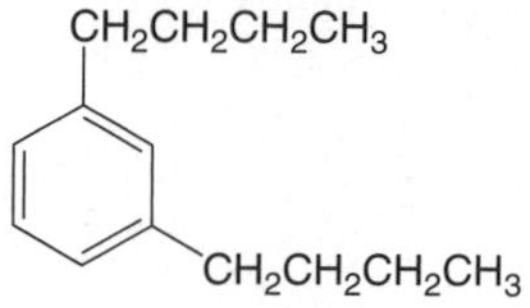

c.

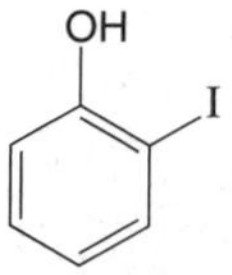

d.

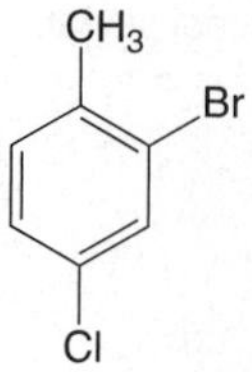

e.

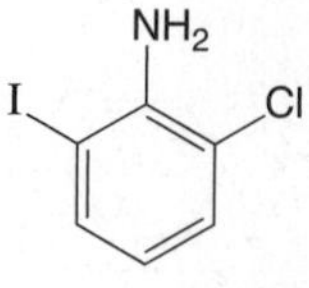

13.83 a. 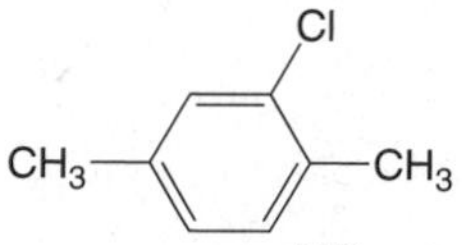   c.

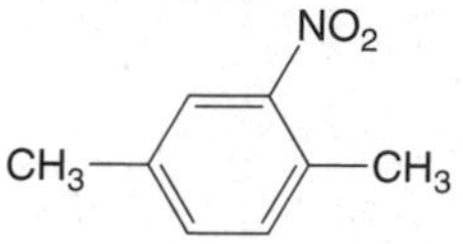

b.

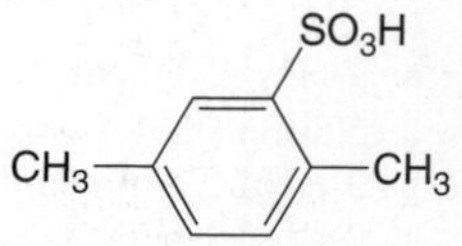

13.85

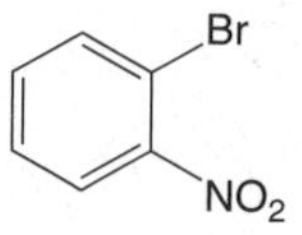

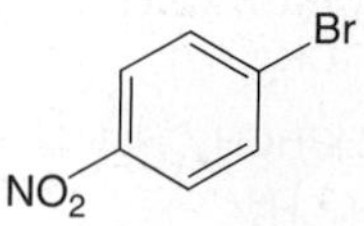

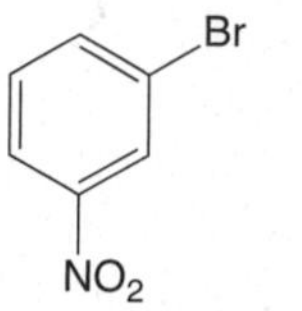

13.87 Vitamin E is an antioxidant.
13.89 Methoxychlor is more water soluble. The OCH_3 groups can hydrogen bond to water. This increase in water solubility makes methoxychlor more biodegradable.
13.91 a.

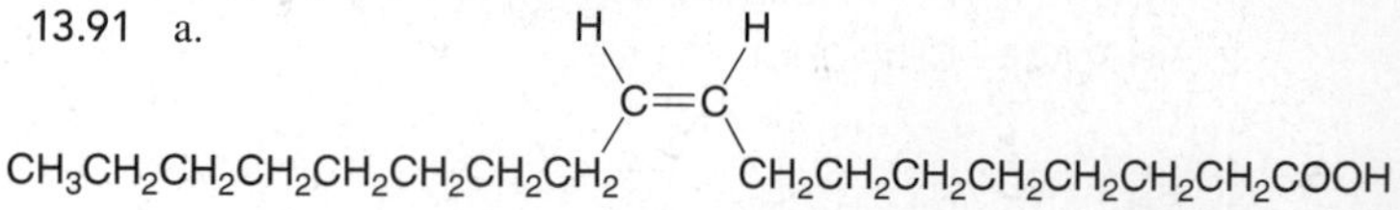

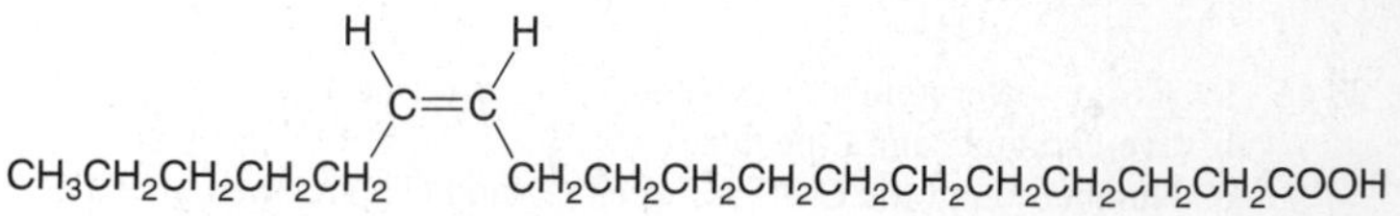

b.
$CH_3CH_2CH_2CH_2CH_2CH_2CH_2CH_2CH_2CH_2CH_2CH_2CH_2CH_2CH_2CH_2CH_2COOH$

c.
one possibility:

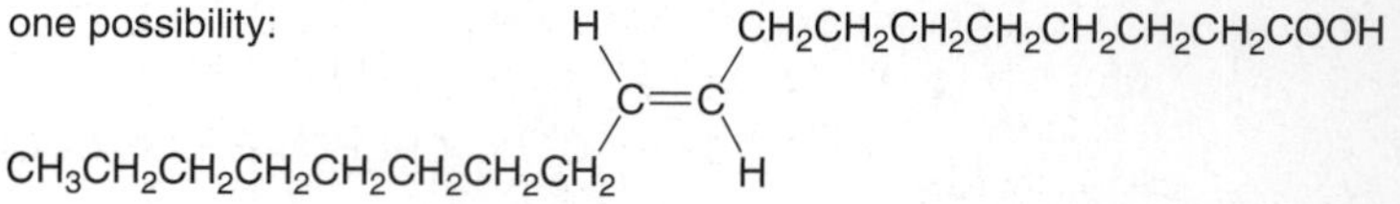

13.93 c.

13.95 Benzene is converted to a more water-soluble compound that can then be excreted in the urine.

13.97 a.

$$CH_3(CH_2)_5 \quad C=C \quad (CH_2)_7COOH$$

b.

$$CH_3(CH_2)_5 \quad C=C \quad (CH_2)_7COOH$$

c.

$$CH_3(CH_2)_4 \quad C=C \quad (CH_2)_8COOH \quad \text{is one possibility}$$

13.99 All the carbons in benzene are trigonal planar with 120° bond angles, resulting in a flat ring. In cyclohexane, all the carbons are tetrahedral so the ring is puckered.

13.101 a. $CH_2{=}CH(CH_2)_4CH_3$ 1-heptene
  b. $CH_3(CH_2)_5CH_3$
  c. $CH_3CH(OH)CH_2CH_2CH_2CH_2CH_3$
  d. $-CH_2C{-}CH_2C{-}CH_2C-$ R = $(CH_2)_4CH_3$

13.103 They are constitutional isomers because the double bond is located in a different place on the carbon chain.

CHAPTER 14

14.1 a.

b. The OH on the benzene ring of salmeterol is part of a phenol.

14.3 a. 3° b. 1° c. 2°

14.5 a.

b. $(CH_3)_3C{-}OH$

14.7 a. 2-heptanol
  b. 4-ethyl-3-hexanol
  c. 2-methylcyclohexanol
  d. 5-ethyl-6-methyl-3-nonanol

14.9 a. $CH_3{-}C{=}CH_2$ b. c.
        $|$
        H

14.11 **B** has no H on the carbon adjacent to the carbon with the OH group, so H_2O cannot be lost.

14.12 a. $CH_3CCH_2CH_2CH_3$ c.
    b. $(CH_3)_3CCH_2C{-}OH$ d. no reaction

14.13 $H{-}C{-}C{-}H$ which is further oxidized to $HO{-}C{-}C{-}OH$

14.15 a. $CH_3(CH_2)_5OCH_3$ c. $CH_3(CH_2)_6OH$
    b.   d. $CH_3(CH_2)_5OCH_3$

14.17 a. 1-methoxybutane (or butyl methyl ether)
  b. methoxycyclohexane
  c. dipropyl ether

14.19

14.21 a. 3°
  b. 2° OH on six-membered ring, 3° OH on five-membered ring, 1° OH bonded to CH_2 group

14.23 a. 2-bromohexane
  b. 3-chloro-2-methylpentane
  c. 1-bromo-2-methylcyclohexane

14.25 a. CFC b. HCFC c. HFC

14.26 a. 3-pentanethiol
  b. cyclohexanethiol
  c. 5-ethyl-1-heptanethiol

14.27

14.29 a. 1° b. 3° c. 2° d. 2°
14.31 a. 2° b. 3° c. 2° d. 1°

14.33 a. $CH_3CH_2CHCH_2CH_2CH_3$ c. $CH_3CH_2C{-}Br$
                    $|$ $|$
                   OH CH_3 / CH_3
    b. $CH_3{-}O{-}CH_2CH_2CH_2CH_2CH_3$

14.35

$CH_3{-}O{-}CHCH_2CH_3$ $CH_3{-}O{-}CH_2CH_2CH_2CH_3$ $CH_3{-}C{-}O{-}CH_3$
          $|$ $|$
         CH_3 CH_3 / CH_3

$CH_3CH_2CH_2OCH_2CH_3$ $CH_3{-}C{-}O{-}CH_2CH_3$ $(CH_3)_2CHCH_2OCH_3$
                                    $|$
                                    H

14.37 a. 2-methyl-3-pentanol   b. 1-chloro-2-methylcyclopentane
14.39 a. $CH_3CH_2C(CH_3)_2CH(OH)CH_3$
  b. 2°
  c. 3,3-dimethyl-2-pentanol
14.41 a. 2-pentanol
  b. 3,3-dimethyl-2-hexanol
  c. 4-ethyl-6-methyl-1-heptanol
  d. 4-butylcyclohexanol
  e. 2,2-dimethylcyclobutanol
  f. 2,5-diethylcyclopentanol

14.43 a. 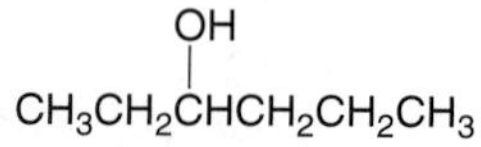
b. $CH_3CH_2CH_2OH$
c. 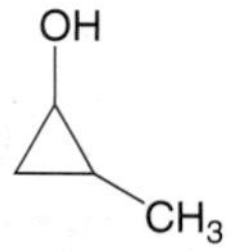
d. 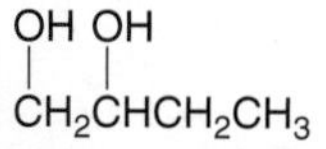
e. 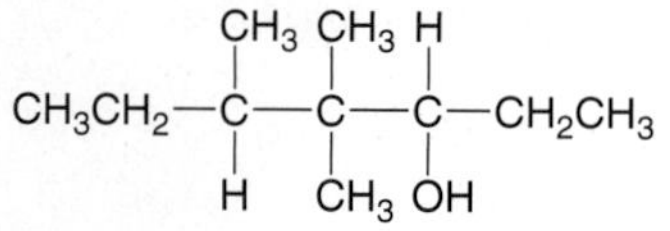
f. 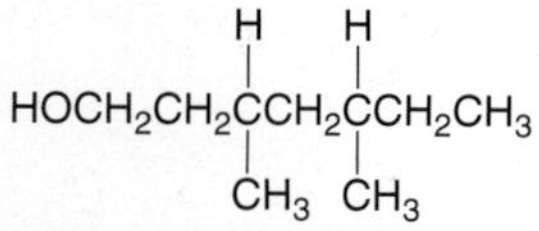

14.45 a. 1-ethoxybutane (or butyl ethyl ether)
b. 2-ethoxypentane
c. ethoxycyclopentane

14.47 2-methoxy-2-methylpropane

14.49 $CH_3CH_2CH_2CH_2CH_2CH_2CH_2OH$ 1-heptanol

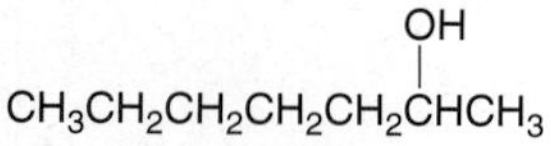 2-heptanol

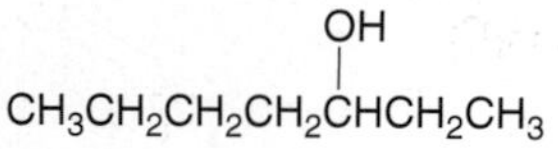 3-heptanol

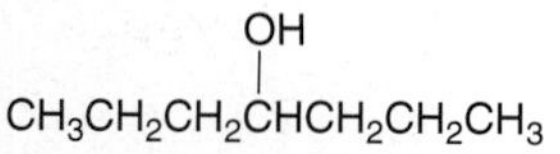 4-heptanol

14.51 a. 4-bromoheptane
b. 1-chloro-3-methylcyclobutane
c. 1-pentanethiol

14.53 a. 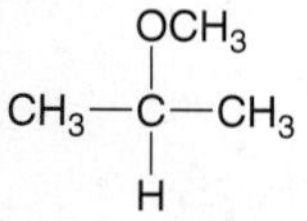 d. $CH_3CH_2CH_2CH_2Cl$
b. 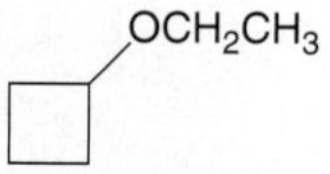 e. 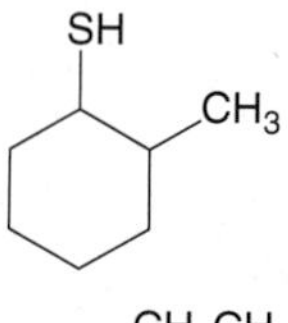
c. 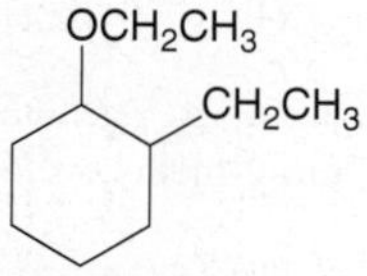 f. 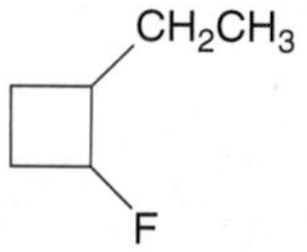

14.55 a. $CH_3CH_2CH_2I$ b. $HOCH_2CH_2OH$ c. $CH_3CH_2CH_2OH$

14.57 Ethanol is a polar molecule capable of hydrogen bonding with itself and water. The greater intermolecular forces make its boiling point higher. Both ethanol and dimethyl ether have only two carbons and can hydrogen bond to H_2O, so both are water soluble.

14.59 1-Butanol is capable of hydrogen bonding with H_2O and is therefore water soluble. 1-Butene is not polar and cannot hydrogen bond with H_2O, so it is not water soluble.

14.61 a. 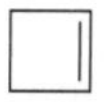
b. 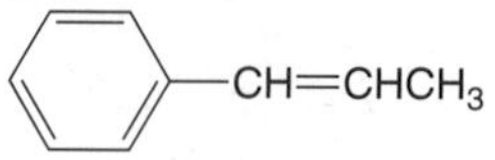
c. $CH_3CH{=}CHCH_2CH_2CH_3$ (major product) + $CH_2{=}CH(CH_2)_3CH_3$
d. 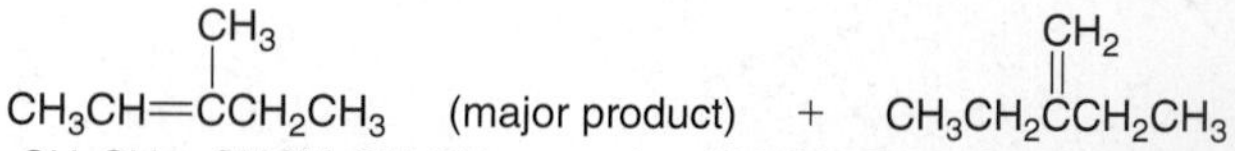

14.63 a. $CH_3CH{=}CHCH_2CH_2CH_3$ and $CH_3CH_2CH{=}CHCH_2CH_3$
b. The carbons of both double bonds are bonded to an equal number of H's; therefore, equal amounts of both isomers are formed.

14.65 a. 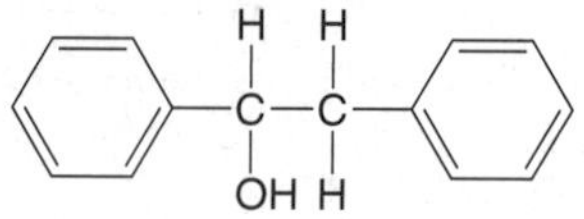 b. 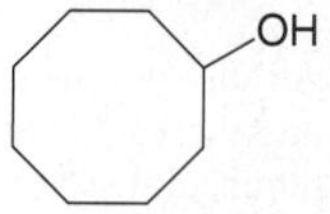

14.67 $CH_3CH_2CH_2OH$ and 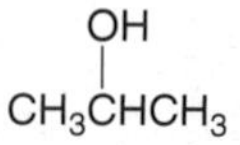

14.69 a. 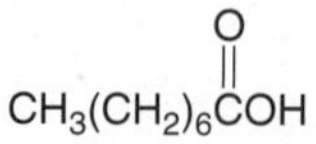 c. 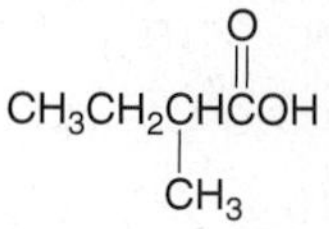
b. 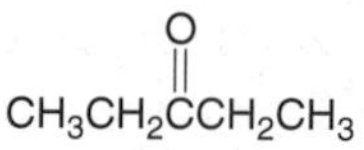 d. no reaction

14.71 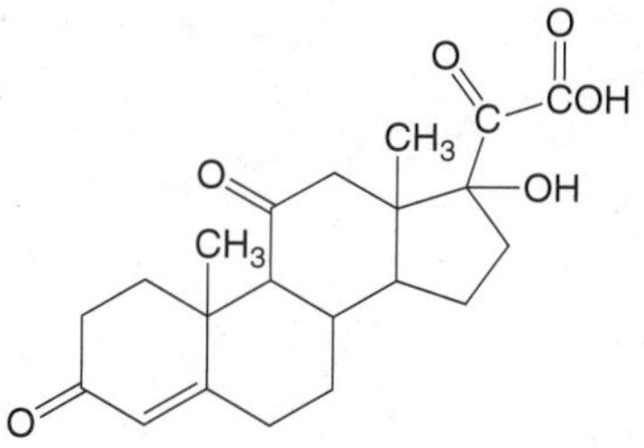

14.73 a. 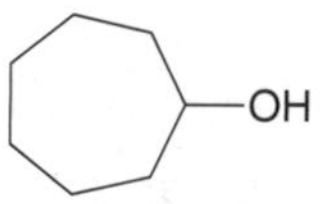 b. 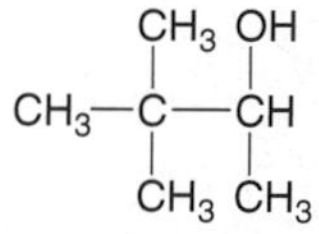 c. 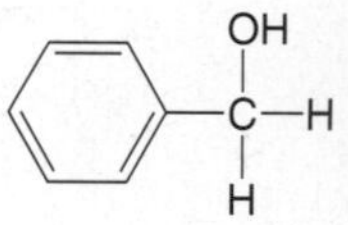

14.75 a. $CH_3CH_2CH_2CH{=}CHCH_2CH_3$
b. 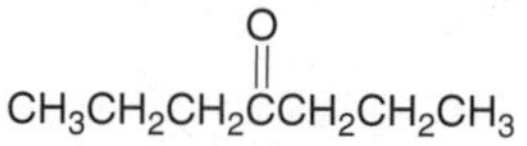

14.77 a. 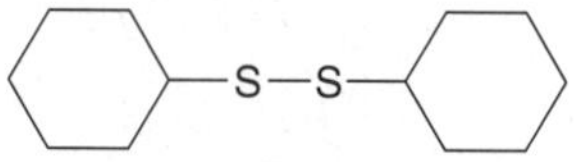
b. $CH_3(CH_2)_4S{-}S(CH_2)_4CH_3$

14.79 a. CH_3SH and $HSCH_2CH_2CH_3$
b. $CH_2{=}CHCH_2SH$ and $HSCH_2CH_2CH_3$

14.81 $C_4H_{10}O + 6\,O_2 \longrightarrow 4\,CO_2 + 5\,H_2O$

14.83 a. CFCs are chlorofluorocarbons with a general formula of CF_xCl_{4-x}. HCFCs have fluorine, chlorine, and hydrogen bonded to carbons, and HFCs have only hydrogen and fluorine bonded to carbon.
b. CFCs interact and destroy the ozone layer, whereas HCFCs and HFCs decompose before ascending to the ozone layer.

14.85 PEG is capable of hydrogen bonding with water and this makes it water soluble. PVC cannot hydrogen bond to water so it is water insoluble.

14.87

$$CH_3CH_2OH \ + \ K_2Cr_2O_7 \ \longrightarrow \ CH_3\overset{O}{\overset{\|}{C}}OH \ + \ Cr^{3+} \ \text{ (green color)}$$
(orange)

The greater the blood alcohol level, the greater the color change from red-orange to green on the Breathalyzer.

14.89 $CH_3\overset{O}{\overset{\|}{C}}-\overset{O}{\overset{\|}{C}}OH$

pyruvic acid

14.91

$CH_3CH_2OH \longrightarrow$ acetaldehyde $\longrightarrow$ acetic acid

Antabuse
(blocks conversion)

Antabuse blocks the conversion of acetaldehyde to acetic acid and the accumulation of acetaldehyde makes people ill.

14.93 $(CH_3)_3COH$

14.95 Ether molecules have no H's on O's capable of hydrogen bonding to other ether molecules, but the hydrogens in water can hydrogen bond to the oxygen of the ether.

14.97 a. 3-ethylcyclopentanol
b. 2°
c. [structure] —CH₂CH₃ and [structure] —CH₂CH₃
d. [structure] —CH₂CH₃
e. [structure] —CH₂CH₃
f. [structure] —OCH₂CH₃

14.99 a. $CH_3CH_2\overset{CH_3}{\underset{H}{C}}CH_2OH$ **A** b. $CH_3CH{=}\overset{CH_3}{C}{-}CH_3$

$CH_3CH_2\overset{CH_3}{\underset{OH}{C}}CH_3$ **B**

CHAPTER 15

15.1 a. constitutional isomers   c. identical
b. stereoisomers   d. constitutional isomers

15.3 a, d: achiral   b, c: chiral

15.5 a. $CH_3\overset{}{\underset{Cl}{C}}HCH_2CH_3$ c. $CH_2{=}CHCHCH_3$ (OH)
b. none   d. [benzene ring]—$\overset{H}{\underset{Br}{C}}$—CH₃

15.7 a. $CH_3CH_2CH_2{-}\overset{H}{\underset{OH}{C}}{-}CH_3$

b. $H_2N{-}\overset{COOH}{\underset{}{C}}{-}H$; $CH_3{-}\overset{}{\underset{CH_2CH_3}{C}}{-}H$

c. $CH_3CH_2{-}\overset{Br}{\underset{H}{C}}{-}CH_2CH_2{-}\overset{Cl}{\underset{H}{C}}{-}CH_3$

15.9 a. [wedge structure with CH₃, Cl, H, CH₂CH₃] and [mirror image with CH₃, H, CH₃CH₂, Cl]

b. [structure with OH, H, CH₂CH₃, CH₂OH] and [structure CH₃CH₂, HO, H, HOCH₂]

15.11 $CH_3NH{-}$[fused bicyclic structure with aryl group, Cl, Cl]

15.13 a. $H{-}\overset{CH_3}{\underset{Cl}{|}}{-}Br$ b. $H{-}\overset{COOH}{\underset{CH_2Cl}{|}}{-}OH$

15.15 a. $CH_3{-}\overset{H}{\underset{OH}{|}}{-}CH_2CH_2CH_3$ $CH_3CH_2CH_2{-}\overset{H}{\underset{OH}{|}}{-}CH_3$

b. $ClCH_2{-}\overset{H}{\underset{Cl}{|}}{-}CH_2CH_3$ $CH_3CH_2{-}\overset{H}{\underset{Cl}{|}}{-}CH_2Cl$

15.16 b. optically active; a, c, d: optically inactive
15.17 optically inactive
15.18 a. levorotatory   b. +32
15.19 a. [structure with COO⁻, H, CH₃, H₃N⁺]

(R)-alanine

15.20 a. **Z**   b. **Y**   c. **Z** and **W**   d. **Y** and **X**
15.21

W	X	Y	Z
CH₃	CH₃	CH₃	CH₃
H—Cl	H—Cl	Cl—H	Cl—H
H—Br	Br—H	H—Br	Br—H
CH₂CH₃	CH₂CH₃	CH₂CH₃	CH₂CH₃
W	**X**	**Y**	**Z**

15.23 a, d: achiral   b, c: chiral
15.25 Butane does not have an enantiomer since the molecule and its mirror image *are* superimposable and therefore not enantiomers.

15.27 a. [structure CF₃, Cl, H, Br]   b. [structure H, H, Cl, Cl]

chiral   achiral

15.29 **B** enantiomer; **C** identical

15.31 a. none   c. none

b. CH₃CHCHCl₂
         |
         Cl

d. CH₃CH₂CHCH₃ with CH₃, Cl, H substituents (CH₃CCH₂CHCH₃)

15.33 a. none

c. cyclopentene ring with CH₃

b. cyclohexene ring with —OH

d. none

15.35
                    CH₃
                    |
a. CH₃CH₂—C—CH₂CH₂CH₃
                    |
                    H

                    OH
                    |
b. CH₃CH₂—C—CH₂CH₂CH₃
                    |
                    H

15.37 A chirality center must have a carbon bonded to four groups and a carbonyl carbon has only three groups.

15.39 a. (pyridine-pyrrolidine structure with N—CH₃)

b. HO₂CCH₂CHCNHCHCH₂—(phenyl)
              | ‖ |
             NH₂ O   CO₂CH₃

15.41 (phenyl)—CH₂CHNCH₃
                         | |
                        CH₃ H

(two structures: C with CH₃, H, CH₂(phenyl), NHCH₃) and (mirror image with CH₃, H, CH₃NH, CH₂(phenyl))

15.43 a. identical   b, c: enantiomers

15.45 a. constitutional isomers   c. identical
          b. enantiomers   d. diastereomers

15.47 a. CH₃CH₂CCOOH
                        |
                       CH₃

c. CH₃CH₂CHCH₂CH (with OH and O)

b. CH₃CH₂CH₂CH₂COOH

15.49
          CHO
          |
CH₃—C—CH₃
          |
          CH₃

CH₃—C—CH₂CH₃ (chirality center, with CHO and H)

CH₃CH₂CH₂CH₂CHO   CH₃CHCH₂CHO
                                      |
                                     CH₃

15.51
          CHO
          |
Br—|—H
          |
         CH₃

15.53
          CHO   OCH₃
          | |
a. H—|—OH   b. CH₃—|—H
          | |
         CH₃   CH₃—|—OH CH₂CH₃
                                      CH₂CH₃

15.55
          CH₃   COOH
          | |
a. H—C—F   b. H—C—NH₂
          | |
     CH(CH₃)₂   CH₃—C—H
                                      |
                                   CH₂CH₃

15.57 a, d: identical   b, c: enantiomers

15.59 a. An optically active compound rotates the plane of polarized light. An optically inactive compound does not rotate the plane of polarized light.

b. one possibility: CH₃CH₂CH₂CH₂OH

c. one possibility:
                    CH₃
                    |
CH₃CH₂—C⋯H
                    OH

chiral and optically active

15.61 a. optically active   b, c: optically inactive

15.63 a. dextrorotatory   b. −52   c. 22 g

15.65 Enantiomers are stereoisomers that are nonsuperimposable mirror images of one another, whereas diastereomers are stereoisomers that are not mirror images of one another.

15.67 a. 1, 2, 5, 6: diastereomers   3, 4: enantiomers

b.
          CH₂OH
          |
          C=O
          |
     H—C—OH
          |
         CH₂OH

15.69 They are diastereomers because they are not mirror images of one another.

15.71 a. CH₃CHCO₂H
                        |
                       OH

                    H   H
                    | |
b. CH₃—C—COOH   HOOC—C—CH₃
                    | |
                   OH   OH

                    H   H
                    | |
c. CH₃—|—COOH   HOOC—|—CH₃
                    | |
                   OH   OH

15.73
          OH   CH₃
          | |
a. CH₃CCH₂CH₂CH₂CH—CH₂CHO
          |
         CH₃

b. CH₃CCH₂CH₂CH₂—C—CH₂CHO (HO, CH₃, H)   OHCCH₂—C—CH₂CH₂CH₂CCH₃ (CH₃, H, OH, CH₃)

c. CH₃CCH₂CH₂CH₂—|—CH₂CHO (HO, CH₃, H)   OHCCH₂—|—CH₂CH₂CH₂CCH₃ (CH₃, H, OH, CH₃)

15.75 a.

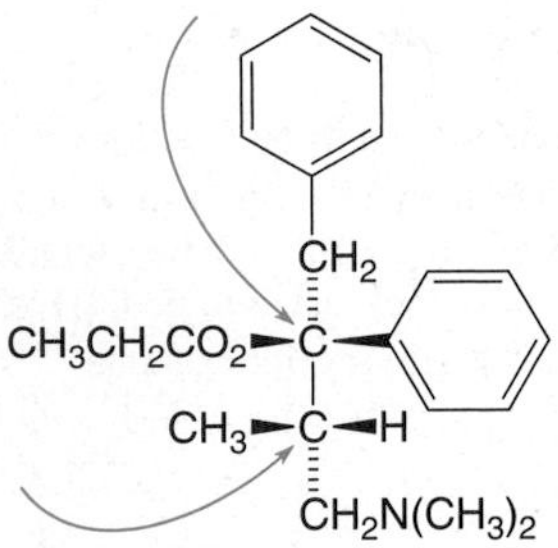

b.

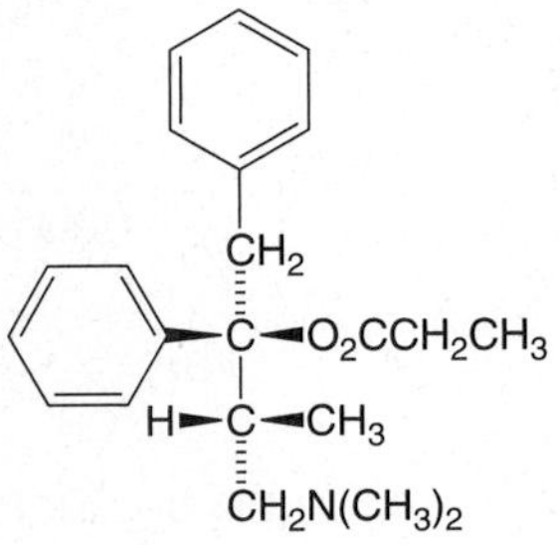

c.

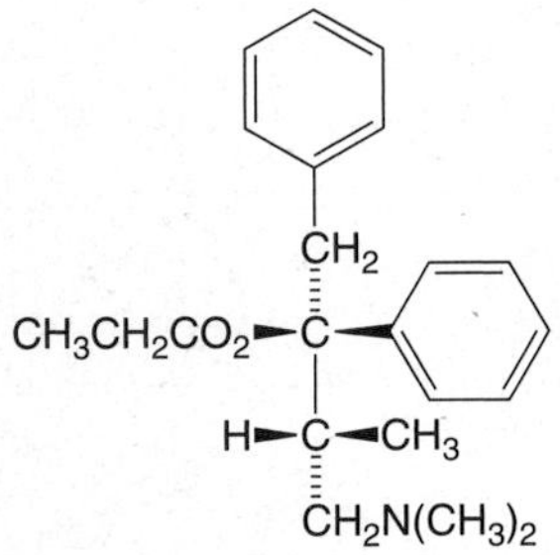

d.

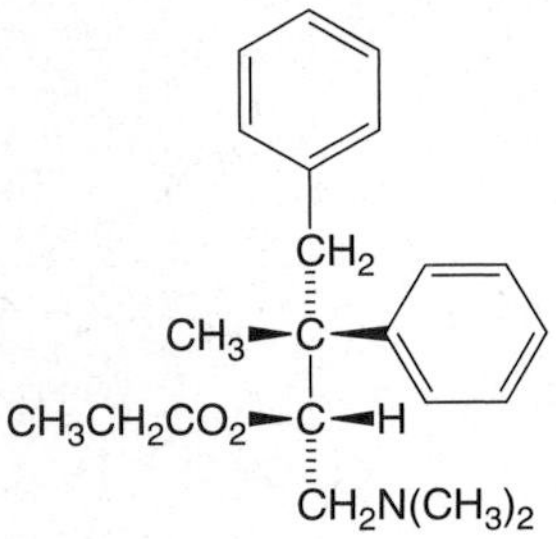

e.

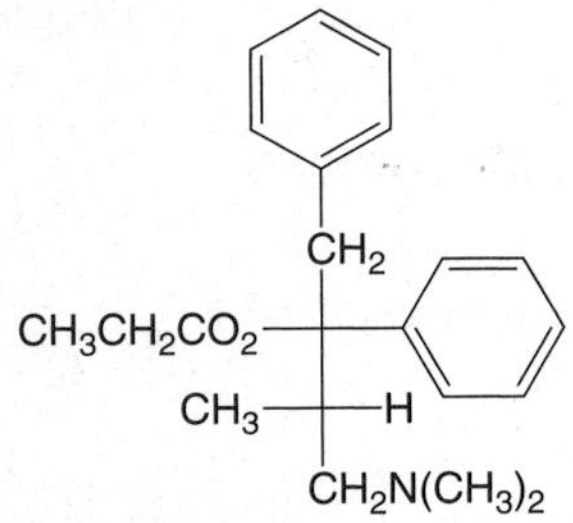

15.77 * = chirality center

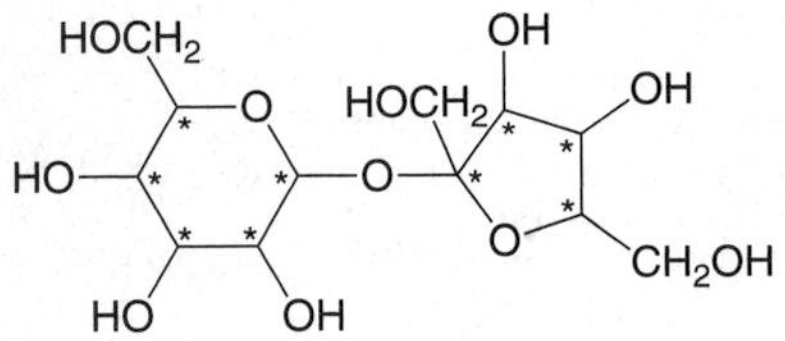

CHAPTER 16

16.1 a. 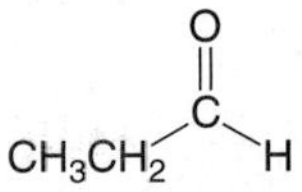 aldehyde

b. 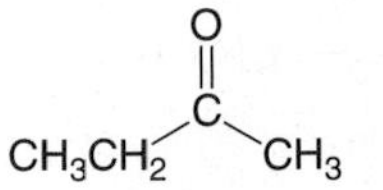 ketone

c. 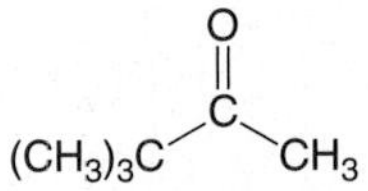 ketone

d. 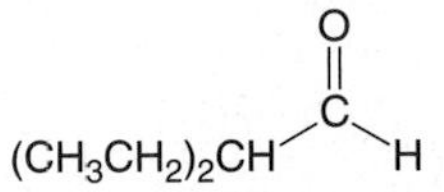 $(CH_3CH_2)_2CH$ aldehyde

16.3

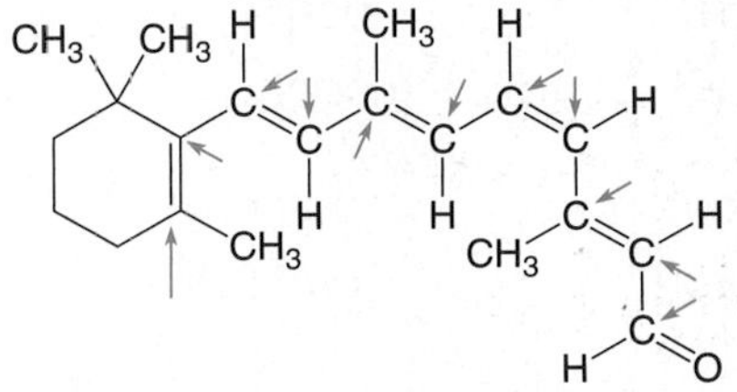

16.4 a. 5-methylhexanal
b. 3,3,4,4-tetramethylpentanal
c. 2,5,6-trimethyloctanal

16.5 a.

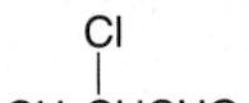

b.

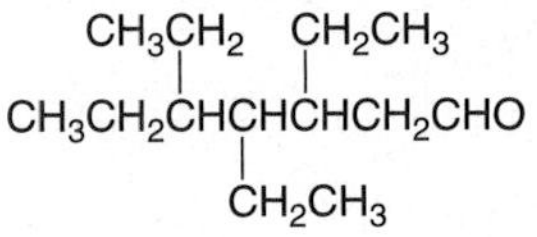

c.

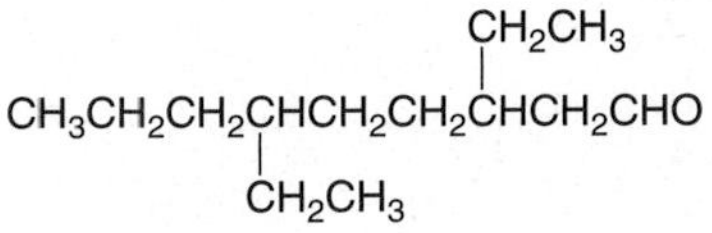

d.

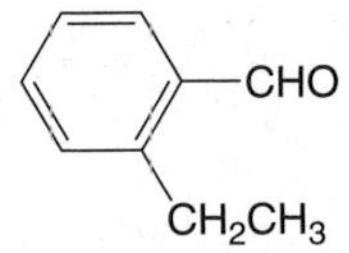

16.7 a. 4-methyl-3-heptanone
b. 2-methylcyclopentanone
c. 2,2-dimethyl-3-heptanone

16.9 a. 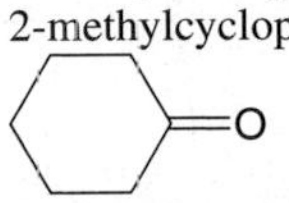 c.
b. $(CH_3CH_2)_2CO$ d. $CH_3(CH_2)_5CHO$

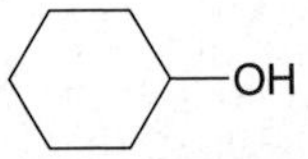

16.11 Hexane is soluble in acetone because both compounds are organic and "like dissolves like." Water is soluble in acetone because acetone has a short hydrocarbon chain and is capable of hydrogen bonding with water.

16.13 a. 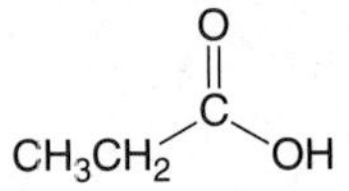 c.
b. no reaction

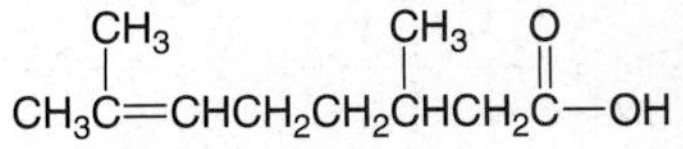

16.14 a. 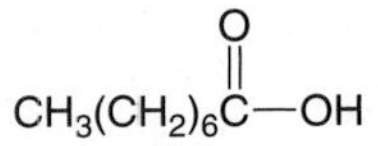 $CH_3(CH_2)_6$ c. 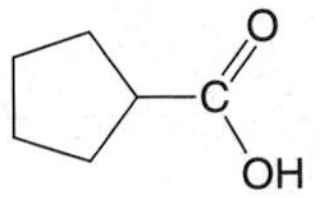
b, d: no reaction

16.15 a. $CH_3CH_2CH_2CH_2OH$ c. $CH_3CH(OH)CH_2CH_3$

b. 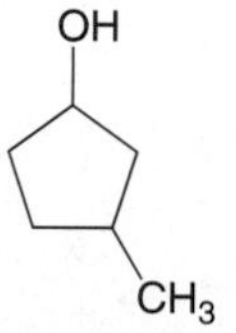

d. 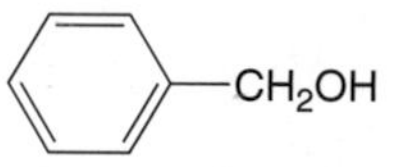

16.17 a. stereoisomers b. not isomers c. stereoisomers

16.18 a. $CH_3CH(OCH_3)OH$ hemiacetal $CH_3CH(OCH_3)OCH_3$ acetal

b. $(CH_3CH_2)_2C(OCH_3)OH$ hemiacetal $(CH_3CH_2)_2C(OCH_3)OCH_3$ acetal

c. 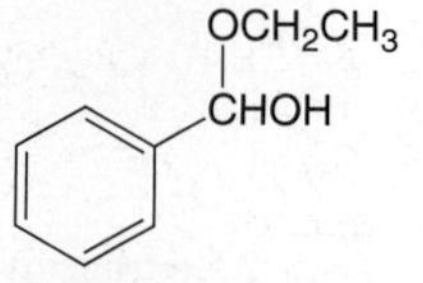

hemiacetal

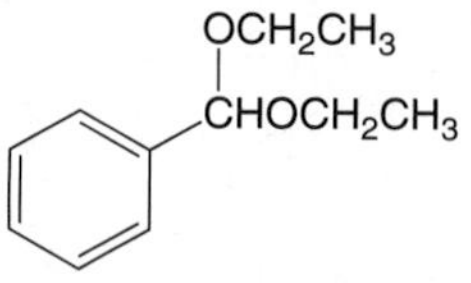

acetal

16.19 a. ether b. acetal c. hemiacetal d. acetal

16.20 a. 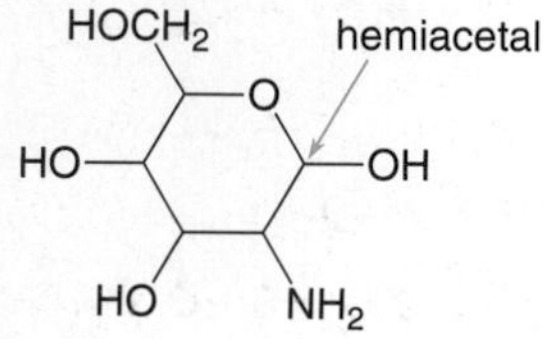

b. 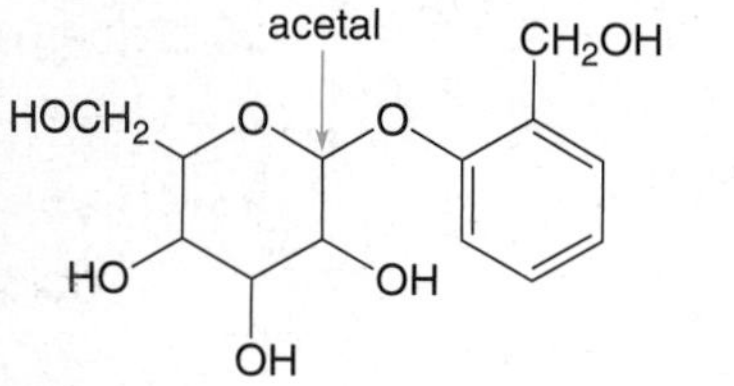

16.21 a. 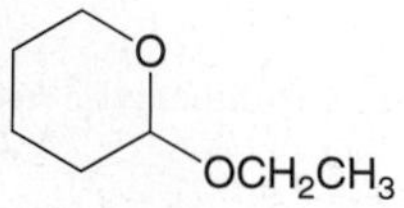

b. 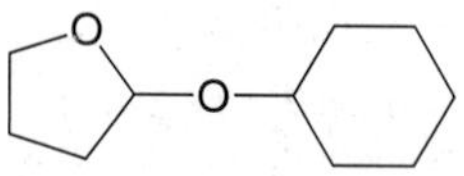

16.22 a. 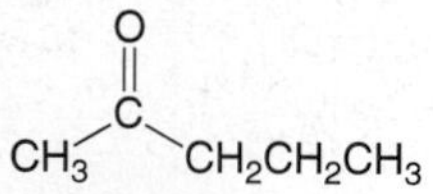 + 2 CH_3OH

b. 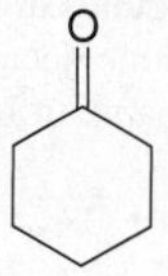 + 2 CH_3CH_2OH

c. 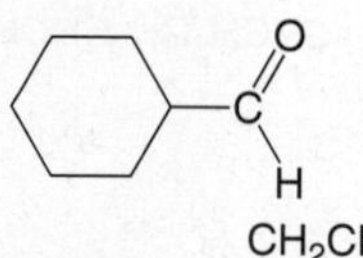 + 2 CH_3OH

16.23 a. $CH_3CH_2CH_2CH(CH_2CH_3)CH_2CHO$

b. $CH_3CH_2C(=O)CH(CH_3)CH_3$

c. 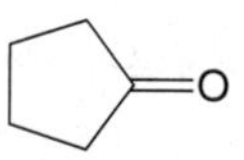

d. 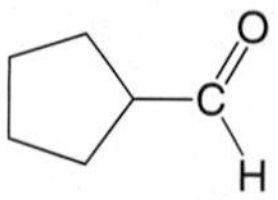

16.25 a. Both are trigonal planar.
b. C=O is polar and C=C is not.
c. Both functional groups undergo addition reactions.

16.27 No, it cannot. $C_5H_{12}O$ has too many H's. Since an aldehyde has a double bond, the number of C's and H's resembles an alkene, not an alkane. A compound with 5 C's would have to be $C_5H_{10}O$.

16.29 a. 2-methylpentanal b. 3-ethylcyclohexanone

16.31 a. 3-methylhexanal
b. 3,5-dimethylheptanal
c. 3-propylhexanal
d. 6,6-diethyl-2,2-dimethyloctanal
e. *p*-chlorobenzaldehyde

16.33 a. $CH_3CH_2CCl_2CH_2CHO$

c. 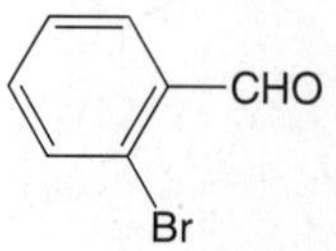

b. $CH_3CH_2CH(CH_3)CH(CH_3)CH_2CHO$

d. $CH_3CH_2CH_2CH(OH)CH_2CH_2CHO$

16.35 a. 4-methyl-2-pentanone
b. 2,6-dimethylcyclohexanone
c. *o*-butylacetophenone
d. 2,4-dimethyl-3-hexanone
e. 3-chlorocyclopentanone

16.37 a. 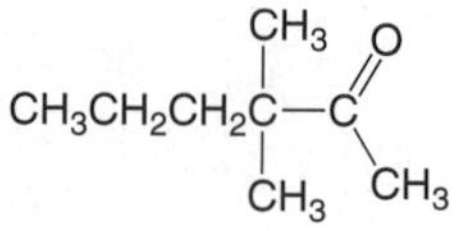

c. 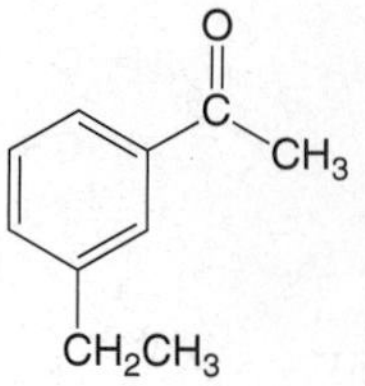

b. 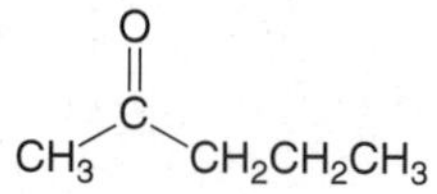

d. 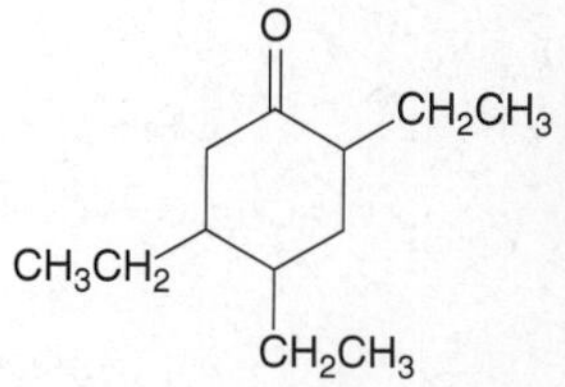

16.39 $CH_3CH_2C(CH_3)_2CHO$ 2,2-dimethylbutanal

$CH_3C(CH_3)_2CH_2CHO$ 3,3-dimethylbutanal

$CH_3CH(CH_3)CH(CH_3)CHO$ 2,3-dimethylbutanal

$CH_3CH_2CH(CH_2CH_3)CHO$ 2-ethylbutanal

16.41 a. $CH_3CH_2CH_2CH_2CH(=O)$ pentanal

c. $CH_3CH_2CH_2CH(CH_3)C(=O)CH_3$ 3-methyl-2-hexanone

b. $CH_3CH_2CH_2C(=O)CH_2CH_3$ 3-hexanone

d. $CH_3CH_2CH_2CH_2CH_2CH_2CH(CH_3)CH(=O)$ 2-methyloctanal

16.43 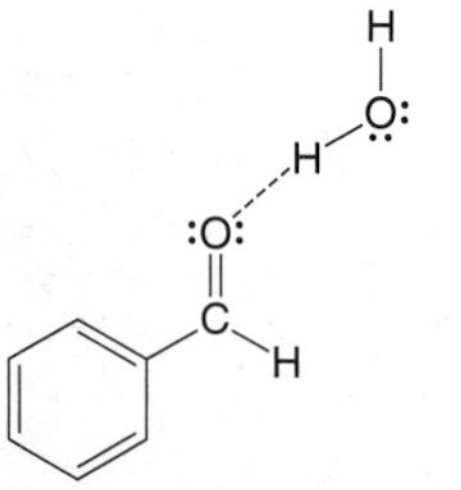

16.45 a. $(CH_3)_3CCH_2CHO$ b. 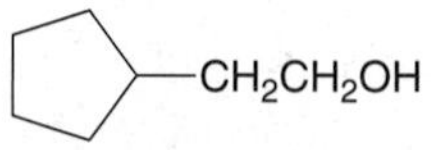

16.47 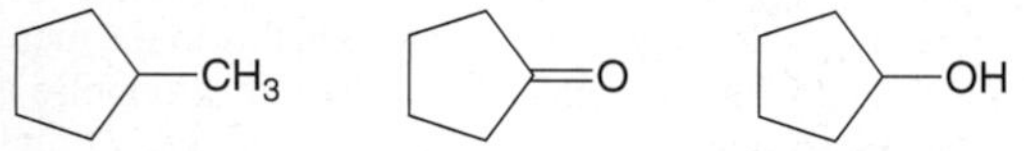

16.49 a. insoluble b. soluble c. insoluble

16.51 2,3-Butanedione has two carbonyl groups capable of hydrogen bonding, whereas acetone has one carbonyl group. It would be soluble in diethyl ether.

16.53 a. $CH_3(CH_2)_4COOH$ c. no reaction

b. 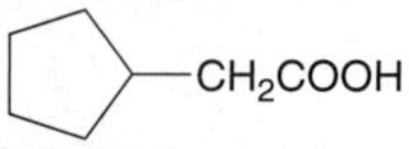 d. $CH_3(CH_2)_4COOH$

16.55 a. $CH_3(CH_2)_4COOH$ c. no reaction

b. 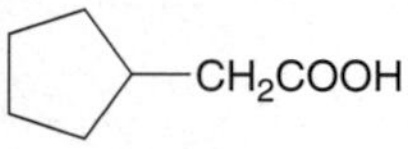 d. no reaction

16.57 a, b: 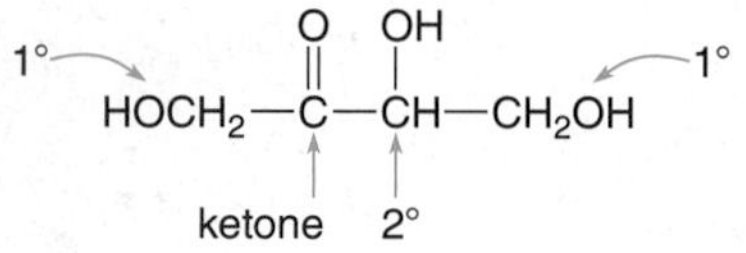
1°
1°
ketone
2°

c. no reaction

d. 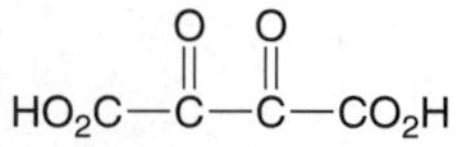

16.59 a. 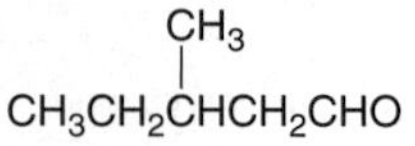 c. 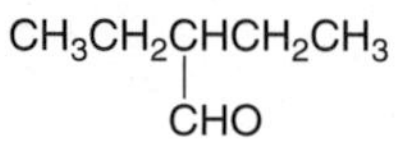

b. 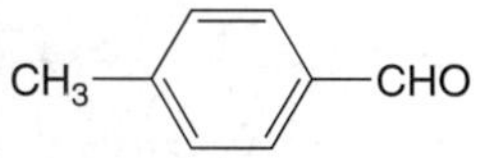

16.61 a. 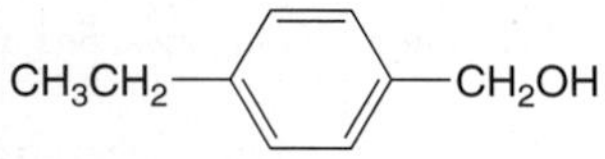 b. 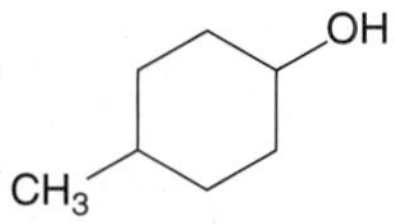

16.63 a, b: 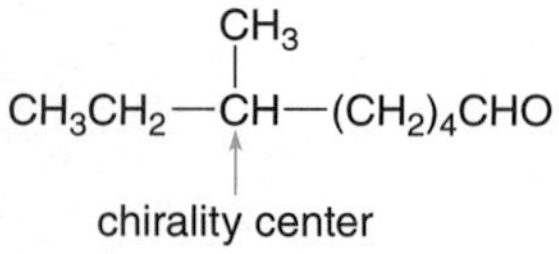
chirality center

c. 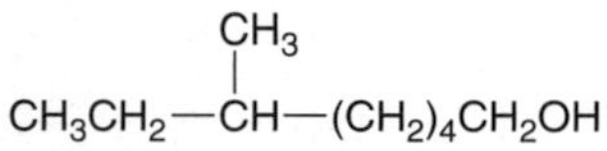

16.65 a. 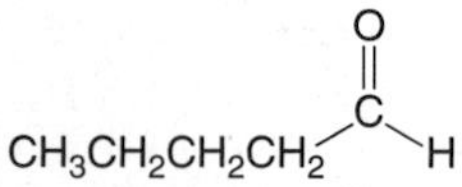 b. 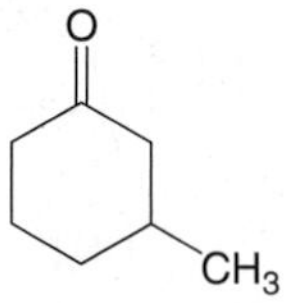

16.67 1-Methylcyclohexanol is a 3° alcohol and cannot be produced from the reduction of a carbonyl compound.

16.69 a. 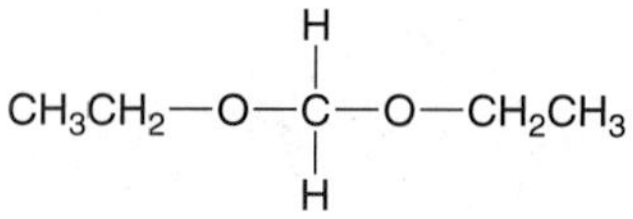

b. 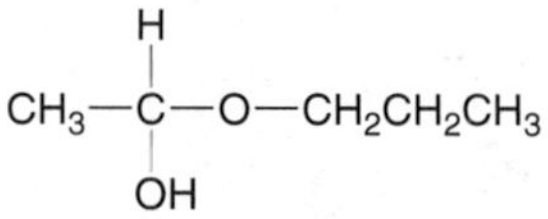

c. 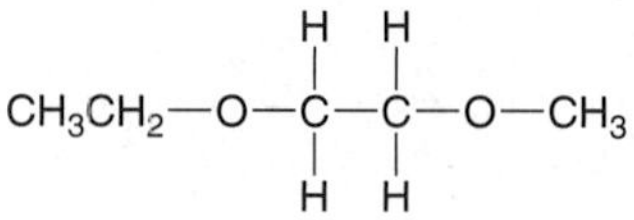

d. 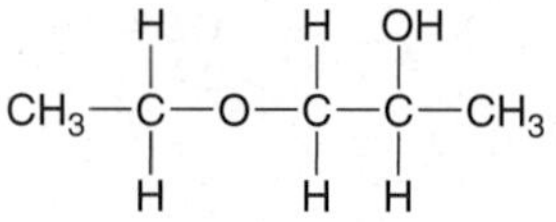

16.71 a. 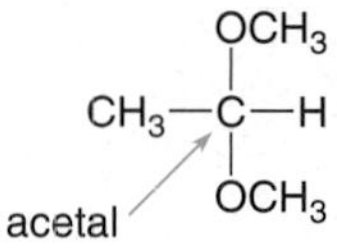
acetal

c. 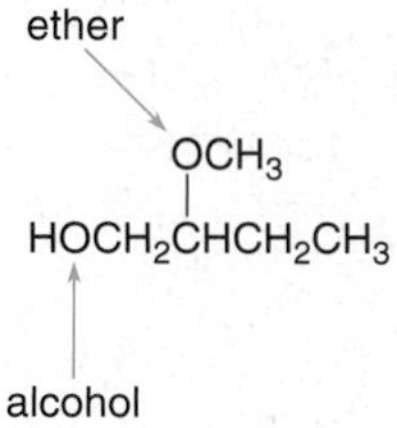
ether
alcohol

b. 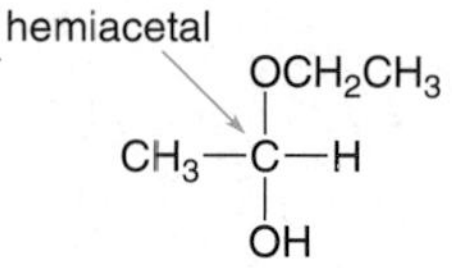
hemiacetal

d. 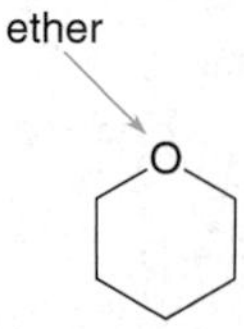
ether

16.73 a. 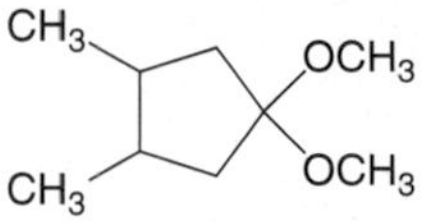 c. 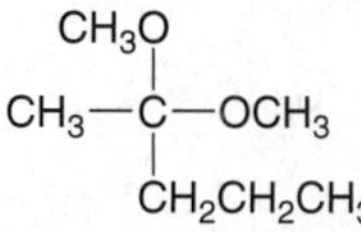

b. $CH_2(OCH_3)_2$ d. 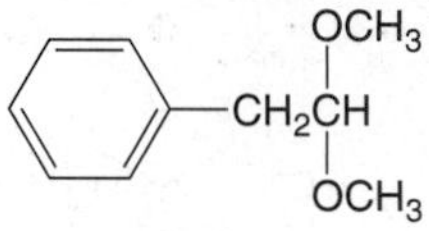

16.75 a. 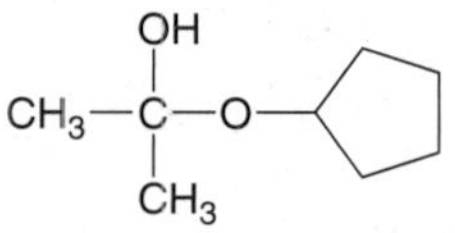 b. 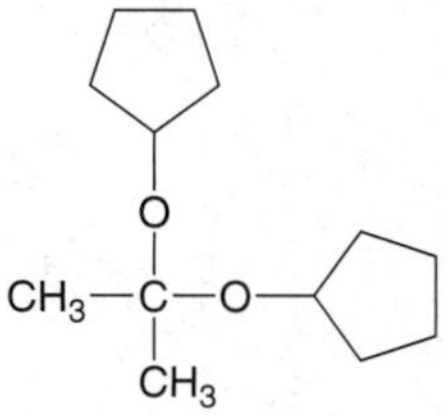

16.77 a. 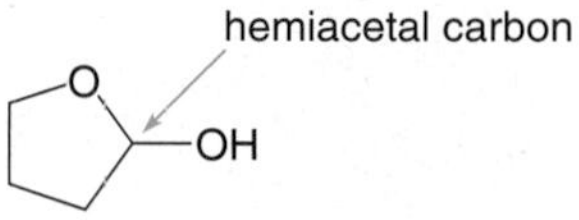
hemiacetal carbon

c. 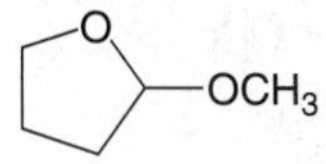

b. 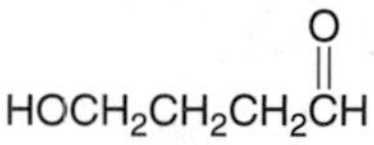

16.79 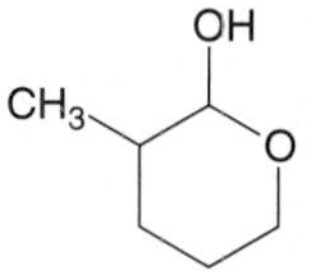

16.81 a. 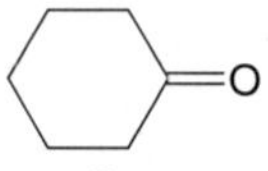 + 2 $HOCH_2CH_2CH_3$

b. 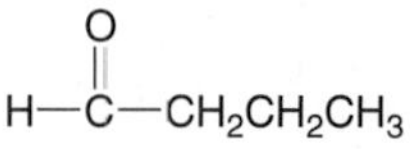 + 2 $HOCH_3$

16.83 a. 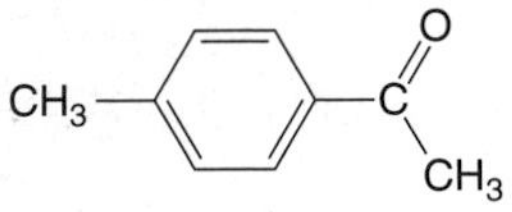

b. *p*-methylacetophenone

c. seven

d. 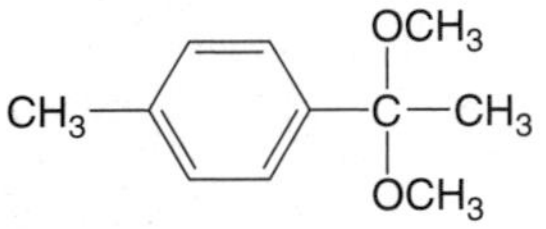

16.85 a. 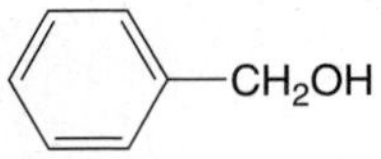

b. 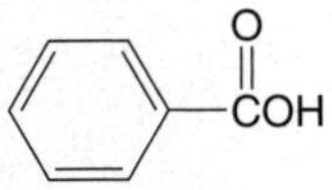

c. 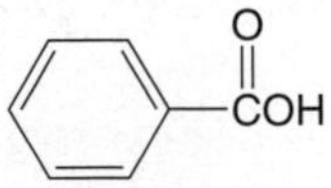

d. 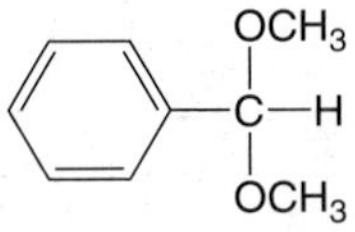

e. 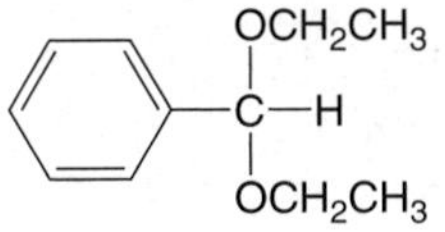

f. 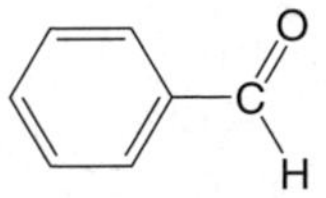

16.87 a. 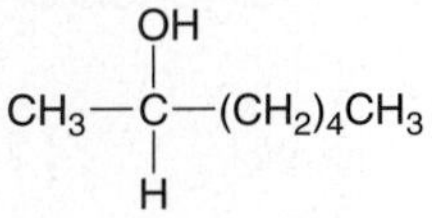

b, c: no reaction

d. 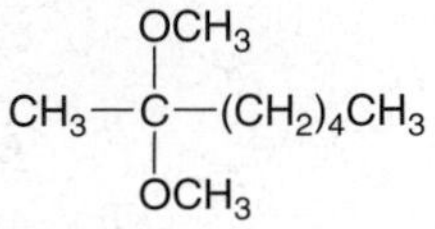

e. 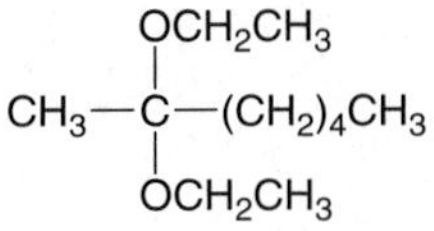

f. 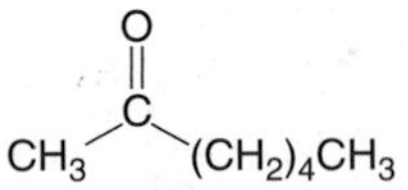

16.89

$CH_2{=}CHCH_2CH_2CHO$ $CH_3CH{=}CHCH_2CHO$ $CH_3CH_2CH{=}CHCHO$

16.91 a. 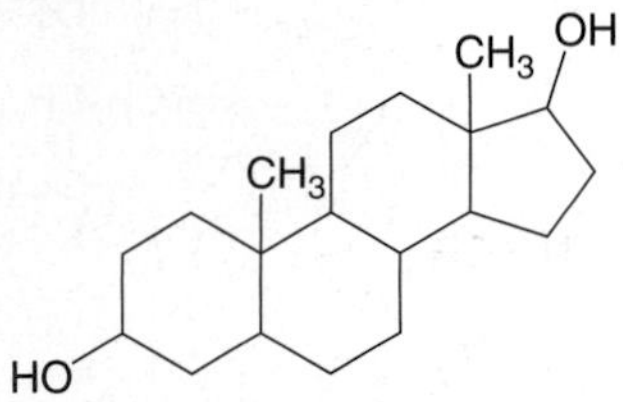

b. 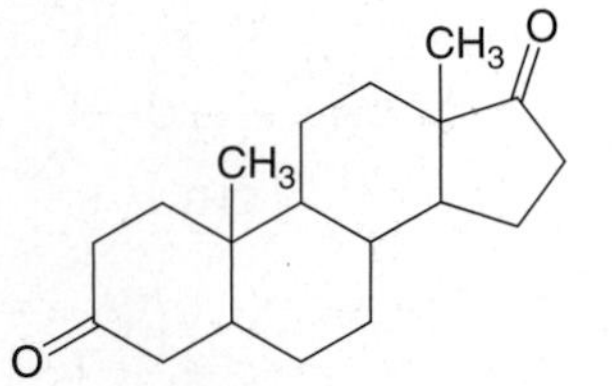

c. 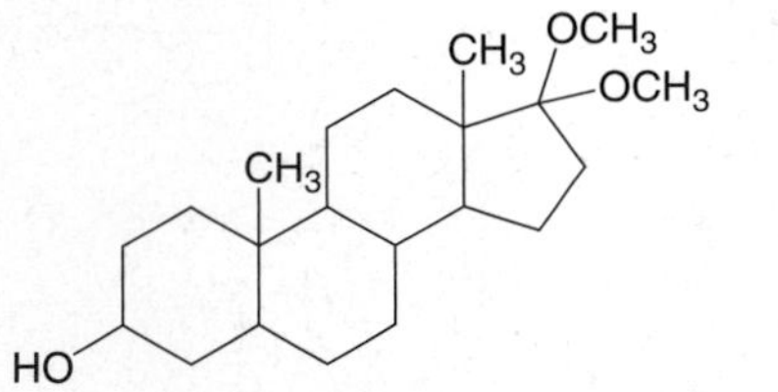

d. 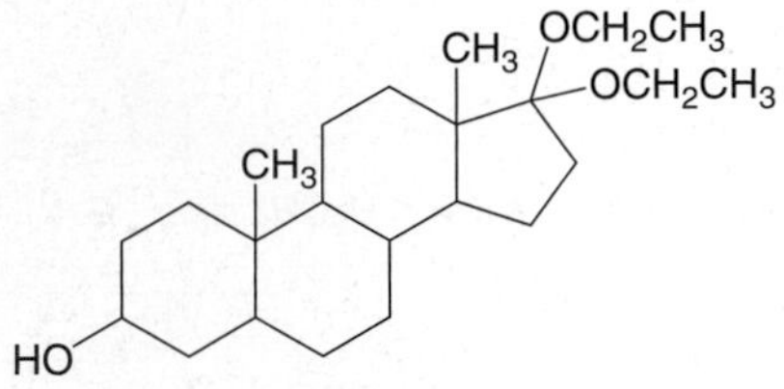

16.93 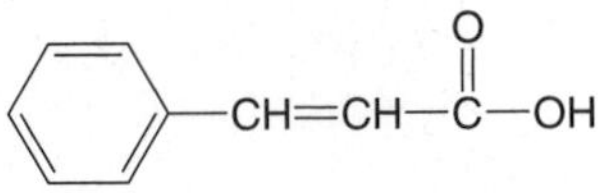

16.95 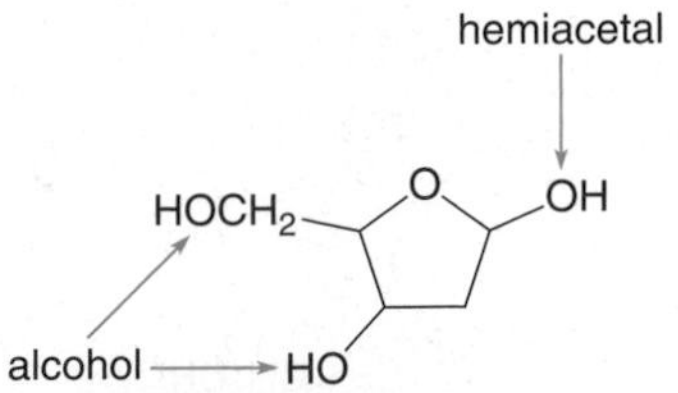
hemiacetal
alcohol

16.97 The cis double bond in 11-*cis*-retinal produces crowding, making the molecule unstable. Light energy converts this to the more stable trans isomer, and with this conversion an electrical impulse is generated in the optic nerve.

16.99 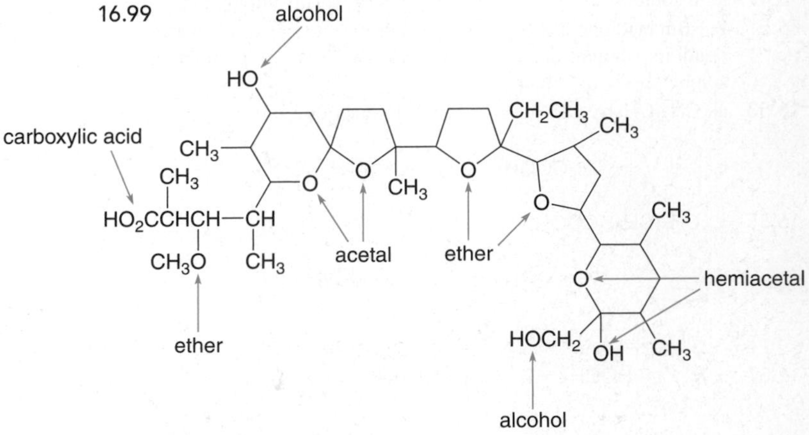
alcohol
carboxylic acid
acetal
ether
hemiacetal
ether
alcohol

CHAPTER 17

17.1 a. 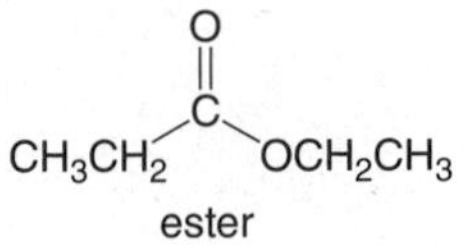
ester

b. 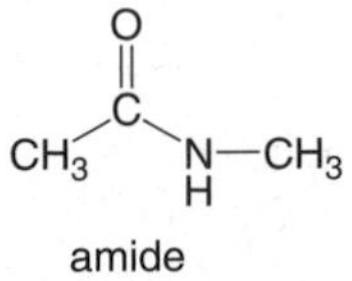
amide

c. 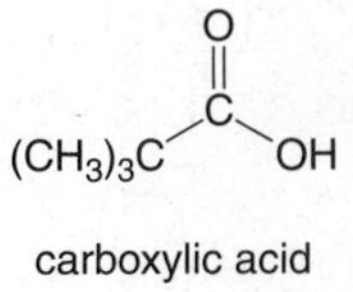
carboxylic acid

d. 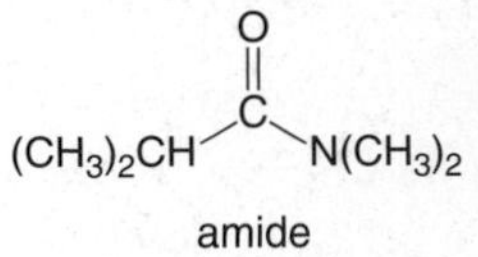
amide

17.3 a. aromatic ring, two carboxyl groups, two amines, one amide
b. nine

17.4 a. 3,3-dimethylhexanoic acid
b. 4-chloropentanoic acid
c. 2,4-diethylhexanoic acid

17.5 a. 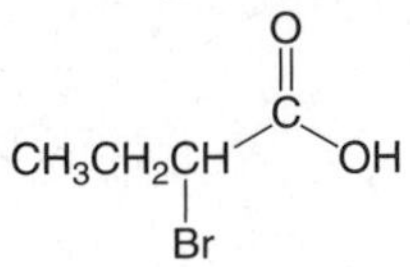

b. 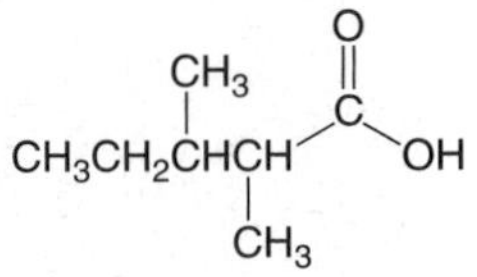

c. 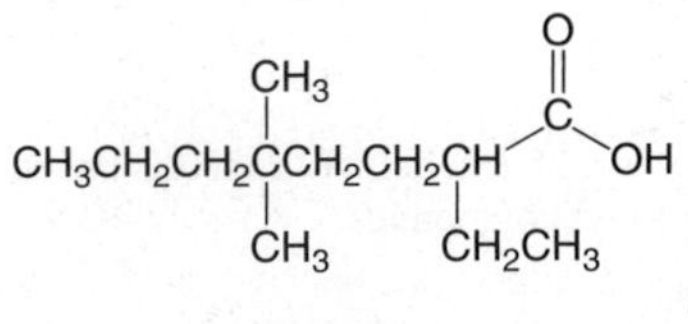

d. 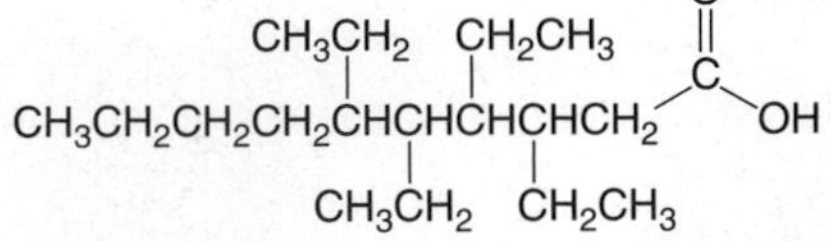

17.6 a. methyl hexanoate
b. ethyl benzoate
c. propyl pentanoate

17.7 a.

$CH_3CH_2-\overset{\overset{\displaystyle O}{\|}}{C}-OCH_2CH_2CH_3$

b.

$CH_3-\overset{\overset{\displaystyle O}{\|}}{C}-OCH_2CH_2CH_2CH_3$

c.

$CH_3CH_2CH_2CH_2CH_2-\overset{\overset{\displaystyle O}{\|}}{C}-OCH_2CH_3$

d.

(benzene ring)$-\overset{\overset{\displaystyle O}{\|}}{C}-OCH_3$

17.8 a. pentanamide
b. N-methylbenzamide
c. N,N-dipropylformamide

17.9 a.

$CH_3CH_2-\overset{\overset{\displaystyle O}{\|}}{C}-NH_2$

b. $CH_3CH_2CH_2CH_2CH_2-\overset{\overset{\displaystyle O}{\|}}{C}-\overset{}{\underset{H}{N}}-CH_2CH_3$

c. $CH_3-\overset{\overset{\displaystyle O}{\|}}{C}-\underset{\underset{\displaystyle CH_3}{|}}{\overset{\overset{\displaystyle CH_3}{|}}{N}}$

d. $CH_3CH_2CH_2-\overset{\overset{\displaystyle O}{\|}}{C}-\underset{\underset{\displaystyle CH_3}{|}}{N}-CH_2CH_2CH_2CH_3$

17.11

cyclohexane–$CH_2CH_2CH_2CH_3$ cyclohexane–$COOCH_3$ cyclohexane–CH_2COOH

lowest bp
least water soluble

highest bp
most water soluble

17.13 $PGF_{2\alpha}$ is more water soluble since it has a COOH and three OH groups.

17.15 a.

cyclohexane$-\overset{\overset{\displaystyle O}{\|}}{C}-O^-Na^+$ + H_2O

b.

$CH_3CH_2CH_2-\overset{\overset{\displaystyle O}{\|}}{C}-O^-Na^+$ + $Na^+HCO_3^-$

17.17 a. sodium butanoate   b. lithium benzoate

17.19

$CH_3CH_2CH_2CH_2CH_2CH_2CH_2CH_2CH_2CH_2CH_2CH_2CH_2CH_2CH_2-\overset{\overset{\displaystyle O}{\|}}{C}-O^-K^+$

17.21 a.

$(CH_3)_2CHCH_2-$(benzene ring)$-\underset{\underset{\displaystyle}{}}{\overset{\overset{\displaystyle CH_3}{|}}{CH}}COOH$ + NaOH

$\longrightarrow$ $(CH_3)_2CHCH_2-$(benzene ring)$-\overset{\overset{\displaystyle CH_3}{|}}{CH}COO^-Na^+$ + H_2O

b. The neutral form is present in the stomach.
c. The ionized form is present in the small intestines.

17.22 a.

$(CH_3)_2CH-\overset{\overset{\displaystyle O}{\|}}{C}-OCH_2CH_3$

c. $CH_3(CH_2)_6-\overset{\overset{\displaystyle O}{\|}}{C}-OCH_2CH_3$

b. $H-\overset{\overset{\displaystyle O}{\|}}{C}-OCH_2CH_3$

d. cyclohexane$-\overset{\overset{\displaystyle O}{\|}}{C}-OCH_2CH_3$

17.23

(benzene ring with OCH_3 top, OCH_3 bottom)$-CH_2O-\overset{\overset{\displaystyle O}{\|}}{C}-CH_2CH(CH_3)_2$

17.25 a. $CH_3CH_2CH_2CH_2-\overset{\overset{\displaystyle O}{\|}}{C}-NH_2$

b. $CH_3CH_2CH_2CH_2-\overset{\overset{\displaystyle O}{\|}}{C}-\underset{\underset{\displaystyle CH_3}{|}}{N}-CH_3$

c. $CH_3CH_2CH_2CH_2-\overset{\overset{\displaystyle O}{\|}}{C}-\underset{\underset{\displaystyle H}{|}}{N}-$cyclohexane

d. $CH_3CH_2CH_2CH_2-\overset{\overset{\displaystyle O}{\|}}{C}-\underset{\underset{\displaystyle H}{|}}{N}-CH_3$

17.27 a. $CH_3(CH_2)_8-\overset{\overset{\displaystyle O}{\|}}{C}-OH$ + CH_3OH

b. $CH_3\underset{\underset{\displaystyle CH_3}{|}}{CH}CH_2-\overset{\overset{\displaystyle O}{\|}}{C}-OH$ + CH_3CH_2OH

c. cyclohexane$-COH$ + $CH_3CH_2CH_2OH$

17.29

(benzene ring with COOH top, OH bottom) + $CH_3\overset{\overset{\displaystyle O}{\|}}{C}OH$

17.30 a. CH$_3$(CH$_2$)$_8$C(=O)OH + NH$_4^+$ HSO$_4^-$

b. CH$_3$CHCH$_2$C(=O)OH + (CH$_3$NH$_3$)$^+$ HSO$_4^-$
with CH$_3$ substituent

c. cyclohexane-C(=O)OH + [(CH$_3$CH$_2$CH$_2$)$_2$NH$_2$]$^+$ HSO$_4^-$

17.31 a. CH$_3$(CH$_2$)$_8$C(=O)O$^-$Na$^+$ + NH$_3$

b. CH$_3$CHCH$_2$C(=O)O$^-$Na$^+$ + CH$_3$NH$_2$
with CH$_3$ substituent

c. cyclohexane-C(=O)O$^-$Na$^+$ + (CH$_3$CH$_2$CH$_2$)$_2$NH

17.33 H$_2$N—(CH$_2$)$_6$—NH$_2$ + HO—C(=O)—(CH$_2$)$_8$—C(=O)—OH

17.35 Polyesters can be converted back to their monomers by acid hydrolysis. The strong C—C bonds in polyethylene are not easily broken.

17.37 a. CH$_3$C(CH$_3$)(CH$_3$)CH$_2$CH$_2$CH$_2$C(=O)OH

c. cyclobutane-C(=O)OCH$_3$

b. CH$_3$CH$_2$CH$_2$CH$_2$C(=O)OCH$_3$

d. cyclobutane with CH$_3$ substituent, C(=O)OH

17.39 a. CH$_3$CH$_2$CH$_2$CH$_2$C(=O)NH$_2$

c. CH$_3$CH$_2$C(=O)N(CH$_3$)—CH$_3$

b. CH$_3$CH$_2$C(=O)N(H)—CH$_2$CH$_3$

17.41 CH$_3$CH$_2$C(=O)O—CH$_3$ CH$_3$C(=O)O—CH$_2$CH$_3$

H—C(=O)OCH$_2$CH$_2$CH$_3$ H—C(=O)OCH(CH$_3$)$_2$

17.43 A lactone is a cyclic ester and a lactam is a cyclic amide.

17.45 a. 4-methylpentanamide   **c.** *o*-chlorobenzoic acid
b. ethyl formate

17.47 a. 4-methylpentanoic acid   **c.** 2-ethylheptanoic acid
b. 4,5-diethyloctanoic acid

17.49 a. propyl butanoate   **b.** butyl benzoate

17.51 a. hexanamide
b. *N*-ethyl-*N*-methylbenzamide

17.53 a. formamide   **c.** 2-hydroxybutanoic acid
b. lithium acetate   **d.** propyl propanoate

17.55 a. CH$_3$CH$_2$CH$_2$CH$_2$CH$_2$CH(OH)C(=O)OH

b. CH$_3$CH$_2$CH$_2$CH$_2$CH$_2$CHClCH$_2$CH$_2$C(=O)OH

c. benzene ring with two Br substituents, C(=O)OH

d. CH$_3$CH$_2$C(=O)O$^-$Li$^+$

e. CH$_3$CH$_2$C(Br)(Br)C(=O)OH

f. CH$_3$CH(CH$_3$)C(=O)O—CH$_2$CH$_3$

17.57 a. H—C(=O)OCH$_2$CH$_2$CH$_3$

b. CH$_3$CH$_2$CH$_2$C(=O)OCH$_2$CH$_2$CH$_2$CH$_3$

c. benzene-C(=O)OCH$_2$CH$_2$CH$_2$CH$_2$CH$_2$CH$_2$CH$_3$

d. CH$_3$CH$_2$CH$_2$CH$_2$CH$_2$C(=O)NHCH$_2$CH$_3$

e. CH$_3$CH$_2$CH$_2$CH$_2$CH$_2$CH$_2$C(=O)N(CH$_3$)—CH$_2$CH$_3$

17.59 CH$_3$CH$_2$CH$_2$CH$_2$C(=O)OH   CH$_3$CHCH$_2$C(=O)OH with CH$_3$ substituent

pentanoic acid   3-methylbutanoic acid

CH$_3$CH$_2$CH(CH$_3$)C(=O)OH   CH$_3$C(CH$_3$)(CH$_3$)C(=O)OH

2-methylbutanoic acid   2,2-dimethylpropanoic acid

17.61 (a) HCO_2CH_3 can hydrogen bond to water.
(b) CH_3CH_2COOH can hydrogen bond to itself and to water.

17.63 $CH_3CH_2CH(CH_3)_2 < CH_3CH_2COCH_3 < CH_3CH_2CO_2H$

17.65 $CH_3CH_2CONH_2$ can intermolecularly hydrogen bond, so it has stronger intermolecular forces.

17.67 a. $CH_3(CH_2)_3\overset{O}{\underset{}{C}}O^-K^+ \quad + \quad H_2O$

b. $(CH_3)_2CHCH_2CH_2\overset{O}{\underset{}{C}}O^-Na^+ \quad + \quad NaHCO_3$

17.69 a. $CH_3CH_2CH_2\overset{O}{\underset{}{C}}OCH_3$

b. $CH_3CH_2CH_2\overset{O}{\underset{}{C}}OCH_2CH_2CH_3$

c. $CH_3CH_2CH_2\overset{O}{\underset{}{C}}O-$ (cyclohexyl)

d. $CH_3CH_2CH_2\overset{O}{\underset{}{C}}O-CH_2CH_2-$ (phenyl)

17.71 $HO-$ (benzene ring) $-CO_2H \quad$ and $\quad CH_3OH$

17.73 a. $CH_3CH_2CH_2\overset{O}{\underset{}{C}}NH_2$

b. $CH_3CH_2CH_2\overset{O}{\underset{}{C}}\underset{H}{N}-CH_2CH_3$

c. $CH_3CH_2CH_2\overset{O}{\underset{}{C}}\underset{CH_2CH_3}{N}-CH_2CH_3$

d. $CH_3CH_2CH_2\overset{O}{\underset{}{C}}\underset{CH_2CH_3}{N}-CH_3$

17.75 a. (cyclohexyl)$\overset{O}{\underset{}{C}}OH \quad + \quad CH_3OH$

b. $HO\overset{O}{\underset{}{C}}CH_3 \quad + \quad$ (cyclohexyl)$-OH$

17.77 CH_3CH_2O- (benzene ring) $-NH_2 \quad + \quad HO\overset{O}{\underset{}{C}}CH_3$

17.79 a. $CH_3CH_2CH_2\overset{O}{\underset{}{C}}OH \quad + \quad HOCH(CH_3)_2$

b. (decalin-OH structure) $\quad + \quad HO\overset{O}{\underset{}{C}}CH_3$

c. (cyclohexyl)$-CH_2CH_2-OH \quad + \quad HO-\overset{O}{\underset{}{C}}H$

17.81 a. (benzene ring)$\overset{O}{\underset{}{C}}OH$ with $OCH_3 \quad + \quad NH_4^+Cl^-$

b. $(CH_3)_3C\overset{O}{\underset{}{C}}OH \quad + \quad [(CH_3)_2NH_2]^+Cl^-$

c. (cyclohexyl)$-NH_3^+ Cl^- \quad + \quad HO-\overset{O}{\underset{}{C}}CH_3$

17.83 (benzene ring)$-CH_2-\overset{O}{\underset{OH}{C}} \quad + \quad CH_3CH_2OH$

17.85 $HO-\overset{O}{\underset{}{C}}-$ (benzene ring) $-\overset{O}{\underset{}{C}}-OH \qquad NH_2-(CH_2)_4-NH_2$

17.87

$-O-\overset{O}{\underset{}{C}}-$ (benzene ring) $-\overset{O}{\underset{}{C}}-OCH_2CH_2CH_2O-\overset{O}{\underset{}{C}}-$ (benzene ring) $-\overset{O}{\underset{}{C}}-O-CH_2CH_2CH_2-$

17.89 Saponification is the hydrolysis of an ester with strong base and forms a metal salt, $RCOO^-M^+$. Esterification forms a new ester, $RCOOR'$.

17.91 a. $CH_3\overset{O}{\underset{}{C}}OCH_3$

b. $(CH_3)_2CHOH \quad + \quad HO\overset{O}{\underset{}{C}}CH_3$

c. $Na^+{}^-O\overset{O}{\underset{}{C}}CH(CH_3)_2 \quad + \quad (CH_3)_2CHCH_2OH$

d. $CH_3(CH_2)_4\overset{O}{\underset{}{C}}O^-Na^+ \quad + \quad H_2O$

17.93 a. 5-methylhexanoic acid

b.

CH₃CH₂CHCH₂CH₂—C(=O)—OH (with CH₃ branch)

c.

CH₃CH₂CH₂CH₂CH₂—C(=O)—OCH₃

d.

CH₃CHCH₂CH₂CH₂—C(=O)—O⁻ Na⁺ (with CH₃ branch)   +   H₂O

e. **A** is insoluble in H₂O, but soluble in organic solvent.

f.

CH₃CHCH₂CH₂CH₂—C(=O)—OCH₂CH₃ (with CH₃ branch)

g.

CH₃CHCH₂CH₂CH₂—C(=O)—NHCH₂CH₃ (with CH₃ branch)

17.95 b. This is a sodium salt of a long-chain carboxylic acid.

17.97 a.

(naproxen structure: CH₃O-naphthalene-CHCOOH with CH₃)   +   NaOH

→ (naproxen sodium salt: CH₃O-naphthalene-CHCOO⁻Na⁺ with CH₃)   +   H₂O

b. In the stomach naproxen exists as the neutral carboxylic acid.
c. In the intestines naproxen exists as the ionized carboxylate anion.

17.99 Aspirin inhibits the production of prostaglandins.

17.101 The nonpolar end of a soap molecule binds to dirt and hydrocarbons while the polar end then hydrogen bonds with water, thereby rendering the dirt soluble in water.

17.103

(structure: HO—C(=O)—CH₂CH—C(=O)—OH with NH₂)   +   (structure: phenyl-CH₂CH(NH₂)—C(=O)—OH with H)   +   CH₃OH

17.105 a. (six-membered lactone ring)   b. (five-membered lactone ring)

CHAPTER 18

18.1 a.

1° 2° 2° 1°
H₂N(CH₂)₃NH(CH₂)₄NH(CH₂)₃NH₂

b. CH₃CH₂O—C(=O)—(ring with C₆H₅ and N—CH₃ 3°)

18.3 a. 2° amine
b. (1) trigonal planar (2) tetrahedral (3) trigonal pyramidal

18.4 a. 2-butanamine
b. *N*-methyl-1-propanamine
c. *N*,*N*-dimethylcyclohexanamine
d. dibutylamine

18.5 a. (benzene with NHCH₃)
c. (CH₃CH₂-benzene-NH₂ with CH₂CH₃)
b. (benzene with NH₂ and CH₂CH₃)
d. (CH₃CH₂-benzene-N(CH₂CH₃)₂)

18.7 a. (CH₃)₂CHCH₂NH₂
c. (cyclohexane—NH₂)
b. (CH₃)₂CHCH₂OH

18.9 pyridine and pyrrolidine

18.11 3°

18.13 a. 11   b. 9

18.14 a. (CH₃CH₂NH₃)⁺   +   Cl⁻
b. [(CH₃CH₂)₂NH₂]⁺   +   Cl⁻
c. [(CH₃CH₂)₃NH]⁺   +   Cl⁻

18.15 a. (CH₃CH₂CH₂CH₂—NH₃)⁺   +   Cl⁻
b. [(CH₃)₂NH₂]⁺   +   C₆H₅COO⁻
c. (piperidinium ring with N, H, H)⁺   +   OH⁻

18.17 a. methylammonium chloride
b. dipropylammonium bromide
c. ethyldimethylammonium acetate

18.19 a. (CH₃CH₂)₃N   b. CH₃CH₂NH₂   c. (piperidine ring NH)

18.21 A quaternary ammonium salt has four R groups bonded to N so there is no proton available that can be removed.

18.23 COOH must be removed and OH must be added.

18.25 This would require addition of a methyl group and removal of two OH groups.

18.27 albuterol: 1° and 2° alcohols, 2° amine
salmeterol: 1° and 2° alcohols, 2° amine

18.29 2° amide and 3° amine

18.31 a. 2°   b. 3°

18.33 a. CH₃CH₂CH₂CH₂CH₂NH₂
c. (piperidine ring N—CH₃)

b. CH₃CH₂CH₂NCH₂CH₂CH₃ (with H below N)
d. [CH₃CH₂NCH₂CH₃ with CH₂CH₃ groups]⁺

18.35 a. cyclohexanamine   b. *N*-ethyl-*N*-methylaniline

18.37 a. diethylamine   c. *N*-methyl-3-hexanamine
b. 3-octanamine   d. *N*-ethyl-2-heptanamine

18.39 a. $CH_3CH_2CH_2CH_2CH_2CH_2CH_2CH_2CH_2NH_2$

b.

c.

d. CH_3CHCH_2COOH
$\quad\ \ |$
$\quad\ \ NH_2$

e. $CH_3CH_2CH_2CH_2CH_2CH_2CHCH_3$
$\qquad\qquad\qquad\qquad\quad |$
$\qquad\qquad\qquad\qquad N(CH_2CH_2CH_3)_2$

f. $CH_3CH_2NHCH_2CH_2CH_2CH_2CH_2CH_3$

18.41

N,N-dimethylaniline   2,4-diethylaniline

18.43 a. $[(CH_3CH_2CH_2)_2NH_2]^+ \ Cl^-$

b. $(CH_3CH_2CH_2CH_2NH_3)^+ \ Br^-$

c. $\left[CH_3CH_2N(CH_3)_2\atop |\ \ \ \ \ \ \ \ \ \ H\right]^+ OH^-$

18.45

trimethylamine   1-propanamine   N-methylethanamine   2-propanamine

18.47 Pyridine is capable of hydrogen bonding with water, so it is more water soluble. Pyridine has a higher boiling point than benzene.

18.49 a. $CH_3(CH_2)_7NH_2$ c.

b. $CH_3(CH_2)_6OH$

18.51

18.53 Primary amines can hydrogen bond to each other, whereas 3° amines cannot. Therefore, 1° amines will have a higher boiling point than 3° amines of similar size. Any amine can hydrogen bond to water so both 1° and 3° amines have similar solubility properties.

18.55 a. $CH_3CH_2NH_2 + H_2O \longrightarrow (CH_3CH_2NH_3)^+ + OH^-$

b. $(CH_3CH_2)_2NH + H_2O \longrightarrow [(CH_3CH_2)_2NH_2]^+ + OH^-$

c. $(CH_3CH_2)_3N + H_2O \longrightarrow [(CH_3CH_2)_3NH]^+ + OH^-$

18.57 a. $[CH_3CH_2CH_2NH(CH_3)_2]^+ + Cl^-$

b. $\left[CH_3CH_2CHCH_2CH_3 \atop \quad\quad |\ NH_3\right]^+ + HSO_4^-$

c. $+ Br^-$

d. $CH_3CH_2-\underset{\underset{CH_2CH_3}{|}}{N}-CH_2CH_3 + H_2O + Na^+$

18.59 a.

b.

18.61 piperidine

18.63 Caffeine is a mild stimulant, imparting a feeling of alertness after consumption. It also increases heart rate, dilates airways, and stimulates the secretion of stomach acid. These effects are observed because caffeine increases glucose production, making an individual feel energetic.

18.65 An alkaloid solution is slightly basic since its amine pulls off a proton from water, forming OH^-.

18.67 Dopamine affects brain processes that control movement, emotions, and pleasure. Normal dopamine levels give an individual a pleasurable, satisfied feeling. Increased levels result in an intense "high." Drugs such as heroin, cocaine, and alcohol increase dopamine levels. When there is too little dopamine in the brain, an individual loses control of fine motor skills and Parkinson's disease results.

18.69 Serotonin plays an important role in mood, sleep, perception, and temperature regulation. We get sleepy after eating a turkey dinner on Thanksgiving because the unusually high level of tryptophan in turkey is converted to serotonin. A deficiency of serotonin causes depression.

18.71 Dopamine and norepinephrine are derived from tyrosine, serotonin from tryptophan, and histamine from histidine.

18.73

a.   c.

18.75

18.77 Chlorpheniramine is an example of an antihistamine. Antihistamines bind to the H1 histamine receptor, but they evoke a different response. An antihistamine like chlorpheniramine or diphenhydramine, for example, inhibits vasodilation, so it is used to treat the symptoms of the common cold and environmental allergies.

18.79 a, b:

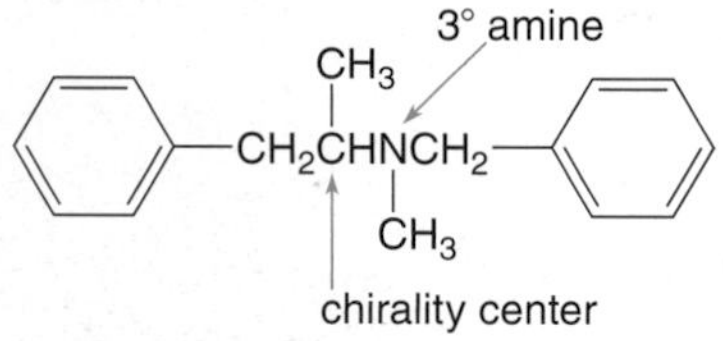

c.

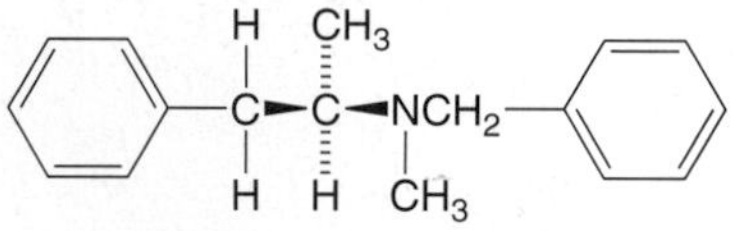

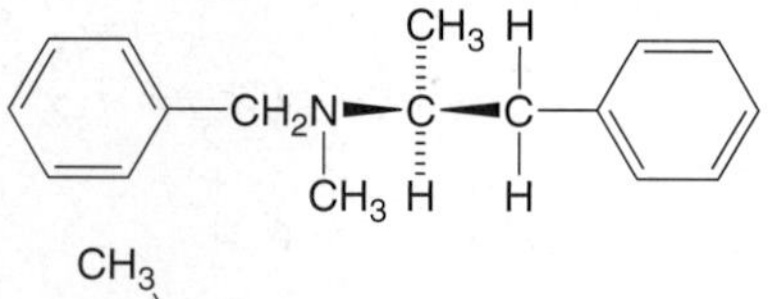

d.

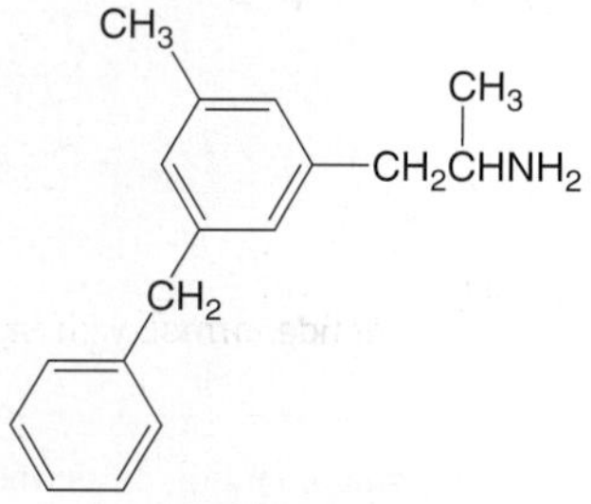

e.

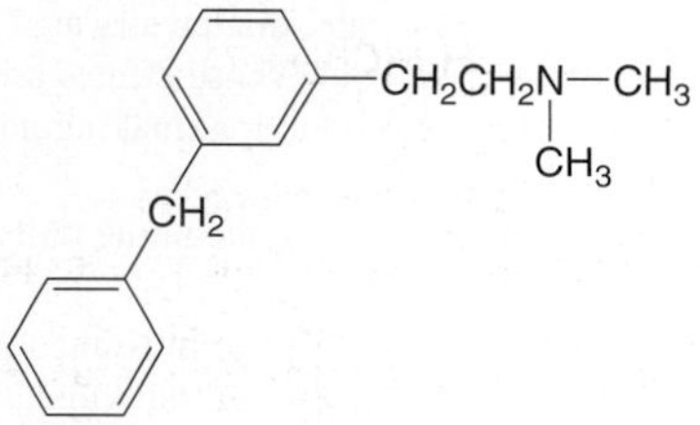

f.

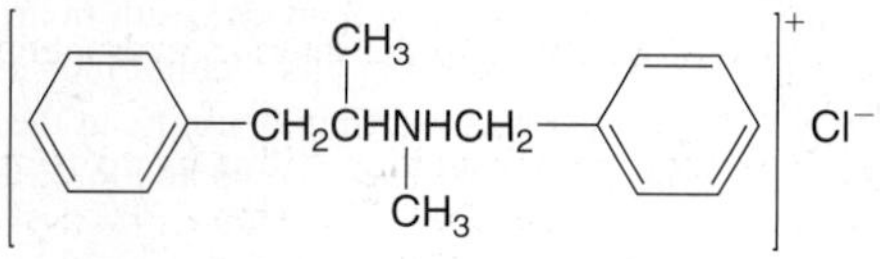

g.

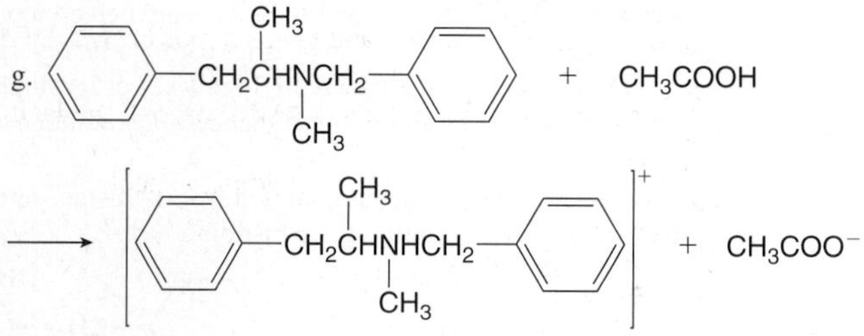

18.81 a, b, c, d:

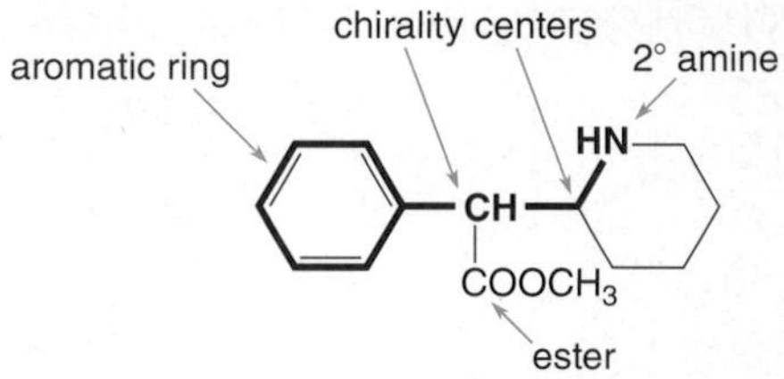

2-phenylethylamine in bold

e.

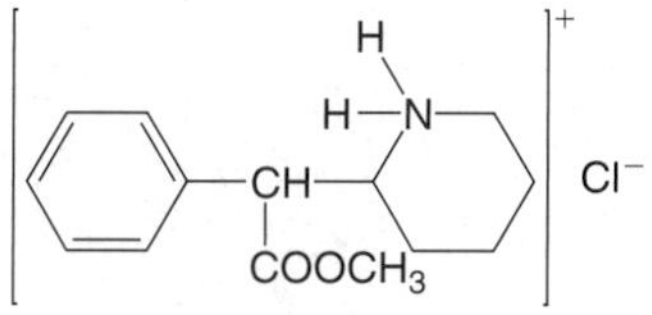

18.83

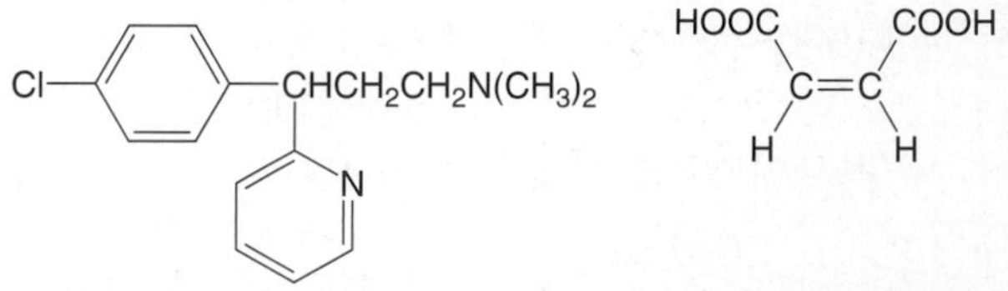

18.85 A vasodilator dilates blood vessels and a bronchodilator dilates airways in the lungs. Histamine is a vasodilator and albuterol is a bronchodilator.

18.87 Albuterol will exist in the ionic form in the stomach and as the neutral form in the intestines.

18.89 Heroin has two esters, which can be made from the two OH groups in morphine. Add acetic acid (CH_3COOH) and H_2SO_4 to make the two esters in heroin.

CHAPTER 19

19.1 b. and c.

19.3 a, b:

A =

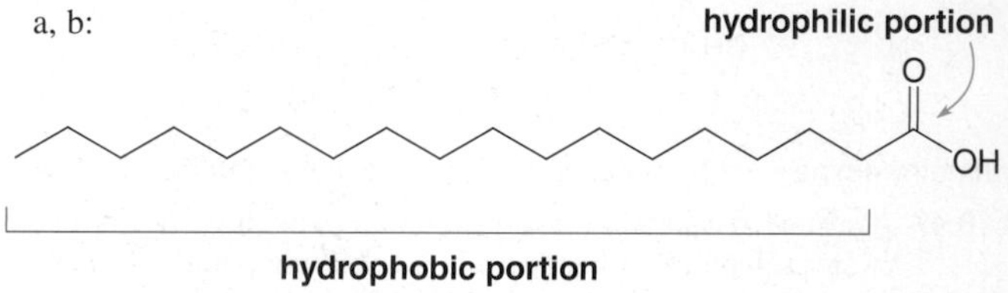

B =

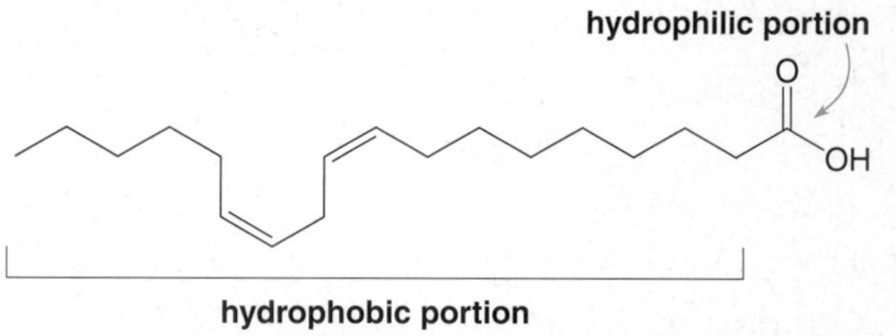

c. **A** will have the higher melting point because the molecules can pack together better.

19.5 a. omega-9   b. omega-6

19.6 a. $CH_3(CH_2)_{16}CO(CH_2)_9CH_3$ c. $CH_3(CH_2)_{16}CO(CH_2)_{29}CH_3$

b. $CH_3(CH_2)_{16}CO(CH_2)_{11}CH_3$

19.7

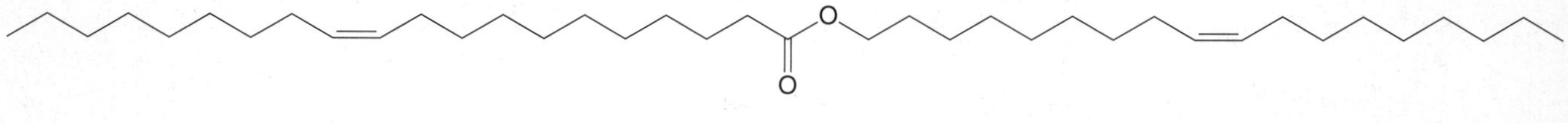

19.9

$$CH_3(CH_2)_{12}\overset{\overset{\displaystyle O}{\|}}{C}OH \quad + \quad HO(CH_2)_{15}CH_3$$

19.10 a.

$$CH_2{-}O{-}\overset{\overset{\displaystyle O}{\|}}{C}{-}(CH_2)_{16}CH_3$$
$$CH{-}O{-}\overset{\overset{\displaystyle O}{\|}}{C}{-}(CH_2)_{16}CH_3$$
$$CH_2{-}O{-}\overset{\overset{\displaystyle O}{\|}}{C}{-}(CH_2)_{16}CH_3$$

b.

$$CH_2{-}O{-}\overset{\overset{\displaystyle O}{\|}}{C}{-}(CH_2)_7\overset{H}{C}{=}\overset{H}{C}(CH_2)_7CH_3$$
$$CH{-}O{-}\overset{\overset{\displaystyle O}{\|}}{C}{-}(CH_2)_7\overset{H}{C}{=}\overset{H}{C}(CH_2)_7CH_3$$
$$CH_2{-}O{-}\overset{\overset{\displaystyle O}{\|}}{C}{-}(CH_2)_7\overset{H}{C}{=}\overset{H}{C}(CH_2)_7CH_3$$

19.11

$$CH_2{-}O{-}\overset{\overset{\displaystyle O}{\|}}{C}{-}(CH_2)_{16}CH_3$$
$$CH{-}O{-}\overset{\overset{\displaystyle O}{\|}}{C}{-}(CH_2)_{16}CH_3$$
$$CH_2{-}O{-}\overset{\overset{\displaystyle O}{\|}}{C}{-}(CH_2)_{14}CH_3$$

$$CH_2{-}O{-}\overset{\overset{\displaystyle O}{\|}}{C}{-}(CH_2)_{16}CH_3$$
$$CH{-}O{-}\overset{\overset{\displaystyle O}{\|}}{C}{-}(CH_2)_{14}CH_3$$
$$CH_2{-}O{-}\overset{\overset{\displaystyle O}{\|}}{C}{-}(CH_2)_{16}CH_3$$

19.13 a.

$$CH_2{-}OH$$
$$CH{-}OH \quad + \quad 3\,HO{-}\overset{\overset{\displaystyle O}{\|}}{C}{-}(CH_2)_{12}CH_3$$
$$CH_2{-}OH$$

b.

$$CH_2{-}OH$$
$$CH{-}OH \quad + \quad HO{-}\overset{\overset{\displaystyle O}{\|}}{C}{-}(CH_2)_{12}CH_3$$
$$CH_2{-}OH \qquad HO{-}\overset{\overset{\displaystyle O}{\|}}{C}{-}(CH_2)_7CH{=}CH(CH_2)_5CH_3$$

$$HO{-}\overset{\overset{\displaystyle O}{\|}}{C}{-}(CH_2)_7CH{=}CH(CH_2)_7CH_3$$

19.15 a. $3\,Na^+ \ {}^-O{-}\overset{\overset{\displaystyle O}{\|}}{C}{-}(CH_2)_{12}CH_3$

b. $Na^+ \ {}^-O{-}\overset{\overset{\displaystyle O}{\|}}{C}{-}(CH_2)_{12}CH_3$

$Na^+ \ {}^-O{-}\overset{\overset{\displaystyle O}{\|}}{C}{-}(CH_2)_7CH{=}CH(CH_2)_5CH_3$

$Na^+ \ {}^-O{-}\overset{\overset{\displaystyle O}{\|}}{C}{-}(CH_2)_7CH{=}CH(CH_2)_7CH_3$

19.16

$$CH_2{-}O{-}\overset{\overset{\displaystyle O}{\|}}{C}{-}(CH_2)_{14}CH_3$$
$$CH{-}O{-}\overset{\overset{\displaystyle O}{\|}}{C}{-}(CH_2)_7\overset{H}{C}{=}\overset{H}{C}(CH_2)_7CH_3$$
$$CH_2{-}O{-}\overset{\overset{\displaystyle O}{\|}}{P}{-}O{-}CH_2CH_2\overset{+}{N}H_3$$
$$\qquad\quad O^-$$

$$CH_2{-}O{-}\overset{\overset{\displaystyle O}{\|}}{C}{-}(CH_2)_7\overset{H}{C}{=}\overset{H}{C}(CH_2)_7CH_3$$
$$CH{-}O{-}\overset{\overset{\displaystyle O}{\|}}{C}{-}(CH_2)_{14}CH_3$$
$$CH_2{-}O{-}\overset{\overset{\displaystyle O}{\|}}{P}{-}O{-}CH_2CH_2\overset{+}{N}H_3$$
$$\qquad\quad O^-$$

19.17 a. phosphoacylglycerol, cephalin

glycerol
$$CH_2{-}O{-}\overset{\overset{\displaystyle O}{\|}}{C}{-}(CH_2)_{12}CH_3 \leftarrow$$
$$CH{-}O{-}\overset{\overset{\displaystyle O}{\|}}{C}{-}(CH_2)_{12}CH_3 \leftarrow \text{fatty acids}$$
$$CH_2{-}O{-}\overset{\overset{\displaystyle O}{\|}}{P}{-}O{-}CH_2CH_2\overset{+}{N}H_3$$
$$\qquad\quad O^-$$
phosphate   ethanolamine

b. triacylglycerol

glycerol
$$CH_2{-}O{-}\overset{\overset{\displaystyle O}{\|}}{C}{-}(CH_2)_{12}CH_3 \leftarrow$$
$$CH{-}O{-}\overset{\overset{\displaystyle O}{\|}}{C}{-}(CH_2)_7CH{=}CH(CH_2)_5CH_3 \leftarrow \text{fatty acids}$$
$$CH_2{-}O{-}\overset{\overset{\displaystyle O}{\|}}{C}{-}(CH_2)_{12}CH_3 \leftarrow$$

c. sphingomyelin

sphingosine
$$HO{-}CH{-}CH{=}CH(CH_2)_{12}CH_3$$
$$CH{-}NH{-}\overset{\overset{\displaystyle O}{\|}}{C}{-}(CH_2)_{12}CH_3 \leftarrow \text{amide formed with myristic acid}$$
$$CH_2{-}O{-}\overset{\overset{\displaystyle O}{\|}}{P}{-}O{-}CH_2CH_2\overset{+}{N}(CH_3)_3$$
$$\qquad\quad O^-$$
phosphate   derived from choline

19.19 Membrane **A** will be more fluid or pliable as it contains unsaturated fatty acids.

19.21 Cholesterol is a lipid since it contains many C—C and C—H bonds and it is not water soluble.

19.23 Triacylglycerols would be found in the interior, hydrophobic portion of lipoproteins.

19.25 a. Estrone has a phenol (a benzene ring with a hydroxyl group) and progesterone has a ketone and C=C in ring A. Progesterone also has a methyl group bonded to C10.
b. Estrone has a ketone at C17 and progesterone has a C—C bond, which is attached to a ketone.

19.27 Testosterone has a methyl group at C10 that nandrolone lacks.

19.29 a.

ketone   carboxylic acid
$$CH_2CH{=}CH(CH_2)_3COOH$$
alkene
$$CH{=}CHCH(CH_2)_4CH_3$$
HO   OH
alcohol

b.
HO   COOH   OH

19.31 b, e, f: hydrolyzable   a, c, d, g: nonhydrolyzable

19.33 b. and c.

19.35 a. $CH_3(CH_2)_3CH=CH(CH_2)_7COOH$,
$CH_3(CH_2)_{12}COOH$, $CH_3(CH_2)_{14}COOH$
   b. $CH_3(CH_2)_5CH=CH(CH_2)_7COOH$,
$CH_3(CH_2)_7CH=CH(CH_2)_7COOH$, $CH_3(CH_2)_{16}COOH$

19.37 a. Increasing the number of carbon atoms increases the melting point.
   b. Increasing the number of double bonds decreases the melting point.

19.39 a, b:

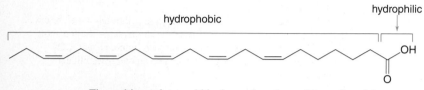

hydrophobic

hydrophilic

   c. The melting point would be lower than the melting point of the trans isomer.
   d. liquid
   e. omega-3 fatty acid

19.41 a. [structure] $-CO_2H$

   b. omega-3 acid

   c. [structure] CO_2H

   d. [structure]

19.43 a. $CH_3(CH_2)_{14}\overset{O}{\overset{\|}{C}}O(CH_2)_{21}CH_3$ c. $CH_3(CH_2)_{14}\overset{O}{\overset{\|}{C}}O(CH_2)_9CH_3$

   b. $CH_3(CH_2)_{14}\overset{O}{\overset{\|}{C}}O(CH_2)_{11}CH_3$

19.45 a. $CH_3(CH_2)_{16}COOH + HO(CH_2)_{17}CH_3$
   b. $CH_3(CH_2)_{12}COOH + HO(CH_2)_{25}CH_3$
   c. $CH_3(CH_2)_{14}COOH + HO(CH_2)_{27}CH_3$
   d. $CH_3(CH_2)_{22}COOH + HO(CH_2)_{13}CH_3$

19.47 a.

$CH_2-O-\overset{O}{\overset{\|}{C}}-(CH_2)_{10}CH_3$
$CH-O-\overset{O}{\overset{\|}{C}}-(CH_2)_{12}CH_3$
$CH_2-O-\overset{O}{\overset{\|}{C}}-(CH_2)_7CH=CHCH_2CH=CH(CH_2)_4CH_3$

   b.

$CH_2-O-\overset{O}{\overset{\|}{C}}-$ [chain]
$CH-O-\overset{O}{\overset{\|}{C}}-$ [chain]
$CH_2-O-\overset{O}{\overset{\|}{C}}-(CH_2)_7\underset{H}{C}=\underset{H}{C}CH_2\underset{H}{C}=\underset{H}{C}(CH_2)_4CH_3$

   c.

$CH_2-O-\overset{O}{\overset{\|}{C}}-(CH_2)_{12}CH_3$
$CH-O-\overset{O}{\overset{\|}{C}}-(CH_2)_{12}CH_3$
$CH_2-O-\overset{O}{\overset{\|}{C}}-(CH_2)_{12}CH_3$

   d.

$CH_2-O-\overset{O}{\overset{\|}{C}}-(CH_2)_{12}CH_3$
$CH-O-\overset{O}{\overset{\|}{C}}-(CH_2)_{12}CH_3$
$CH_2-O-\overset{O}{\overset{\|}{C}}-(CH_2)_7\underset{H}{C}=\underset{H}{C}(CH_2)_7CH_3$

19.49

$CH_2-O-\overset{O}{\overset{\|}{C}}-(CH_2)_3CH=CH(CH_2)_3CH_3$
$CH-O-\overset{O}{\overset{\|}{C}}-(CH_2)_3CH=CH(CH_2)_3CH_3$
$CH_2-O-\overset{O}{\overset{\|}{C}}-(CH_2)_3CH=CH(CH_2)_3CH_3$

19.51

Compound	a. General Structure	b. Example	c. Water Soluble (Y/N)	d. Hexane Soluble (Y/N)
[1] Fatty acid	RCOOH	[structure] COOH	N	Y
[2] Soap	RCOO⁻ Na⁺	[structure] COO⁻ Na⁺	Y	N
[3] Wax	RCOOR'	[structure] COO [structure]	N	Y
[4] Triacylglycerol	$CH_2-O-\overset{O}{\overset{\|}{C}}-R$ $CH-O-\overset{O}{\overset{\|}{C}}-R'$ $CH_2-O-\overset{O}{\overset{\|}{C}}-R''$	$CH_2-O-\overset{O}{\overset{\|}{C}}-(CH_2)_{12}CH_3$ $CH-O-\overset{O}{\overset{\|}{C}}-(CH_2)_{12}CH_3$ $CH_2-O-\overset{O}{\overset{\|}{C}}-(CH_2)_{12}CH_3$	N	Y

19.53
a. arachidic acid, stearic acid, and lauric acid
b. solid
c. The long hydrocarbon chains are hydrophobic.
d. The ester linkages are hydrophilic.

e.
CH_2—OH $HOOC(CH_2)_{10}CH_3$
CH—OH   + $HOOC(CH_2)_{16}CH_3$
CH_2—OH $HOOC(CH_2)_{18}CH_3$

19.55
a.   [1] water and H_2SO_4

CH_2—OH
CH—OH   +   2 HOC—$(CH_2)_{14}CH_3$ (with C=O)
CH_2—OH HOC—$(CH_2)_{16}CH_3$ (with C=O)

[2] water and NaOH

CH_2—OH
CH—OH   +   2 $Na^{+-}OC$—$(CH_2)_{14}CH_3$ (with C=O)
CH_2—OH $Na^{+-}OC$—$(CH_2)_{16}CH_3$ (with C=O)

b.   [1] water and H_2SO_4

CH_2—OH HOC—$(CH_2)_7CH=CH(CH_2)_7CH_3$ (with C=O)
CH—OH   + HOC—$(CH_2)_{14}CH_3$ (with C=O)
CH_2—OH HOC—$(CH_2)_7CH=CH(CH_2)_5CH_3$ (with C=O)

[2] water and NaOH

CH_2—OH $Na^{+-}OC$—$(CH_2)_7CH=CH(CH_2)_7CH_3$ (with C=O)
CH—OH   + $Na^{+-}OC$—$(CH_2)_{14}CH_3$ (with C=O)
CH_2—OH $Na^{+-}OC$—$(CH_2)_7CH=CH(CH_2)_5CH_3$ (with C=O)

19.57 c.

CH_2—O—C—$(CH_2)_7CH=CH(CH_2)_5CH_3$ (with C=O)
CH—O—C—$(CH_2)_7CH=CH(CH_2)_5CH_3$ (with C=O)
CH_2—O—P—O—$CH_2CH_2\overset{+}{N}H_3$ (with P=O and O^-)

19.59 a. (same glycerophospholipid structure as above)

b.
CH_2—O—C—$(CH_2)_{10}CH_3$ (with C=O)
CH—O—C—$(CH_2)_{10}CH_3$ (with C=O)
CH_2—O—P—O—$CH_2CH_2\overset{+}{N}(CH_3)_3$ (with P=O and O^-)

c.
HO—CH—$CH=CH(CH_2)_{12}CH_3$
CH—NH—C—$(CH_2)_{16}CH_3$ (with C=O)
CH_2—O—P—O—$CH_2CH_2\overset{+}{N}H_3$ (with P=O and O^-)

19.61 Triacylglycerols do not have a strongly hydrophilic region contained in a polar head.

19.63 Diffusion is the movement of small molecules through a membrane along a concentration gradient. Facilitated transport is the transport of molecules through channels in a cell membrane. O_2 and CO_2 move by diffusion whereas glucose and Cl^- move by facilitated transport.

19.65

19.67 Cholesterol is insoluble in the aqueous medium of the bloodstream. By being bound to a lipoprotein particle, it can be transported in the aqueous solution.

19.69 Low-density lipoproteins (LDLs) transport cholesterol from the liver to the tissues where it is incorporated in cell membranes. High-density lipoproteins (HDLs) transport cholesterol from the tissues back to the liver. When LDLs supply more cholesterol than is needed, LDLs deposit cholesterol on the wall of arteries, forming plaque. Atherosclerosis is a disease that results from the buildup of these fatty deposits, restricting the flow of blood, increasing blood pressure, and increasing the likelihood of a heart attack or stroke. As a result, LDL cholesterol is often called "bad" cholesterol.

19.71 a.
estrone   testosterone

b. The estrogen (left) and androgen (right) both contain the four rings of the steroid skeleton. Both contain a methyl group bonded to C13.
c. The estrogen has an aromatic A ring and a hydroxyl group on this ring. The androgen has a carbonyl on the A ring but does not contain an aromatic ring. The androgen also contains a C=C in the A ring and an additional CH_3 group at C10. The D rings are also different. The estrogen contains a carbonyl at C17 and the androgen has an OH group.
d. Estrogens, synthesized in the ovaries, control the menstrual cycle and secondary sexual characteristics of females. Androgens, synthesized in the testes, control the development of male secondary sexual characteristics.

19.73 Prostaglandins and leukotrienes are two types of eicosanoids, a group of biologically active compounds containing 20 carbon atoms derived from the fatty acid arachidonic acid. Prostaglandins are a group of carboxylic acids that contain a five-membered ring. Leukotrienes do not contain a ring. They both mediate biological activity at the site where they are formed. Prostaglandins mediate inflammation and uterine contractions. Leukotrienes stimulate smooth muscle contraction in the lungs and lead to the narrowing of airways as associated with asthma.

19.75 Prostaglandins contain a five-membered ring and a carboxyl group (COOH).

19.77 Aspirin inhibits the activity of both COX-1 and COX-2 enzymes, whereas celecoxib inhibits the activity of only COX-2.

19.79 Vitamins are organic compounds required in small quantities for normal metabolism and must be obtained in the diet since our cells cannot synthesize these compounds.

19.81

	Vitamin A	Vitamin D
a.	10	21
b.	10	6
e.	Required for normal vision	Regulates calcium and phosphorus metabolism
f.	Night blindness	Rickets and skeletal deformities
g.	Liver, kidney, oily fish, dairy	Milk and breakfast cereals

c. and d.

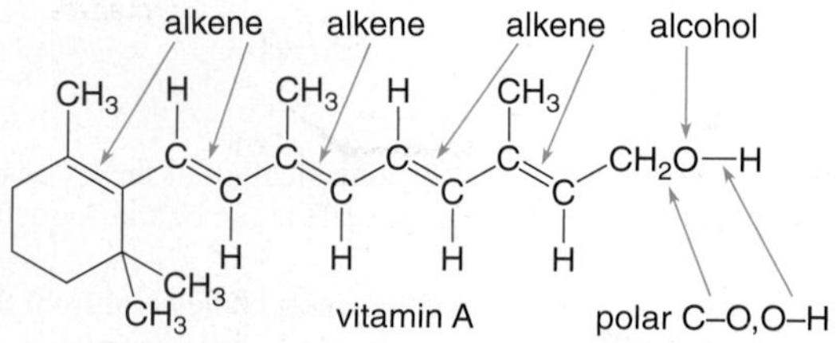

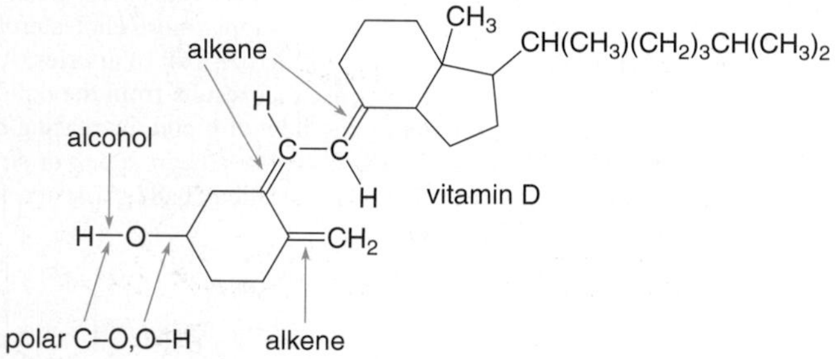

19.83 a.

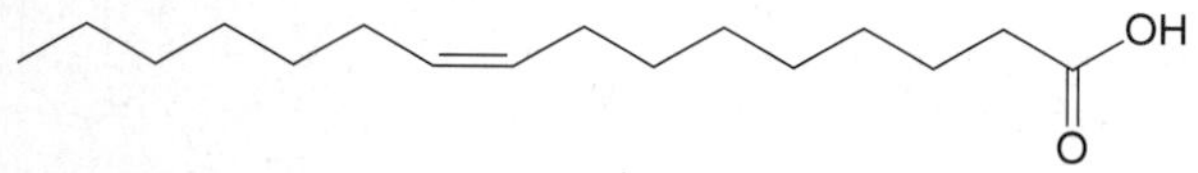

b. $CH_3(CH_2)_{12}COO(CH_2)_{15}CH_3$

c.

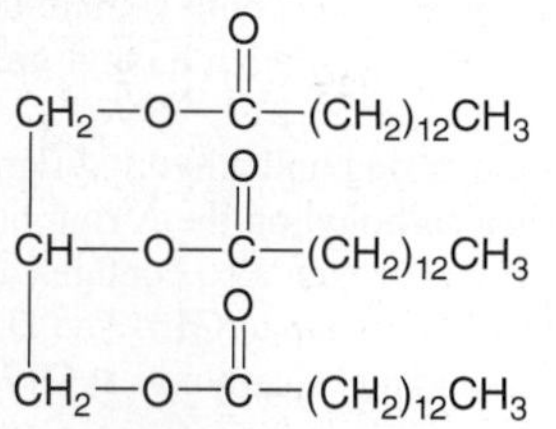

d.

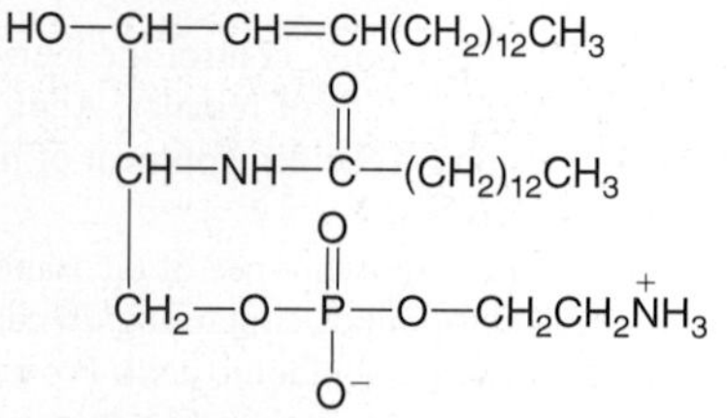

19.85 **A:** a, c, e **B:** a, c, d **C:** b, c

19.87 They contain an ionic head, making them more polar than triacylglycerols.

19.89 The hydrocarbon chains have only 12 carbons in them, making them short enough so that the triacylglycerol remains a liquid at room temperature.

19.91 Vegetable oils are composed of triacylglycerols while motor oil, derived from petroleum, is mostly alkanes and other long-chain hydrocarbons.

19.93 No, certain fatty acids and fat-soluble vitamins are required in the diet.

19.95 Saturated fats are more likely to lead to atherosclerosis and heart disease.

19.97 The unsaturated fats have lower melting points, thus remaining liquid at low temperatures. These unsaturated fats allow the cells to remain more fluid with less rigid cell membranes than saturated triacylglycerols would allow for.

19.99 a. reduction b. oxidation c. reduction

CHAPTER 20

20.1

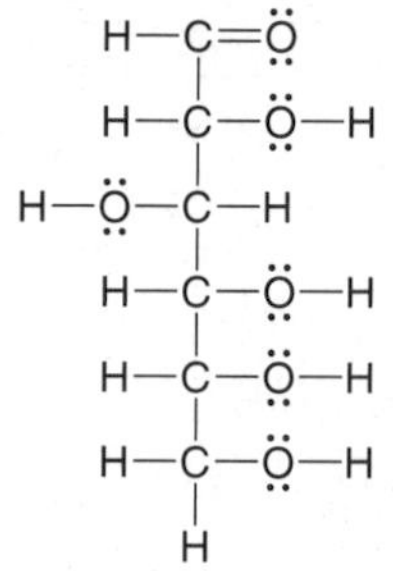

20.3 a. aldopentose b. aldotetrose c. ketotetrose

20.5 Hexane < 1-decanol < glucose. Hexane is a nonpolar hydrocarbon, insoluble in water. 1-Decanol is a long-chain alcohol and minimally soluble in water, due to the polar OH group. Glucose, with multiple hydroxyl groups, is water soluble.

20.7

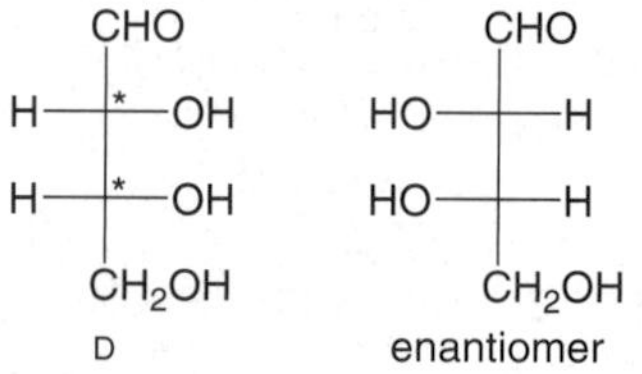

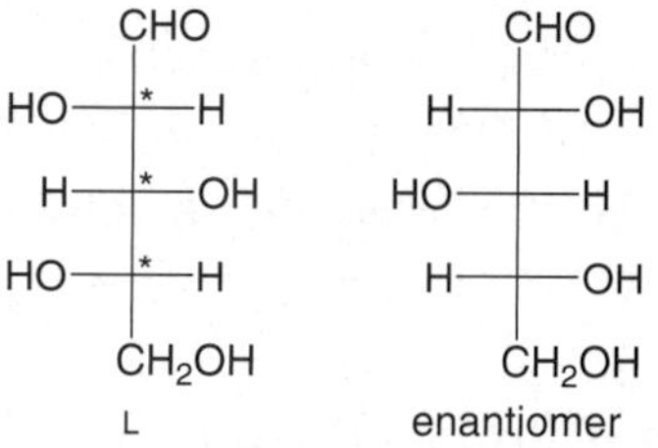

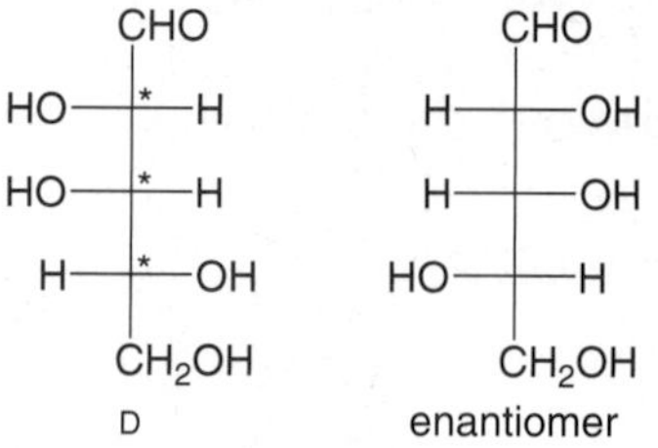

* chirality center

20.9 D-Glucose and D-fructose are constitutional isomers.
D-Galactose and D-fructose are also constitutional isomers.

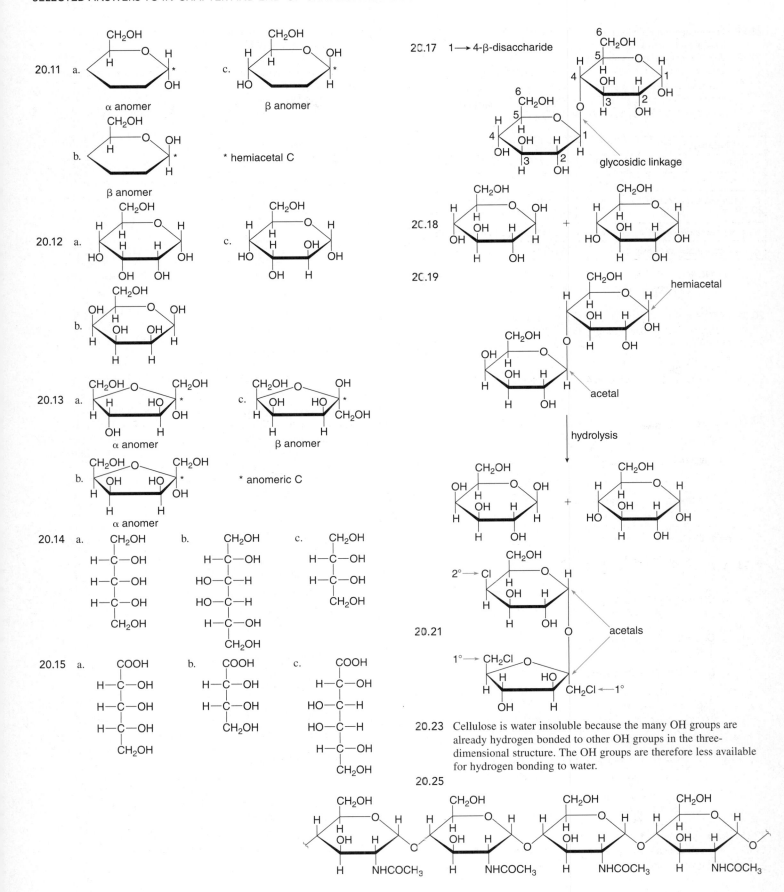

20.23 Cellulose is water insoluble because the many OH groups are already hydrogen bonded to other OH groups in the three-dimensional structure. The OH groups are therefore less available for hydrogen bonding to water.

20.27 Aldoses are monosaccharides with a carbonyl group at C1, forming an aldehyde, and ketoses are monosaccharides with a carbonyl group at C2, forming a ketone.

$$\begin{array}{c} \text{CHO} \\ \text{H}-\text{C}-\text{OH} \\ \text{H}-\text{C}-\text{OH} \\ \text{H}-\text{C}-\text{OH} \\ \text{CH}_2\text{OH} \end{array} \qquad \begin{array}{c} \text{CH}_2\text{OH} \\ \text{C}=\text{O} \\ \text{HO}-\text{C}-\text{H} \\ \text{H}-\text{C}-\text{OH} \\ \text{H}-\text{C}-\text{OH} \\ \text{CH}_2\text{OH} \end{array}$$

ribose, an aldose   fructose, a ketose

20.29 a.
$$\begin{array}{c} \text{CHO} \\ \text{H}-\text{C}-\text{OH} \\ \text{H}-\text{C}-\text{OH} \\ \text{HO}-\text{C}-\text{H} \\ \text{CH}_2\text{OH} \end{array}$$
b.
$$\begin{array}{c} \text{CHO} \\ \text{H}-\text{C}-\text{OH} \\ \text{H}-\text{C}-\text{OH} \\ \text{CH}_2\text{OH} \end{array}$$
c.
$$\begin{array}{c} \text{CH}_2\text{OH} \\ \text{H}-\text{C}-\text{OH} \\ \text{H}-\text{C}-\text{OH} \\ \text{HO}-\text{C}-\text{H} \\ \text{CH}_2\text{OH} \end{array}$$

20.31 α-D-Glucose and β-D-glucose are not enantiomers because they differ in the orientation of only one OH at C1.

20.33 a. aldotetrose   b. aldohexose   c. ketopentose

20.35 a.
$$\begin{array}{c} \text{CHO} \\ \text{H}-\!\!\!\!-\text{OH} \\ \text{CH}_2\text{OH} \end{array}$$
b. aldotriose

20.37 a.
$$\begin{array}{c} \text{CHO} \\ \text{HO}-\overset{*}{\text{C}}-\text{H} \\ \text{HO}-\overset{*}{\text{C}}-\text{H} \\ \text{CH}_2\text{OH} \end{array}$$
L-tetrose
$$\begin{array}{c} \text{CHO} \\ \text{H}-\text{C}-\text{OH} \\ \text{H}-\text{C}-\text{OH} \\ \text{CH}_2\text{OH} \end{array}$$
enantiomer
$$\begin{array}{c} \text{CHO} \\ \text{HO}-\!\!\!\!-\text{H} \\ \text{HO}-\!\!\!\!-\text{H} \\ \text{CH}_2\text{OH} \end{array}$$
Fischer projection

b.
$$\begin{array}{c} \text{CHO} \\ \text{HO}-\overset{*}{\text{C}}-\text{H} \\ \text{HO}-\overset{*}{\text{C}}-\text{H} \\ \text{HO}-\overset{*}{\text{C}}-\text{H} \\ \text{H}-\overset{*}{\text{C}}-\text{OH} \\ \text{CH}_2\text{OH} \end{array}$$
D-hexose
$$\begin{array}{c} \text{CHO} \\ \text{H}-\text{C}-\text{OH} \\ \text{H}-\text{C}-\text{OH} \\ \text{H}-\text{C}-\text{OH} \\ \text{HO}-\text{C}-\text{H} \\ \text{CH}_2\text{OH} \end{array}$$
enantiomer
$$\begin{array}{c} \text{CHO} \\ \text{HO}-\!\!\!\!-\text{H} \\ \text{HO}-\!\!\!\!-\text{H} \\ \text{HO}-\!\!\!\!-\text{H} \\ \text{H}-\!\!\!\!-\text{OH} \\ \text{CH}_2\text{OH} \end{array}$$
Fischer projection

c.
$$\begin{array}{c} \text{CH}_2\text{OH} \\ \text{C}=\text{O} \\ \text{H}-\overset{*}{\text{C}}-\text{OH} \\ \text{HO}-\overset{*}{\text{C}}-\text{H} \\ \text{CH}_2\text{OH} \end{array}$$
L-pentose
$$\begin{array}{c} \text{CH}_2\text{OH} \\ \text{C}=\text{O} \\ \text{HO}-\text{C}-\text{H} \\ \text{H}-\text{C}-\text{OH} \\ \text{CH}_2\text{OH} \end{array}$$
enantiomer
$$\begin{array}{c} \text{CH}_2\text{OH} \\ \text{C}=\text{O} \\ \text{H}-\!\!\!\!-\text{OH} \\ \text{HO}-\!\!\!\!-\text{H} \\ \text{CH}_2\text{OH} \end{array}$$
Fischer projection

* chirality center

20.39 a. **A** and **B**
b. **B** and **C** (or **A** and **C**)
c.
$$\begin{array}{c} \text{CHO} \\ \text{HO}-\text{C}-\text{H} \\ \text{H}-\text{C}-\text{OH} \\ \text{CH}_2\text{OH} \end{array}$$
d.
$$\begin{array}{c} \text{CHO} \\ \text{H}-\!\!\!\!-\text{OH} \\ \text{H}-\!\!\!\!-\text{OH} \\ \text{CH}_2\text{OH} \end{array}$$

20.41

β anomer   α anomer

20.43 Using a skeletal structure:
1° HO—
2° HO—
hemiacetal C
—OH ← OH on the anomeric C
HO— OH—
2° 2°

20.45
a. hemiacetal carbon
b. β anomer

c.

d.

20.47 a.
hemiacetal anomeric carbon β anomer

b.
hemiacetal anomeric carbon α anomer

20.49 A ketotriose has no stereoisomers.

20.51 a.

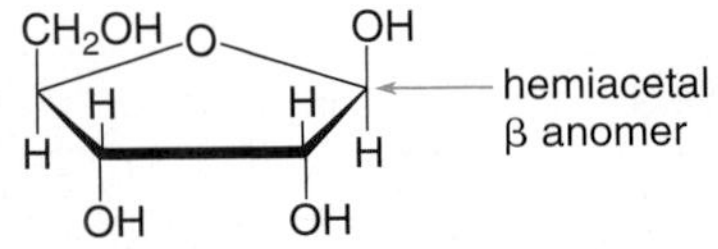

CH$_2$OH, OH — hemiacetal, β anomer

b.

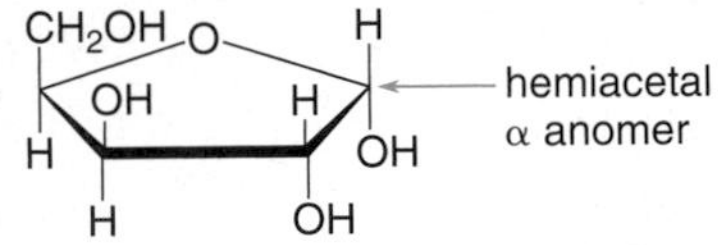

CH$_2$OH, H — hemiacetal, α anomer

20.53

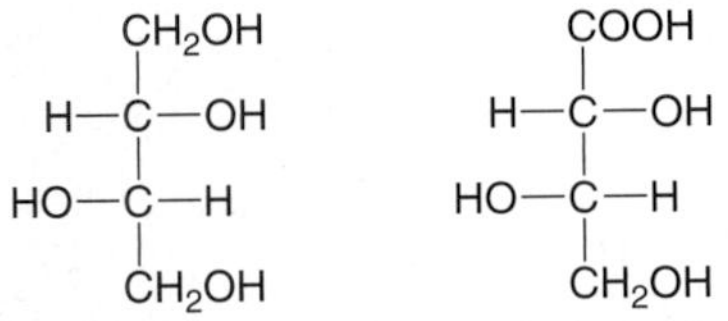

CH$_2$OH	COOH
H—C—OH	H—C—OH
HO—C—H	HO—C—H
CH$_2$OH	CH$_2$OH
alditol	aldonic acid

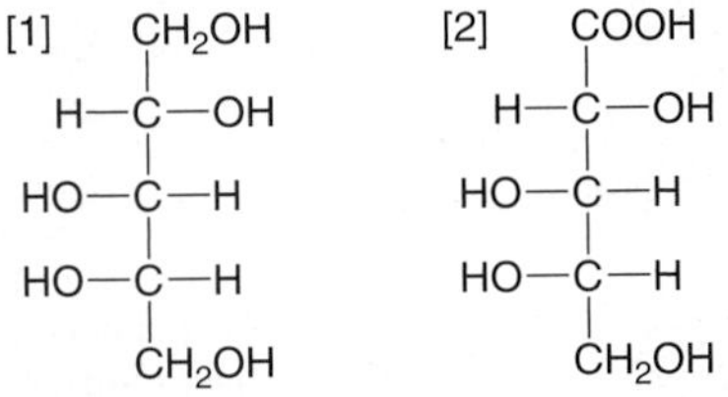

20.55 a.

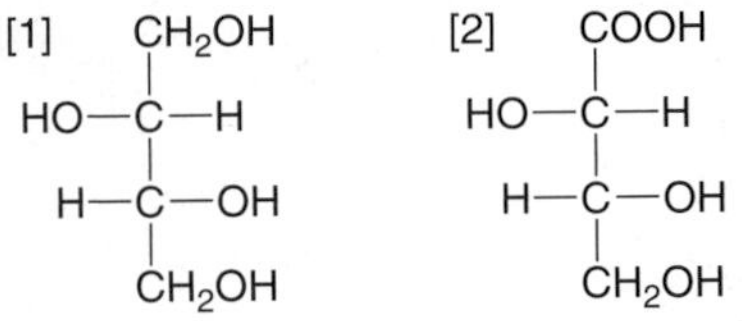

[1]
CH$_2$OH
HO—C—H
H—C—OH
CH$_2$OH

[2]
COOH
HO—C—H
H—C—OH
CH$_2$OH

b.

[1]
CH$_2$OH
H—C—OH
HO—C—H
HO—C—H
CH$_2$OH

[2]
COOH
H—C—OH
HO—C—H
HO—C—H
CH$_2$OH

c.

[1]
CH$_2$OH
H—C—OH
H—C—OH
HO—C—H
HO—C—H
CH$_2$OH

[2]
COOH
H—C—OH
H—C—OH
HO—C—H
HO—C—H
CH$_2$OH

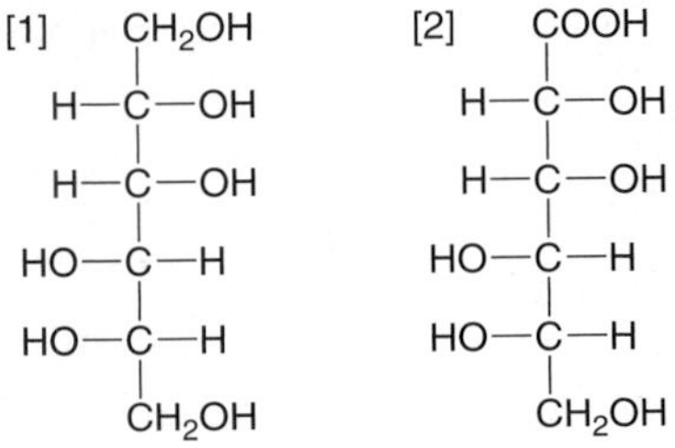

20.57 a.

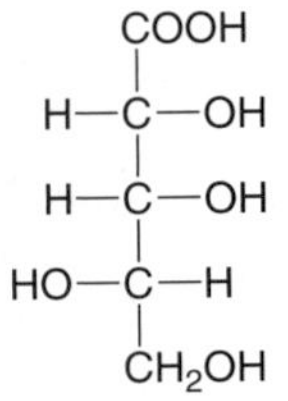

COOH
H—C—OH
H—C—OH
HO—C—H
CH$_2$OH

b.

COOH
H—C—OH
H—C—OH
H—C—OH
CH$_2$OH

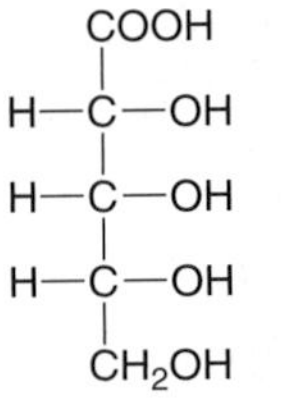

20.59 Reducing sugars are carbohydrates that are oxidized with Benedict's reagent (Cu^{2+}). Glucose, an aldohexose, is a reducing sugar.

20.61 a.

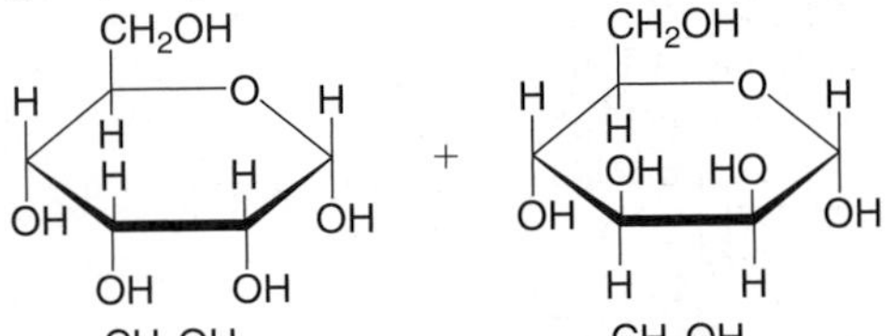

CH$_2$OH ring + CH$_2$OH ring

b.

CH$_2$OH ring + CH$_2$OH ring

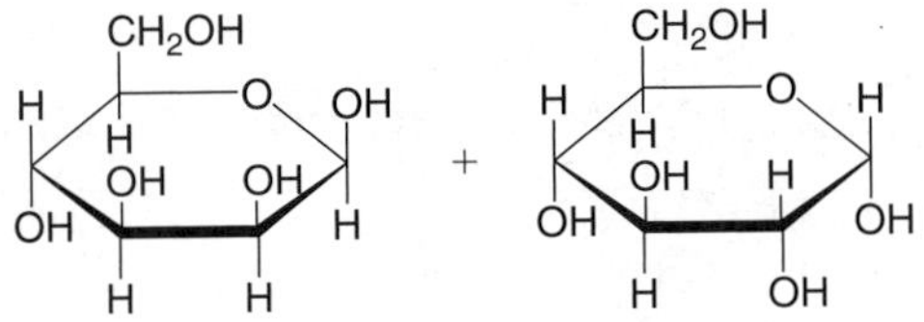

20.63 An α anomer has a hydroxyl at C1, the hemiacetal C, in the down position. An α glycoside has the glycosidic linkage in the down position.

20.65

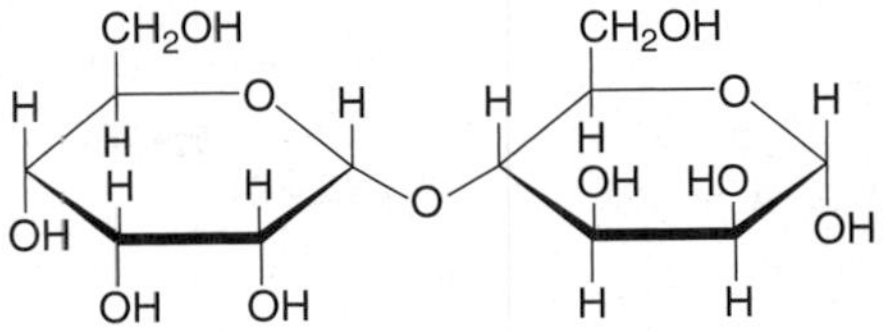

CH$_2$OH ring — O — CH$_2$OH ring

20.67 a, b:

6 CH$_2$OH ring — acetal
O—6 CH$_2$ ring — hemiacetal

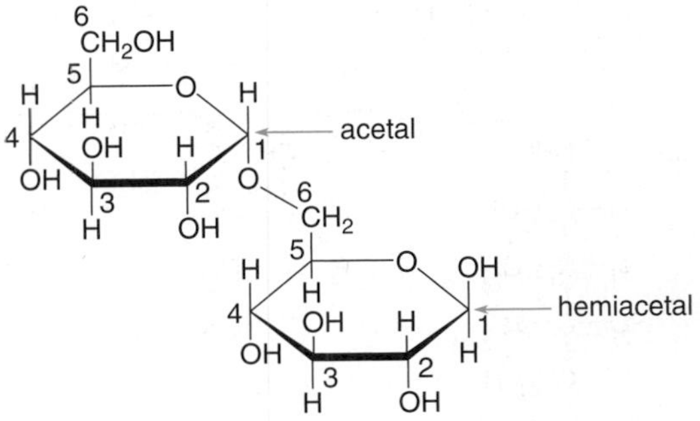

c. 1→6-α-glycosidic linkage

d. β anomer

e.

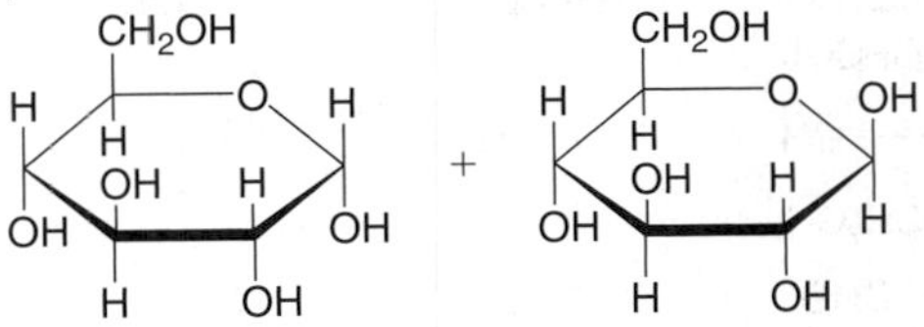

CH$_2$OH ring
α anomer
+
CH$_2$OH ring
β anomer

20.69

CH$_2$OH ring — O — CH$_2$OH ring

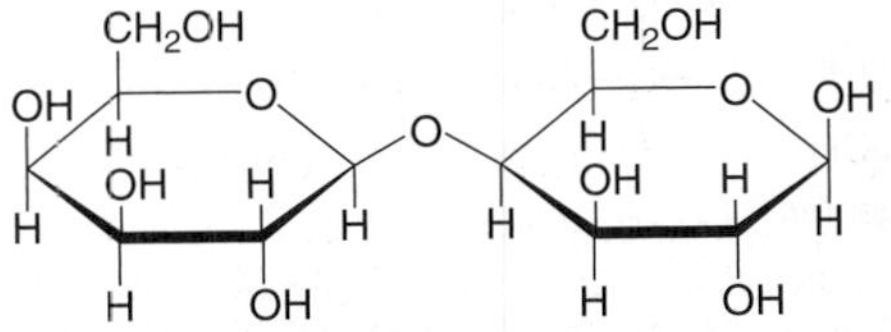

20.71 Cellulose and amylose are both composed of repeating glucose units. In cellulose the glucose units are joined by a 1→4-β-glycosidic linkage, but in amylose they are joined by an α-(1→4) linkage. This leads to very different three-dimensional shapes, with cellulose forming sheets and amylose forming helices.

20.73

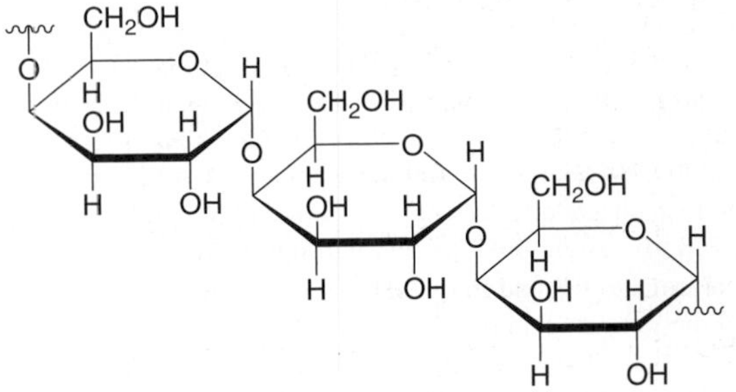

CH$_2$OH ring — O — CH$_2$OH ring — O — CH$_2$OH ring

20.75 a. D sugar

b. aldohexose

c.
CHO
H—C—OH
H—C—OH
H—C—OH
HO—C—H
CH₂OH
enantiomer

d.
CHO
HO—C*—H
HO—C*—H
HO—C*—H
H—C*—OH
CH₂OH
* chirality center

e.
CH₂OH
OH   O   H
H
OH   OH
H   OH
H   H

f.
COOH
HO—C—H
HO—C—H
HO—C—H
H—C—OH
CH₂OH

g.
CH₂OH
HO—C—H
HO—C—H
HO—C—H
H—C—OH
CH₂OH

h. a reducing sugar

20.77 Lactose intolerance results from a lack of the enzyme lactase. It results in abdominal cramping and diarrhea. Galactosemia results from the inability to metabolize galactose. Therefore, it accumulates in the liver, causing cirrhosis, and in the brain, leading to mental retardation.

20.79 Fructose is a naturally occurring sugar with more perceived sweetness per gram than sucrose. Sucralose is a synthetic sweetener; that is, it is not naturally occurring.

20.81 An individual with type A blood can receive only blood types A and O, because he or she will produce antibodies and an immune response to B or AB blood. He or she can donate to individuals with either type A or AB blood as the type A polysaccharides are common to both and no immune response will be generated.

20.83 The long sheets of polysaccharides in chitin, similar to cellulose, have β glycosidic linkages and will not be digestible.

20.85 Hyaluronate is found in the extracellular fluid that lubricates joints and the vitreous humor of the eye. Chondroitin is a component of cartilage and tendons. Heparin is stored in the mast cells of the liver and other organs and prevents blood clotting.

20.87

CH₂OH
C=O
HO—C—H
H—C—OH
H—C—OH
CH₂OH
fructose

→ reduction →

CH₂OH
HO—C—H
HO—C—H
H—C—OH
H—C—OH
CH₂OH

+

CH₂OH
H—C—OH
HO—C—H
H—C—OH
H—C—OH
CH₂OH

stereoisomers
They differ in configuration at a single carbon.

CHAPTER 21

21.1 a. amide   b. alcohol   c. thiol

21.3 a.
COO⁻
H₃N⁺—C—H
CH₂
(phenyl ring)
L

COO⁻
H—C—NH₃⁺
CH₂
(phenyl ring)
D

b.
COO⁻
H₃N⁺—C—H
CH₂CH₂SCH₃
L

COO⁻
H—C—NH₃⁺
CH₂CH₂SCH₃
D

21.5 a.
H
H₃N⁺—C—COO⁻
CH(CH₃)₂
predominant at p*I*

c.
H
H₂N—C—COO⁻
CH(CH₃)₂

b.
H
H₃N⁺—C—COOH
CH(CH₃)₂

21.7
a. N-terminal: leucine   C-terminal: alanine
b. N-terminal: arginine   C-terminal: tyrosine
c. N-terminal: phenylalanine   C-terminal: glutamine
d. N-terminal: valine   C-terminal: phenylalanine

21.9 a.
H   O   H
H₃N⁺—C—C—N—C—COO⁻
H   H
CH₂(phenyl)

b.
H   O   H
H₃N⁺—C—C—N—C—COO⁻
CH₂   H   CH(CH₃)CH₂CH₃
CH₂CONH₂

c.
H   O   H
H₃N⁺—C—C—N—C—COO⁻
CH₂   H   CH₂SH
CH(CH₃)₂

21.11 a. alanine and isoleucine: Ala–Ile
b. tyrosine and valine: Tyr–Val

21.12

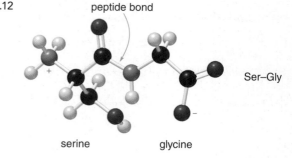

peptide bond

Ser–Gly

serine   glycine

21.13 a.

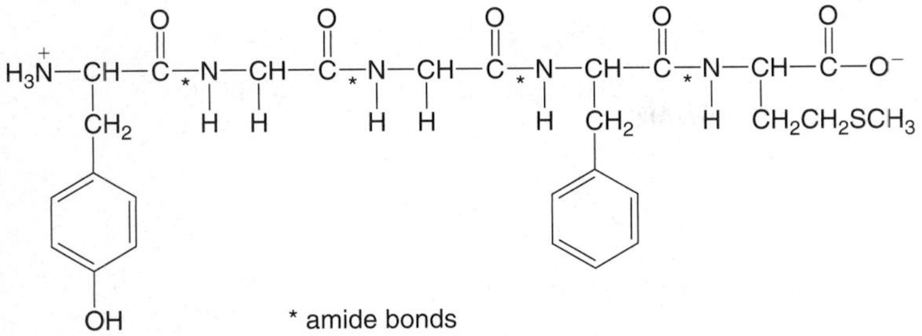

$$H_3\overset{+}{N}-CH-\overset{O}{\overset{\|}{C}}-\overset{*}{N}-CH-\overset{O}{\overset{\|}{C}}-\overset{*}{N}-CH-\overset{O}{\overset{\|}{C}}-\overset{*}{N}-CH-\overset{O}{\overset{\|}{C}}-\overset{*}{N}-CH-\overset{O}{\overset{\|}{C}}-O^-$$

with side chains: CH₂ (—OH phenol, tyrosine); H H; H H; H CH₂ (phenyl); H CH₂CH₂SCH₃

* amide bonds

b. tyrosine

c. 3

21.15 Yes, the amino acids may be ordered differently.

21.17 Glycine has no large side chain and this allows for the β-sheets to stack well together.

21.19 a.

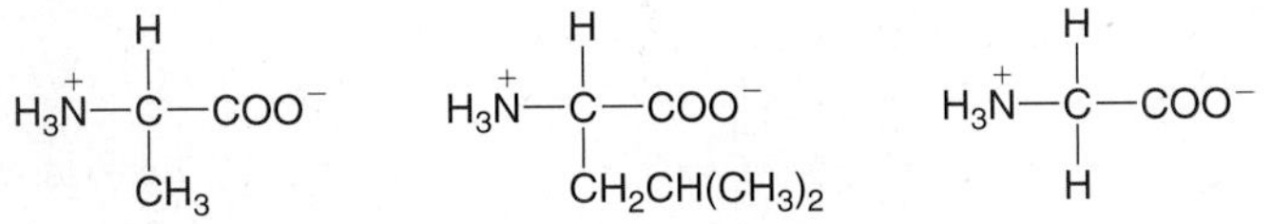

$$H_3\overset{+}{N}-\overset{H}{\underset{CH_3}{\overset{|}{C}}}-COO^- \qquad H_3\overset{+}{N}-\overset{H}{\underset{CH_2CH(CH_3)_2}{\overset{|}{C}}}-COO^- \qquad H_3\overset{+}{N}-\overset{H}{\underset{H}{\overset{|}{C}}}-COO^-$$

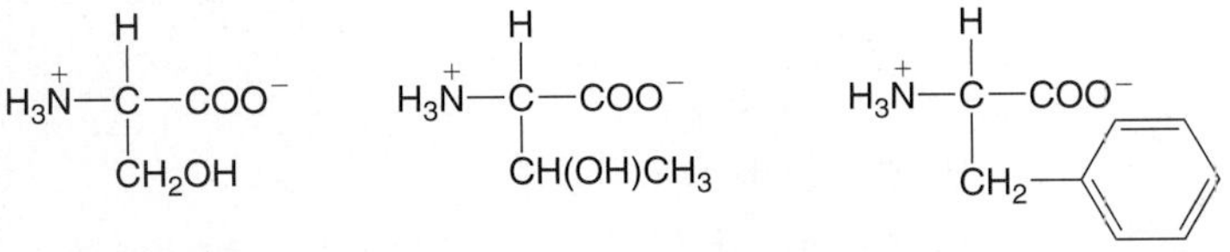

b.

$$H_3\overset{+}{N}-\overset{H}{\underset{CH_2OH}{\overset{|}{C}}}-COO^- \qquad H_3\overset{+}{N}-\overset{H}{\underset{CH(OH)CH_3}{\overset{|}{C}}}-COO^- \qquad H_3\overset{+}{N}-\overset{H}{\underset{CH_2}{\overset{|}{C}}}-COO^- \text{(phenyl)}$$

c.

$$H_3\overset{+}{N}-\overset{H}{\underset{CH_2CH(CH_3)_2}{\overset{|}{C}}}-COO^- \qquad H_3\overset{+}{N}-\overset{H}{\underset{CH_2}{\overset{|}{C}}}-COO^- \text{(phenol —OH)} \qquad H_3\overset{+}{N}-\overset{H}{\underset{CH_2CONH_2}{\overset{|}{C}}}-COO^-$$

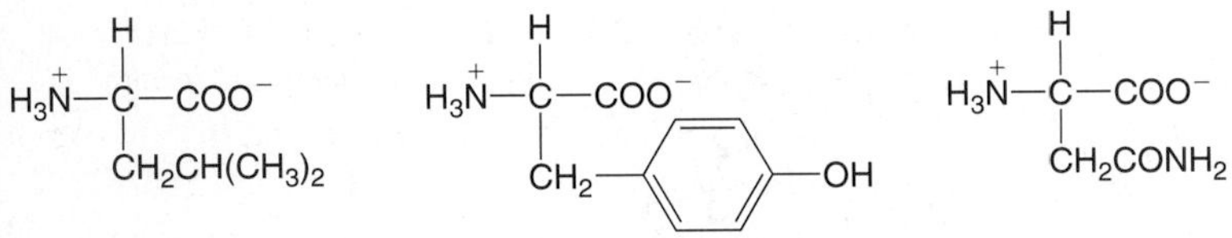

21.21 b, d, e

21.23

substrate

Inhibitor blocks substrate access to the active site.

enzyme

21.25 Fibrin and thrombin circulate as inactive zymogens so that the blood does not clot unnecessarily. They are activated as required at a bleeding point to form a clot.

21.27 The L designation refers to the configuration at the chirality center. With a vertical carbon chain in the Fischer projection, the L isomer has the –NH₃⁺ drawn on the left side. The α-amino acid designation indicates that the amino group is bonded to the carbon adjacent to the carbonyl group.

21.29 Alanine is an ionic salt with strong electrostatic forces, leading to its high melting point, and making it a solid at room temperature. Pyruvic acid has much weaker intermolecular forces so it is a liquid at room temperature.

21.31 a.
$$H_3\overset{+}{N}-\overset{H}{\underset{CH_2OH}{\overset{|}{C}}}-COO^-$$

c.
$$H_3\overset{+}{N}-\overset{H}{\underset{CH_2}{\overset{|}{C}}}-COO^- \text{(phenyl)}$$

b.
$$H_3\overset{+}{N}-\overset{H}{\underset{CH_2CONH_2}{\overset{|}{C}}}-COO^-$$

d.
$$H_3\overset{+}{N}-\overset{H}{\underset{CH(CH_3)_2}{\overset{|}{C}}}-COO^-$$

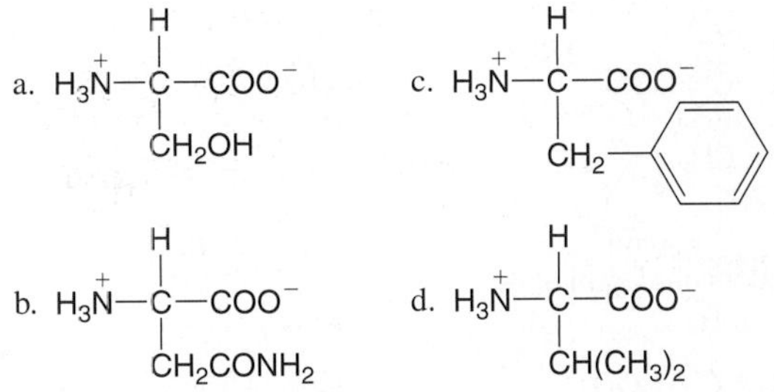

21.33 isoleucine and threonine

	[1]	[2]	[3]	[4]
21.35 a.	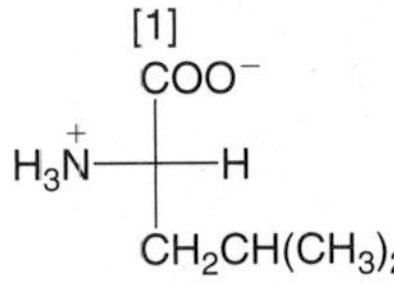 $H_3\overset{+}{N}-\underset{CH_2CH(CH_3)_2}{\overset{COO^-}{\mid}}-H$	neutral	Leu	L
b.	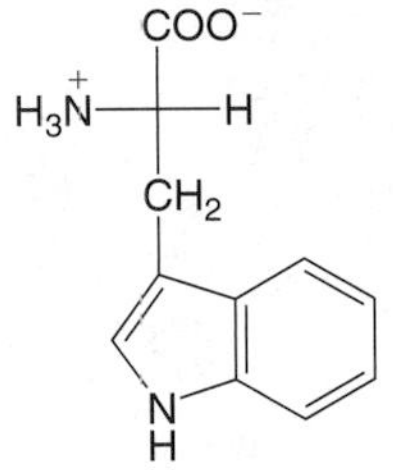 $H_3\overset{+}{N}-\underset{CH_2\text{(indole)}}{\overset{COO^-}{\mid}}-H$	neutral	Trp	W
c.	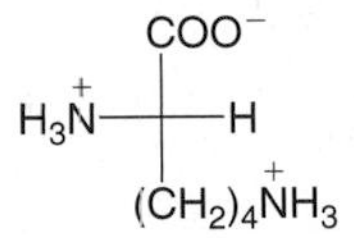 $H_3\overset{+}{N}-\underset{(CH_2)_4\overset{+}{N}H_3}{\overset{COO^-}{\mid}}-H$	basic	Lys	K
d.	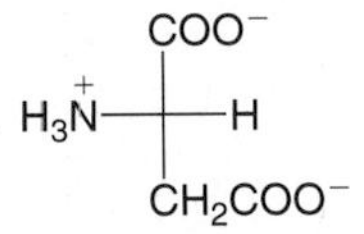 $H_3\overset{+}{N}-\underset{CH_2COO^-}{\overset{COO^-}{\mid}}-H$	acidic	Asp	D

21.37 a.
$$H_3\overset{+}{N}-\underset{CH_2CH_2SCH_3}{\overset{COO^-}{\mid}}-H \qquad H-\underset{CH_2CH_2SCH_3}{\overset{COO^-}{\mid}}-\overset{+}{N}H_3$$
L   D

b.
$$H_3\overset{+}{N}-\underset{CH_2CONH_2}{\overset{COO^-}{\mid}}-H \qquad H-\underset{CH_2CONH_2}{\overset{COO^-}{\mid}}-\overset{+}{N}H_3$$
L   D

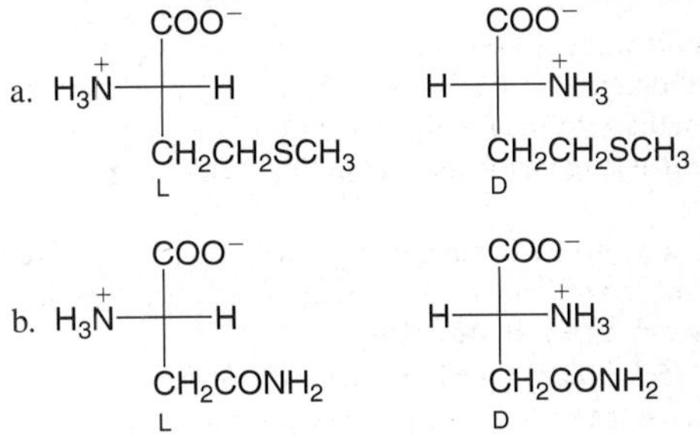

21.39

	[1]	[2]	[3]	[4]
a.	glutamine	Gln	Q	neutral
b.	tyrosine	Tyr	Y	neutral

21.41 a.
$$H_3\overset{+}{N}-\overset{H}{\underset{CH_2CH(CH_3)_2}{\overset{|}{C}}}-COO^-$$

c.
$$H_3\overset{+}{N}-\overset{H}{\underset{CH_2CH(CH_3)_2}{\overset{|}{C}}}-COOH$$

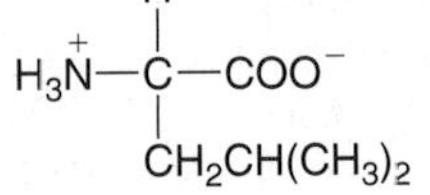

predominant form at p*I*

b.
$$H_2N-\overset{H}{\underset{CH_2CH(CH_3)_2}{\overset{|}{C}}}-COO^-$$

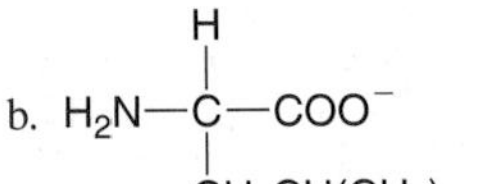

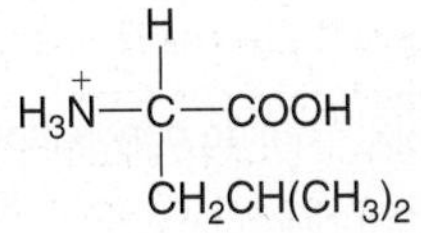

21.43

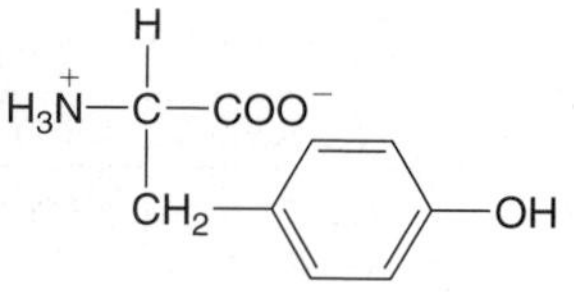

neutral
predominant form at pI

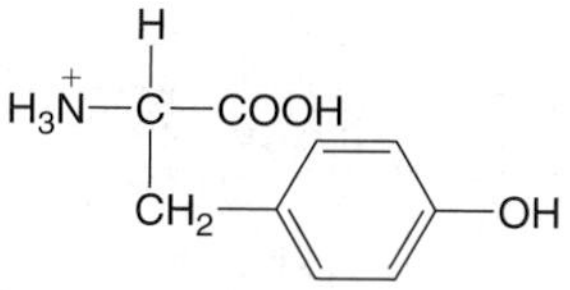

positive charge
pH = 1

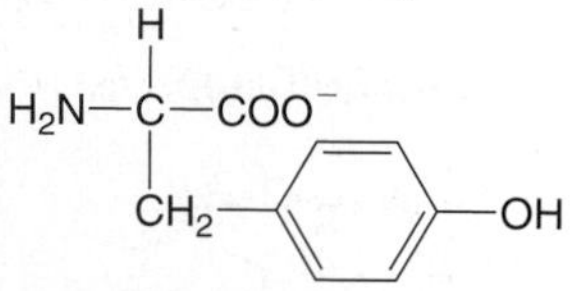

negative charge
pH = 11

21.45

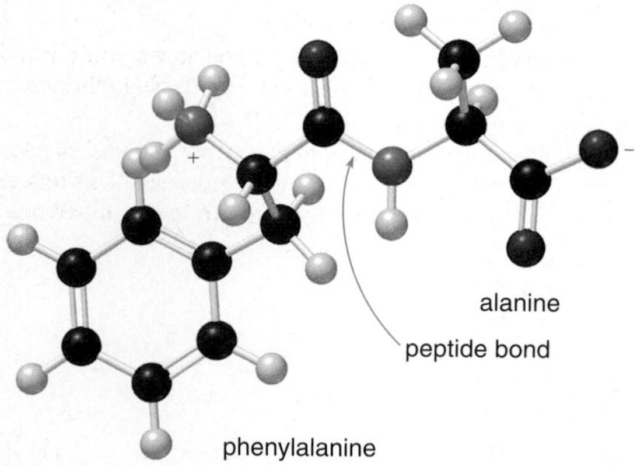

Phe–Ala

alanine

peptide bond

phenylalanine

21.47 a, b, c:

N-terminal amino acid

Val–Phe

Phe–Val

C-terminal amino acid

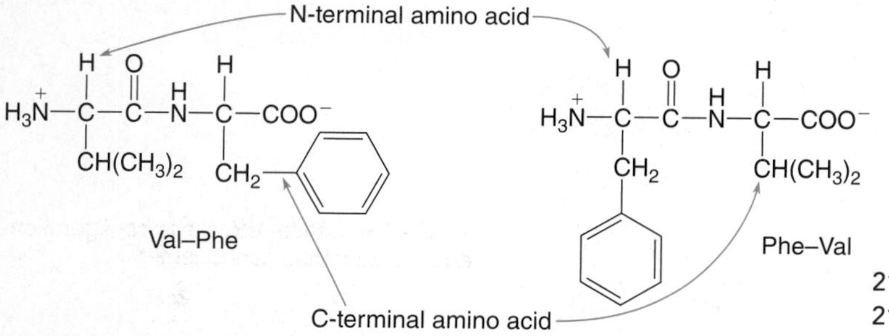

21.49 a. [1]

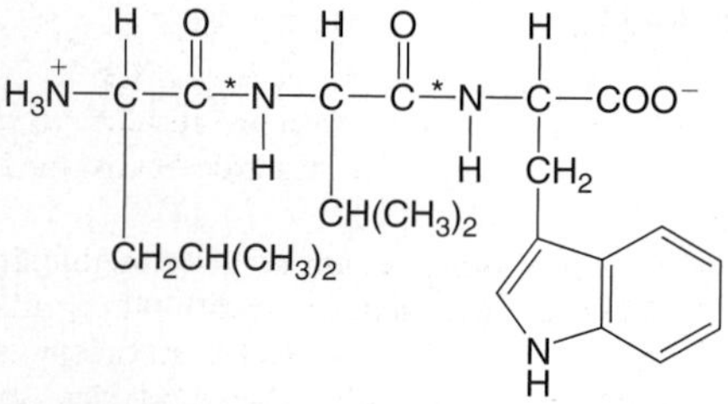

[2] * amide bonds labeled

[3] N-terminal: leucine
C-terminal: tryptophan

[4] Leu–Val–Trp

b. [1]

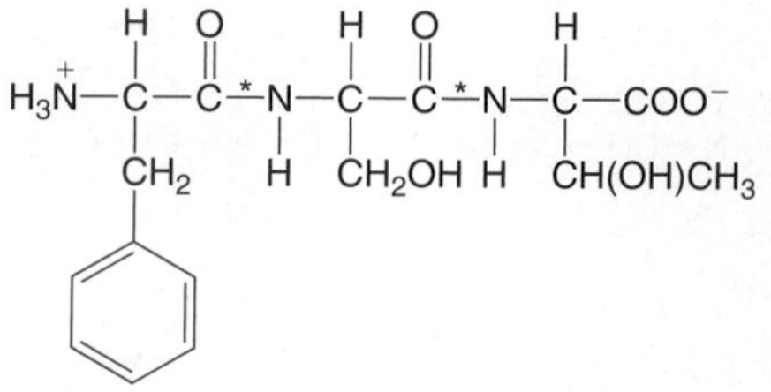

[2] * amide bonds labeled

[3] N-terminal: phenylalanine
C-terminal: threonine

[4] Phe–Ser–Thr

21.51 a. [1], [2] valine: N-terminal, glycine, phenylalanine:
C-terminal [3] Val–Gly–Phe

b. [1], [2] leucine: N-terminal, tyrosine, methionine:
C-terminal [3] Leu–Tyr–Met

21.53

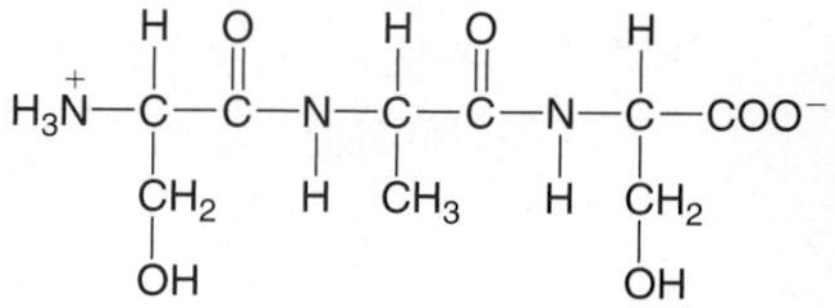

Ser–Ala–Ser

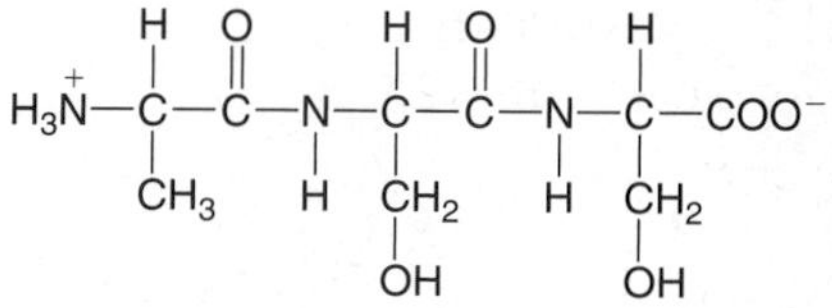

Ala–Ser–Ser

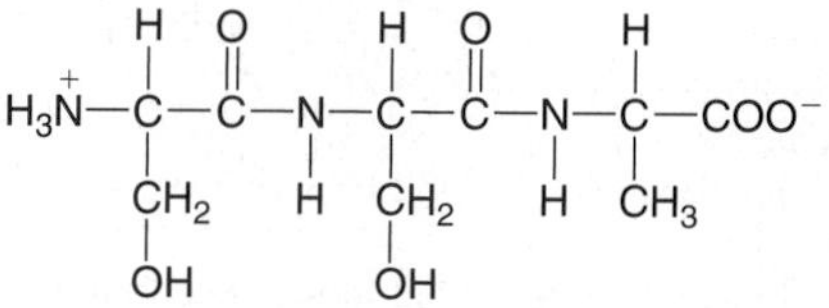

Ser–Ser–Ala

21.55 alanine, cysteine, glycine

21.57 a.

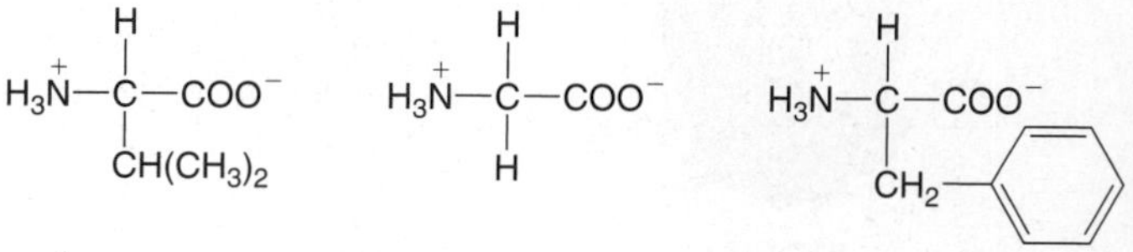

b.

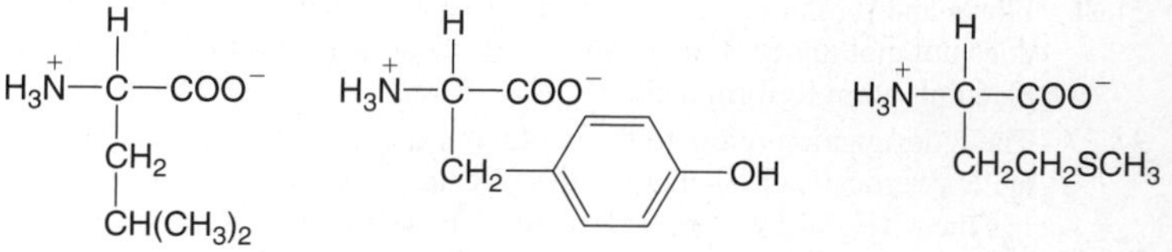

21.59

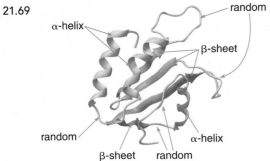

3 moles Pro

2 moles each, Arg and Phe

1 mole each, Gly and Ser

21.61

Gly–Tyr

Val

Gly–Ala–Phe

21.63 The primary structure of a protein is the order of its amino acids. The secondary structure refers to the three-dimensional arrangements of regions within the protein.

21.65 a. London dispersion forces   c. electrostatic
        b. London dispersion forces   d. electrostatic

21.67

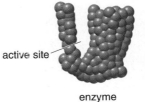

hydrogen bonding

21.69

α-helix
random
β-sheet
random
α-helix
β-sheet   random

21.71

	a. Secondary Structure	b. H$_2$O Solubility	c. Function	d. Location
Hemoglobin	Globular with much α-helix	Soluble	Carries oxygen to tissues	Blood
Keratin	α-Helix	Insoluble	Firm tissues	Nail, hair

21.73 When heated, a protein's primary structure is unaffected. The 2°, 3°, and 4° structures may be altered.

21.75 a. Insulin is a hormone that controls glucose levels.
        b. Myoglobin stores oxygen in muscle.
        c. α-Keratin forms hard tissues such as hair and nails.
        d. Chymotrypsin is a protease that hydrolyzes peptide bonds.
        e. Oxytocin is a hormone that stimulates uterine contractions and induces the release of breast milk.

21.77 Reversible enzyme inhibition occurs when an enzyme's activity is restored when an inhibitor is released. Irreversible inhibition renders an enzyme incapable of further activity.

21.79 Captopril inhibits the angiotensin-converting enzyme, blocking the conversion of angiotensinogen to angiotensin. This reduces the concentration of angiotensin, which in turn lowers blood pressure.

21.81

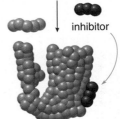

substrate

active site

enzyme

inhibitor

The inhibitor alters active site configuration and the substrate cannot enter.

21.83 The α-keratin in nails has more cysteine residues to form disulfide bonds. The larger the number of disulfide bonds, the harder the substance.

21.85 Humans cannot synthesize the amino acids methionine and lysine. Diets that include animal products readily supply all the needed amino acids, but no one plant source has sufficient amounts of all the essential amino acids. Grains—wheat, rice, and corn—are low in lysine, and legumes—beans, peas, and peanuts—are low in methionine, but a combination of these foods provides all the needed amino acids.

21.87 Cauterization denatures the proteins in a wound.

21.89 In sickle hemoglobin there is a substitution of a single amino acid, valine for glutamic acid.

21.91 Penicillin inhibits the formation of the bacterial cell wall by irreversibly binding to an enzyme needed for its construction. It does not affect humans since human cells have a cell membrane, but not a rigid cell wall. Sulfanilamide inhibits the production of folic acid and therefore reproduction in bacteria, but humans do not synthesize folic acid (they must ingest it instead), so it does not affect humans.

21.93 Both aspartic acid and glutamic acid have two carboxylic acid groups. At low pH they have a +1 charge with both acid groups protonated, but at a high pH both acid groups are ionized, leading to a net charge of −2.

Form of Asp at low pH

$$H_3\overset{+}{N}-\overset{\displaystyle H}{\underset{\displaystyle CH_2COOH}{C}}-COOH$$

Form of Asp at high pH

$$H_2N-\overset{\displaystyle H}{\underset{\displaystyle CH_2COO^-}{C}}-COO^-$$

CHAPTER 22

22.1 a. base = uracil, sugar = D-ribose, nucleoside = uridine
   b. base = guanine, sugar = D-2-deoxyribose, nucleoside = deoxyguanosine

22.3 a. base = uracil, sugar = ribose, uridine 5'-monophosphate, UMP
   b. base = thymine, sugar = D-2-deoxyribose, deoxythymidine 5'-monophosphate, dTMP

22.5 a.

UMP

b.

dTMP

c.

AMP

22.7

22.9 a. 3'–TTTGCAGG–5'   c. 3'–TAACGTGGGCG–5'
   b. 3'–ATATGCGG–5'   d. 3'–GTGAACTAGCC–5'

22.10 a. 5'–TCTCAGAG–3'   c. 5'–TAGGACATG–3'
   b. 3'–TAACAG–5'   d. 3'–CCGGTATGAG–5'

22.11 a. [1] 5'–ACGGAUUGC–3'   [2] 5'–ACGGATTGC–3'
   b. [1] 5'–CUGAGG–3'   [2] 5'–CTGAGG–3'
   c. [1] 5'–AAUUGCGCU–3'   [2] 5'–AATTGCGCT–3'
   d. [1] 5'–GUCACUGGCAUG–3'   [2] 5'–GTCACTGGCATG–3'

22.13 a. Ala   c. Leu   e. Gln
   b. Asn   d. Ser   f. Lys

22.15 a. Gln–Glu–Val–Ser–Tyr–Arg
   b. Val–Ile–Trp–Arg–Gly–Ile
   c. Leu–Cys–Ser–Arg–Thr–Pro

22.17 a. 3'–CTC GGG CAT ATG CGG TGC–5'
   b. Glu–Pro–Val–Tyr–Ala–Thr

22.19 a. Pro–Pro–Ala–Asn–Glu–Ala
      GGU GGC CGU UUG CUU CGU
   b. Ala–Pro–Leu–Arg–Asp
      CGU GGU GAU UCU CUG

22.20 a. Arg–Val–Ala–Leu–Leu–Ser
   b. Arg–Gly–Phe–Ile–Val–Asn

22.21 a. Leu–Thr
   b. [1] Leu–Pro
      [2] Stop codon, so no dipeptide is formed.
      [3] Leu–Thr

22.23

5' ∼∼∼ C C A [   ]   A G C T T G G A T T ∼∼∼ 3'
                     sticky ends
3' ∼∼∼ G G T T C G A   [   ] A C C T A A ∼∼∼ 5'

22.25 A ribonucleoside contains ribose (a monosaccharide) and a nitrogen-containing base (A, G, C, or U), and a ribonucleotide has these components plus a phosphate group attached to the 5' position of the ribose.

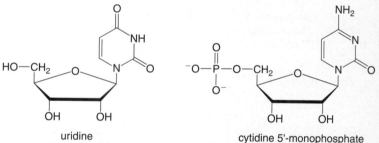

uridine
a ribonucleoside

cytidine 5'-monophosphate
a ribonucleotide

22.27 A gene is a portion of the DNA molecule responsible for the synthesis of a single protein. Many genes form each chromosome.

22.29 a, c: DNA   b. both   d. RNA

22.31 a. base: cytosine
      monosaccharide: 2'-deoxyribose
      deoxycytidine
   b. base: guanine
      monosaccharide: ribose
      guanosine 5'-monophosphate

22.33 a.

b. 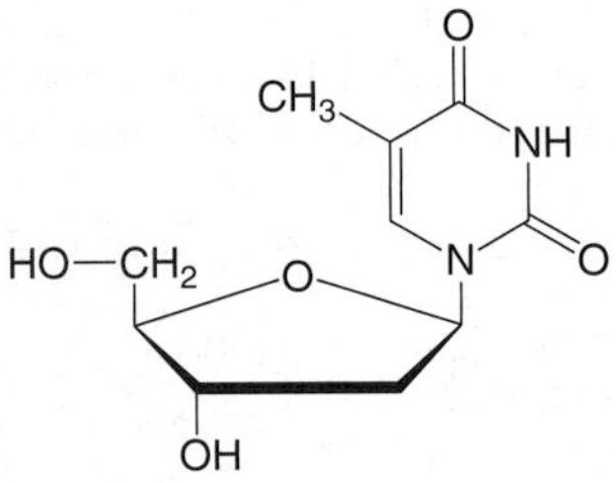 (structure)

c. 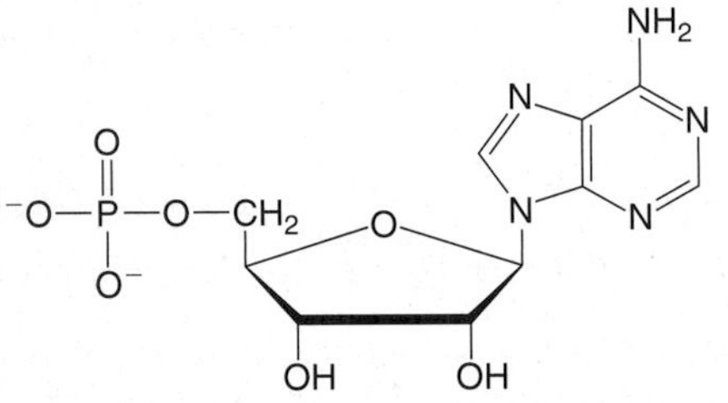 (structure)

d. 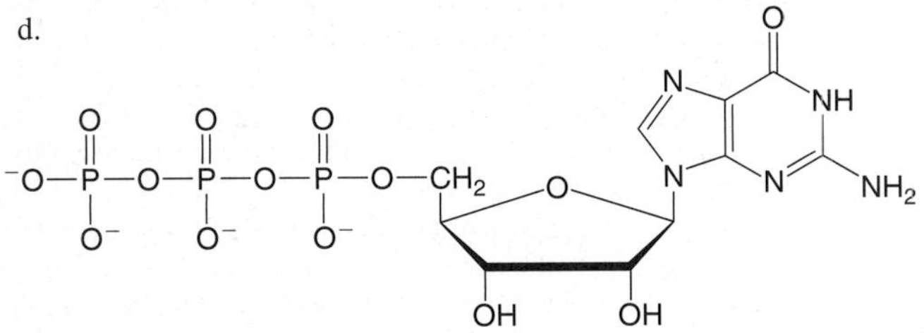 (structure)

22.35 a. 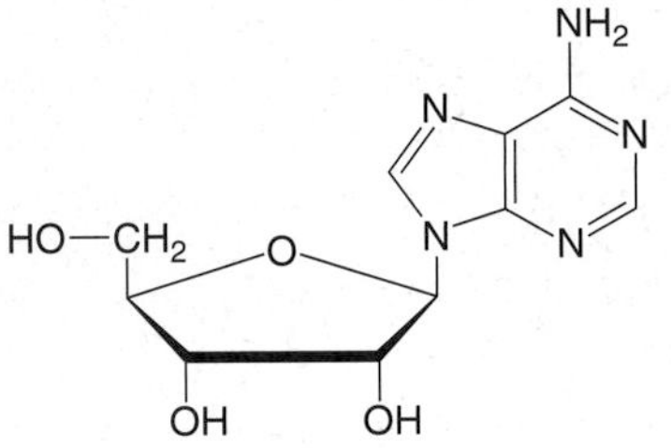 (structure)

b. 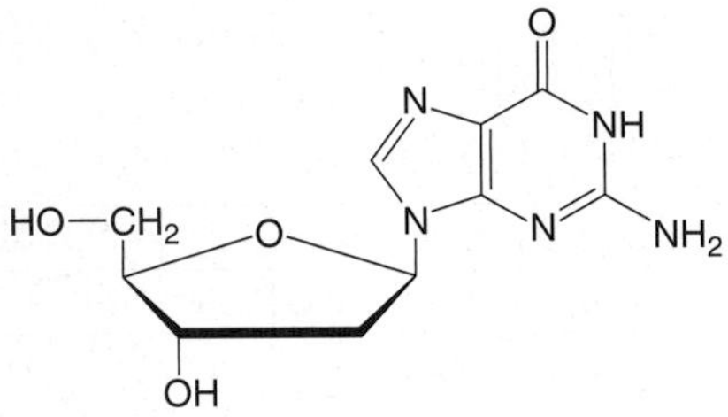 (structure)

c. 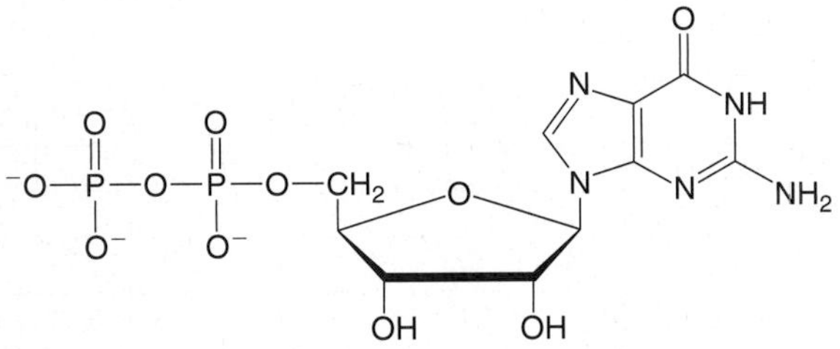 (structure)

d. 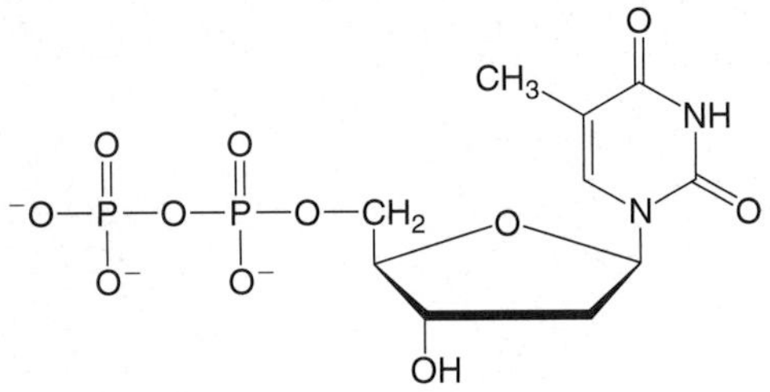 (structure)

22.37 a. uracil, adenine
b. The 5' end has the free phosphate and the 3' end has two OH groups on the five-membered sugar ring.
c. UMP, AMP
d. This dinucleotide is a ribonucleotide because the sugar rings contain an OH group on C2'.
e. UA

22.39 (structure)

(structure)

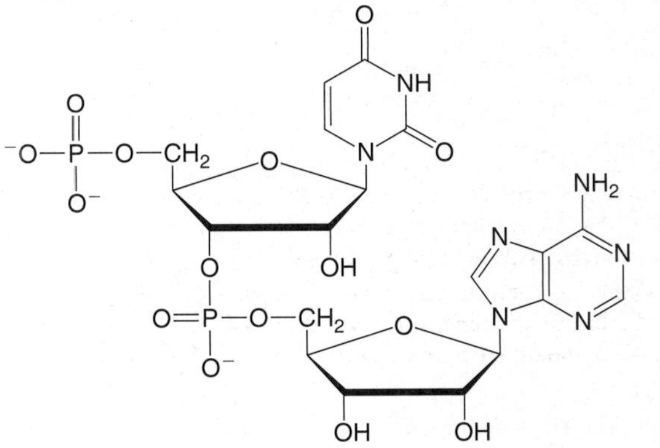

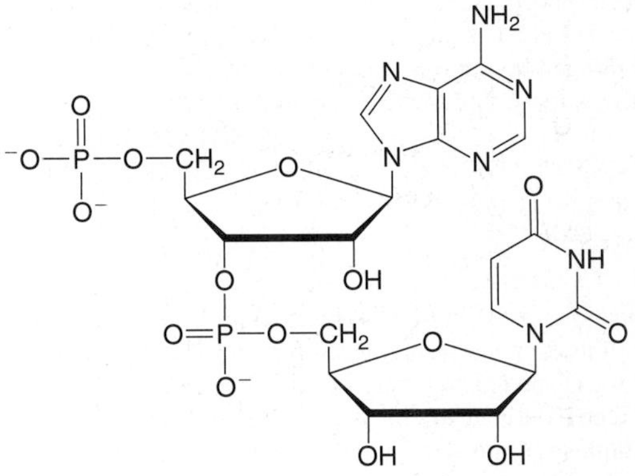

22.41 a. 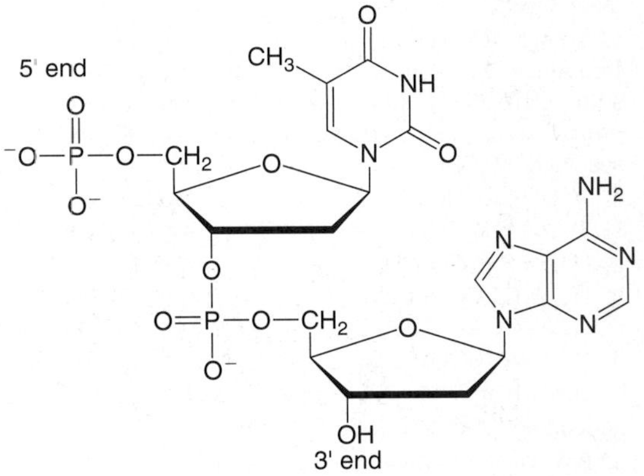 (structure)
5' end
3' end

b. 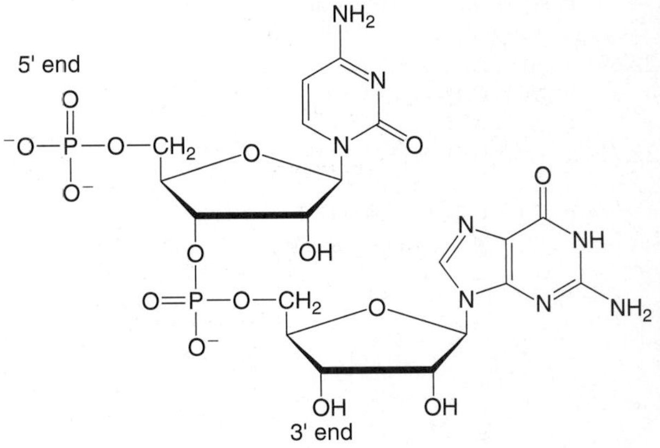 (structure)
5' end
3' end

22.43

22.45 a. The DNA double helix has 2-deoxyribose as the only sugar. The sugar–phosphate groups are on the outside of the helix.
b. The 5' end has a phosphate and the 3' end has an OH group.
c. Hydrogen bonding occurs in the interior of the helix between base pairs: A pairs with T and G pairs with C.

22.47 a. 3'–TTTATTG–5' c. 3'–GCTATAGGGC–5'
b. 3'–TGACCTGA–5' d. 3'–AAGGGCCCTAT–5'

22.49 27% T, 23% G, 23% C

22.51 G and C

22.53 5'–TACCGGATACGCTA–3'

22.55 Replication occurs in only one direction, from the 3' end to the 5' end of the template strand, but the strands of DNA run in opposite directions. The leading strand can be formed continuously from the 3' end as it is unwound. The lagging strand runs in the opposite direction, so it must be formed in segments that are then joined by DNA ligase.

22.57 Messenger RNA carries the specific sequence of the DNA code from the cell nucleus to the ribosomes in the cytoplasm to make a protein. Each transfer RNA brings a specific amino acid to the growing protein chain on the ribosome according to the sequence specified by the mRNA.

22.59 a. 3'–UUUAUUG–5' c. 3'–GCUAUAGGGC–5'
b. 3'–UGACCUGA–5' d. 3'–AAGGGCCCUAU–5'

22.61 a. [1] 5'-UACCGAAU-3' [2] 5'-TACCGAAT-3'
b. [1] 5'-GCCGCGAAU-3' [2] 5'-GCCGCGAAT-3'
c. [1] 5'-CCAUAUGGC-3' [2] 5'-CCATATGGC-3'
d. [1] 5'-AUCCGGCAU-3' [2] 5'-ATCCGGCAT-3'

22.63 a. GAC: Leu b. AAA: Phe c. UUC: Lys d. CGU: Ala

22.65 anticodon: CGC; amino acid: alanine

22.67 a. Pro–Thr–Trp–Val–Glu
b. Met–Phe–Leu–Trp–Trp
c. Val–Asp–Glu–Pro–Gln

22.69 a. AUU AUG AAA AGU UAU
b. CCU CAA GAA GAU UUU
c. ACU AGU AAU CGU

22.71 a. [1] 3' ATA AGT TAT TTT TTG 5'
[2] Tyr–Ser–Ile–Lys–Asn
b. [1] 3' CTA CAT TTG TTC GGC 5'
[2] Asp–Val–Asn–Lys–Pro

22.73 A point mutation results in the substitution of one nucleotide for another in a DNA molecule. A silent mutation is a point mutation in DNA that results in no change in an amino acid sequence.

22.75 a. Leu–Gln–His
b. Leu–Gln–Asn
c. Leu–Gln–His, no change
d. This is a stop codon so the chain is terminated.
e. A dipeptide, Ser–Ala, is synthesized.

22.77 a. Asn–Ala b. Asn–Ala c. Asn–Gly d. Asn–Ser

22.79 A restriction endonuclease is an enzyme that cleaves plasmid DNA at a specific site.

22.81

5' ~~~~ C C G G T T G ⌐‾‾‾‾ G A T C C T T ~~~~ 3'
          sticky ends
3' ~~~~ G G C C A A C C T A G ⌐‾‾‾‾ G A A ~~~~ 5'

22.83 Circular plasmid DNA is isolated from bacteria and cleaved at a specific site with a restriction endonuclease. This forms "sticky ends" of DNA that are then combined with another DNA source, perhaps human, with complementary "sticky ends" to the plasmid DNA. These DNA strands come together and then a DNA ligase is used to re-form a circular DNA that is then reproduced by the bacteria.

22.85 a. Lanes 3 and 5 represent DNA of children that share both parents because they both have DNA fragments common to both parents.
b. Lane 4 represents DNA from an adopted child because the DNA fragments have little relationship to the parental DNA fragments.

22.87 a. cytidine
b. Lamivudine is a nucleoside analogue that gets incorporated into a DNA chain, but since it does not contain a 3' hydroxyl group, synthesis is terminated.

22.89 a. 5' GTT ACA TAA AAA CGA 3'
b. 5' GUU ACA UAA AAA CGA 3'
c. Val–Thr

22.91

DNA informational strand:	5' end	AAC	TAT	CCA	ACG	AAG	ATG	3' end
DNA template strand:	3' end	TTG	ATA	GGT	TGC	TTC	TAC	5' end
mRNA codons:	5' end	AAC	UAU	CCA	ACG	AAG	AUG	3' end
tRNA anticodons:		UUG	AUA	GGU	UGC	UUC	UAC	
Polypeptide:		Asn	Tyr	Pro	Thr	Lys	Met	

22.93

DNA informational strand:	5' end	AAC	GTA	TCA	ACT	CAC	ATG	3' end
DNA template strand:	3' end	TTG	CAT	AGT	TGA	GTG	TAC	5' end
mRNA codons:	5' end	AAC	GUA	UCA	ACU	CAC	AUG	3' end
tRNA anticodons:		UUG	CAU	AGU	UGA	GUG	UAC	
Polypeptide:		Asn	Val	Ser	Thr	His	Met	

22.95 975

22.97 ATA CCA CCA AAA TAC

22.99 TAA CCT AAA

CHAPTER 23

23.1 This makes it possible to use the same reactions and the same enzyme systems to metabolize all types of biomolecules.

23.3 a. glucose + ATP $\longrightarrow$ glucose 1-phosphate + ADP
b. −2.3 kcal/mol

23.5 −3.0 kcal/mol of energy released

23.6 a. reduction using NADH   b. oxidation using NAD^+

23.7 Riboflavin has numerous polar groups (OH and NH) that can hydrogen bond to water, making it water soluble.

23.9 $CH_3CH_2CH_2\overset{\displaystyle O}{\overset{\|}{C}}O^-$ + HSCoA

23.10 a.
$$\begin{array}{c} CO_2^- \\ | \\ HO-C-H \\ | \\ CH_2 \\ | \\ CO_2^- \end{array} \xrightarrow{\overset{NAD^+ \quad NADH+H^+}{\curvearrowright}} \begin{array}{c} CO_2^- \\ | \\ C=O \\ | \\ CH_2 \\ | \\ CO_2^- \end{array}$$

b. oxidation

23.11 Succinate dehydrogenase is so named because the elements of hydrogen (H_2) are removed from succinate.

23.13 a. reduction   b. oxidizing agent

23.15 Mitochondria contain an outer membrane and an inner membrane with many folds. The area between these two membranes is called the intermembrane space. Energy production occurs within the matrix, the area surrounded by the inner membrane.

23.17 hydrolysis of starch, the conversion of glucose to acetyl CoA, the citric acid cycle, electron transport chain, oxidative phosphorylation

23.19 a. stage [1]   c. stage [3]   e. stage [1]
b. stage [2]   d. stage [4]

23.21 Coupled reactions are pairs of reactions that occur together. The energy released by one reaction provides the energy to drive the other reaction.

23.23 $CH_3\overset{\displaystyle O}{\overset{\|}{C}}O^-$ + HPO_4^{2-}

23.25

	Energy change
a. ATP + succinate + HSCoA $\longrightarrow$ succinyl CoA + ADP + HPO_4^{2-}	+2.1 kcal/mol

b. The reaction is not energetically favored because an input of energy is required.

23.27 a. glucose + HPO_4^{2-} $\longrightarrow$ glucose 1-phosphate + H_2O
b. glucose + ATP $\longrightarrow$ glucose 1-phosphate + ADP
c. −2.3 kcal/mol

23.29 a. −3.9 kcal/mol
b. fructose 6-phosphate + HPO_4^{2-} $\longrightarrow$ fructose 1,6-bisphosphate + H_2O

$\underline{\text{ATP} + H_2O \longrightarrow \text{ADP} + HPO_4^{2-}}$
fructose 6-phosphate + ATP $\longrightarrow$ fructose 1,6-bisphosphate + ADP

c. +3.9 + (−7.3) = −3.4 kcal/mol

23.31 a. 1,3-bisphosphoglycerate + ADP $\longrightarrow$ 3-phosphoglycerate + ATP
b. −4.5 kcal/mol
c. Yes, this is an energetically favorable coupled reaction that could be used to synthesize ATP from ADP.

23.33

a.
GTP

b.
GDP

23.35 a. reducing agent   b. neither   c. oxidizing agent

23.37 When a substrate is oxidized, NAD^+ is reduced. NAD^+ is an oxidizing agent.

23.39 a.
$$\text{cyclohexanol} \xrightarrow[\text{oxidation}]{\overset{NAD^+ \quad NADH+H^+}{\curvearrowright}} \text{cyclohexanone}$$

b.
$$\text{benzaldehyde (CHO)} \xrightarrow[\text{reduction}]{\overset{NADH+H^+ \quad NAD^+}{\curvearrowright}} \text{benzyl alcohol (CH}_2\text{OH)}$$

23.41 a. steps [3], [4], and [8]   c. step [6]
b. steps [3] and [4]   d. step [1]

23.43 a.
$$\begin{array}{c} H \quad\quad CO_2^- \\ \diagdown\quad\diagup \\ C=C \\ \diagup\quad\diagdown \\ {}^-O_2C \quad\quad H \end{array}$$
fumarate
    b. succinate   c. malate

23.45 a. isocitrate   b. malate, isocitrate

23.47 a. oxidation   b. decarboxylation   c. step [3a]
d. The elements of H_2 (hydrogen) are removed in converting isocitrate to oxalosuccinate.

23.49 step [7]

23.51 They require oxygen.

23.53 a. $FADH_2$ donates electrons to the electron transport chain.
b. ADP is a substrate for the formation of ATP.
c. ATP synthase catalyzes the formation of ATP from ADP.
d. The inner mitochondrial membrane contains the four complexes for the electron transport chain. ATP synthase is also embedded in the membrane and contains the H^+ ion channel that allows H^+ to return to the matrix.

23.55 NAD^+, FAD, and H_2O

23.57 $FADH_2$ enters the electron transport chain at complex II, whereas NADH enters at complex I.

23.59 a. Pepsin catalyzes the hydrolysis of proteins to amino acids in the stomach.
b. Succinate dehydrogenase catalyzes the conversion of succinate to fumarate in step [6] of the citric acid cycle.
c. ATP synthase catalyzes the oxidative phosphorylation of ADP to ATP.

23.61 Each two-carbon fragment of acetyl CoA that enters the citric acid cycle produces three molecules of NADH and one molecule of $FADH_2$. These then enter the electron transport chain and serve as reducing agents. For each NADH that enters the electron transport chain, there are 2.5 ATPs produced, and for each $FADH_2$, there are 1.5 ATPs produced. In addition, there is one GTP (an ATP equivalent) produced in the citric acid cycle.
In total: 3 NADH × 2.5 ATP/NADH = 7.5 ATP
              1 $FADH_2$ × 1.5 ATP/$FADH_2$ = 1.5 ATP
              1 GTP (ATP equivalent) = 1 ATP
              _____
                                      10 ATP

23.63 ATP has three phosphate groups and ADP has two.

23.65 a. and b.

glucose 1-phosphate

23.67 The citric acid cycle generates the reducing agents NADH and $FADH_2$ that then enter the electron transport chain.

23.69 There would be more mitochondria in the heart because it has far more metabolic needs than bone.

23.71 Creatine phosphate, stored in muscles, is a high-energy phosphate that generates energy upon hydrolysis.

23.73 68 moles, 4.1×10^{25} molecules of ATP

CHAPTER 24

24.1 The reactant and product are constitutional isomers that differ in the location of a carbonyl and hydroxyl group. Thus, an isomerase enzyme converts one isomer to another.

24.3 They are constitutional isomers with a different arrangement of atoms but the same molecular formula.

24.5 step [1]: glucose; step [3]: fructose 6-phosphate; step [7]: ADP; step [10]: ADP

24.7 The rate of glycolysis would decrease.

24.9 NADH serves as the reducing agent for the conversion of pyruvate to both lactate and ethanol. The NAD^+ formed in the process can then be used as the oxidant in step [6] of glycolysis, making the process anaerobic.

24.11 a. Both use NADH to generate a reduced compound.
b. Ethanol is a two-carbon product formed by decarboxylation, whereas lactate is a three-carbon compound.

24.13 the conversion of pyruvate to acetyl CoA and steps [3] and [4] of the citric acid cycle

24.15

	Starting Material	Product
a.	Pyruvate	Phosphoenolpyruvate
b.	2-Phosphoglycerate	3-Phosphoglycerate
c.	Glucose 6-phosphate	Glucose

24.17 a. [1] 10; [2] 9 cycles   b. [1] 8; [2] 7 cycles

24.18 106

24.19 134

24.21 a. 5.3 ATP/carbon in glucose
b. 6.7 ATP/carbon in stearic acid
c. supports

24.23 β-Hydroxybutyrate contains an alcohol and a carboxylate anion, but no ketone.

24.25 An increased concentration of acetyl CoA increases the production of ketone bodies.

24.26 a.

b.

c.

24.27 a.

b.

c.

24.29 a. Oxidation occurs with loss of hydrogen by a dehydrogenase enzyme. The coenzyme NAD^+ serves as an oxidant.
b. Transfer of phosphate from GTP to the reactant occurs, forming GDP. The loss of carbon dioxide takes place with the carboxykinase enzyme.

24.31 This reaction converts one isomer to another, so there is a change in position of the phosphate; thus, the enzyme is called a "mutase."

24.33 a.   b. 2-phosphoglycerate   c. pyruvate

phosphoenolpyruvate

24.35 Energy-investment phase:
a. glucose, glyceraldehyde 3-phosphate
b. 2 ATP utilized
c. no coenzymes used or formed
Energy-generating phase:
a. glyceraldehyde 3-phosphate, pyruvate
b. 4 ATP/glucose produced
c. 2 NAD^+ used and 2 NADH produced per glucose

24.37 a. 7, 10   b. 1, 3   c. 6   d. 4

24.39 The conversion of pyruvate to acetyl CoA forms one CO_2 for each pyruvate.

The conversion of isocitrate to α-ketoglutarate and α-ketoglutarate to succinyl CoA in the citric acid cycle forms one CO_2 for each acetyl CoA.

24.41 a.

$$C_6H_{12}O_6 + 2\ NAD^+ \xrightarrow[\text{2 ADP} \quad \text{2 ATP}]{} 2\ CH_3COCO_2^- + 2\ NADH + 2\ H^+$$
glucose   pyruvate

b.

$$C_6H_{12}O_6 \xrightarrow[\text{2 ADP} \quad \text{2 ATP}]{} 2\ CH_3CH_2OH + 2\ CO_2$$
glucose   ethanol

c.

24.43 a. aerobic: CO_2
anaerobic: lactate

b. aerobic: NAD^+ and FAD are used and NADH and $FADH_2$ are formed.
anaerobic: NADH is used to convert pyruvate to lactate and NAD^+ is formed.

24.45 Glycolysis takes glucose and breaks it into smaller units, producing pyruvate. Gluconeogenesis is the synthesis of glucose from lactate, amino acids, and glycerol.

24.47 a. increased   c. increased
b. decreased   d. decreased

24.49 In the Cori cycle, glucose in muscle is catabolized to pyruvate and then converted to lactate, which is transported to the liver. In the liver, lactate is converted to glucose by gluconeogenesis and then transported back to the muscle.

24.51 a. lactate   b. ethanol   c. CO_2

24.53 During glycolysis: 2 ATP and 2 NADH generated.
Each NADH in turn leads to 2.5 ATP,
so glycolysis leads to: total 7 ATP
Conversion of 2 pyruvate to 2 acetyl CoA
yields 2 NADH, which leads to: 5 ATP
In the citric acid cycle, 20 additional ATP
are formed for 2 $CH_3COSCoA$:
  2 GTP (ATP), 6 NADH $\longrightarrow$ 15 ATP,
  2 $FADH_2$ $\longrightarrow$ 3 ATP: total 20 ATP
                                                                        = 32 ATP

24.55 two carbons in two molecules of CO_2 and four in two molecules of CH_3CH_2OH

24.57 Two phosphate bonds of ATP are hydrolyzed forming AMP; therefore, 2 ATP equivalents are used.

24.59 a. 7   b. 6

24.61 a. 3   b. 2

24.63 92

24.65

24.67 a. $CH_3(CH_2)_6-CH_2-CH_2-\overset{\displaystyle O}{\overset{\|}{C}}-OH$
                              β α

b. $CH_3(CH_2)_6-CH_2-CH_2-\overset{\displaystyle O}{\overset{\|}{C}}-SCoA$
                        β α

c. 5   d. 4   e. 64

24.69 0.37 mol ATP/g decanoic acid

24.71 Ketosis is the condition under which ketone bodies accumulate. Ketogenesis is the synthesis of ketone bodies from acetyl CoA.

24.73 In poorly controlled diabetes, glucose cannot be metabolized. Fatty acids are used for metabolism and ketone bodies are formed to a greater extent.

24.75 Ketogenic amino acids are converted to acetyl CoA or a related thioester and can be converted to ketone bodies. Glucogenic amino acids are catabolized to pyruvate or another intermediate in the citric acid cycle.

24.77 a. $H-\overset{\displaystyle O}{\overset{\|}{C}}-CO_2^-$ b.

24.79 a. $CH_3-\overset{O}{\overset{\|}{C}}-CO_2^-$ + $^-O_2CCH_2-\overset{\overset{+}{N}H_3}{\underset{H}{\overset{|}{C}}}-CO_2^-$

b. $(CH_3)_2CHCH_2-\overset{O}{\overset{\|}{C}}-CO_2^-$ + $^-O_2CCH_2-\overset{\overset{+}{N}H_3}{\underset{H}{\overset{|}{C}}}-CO_2^-$

24.81 a. $(CH_3)_2CHCH_2-\overset{O}{\overset{\|}{C}}-CO_2^-$ + NH_4^+

b. $CH_2-\overset{O}{\overset{\|}{C}}-CO_2^-$ + NH_4^+

24.83 a. acetoacetyl CoA, fumarate
b. α-ketoglutarate
c. oxaloacetate
d. pyruvate

24.85 Yes, phenylalanine, for example, can be degraded by multiple routes and can be both ketogenic and glucogenic.

24.87 A spiral pathway involves the same set of reactions repeated on increasingly smaller substrates; example: β-oxidation of fatty acids. A cyclic pathway is a series of reactions that regenerates the first reactant; example: citric acid cycle.

24.89 Glucose is metabolized anaerobically to form CO_2 and ethanol. The CO_2 causes bread to rise.

24.91 Pyruvate is metabolized anaerobically to lactate.

24.93 The diet calls for ingestion of protein and fat, so in the absence of carbohydrates to be metabolized, ketone bodies are formed.

24.95 a. kinase   b. dehydrogenase   c. carboxylase

24.97 18.5 ATP

24.99 One gram of arachidic acid produces more ATP than one gram of glucose (0.429 mol/g compared to 0.18 mol/g). This result supports the fact that lipids are more efficient at storing energy than carbohydrates.

Glossary

A

Acetal (16.8) A compound that contains two OR groups (alkoxy groups) bonded to the same carbon; general formula $R_2C(OR)_2$.

Acetyl CoA (23.4) A compound formed when an acetyl group ($CH_3CO–$) is bonded to coenzyme A (HS–CoA); $CH_3COSCoA$.

Achiral (15.2) Being superimposable on a mirror image.

Acid (9.1) In the Arrhenius definition, a substance that contains a hydrogen atom and dissolves in water to form a hydrogen ion, H^+.

Acid dissociation constant, K_a (9.4) A constant, K_a, related to acid strength. The stronger the acid (HA), the larger the value of K_a; $K_a = [H_3O^+][A:^-]/[HA]$.

Acidic solution (9.5) A solution in which $[H_3O^+] > [OH^-]$; thus, $[H_3O^+] > 10^{-7}$ M.

Actinides (2.4) A group of elements in the periodic table beginning with thorium ($Z = 90$), and immediately following the element actinium (Ac).

Active site (6.4, 21.9) The region in an enzyme that binds a substrate, which then undergoes a very specific reaction with an enhanced rate.

Active transport (19.7) The process of moving an ion across a cell membrane that requires energy input.

Actual yield (5.7) The amount of product formed in a reaction, determined by weighing the product on a balance.

Acyclic alkane (12.1) An alkane with molecular formula C_nH_{2n+2}, which contains a chain of carbon atoms but no rings. An acyclic alkane is also called a saturated hydrocarbon.

Acyl CoA (24.7) The thioester formed from a fatty acid and coenzyme A that undergoes β-oxidation in mitochondria; general structure RCOSCoA.

Acyl group (17.1) A substituent having the formula RCO–.

Addition reaction (13.6) A reaction in which elements are added to a compound.

Adenosine 5'-diphosphate (ADP, 23.3) A nucleoside diphosphate formed by adding two phosphates to the 5'-OH group of adenosine.

Adenosine 5'-triphosphate (ATP, 23.3) A nucleoside triphosphate formed by adding three phosphates to the 5'-OH group of adenosine. ATP is the most prominent member of a group of "high-energy" molecules that release energy by cleavage of a P–O bond during hydrolysis.

Adrenal cortical steroid (19.9) A steroid hormone synthesized in the outer layer of the adrenal gland.

Alcohol (11.5) A compound containing a hydroxyl group (OH) bonded to a tetrahedral carbon atom; general formula ROH.

Aldehyde (11.5) A compound that has a hydrogen atom bonded directly to a carbonyl carbon; general formula RCHO.

Alditol (20.4) A compound produced when the carbonyl group of an aldose is reduced to a 1° alcohol.

Aldonic acid (20.4) A compound produced when the aldehyde carbonyl of an aldose is oxidized to a carboxyl group.

Aldose (20.2) A monosaccharide with an aldehyde carbonyl group at C1.

Alkali metal (2.4) An element located in group 1A (group 1) of the periodic table. Alkali metals include lithium (Li), sodium (Na), potassium (K), rubidium (Rb), cesium (Cs), and francium (Fr).

Alkaline earth element (2.4) An element located in group 2A (group 2) of the periodic table. Alkaline earth elements include beryllium (Be), magnesium (Mg), calcium (Ca), strontium (Sr), barium (Ba), and radium (Ra).

Alkaloid (18.4) A naturally occurring amine derived from a plant source.

Alkane (11.5) A compound having only C–C and C–H single bonds.

Alkene (11.5) A compound having a carbon–carbon double bond.

Alkoxy group (14.7) An OR group. An alkoxy group is named by changing the -yl ending of an alkyl group to -oxy.

Alkyl group (12.4) A group formed by removing one hydrogen from an alkane.

Alkyl halide (11.5) A compound with the general structure R–X that contains a halogen atom (X = F, Cl, Br, or I) bonded to a tetrahedral carbon.

Alkyne (11.5) A compound with a carbon–carbon triple bond.

Alpha (α) carbon (17.2) The carbon adjacent to a carbonyl group.

Alpha (α) particle (10.1) A high-energy particle that is emitted from a radioactive nucleus and contains two protons and two neutrons.

Amide (11.5) A compound that contains a nitrogen atom bonded directly to a carbonyl carbon; general structure $RCONR'_2$, where R' = H or alkyl.

Amine (11.5) An organic compound that contains a nitrogen atom bonded to one, two, or three alkyl groups; general structure RNH_2, R_2NH, or R_3N.

Amino acid (21.2) A compound that contains two functional groups—an amino group (NH_2) and a carboxyl group (COOH) bonded to the same carbon.

Amino group (11.5) An $–NH_2$ group.

Ammonium ion (3.6) An NH_4^+ ion.

Ammonium salt (18.6) An ionic compound that contains a positively charged ammonium ion and an anion. $(CH_3CH_2CH_2NH_3)^+Cl^-$ is an ammonium salt.

Amorphous solid (7.9) A solid with no regular arrangement of its particles.

Amphoteric compound (9.2) A compound that contains both a hydrogen atom and a lone pair of electrons so that it can be either an acid or a base.

Anabolic steroid (19.9) A synthetic androgen analogue that promotes muscle growth.

Anabolism (23.1) The synthesis of large molecules from smaller ones in a metabolic pathway.

Androgen (19.9) A hormone that controls the development of secondary sex characteristics in males.

Anion (3.2) A negatively charged ion with more electrons than protons.

α Anomer (20.3) The cyclic form of a monosaccharide that contains a hemiacetal with the OH group drawn down, below the ring.

β Anomer (20.3) The cyclic form of a monosaccharide that contains a hemiacetal with the OH group drawn up, above the ring.

Anomeric carbon (20.3) The carbon atom that is part of the hemiacetal in a cyclic monosaccharide.

Anticodon (22.8) Three nucleotides in a tRNA molecule that are complementary to the codon in mRNA and identify an individual amino acid.

Antihistamine (18.10) A compound that binds to the H1 histamine receptor and prevents the action of histamine.

Antioxidant (13.4) A compound that prevents an unwanted oxidation reaction from occurring.

Anti-ulcer drug (18.10) A drug that binds to the H2 histamine receptor, thus reducing acid secretion in the stomach.

Aqueous solution (8.1) A solution with water as the solvent.

Aromatic compound (11.5) A compound that contains a benzene ring, a six-membered ring with three double bonds.

Aryl halide (13.13) An organic halide with the halogen bonded directly to a benzene ring.

Atmosphere (7.2) A unit used to measure pressure; 1 atm = 760 mm Hg.

Atom (2.2) The basic building block of matter composed of a nucleus and an electron cloud.

Atomic mass unit (2.2) A unit abbreviated as amu, which equals one-twelfth the mass of a carbon atom that has six protons and six neutrons; 1 amu = 1.661×10^{-24} g.

Atomic number (2.2) The number of protons in the nucleus of an atom; symbolized as Z.

Atomic weight (2.3) The weighted average of the mass of all naturally occurring isotopes of a particular element, reported in atomic mass units.

Avogadro's law (7.4) A gas law that states that the volume of a gas is proportional to the number of moles present when the pressure and temperature are held constant.

Avogadro's number (5.3) A quantity that contains 6.02×10^{23} items—usually atoms, molecules, or ions.

Axon (18.8) The long stem that protrudes from the cell body of a neuron.

B

Balanced chemical equation (5.2) An equation written so that an equal number of atoms of each element is present on both sides.

Barometer (7.2) A device for measuring atmospheric pressure.

Base (9.1) In the Arrhenius definition, a substance that contains hydroxide and dissolves in water to form OH^-.

Basic solution (9.5) A solution in which $[OH^-] > [H_3O^+]$; thus, $[OH^-] > 10^{-7}$ M.

Becquerel (10.4) An SI unit used to measure radioactivity, abbreviated as Bq; 1 Bq = 1 disintegration/s.

Benedict's reagent (20.4) A Cu^{2+} reagent that oxidizes the aldehyde carbonyl of an aldose to a carboxyl group, yielding an aldonic acid.

Beta (β) carbon (17.2) The carbon bonded to the α (alpha) carbon and located two carbons from a carbonyl group.

Beta (β) particle (10.1) A high-energy electron emitted from a radioactive nucleus.

Boiling point (bp, 7.7) The temperature at which a liquid is converted to the gas phase.

Boiling point elevation (8.7) The increase in the boiling point of a liquid solution due to the presence of a dissolved nonvolatile solute.

Bond dissociation energy (6.2) The energy needed to break a covalent bond by equally dividing the electrons between the two atoms in the bond.

Bonding (3.1) The joining of two atoms in a stable arrangement.

Boyle's law (7.3) A gas law that relates pressure and volume. Boyle's law states that for a fixed amount of gas at constant temperature, the pressure and volume of the gas are inversely related.

Branched-chain alkane (12.2) An alkane that contains one or more carbon branches bonded to a carbon chain.

Brønsted–Lowry acid (9.1) A proton donor.

Brønsted–Lowry base (9.1) A proton acceptor.

Buffer (9.10) A solution whose pH changes very little when acid or base is added. Most buffers are solutions composed of approximately equal amounts of a weak acid and the salt of its conjugate base.

Building-block element (2.1) One of the four nonmetals—oxygen, carbon, hydrogen, and nitrogen—that comprise 96% of the mass of the human body.

C

Calorie (6.1) A unit of energy that equals the amount of energy needed to raise the temperature of 1 g of water by 1 °C; abbreviated as cal, where 1 cal = 4.184 J.

Carbohydrate (20.1) A polyhydroxy aldehyde or ketone, or a compound that can be hydrolyzed to a polyhydroxy aldehyde or ketone.

Carbonate (3.6) A polyatomic anion with the structure CO_3^{2-}.

Carbonyl group (11.5) A carbon–oxygen double bond (C=O).

Carboxylate anion (17.6) The conjugate base of a carboxylic acid; general structure $RCOO^-$.

Carboxyl group (17.1) A COOH group.

Carboxylic acid (11.5) A compound that contains an OH group bonded directly to the carbonyl carbon; general structure RCOOH or RCO_2H.

Catabolism (23.1) The breakdown of large molecules into smaller ones during metabolism.

Catalyst (6.4) A substance that increases the rate of a reaction but is recovered unchanged at the end of the reaction.

Cation (2.8) A positively charged particle with fewer electrons than protons.

Cell membrane (19.7) The semipermeable membrane that surrounds the cell, composed of a lipid bilayer.

Celsius scale (1.9) One of three temperature scales in which water freezes at 0 °C and boils at 100 °C.

Cephalin (19.6) A phosphoacylglycerol in which the identity of the R group esterified to the phosphodiester is $-CH_2CH_2NH_3^+$. A cephalin is also called a phosphatidylethanolamine.

Chain reaction (10.6) The process by which each neutron produced during fission can go on to bombard three other nuclei to produce more nuclei and more neutrons.

Charles's law (7.3) A gas law that states that for a fixed amount of gas at constant pressure, the volume of the gas is proportional to its Kelvin temperature.

Chemical equation (5.1) An expression that uses chemical formulas and other symbols to illustrate what reactants constitute the starting materials in a reaction and what products are formed.

Chemical formula (2.1) A representation that uses element symbols to show the identity of elements in a compound, and subscripts to show the number of atoms of each element contained in the compound.

Chemical properties (1.2) Those properties that determine how a substance can be converted to another substance by a chemical reaction.

Chemistry (1.1) The study of matter—its composition, properties, and transformations.

Chiral (15.2) Not superimposable on a mirror image.

Chirality center (15.2) A carbon atom bonded to four different groups.

Chlorination (13.13) A reaction with chlorine in which a Cl atom substitutes for a hydrogen atom.

Chlorofluorocarbon (14.9) A halogen-containing compound having the general molecular formula CF_xCl_{4-x}.

Cis isomer (13.3) An alkene with two R groups on the same side of the double bond.

Citric acid cycle (23.5) A cyclic metabolic pathway that begins with the addition of acetyl CoA to a four-carbon substrate and ends when the same four-carbon compound is formed as a product eight steps later.

Codon (22.7) A sequence of three nucleotides (triplet) in mRNA that codes for a specific amino acid.

Coenzyme (14.6, 21.9) An organic molecule needed for an enzyme-catalyzed reaction to occur.

Coenzyme A (23.4) A coenzyme that contains a sulfhydryl group (SH group) making it a thiol (RSH), and abbreviated as HS–CoA.

Cofactor (21.9) A metal ion or a nonprotein organic molecule needed for an enzyme-catalyzed reaction to occur.

Colligative properties (8.7) The properties of a solution that depend on the concentration of the solute but not its identity.

Colloid (8.1) A homogeneous mixture with large particles, often having an opaque appearance.

Combined gas law (7.3) A gas law that relates pressure, volume, and temperature. For a constant number of moles, the product of pressure and volume divided by temperature is a constant.

Combustion (12.8) An oxidation reaction in which carbon-containing compounds react with oxygen to form carbon dioxide (CO_2) and water.

Competitive inhibitor (21.9) An enzyme inhibitor that has a shape and structure similar to the substrate, and competes with the substrate for binding to the active site.

Complementary base pairs (22.3) The predictable pairing of bases between two strands of DNA. Adenine pairs with thymine using two hydrogen bonds, forming an A–T base pair, and cytosine pairs with guanine using three hydrogen bonds, forming a C–G base pair.

Compound (1.3) A pure substance formed by chemically combining two or more elements.

Concentration (8.4) The amount of solute dissolved in a given amount of solution.

Condensation (7.8, 7.10) The conversion of a gas to a liquid.

Condensation polymer (17.10) A polymer formed when monomers containing two functional groups come together with loss of a small molecule such as water.

Condensed structure (11.4) A representation used for a compound having a chain of atoms bonded together. The atoms are drawn in, but the two-electron bond lines and lone pairs on heteroatoms are generally omitted.

Conjugate acid (9.2) The product formed by the gain of a proton by a base.

Conjugate acid–base pair (9.2) Two species that differ by the presence of a proton.

Conjugate base (9.2) The product formed by loss of a proton from an acid.

Conjugated protein (21.7) A compound composed of a protein unit and a nonprotein molecule.

Constitutional isomers (12.2) Isomers that differ in the way the atoms are connected to each other.

Conversion factor (1.7) A term that converts a quantity in one unit to a quantity in another unit.

Cooling curve (7.11) A graph that shows how the temperature of a substance changes as heat is removed.

Cori cycle (24.6) The cycling of lactate from the muscle to the liver, where it is re-oxidized to pyruvate and converted to glucose. Glucose is then transported back to the muscle, where it undergoes glycolysis.

Coupled reactions (23.3) Pairs of reactions that occur together. The energy released by an energetically favorable reaction drives an energetically unfavorable reaction.

Covalent bond (3.1) A chemical bond that results from the sharing of electrons between two atoms.

Critical mass (10.6) The amount of a radioactive element required to sustain a chain reaction.

Cross formula (15.6) A Fischer projection formula that replaces a chirality center with a cross. The horizontal lines represent wedged bonds and the vertical lines represent dashed bonds.

Crystalline solid (7.9) A solid with a regular arrangement of particles—atoms, molecules, or ions—with a repeating structure.

C-Terminal amino acid (21.4) In a peptide, the amino acid with the free –COO^- group on the α carbon.

Cubic centimeter (1.4) A unit of volume equal to one milliliter; one cubic centimeter = 1 cm^3 = 1 cc.

Curie (10.4) A unit used to measure radioactivity and equal to 3.7×10^{10} disintegrations/s. A curie corresponds to the decay rate of one gram of the element radium.

Cyclic hemiacetal (16.8) A compound formed by an intramolecular reaction of a hydroxyl group and an aldehyde or ketone.

Cycloalkane (12.1) A compound with the general formula C_nH_{2n} that contains carbons joined in one or more rings.

D

Dalton's law (7.6) A law that states that the total pressure (P_{total}) of a gas mixture is equal to the sum of the partial pressures of its component gases.

d Block (2.6) A group of elements consisting of the 10 columns of transition metals in the periodic table. The d subshell is filled last in these elements.

Decarboxylation (24.2) The loss of carbon dioxide (CO_2) from a compound.

Dehydration (14.5) The loss of water (H_2O) from a starting material.

Deletion mutation (22.9) The loss of one or more nucleotides from a DNA molecule.

Denaturation (21.8) The process of altering the shape of a protein without breaking the amide bonds that form the primary structure.

Dendrites (18.8) Numerous small filaments at the end of a neuron.

Density (1.10) A physical property that relates the mass of a substance to its volume; density = g/(mL or cc).

Deoxyribonucleic acid (DNA, 22.1, 22.3) A polymer of deoxyribo-nucleotides that stores the genetic information of an organism and transmits that information from one generation to another.

Deoxyribonucleoside (22.1) A compound that contains the monosaccharide 2-deoxyribose and a purine or pyrimidine base.

Deoxyribonucleotide (22.1) A compound that contains the monosaccharide 2-deoxyribose bonded to a purine or pyrimidine base, as well as a phosphate at the 5'-OH group.

Deposition (7.10) The conversion of a gas directly to a solid.

Deuterium (2.3) A hydrogen atom having one proton and one neutron, giving it a mass number of two.

Dextrorotatory (15.7) Rotating plane-polarized light in the clockwise direction. The rotation is labeled (+).

Dialysis (8.8) A process that involves the selective passage of substances across a semipermeable membrane, called a dialyzing membrane.

Diastereomers (15.8) Stereoisomers that are not mirror images of each other.

Diatomic molecule (4.1) A molecule that contains two atoms. Hydrogen (H_2) is a diatomic molecule.

Dilution (8.6) The addition of solvent to a solution to decrease the concentration of solute.

Diol (14.3) A compound with two hydroxyl groups, also called a glycol.

Dipeptide (21.4) A peptide formed from two amino acids joined together by one amide bond.

Dipole (4.7) The separation of charge in a bond or molecule.

Dipole–dipole interactions (7.7) The attractive intermolecular forces between the permanent dipoles of two polar molecules.

Diprotic acid (9.1) An acid that contains two acidic protons.

Disaccharide (20.1) A carbohydrate composed of two monosaccharides joined together.

Dissociation (9.3) The splitting apart of a covalent molecule (or an ionic compound) into individual ions.

Disulfide (14.10) A compound that contains a sulfur–sulfur bond.

DNA fingerprinting (22.10) A technique in which DNA is amplified using PCR and cut into fragments that are separated by size using gel electrophoresis. This forms a set of horizontal bands, each band corresponding to a segment of DNA, sorted from low to high molecular weight.

Double bond (4.2) A multiple bond that contains four electrons—that is, two two-electron bonds.

Double-headed arrow (13.9) An arrow drawn between resonance structures.

E

Eicosanoids (19.11) A group of biologically active compounds containing 20 carbon atoms derived from arachidonic acid.

Electrolyte (8.1) A substance that conducts an electric current in water.

Electron (2.2) A negatively charged subatomic particle.

Electron cloud (2.2) The space surrounding the nucleus of an atom, which contains electrons and comprises most of the volume of an atom.

Electron-dot symbol (2.7) A symbol that shows the number of valence electrons around an atom.

Electronegativity (4.7) A measure of an atom's attraction for electrons in a bond.

Electronic configuration (2.6) The arrangement of electrons in an atom's orbitals.

Electron transport chain (23.6) A series of reactions that transfers electrons from reduced coenzymes to progressively stronger oxidizing agents, ultimately converting oxygen to water.

Element (1.3) A pure substance that cannot be broken down into simpler substances by a chemical reaction.

Elimination (14.5) A reaction in which elements of the starting material are "lost" and a new multiple bond is formed.

Enantiomers (15.2) Mirror images that are not superimposable.

Endothermic reaction (6.2) A chemical reaction where ΔH is positive (+) and energy is absorbed.

Energy (6.1) The capacity to do work.

Energy diagram (6.3) A schematic representation of the energy changes in a reaction, which plots energy on the vertical axis and the progress of the reaction—the reaction coordinate—on the horizontal axis.

Energy of activation (6.3) The difference in energy between the reactants and the transition state; symbolized by E_a.

English system of measurement (1.4) A system of measurement used primarily in the United States in which units are not systematically related to each other and require memorization.

Enthalpy change (6.2) The energy absorbed or released in any reaction—also called the heat of reaction and symbolized by ΔH.

Enzyme (6.4, 21.9) A biological catalyst composed of one or more chains of amino acids in a very specific three-dimensional shape.

Enzyme–substrate complex (21.9) A structure composed of a substrate bonded to the active site of an enzyme.

Epoxide (14.7) A cyclic ether containing an oxygen atom in a three-membered ring.

Equilibrium (6.5) A reaction that consists of forward and reverse reactions that have equal reaction rates, so the concentration of each species does not change.

Equilibrium constant (6.5) A characteristic value for a reaction at a given temperature and equal to the ratio of the concentrations of the products multiplied together to the concentrations of the reactants multiplied together. Each term is raised to a power equal to its coefficient in the balanced chemical equation.

Ester (11.5) A compound that contains an alkoxy group (OR) bonded directly to the carbonyl carbon; general structure RCOOR.

Estrogen (19.9) A hormone that controls the development of secondary sex characteristics in females and regulates the menstrual cycle.

Ether (14.1) A compound that has two alkyl groups bonded to an oxygen atom; general structure ROR.

Evaporation (7.8) The conversion of liquid molecules to gas molecules.

Exact number (1.5) A number that results from counting objects or is part of a definition.

Exothermic reaction (6.2) A reaction in which energy is released and ΔH is negative (–).

F

Facilitated transport (19.7) The process by which some ions and molecules travel through the channels in a cell membrane created by integral proteins.

Factor–label method (1.7) A method of using conversion factors to convert a quantity in one unit to a quantity in another unit.

FAD (flavin adenine dinucleotide, 23.4) A biological oxidizing agent synthesized in cells from vitamin B_2, riboflavin. FAD is reduced by adding two hydrogen atoms, forming $FADH_2$.

FADH₂ (23.4) A biological reducing agent and coenzyme formed when FAD is reduced.

Fahrenheit scale (1.9) One of three temperature scales in which water freezes at 32 °F and boils at 212 °F.

Fat (13.3, 19.4) A triacylglycerol with few double bonds, making it a solid at room temperature.

Fat-soluble vitamin (11.7, 19.10) A vitamin that dissolves in an organic solvent but is insoluble in water. Vitamins A, D, E, and K are fat soluble.

Fatty acid (13.3, 19.2) A carboxylic acid (RCOOH) with a long carbon chain, usually containing 12–20 carbon atoms.

f **Block** (2.6) A group of elements consisting of the two rows of inner transition metals. The *f* subshell is filled last in these elements.

Fermentation (24.4) The anaerobic conversion of glucose to ethanol and CO_2.

Fibrous protein (21.7) A water-insoluble protein composed of long linear polypeptide chains that are bundled together to form rods or sheets.

Fischer esterification (17.8) Treatment of a carboxylic acid (RCOOH) with an alcohol (R'OH) and an acid catalyst to form an ester (RCOOR').

Fischer projection formula (15.6) A method of drawing chiral compounds with the chirality center at the intersection of a cross. The horizontal bonds are assumed to be wedges and the vertical bonds are assumed to be dashed lines.

Formula weight (5.4) The sum of the atomic weights of all the atoms in a compound, reported in atomic mass units (amu).

Forward reaction (6.5) In equilibrium, a reaction that proceeds from left to right as drawn.

Freezing (7.10) The conversion of a liquid to a solid.

Freezing point depression (8.7) The decrease in the melting point of a liquid solution due to the presence of a nonvolatile solute.

Functional group (11.5) An atom or a group of atoms with characteristic chemical and physical properties.

G

Gamma (γ) ray (10.1) High-energy radiation released from a radioactive nucleus.

Gas (1.2) A state of matter that has no definite shape or volume. The particles of a gas move randomly and are separated by a distance much larger than their size.

Gas laws (7.3) A series of laws that relate the pressure, volume, and temperature of a gas.

Gay–Lussac's law (7.3) A gas law that states for a fixed amount of gas at constant volume, the pressure of the gas is proportional to its Kelvin temperature.

Geiger counter (10.4) A small portable device used for measuring radioactivity.

Gene (22.1) A portion of a DNA molecule responsible for the synthesis of a single protein.

Genetic code (22.7) The sequence of nucleotides in mRNA (coded in triplets) that specifies the amino acid sequence of a protein. Each triplet is called a codon.

Genetic disease (22.9) A disease resulting from a mutation that causes a condition to be inherited from one generation to another.

Genetic engineering (22.10) The process of manipulating DNA in the laboratory that allows a gene in one organism to be spliced into the DNA of another organism.

Globular protein (21.7) A protein that is coiled into a compact shape with a hydrophilic outer surface to make it water soluble.

Glucogenic amino acid (24.9) An amino acid that can be used to synthesize glucose.

Gluconeogenesis (24.6) The synthesis of glucose from noncarbohydrate sources—lactate, amino acids, or glycerol.

Glycol (14.3) A compound with two hydroxyl groups, also called a diol.

Glycolysis (24.3) A linear, 10-step pathway that converts glucose, a six-carbon monosaccharide, to two three-carbon pyruvate molecules.

α Glycoside (20.5) A monosaccharide with the OR group on the anomeric carbon oriented below the plane of the ring.

β Glycoside (20.5) A monosaccharide with the OR group on the anomeric carbon oriented above the plane of the ring.

Glycosidic linkage (20.5) The acetal C–O bond that joins two monosaccharides together.

Gram (1.4) The basic unit of mass in the metric system; abbreviated as g.

Gray (10.4) A unit that measures absorbed radiation; abbreviated as Gy.

Greenhouse gas (12.8) A gas that absorbs thermal energy that normally radiates from the earth's surface, and redirects it back to the surface.

Ground state (2.6) The lowest energy arrangement of electrons.

Group (2.4) A column in the periodic table.

Group number (2.4) A number that identifies a particular column in the periodic table.

H

Half-life (10.3) The time it takes for one-half of a sample to decay.

Half reaction (5.9) An equation written for an individual oxidation or reduction that shows how many electrons are gained or lost.

Halogen (2.4) An element located in group 7A (group 17) of the periodic table. Halogens include fluorine (F), chlorine (Cl), bromine (Br), iodine (I), and astatine (At).

Halogenation (13.6) The reaction of a compound with a halogen, X_2, such as the addition of X_2 to an alkene.

Hardening (13.7) The reaction of an unsaturated liquid vegetable oil with hydrogen to form a fat with a higher melting point.

Haworth projection (20.3) A planar, six-membered ring used to represent the cyclic hemiacetal of glucose and other sugars.

Heating curve (7.11) A graph that shows how the temperature of a substance changes as heat is added.

Heat of fusion (7.10) The amount of energy needed to melt one gram of a substance.

Heat of reaction (6.2) The energy absorbed or released in any reaction and symbolized by ΔH—also called the enthalpy change.

Heat of vaporization (7.10) The amount of energy needed to vaporize one gram of a substance.

α-Helix (21.6) A secondary structure of a protein formed when a peptide chain twists into a right-handed or clockwise spiral.

Heme (21.7) A complex organic compound containing an Fe^{2+} ion complexed with a large nitrogen-containing ring system.

Hemiacetal (16.8) A compound that contains an OH group (hydroxyl) and an OR group (alkoxy) bonded to the same carbon.

Henry's law (8.3) A law that states that the solubility of a gas in a liquid is proportional to the partial pressure of the gas above the liquid.

Heteroatom (11.2) Any atom in an organic compound that is not carbon or hydrogen.

Heterocycle (14.7) A ring that contains a heteroatom.

Heterogeneous mixture (8.1) A mixture that does not have a uniform composition throughout a sample.

Hexose (20.2) A monosaccharide with six carbons.

High-density lipoprotein (19.8) A spherical particle that transports cholesterol from the tissues to the liver.

Homogeneous mixture (8.1) A mixture that has a uniform composition throughout a sample.

Hormone (18.9, 19.9) A compound synthesized in one part of an organism, which then travels through the bloodstream to elicit a response at a target tissue or organ.

Hybrid (13.9) A composite of two or more resonance forms.

Hydration (13.6) The addition of water to a molecule.

Hydrocarbon (11.5) A compound that contains only the elements of carbon and hydrogen.

Hydrochlorofluorocarbon (14.9) A compound such as CF_3CHCl_2 that contains the elements of H, Cl, and F bonded to carbon.

Hydrofluorocarbon (14.9) A compound such as FCH_2CF_3 that contains the elements of H and F bonded to carbon.

Hydrogenation (13.6) The addition of hydrogen (H_2) to an alkene.

Hydrogen bonding (7.7) An attractive intermolecular force that occurs when a hydrogen atom bonded to O, N, or F is electrostatically attracted to an O, N, or F atom in another molecule.

Hydrohalogenation (13.6) The addition of HX (X = Cl or Br) to an alkene.

Hydrolysis (16.8) A cleavage reaction that uses water.

Hydrolyzable lipid (19.1) A lipid that can be converted to smaller molecules by hydrolysis with water.

Hydronium ion (3.6) The H_3O^+ ion.

Hydrophilic (19.2) The polar part of a molecule that is attracted to water.

Hydrophobic (19.2) The nonpolar part of a molecule (C–C and C–H bonds) that is not attracted to water.

Hydroxide (3.6) The OH^- ion.

α-Hydroxy acid (17.4) A compound that contains a hydroxyl group on the α carbon to a carboxyl group.

Hydroxyl group (11.5) An OH group.

Hypertonic solution (8.8) A solution that has a higher osmotic pressure than body fluids.

Hypotonic solution (8.8) A solution that has a lower osmotic pressure than body fluids.

I

Ideal gas law (7.5) A gas law that relates the pressure (P), volume (V), temperature (T), and number of moles (n) of a gas in a single equation; $PV = nRT$, where R is a constant.

Incomplete combustion (12.8) An oxidation reaction that forms carbon monoxide (CO) instead of carbon dioxide (CO_2) because insufficient oxygen is available.

Induced-fit model (21.9) The binding of a substrate to an enzyme such that the shape of the active site adjusts to fit the shape of the substrate.

Inexact number (1.5) A number that results from a measurement or observation and contains some uncertainty.

Inhibitor (21.9) A molecule that causes an enzyme to lose activity.

Inner transition metal elements (2.4) A group of elements consisting of the lanthanides and actinides.

Insertion mutation (22.9) The addition of one or more nucleotides to a DNA molecule.

Intermolecular forces (7.7) The attractive forces that exist between molecules.

Ion (3.1) A charged species in which the number of protons and electrons in an atom is not equal.

Ion–dipole interaction (8.2) The attraction of an ion to a dipole in another molecule.

Ionic bond (3.1) A bond that results from the transfer of electrons from one element to another.

Ionic solid (7.9) A solid composed of oppositely charged ions in a regular arrangement.

Ionization energy (2.8) The energy needed to remove an electron from a neutral atom.

Ion–product constant, K_w (9.5) The product of the concentrations of H_3O^+ and OH^- in water or an aqueous solution—symbolized by K_w and equal to 1×10^{-14}.

Irreversible inhibitor (21.9) An inhibitor that covalently binds to an enzyme, permanently destroying its activity.

Isoelectric point (21.3) The pH at which an amino acid exists primarily in its neutral form; abbreviated as pI.

Isomerase (24.2) An enzyme that catalyzes the conversion of one isomer to another.

Isomers (12.2) Two different compounds with the same molecular formula.

Isotonic solution (8.8) Two solutions with the same osmotic pressure.

Isotopes (2.3) Atoms of the same element having a different number of neutrons.

IUPAC nomenclature (12.3) A systematic method of naming compounds developed by the International Union of Pure and Applied Chemistry.

J

Joule (6.1) A unit of measurement for energy; abbreviated as J, where 1 cal = 4.184 J.

K

Kelvin scale (1.9) A temperature scale commonly used by scientists. The Kelvin scale is divided into kelvins (K); K = °C + 273.

Ketogenesis (24.8) The synthesis of ketone bodies from acetyl CoA.

Ketogenic amino acid (24.9) An amino acid that cannot be used to synthesize glucose, but can be converted to ketone bodies.

Ketone (11.5) A compound that has two alkyl groups bonded to the carbonyl group; general structure RCOR.

Ketone bodies (24.8) Three compounds—acetoacetate, β-hydroxybutyrate, and acetone—formed when acetyl CoA levels exceed the capacity of the citric acid cycle.

Ketose (20.2) A monosaccharide with a carbonyl group at C2.

Ketosis (24.8) The accumulation of ketone bodies during starvation and uncontrolled diabetes.

Kinase (24.2) An enzyme that catalyzes the transfer of a phosphate group from one substrate to another.

Kinetic energy (6.1) The energy of motion.

Kinetic-molecular theory (7.2) A theory that describes the fundamental characteristics of gas particles.

L

Lactam (17.1) A cyclic amide.

Lactone (17.1) A cyclic ester.

Lagging strand (22.4) The strand of DNA synthesized in small fragments during replication, which are then joined together by a DNA ligase enzyme.

Lanthanides (2.4) A group of 14 elements in the periodic table beginning with the element cerium ($Z = 58$) and immediately following the element lanthanum (La).

Law of conservation of energy (6.1) A law that states that the total energy in the universe does not change. Energy cannot be created or destroyed.

Law of conservation of mass (5.1) A law that states that atoms cannot be created or destroyed in a chemical reaction.

LD_{50} (10.4) The lethal dose of radiation (or a poison) that kills 50% of a population.

Leading strand (22.4) The strand of DNA that grows continuously during replication.

Le Châtelier's principle (6.6) A principle that states that if a chemical system at equilibrium is disturbed or stressed, the system will react in the direction that counteracts the disturbance or relieves the stress.

Lecithin (19.6) A phosphoacylglycerol in which the identity of the R group esterified to the phosphodiester is $-CH_2CH_2N(CH_3)_3^+$. A lecithin is also called a phosphatidylcholine.

Leukotriene (19.11) A molecule synthesized in several steps from arachidonic acid, which contributes to the asthmatic response by constricting smooth muscles, especially in the lungs.

Levorotatory (15.7) Rotating plane-polarized light in the counterclockwise direction. The rotation is labeled as (–).

Lewis structure (4.1) An electron-dot structure for a molecule that shows the location of all valence electrons in the molecule, both the shared electrons in bonds and the nonbonded electron pairs.

"Like dissolves like" (11.6) The principle in solubility that compounds dissolve in solvents having similar types of intermolecular forces.

Limiting reactant (5.8) The reactant that is completely used up in a reaction.

Lipid (17.9, 19.1) A biomolecule that is soluble in organic solvents and insoluble in water.

Lipid bilayer (19.7) The basic structure of the cell membrane formed from two layers of phospholipids having their ionic heads oriented on the outside and their nonpolar tails on the inside.

Lipoprotein (19.8) A small water-soluble spherical particle composed of proteins and lipids.

Liquid (1.2) A state of matter that has a definite volume, but takes on the shape of the container it occupies. The particles of a liquid are close together but they can randomly move past each other.

Liter (1.4) The basic unit of volume in the metric system; abbreviated as L.

Lock-and-key model (21.9) The binding of a substrate to a rigid active site, such that the three-dimensional geometry of the substrate exactly matches the shape of the active site.

London dispersion forces (7.7) Very weak intermolecular interactions due to the momentary changes in electron density in a molecule.

Lone pair (4.1) An unshared electron pair.

Low-density lipoprotein (19.8) A spherical particle containing proteins and lipids, which transports cholesterol from the liver to the tissues.

M

Main group element (2.4) An element in groups 1A–8A of the periodic table.

Major mineral (macronutrient, 2.1) One of the seven elements present in the body in small amounts (0.1–2% by mass) and needed in the daily diet.

Markovnikov's rule (13.6) The rule that states that in the addition of HX to an unsymmetrical alkene, the H atom bonds to the less substituted carbon atom.

Mass (1.4) A measure of the amount of matter in an object.

Mass number (2.2) The total number of protons and neutrons in a nucleus; symbolized as A.

Matter (1.1) Anything that has mass and takes up volume.

Melting (7.10) The conversion of a solid to a liquid.

Melting point (mp, 7.7) The temperature at which a solid is converted to the liquid phase.

Messenger RNA (mRNA, 22.5) The carrier of information from DNA (in the cell nucleus) to the ribosomes (in the cell cytoplasm). Each gene of a DNA molecule corresponds to a specific mRNA molecule.

Metabolism (23.1) The sum of all of the chemical reactions that take place in an organism.

Meta isomer (13.10) A 1,3-disubstituted benzene.

Metal (2.1) A shiny element that is a good conductor of heat and electricity.

Metallic solid (7.9) A lattice of metal cations surrounded by a cloud of electrons that move freely.

Metalloid (2.1) An element with properties intermediate between a metal and a nonmetal. Metalloids include boron (B), silicon (Si), germanium (Ge), arsenic (As), antimony (Sb), tellurium (Te), and astatine (At).

Meter (1.4) A unit used to measure length; abbreviated as m.

Metric system (1.4) A measurement system in which each type of measurement has a base unit and all other units are related to the base unit by a prefix that indicates if the unit is larger or smaller than the base unit.

Micelle (17.6) A spherical droplet formed when soap is dissolved in water. The ionic heads of the soap molecules are oriented on the surface and the nonpolar tails are packed in the interior.

Millimeters of mercury (7.2) A unit used to measure pressure; abbreviated as mm Hg and also called "torr."

Mitochondrion (23.1) A small sausage-shaped organelle within a cell in which energy production takes place.

Mixture (1.3) Matter composed of more than one component.

Molarity (8.5) The number of moles of solute per liter of solution; abbreviated as M.

Molar mass (5.4) The mass of one mole of any substance, reported in grams per mole.

Mole (5.3) A quantity that contains 6.02×10^{23} items—usually atoms, molecules, or ions.

Molecular formula (4.2) A formula that shows the number and identity of all of the atoms in a compound, but it does not indicate what atoms are bonded to each other.

Molecular solid (7.9) A solid composed of individual molecules arranged regularly.

Molecular weight (5.4) The formula weight of a covalent compound.

Molecule (4.1) A discrete group of atoms that are held together by covalent bonds.

Monomers (13.8) Small molecules that covalently bond together to form polymers.

Monoprotic acid (9.1) An acid that contains one acidic proton.

Monosaccharide (20.1) A carbohydrate that cannot be hydrolyzed to simpler compounds.

D Monosaccharide (20.2) A carbohydrate that has the OH group on the chirality center farthest from the carbonyl on the right.

L Monosaccharide (20.2) A carbohydrate that has the OH group on the chirality center farthest from the carbonyl on the left.

Multiple bond (4.2) A chemical bond that contains four or six electrons—that is, a double or a triple bond.

Mutarotation (20.3) The process by which a single anomer of a monosaccharide equilibrates to a mixture of anomers.

Mutation (22.9) A change in the nucleotide sequence in a molecule of DNA.

N

NAD$^+$ (nicotinamide adenine dinucleotide, 16.6, 23.4) A biological oxidizing agent and coenzyme synthesized from the vitamin niacin. NAD$^+$ and NADH are interconverted by oxidation and reduction reactions.

NADH (16.6, 23.4) A biological reducing agent and coenzyme formed when NAD$^+$ is reduced.

Net ionic equation (9.7) An equation that contains only the species involved in a reaction.

Network solid (7.9) A solid composed of a vast number of atoms covalently bonded together, forming sheets or three-dimensional arrays.

Neuron (18.8) A nerve cell.

Neurotransmitter (18.8) A chemical messenger that transmits nerve impulses from one nerve cell to another cell.

Neutralization reaction (9.7) An acid–base reaction that produces a salt and water as products.

Neutral solution (9.5) Any solution that has an equal concentration of H_3O^+ and OH^- ions and a pH = 7.

Neutron (2.2) A neutral subatomic particle in the nucleus.

Nitration (13.13) Substitution of a nitro group (NO_2) for a hydrogen.

Nitro group (13.13) An NO_2 group.

Noble gases (2.4) Elements located in group 8A (group 18) of the periodic table. The noble gases are helium (He), neon (Ne), argon (Ar), krypton (Kr), xenon (Xe), and radon (Rn).

Nomenclature (3.4) The system of assigning an unambiguous name to a compound.

Nonbonded electron pair (4.1) An unshared electron pair or lone pair.

Noncompetitive inhibitor (21.9) An inhibitor that binds to an enzyme but does not bind at the active site.

Nonelectrolyte (8.1) A substance that does not conduct an electric current when dissolved in water.

Nonhydrolyzable lipid (19.1) A lipid that cannot be cleaved into smaller units by aqueous hydrolysis.

Nonmetal (2.1) An element that does not have a shiny appearance and poorly conducts heat and electricity.

Nonpolar bond (4.7) A bond in which electrons are equally shared.

Nonpolar molecule (11.6) A molecule that has no net dipole.

Nonreducing sugar (20.4) A sugar that does not react with Benedict's reagent.

Nonvolatile (8.7) Not readily vaporized.

Normal boiling point (7.8) The temperature at which the vapor pressure above a liquid equals 760 mm Hg.

N-Terminal amino acid (21.4) In a peptide, the amino acid with the free $-NH_3^+$ group on the α carbon.

Nuclear fission (10.6) The splitting apart of a nucleus into lighter nuclei and neutrons.

Nuclear fusion (10.6) The joining together of two nuclei to form a larger nucleus.

Nuclear reaction (10.1) A reaction that involves the subatomic particles of the nucleus.

Nucleic acid (22.1, 22.2) An unbranched polymer composed of nucleotides. DNA and RNA are nucleic acids.

Nucleoside (22.1) A compound formed by joining the anomeric carbon of a monosaccharide with a nitrogen atom of a purine or pyrimidine base.

Nucleotide (22.1) A compound formed by adding a phosphate group to the 5'-OH of a nucleoside.

Nucleus (2.2) The dense core of the atom that contains protons and neutrons.

Nylon (17.10) A condensation polymer that contains many amide bonds.

O

Octet rule (3.2) The rule in bonding that states that main group elements are especially stable when they possess eight electrons (an octet) in the outer shell.

Oil (13.3, 19.4) A triacylglycerol that is liquid at room temperature.

Omega-n acid (19.2) An unsaturated fatty acid where n is the carbon at which the first double bond occurs in the carbon chain. The numbering begins at the end of the chain with the CH_3 group.

Optically active (15.7) Able to rotate the plane of polarized light.

Optically inactive (15.7) Not able to rotate the plane of polarized light.

Orbital (2.5) A region of space where the probability of finding an electron is high.

Organic chemistry (11.1) The study of compounds that contain the element carbon.

Ortho isomer (13.10) A 1,2-disubstituted benzene.

Osmosis (8.8) The selective diffusion of solvent, usually water, across a semipermeable membrane from a less concentrated solution to a more concentrated solution.

Osmotic pressure (8.8) The pressure that prevents the flow of additional solvent into a solution on one side of a semipermeable membrane.

Oxidation (5.9, 12.8) The loss of electrons from an atom. Oxidation may result in a gain of oxygen atoms or a loss of hydrogen atoms.

β-Oxidation (24.7) A process in which two-carbon acetyl CoA units are sequentially cleaved from a fatty acid.

Oxidative deamination (24.9) The process by which the C–H and C–NH_3^+ bonds on the α carbon of an amino acid are converted to C=O and an ammonium ion (NH_4^+).

Oxidative phosphorylation (23.6) The process by which the energy released from the oxidation of reduced coenzymes is used to convert ADP to ATP using the enzyme ATP synthase.

Oxidizing agent (5.9) A compound that gains electrons (i.e., is reduced), causing another compound to be oxidized.

P

Para isomer (13.10) A 1,4-disubstituted benzene.

Parent name (12.4) The root that indicates the number of carbons in the longest continuous carbon chain in a molecule.

Partial hydrogenation (13.7) The hydrogenation of some, but not all, of the double bonds in a molecule.

Partial pressure (7.6) The pressure exerted by one component of a mixture of gases.

Parts per million (8.4) A concentration term (abbreviated ppm)—the number of "parts" in 1,000,000 parts of solution.

p Block (2.6) The elements in groups 3A–8A (except helium) in the periodic table. The p subshell is filled last in these elements.

Penicillin (17.11) An antibiotic that contains a β-lactam and interferes with the synthesis of the bacterial cell wall.

Pentose (20.2) A monosaccharide with five carbons.

Peptide (21.4) A compound that contains many amino acids joined together by amide bonds.

Peptide bond (21.4) An amide bond in peptides and proteins.

Percent yield (5.7) The amount of product actually formed in a particular reaction divided by the theoretical yield, multiplied by 100%.

Period (2.4) A row in the periodic table.

Periodic table (2.1) A schematic arrangement of all known elements that groups elements with similar properties.

Petroleum (12.6) A complex mixture of compounds, most of which are hydrocarbons containing 1–40 carbon atoms.

Pheromone (12.1) A chemical substance used for communication in a specific animal species, most commonly an insect population.

Phosphate (3.6) A PO_4^{3-} anion.

Phosphatidylcholine (19.6) A phosphoacylglycerol in which the identity of the R group esterified to the phosphodiester is $-CH_2CH_2N(CH_3)_3^+$; also called a lecithin.

Phosphatidylethanolamine (19.6) A phosphoacylglycerol in which the identity of the R group esterified to the phosphodiester is $-CH_2CH_2NH_3^+$; also called a cephalin.

Phosphoacylglycerol (19.6) A lipid with a glycerol backbone that contains two of the hydroxyls esterified with fatty acids and the third hydroxyl as part of a phosphodiester.

Phosphodiester (19.6) A derivative of phosphoric acid (H_3PO_4) that is formed by replacing two of the H atoms by R groups.

Phospholipid (19.6) A lipid that contains a phosphorus atom.

Phosphorylation (23.3) A reaction that adds a phosphate group to a molecule.

pH scale (9.6) The scale used to report the H_3O^+ concentration; pH = $-\log [H_3O^+]$.

Physical properties (1.2) Those properties of a substance that can be observed or measured without changing the composition of the material.

Plane-polarized light (15.7) Light that consists of waves that oscillate in a single plane. Plane-polarized light arises from passing ordinary light through a polarizer.

Plasmid (22.10) A circular, double-stranded DNA molecule isolated from bacteria.

β-Pleated sheet (21.6) A secondary structure formed when two or more peptide chains, called strands, line up side-by-side.

Point mutation (22.9) The substitution of one nucleotide for another.

Polar bond (4.7) A bond in which electrons are unequally shared and pulled towards the more electronegative element.

Polarimeter (15.7) An instrument that measures the degree which a compound rotates plane-polarized light.

Polar molecule (11.6) A molecule that contains a net dipole.

Polyamide (17.10) A class of condensation polymer that contains many amide bonds.

Polyatomic ion (3.6) A cation or anion that contains more than one atom.

Polycyclic aromatic hydrocarbon (13.11) A compound containing two or more benzene rings that share a carbon–carbon bond.

Polyester (17.10) A class of condensation polymer that contains many ester bonds.

Polymer (13.8) A large molecule made up of repeating units of smaller molecules—called monomers—covalently bonded together.

Polymerase chain reaction (22.10) A technique that produces exact copies of a fragment of DNA.

Polymerization (13.8) The joining together of monomers to make polymers.

Polynucleotide (22.2) A polymer of nucleotides that contains a sugar–phosphate backbone.

Polysaccharide (20.1) Three or more monosaccharides joined together.

***p* Orbital** (2.5) A dumbbell-shaped orbital higher in energy than an *s* orbital in the same shell.

Positron (10.1) A radioactive particle that has a negligible mass and a +1 charge.

Postsynaptic neuron (18.8) A nerve cell that contains the receptors that bind a neurotransmitter.

Potential energy (6.1) Energy that is stored.

Pressure (7.2) The force (*F*) exerted per unit area (*A*); symbolized by *P*.

Presynaptic neuron (18.8) A nerve cell that releases a neurotransmitter.

Primary (1°) alcohol (14.2) An alcohol having the general structure RCH_2OH.

Primary (1°) alkyl halide (14.9) An alkyl halide having the general structure RCH_2X.

Primary (1°) amide (17.1) A compound having the general structure $RCONH_2$.

Primary (1°) amine (18.1) A compound having the general structure RNH_2.

Primary (1°) carbon (12.2) A carbon atom bonded to one other carbon.

Primary structure (21.6) The particular sequence of amino acids that are joined together by peptide bonds in a protein.

Product (5.1) A substance formed in a chemical reaction.

Progestin (19.9) A hormone responsible for the preparation of the uterus for implantation of a fertilized egg.

Prostaglandins (17.4, 19.11) A group of carboxylic acids that contain a five-membered ring, are synthesized from arachidonic acid, and have a wide range of biological activities.

Proteins (21.1) Biomolecules that contain many amide bonds, formed by joining amino acids together.

Proton (2.2) A positively (+) charged subatomic particle that resides in the nucleus of the atom.

Proton transfer reaction (9.2) A Brønsted–Lowry acid–base reaction in which a proton is transferred from an acid to a base.

Pure substance (1.3) A substance that contains a single component, and has a constant composition regardless of the sample size.

Q

Quaternary ammonium ion (18.1) A cation with the general structure R_4N^+.

Quaternary (4°) carbon (12.2) A carbon atom that is bonded to four other carbons.

Quaternary structure (21.6) The shape adopted when two or more folded polypeptide chains come together into one protein complex.

R

Racemic mixture (15.5) An equal mixture of two enantiomers.

Rad (10.4) The radiation absorbed dose; the amount of radiation absorbed by one gram of a substance.

Radioactive decay (10.2) The process by which an unstable radioactive nucleus emits radiation, forming a nucleus of new composition.

Radioactive isotope (10.1) An isotope that is unstable and spontaneously emits energy to form a more stable nucleus.

Radioactivity (10.1) The energy emitted spontaneously by an unstable radioactive isotope.

Radiocarbon dating (10.3) A method to date artifacts that is based on the ratio of the radioactive carbon-14 isotope to the stable carbon-12 isotope.

Reactant (5.1) The starting material in a reaction.

Reaction rate (6.3) A measure of how fast a chemical reaction occurs.

Recombinant DNA (22.10) Synthetic DNA that contains segments from more than one source.

Redox reaction (5.9) A reaction that involves the transfer of electrons from one element to another.

Reducing agent (5.9) A compound that loses electrons (i.e., is oxidized), causing another compound to be reduced.

Reducing sugar (20.4) A carbohydrate that is oxidized with Benedict's reagent.

Reduction (5.9, 12.8) The gain of electrons by an atom. Reduction may result in the loss of oxygen atoms or the gain of hydrogen atoms.

Refining (12.6) The distillation of crude petroleum to form usable fractions that differ in boiling point.

Rem (10.4) The radiation equivalent for man; the amount of radiation absorbed by a substance that also factors in its energy and potential to damage tissue.

Replication (22.4) The process by which DNA makes a copy of itself when a cell divides.

Resonance structures (4.4) Two Lewis structures having the same arrangement of atoms but a different arrangement of electrons.

Restriction endonuclease (22.10) An enzyme that cuts DNA at a particular sequence of bases.

Retrovirus (22.11) A virus that contains a core of RNA.

Reverse reaction (6.5) In equilibrium, a reaction that proceeds from right to left as drawn.

Reverse transcription (22.11) A process by which a retrovirus produces DNA from RNA.

Reversible inhibitor (21.9) An inhibitor that binds to an enzyme, but enzyme activity is restored when the inhibitor is released.

Reversible reaction (6.5) A reaction that can occur in either direction, from reactants to products or from products to reactants.

Ribonucleic acid (RNA, 22.1, 22.5) A polymer of ribonucleotides that translates genetic information to protein synthesis.

Ribonucleoside (22.1) A compound that contains the monosaccharide ribose and a purine or pyrimidine base.

Ribonucleotide (22.1) A compound that contains the monosaccharide ribose bonded to either a purine or pyrimidine base as well as a phosphate at the 5'-OH group.

Ribosomal RNA (rRNA, 22.5) The most abundant type of RNA. rRNA is found in the ribosomes of the cell and provides the site where polypeptides are assembled during protein synthesis.

S

Saponification (17.9, 19.5) The basic hydrolysis of an ester.

Saturated fatty acids (19.2) Fatty acids that have no double bonds in their long hydrocarbon chains.

Saturated hydrocarbon (12.1) An alkane with molecular formula C_nH_{2n+2} that contains a chain of carbon atoms but no rings.

Saturated solution (8.2) A solution that has the maximum number of grams of solute that can be dissolved.

s **Block** (2.6) Elements located in groups 1A and 2A of the periodic table as well as the element helium. The *s* subshell is filled last in these elements.

Scientific notation (1.6) A system in which numbers are written as $y \times 10^x$, where y is a number between 1 and 10 and x can be either positive or negative.

Secondary (2°) alcohol (14.2) An alcohol having the general structure R_2CHOH.

Secondary (2°) alkyl halide (14.9) An alkyl halide having the general structure R_2CHX.

Secondary (2°) amide (17.1) A compound that has the general structure RCONHR'.

Secondary (2°) amine (18.1) A compound that has the general structure R_2NH.

Secondary (2°) carbon (12.2) A carbon atom that is bonded to two other carbons.

Secondary structure (21.6) The three-dimensional arrangement of localized regions of a protein. The α-helix and β-pleated sheet are two kinds of secondary structure.

Semipermeable membrane (8.8) A membrane that allows only certain molecules to pass through.

Shell (2.5) A region where an electron that surrounds a nucleus is confined. A shell is also called a principal energy level.

Sievert (10.4) A unit that measures absorbed radiation; abbreviated as Sv.

Significant figures (1.5) All of the digits in a measured number, including one estimated digit.

SI units (1.4) The International System of Units formally adopted as the uniform system of units for the sciences.

Skeletal structure (11.4) A shorthand method used to draw organic compounds in which carbon atoms are assumed to be at the junction of any two lines or at the end of a line, and all H's on C's are omitted.

Soap (17.6, 19.5) A salt of a long-chain carboxylic acid.

Solid (1.2) A state of matter that has a definite shape and volume. The particles of a solid lie close together, and are arranged in a regular, three-dimensional array.

Solubility (8.2) The amount of solute that dissolves in a given amount of solvent.

Solute (8.1) The substance present in the lesser amount in a solution.

Solution (8.1) A homogeneous mixture that contains small particles. Liquid solutions are transparent.

Solvation (8.2) The process of surrounding particles of a solute with solvent molecules.

Solvent (8.1) The substance present in the larger amount in a solution.

s **Orbital** (2.5) A spherical orbital that is lower in energy than other orbitals in the same shell.

Specific gravity (1.10) A unitless quantity that compares the density of a substance with the density of water at 4 °C.

Specific rotation (15.7) A physical constant for the amount that a chiral compound rotates the plane of polarized light. Specific rotation is defined with a specific sample tube length (usually 10 cm), concentration, temperature (25 °C), and wavelength.

Spectator ion (9.7) An ion that appears on both sides of an equation but undergoes no change in a reaction.

Sphingomyelin (19.6) A phospholipid derived from sphingosine, which contains a single fatty acid bonded with an amide bond to the carbon backbone.

SSRI (18.8) A class of antidepressants that acts by inhibiting the reuptake of serotonin by the presynaptic neuron. SSRI is an abbreviation for "selective serotonin reuptake inhibitor."

Standard molar volume (7.4) The volume of one mole of any gas at STP—22.4 L.

States of matter (1.2) The forms in which most matter exists—that is, gas, liquid, and solid.

Stereochemistry (15.1) The three-dimensional structure of molecules.

Stereoisomers (13.3) Isomers that differ only in their three-dimensional arrangement of atoms.

Steroid (19.8) A lipid whose carbon skeleton contains three six-membered rings and one five-membered ring.

STP (7.4) Standard conditions of temperature and pressure—1 atm (760 mm Hg) for pressure and 273 K (0 °C) for temperature.

Straight-chain alkane (12.2) An alkane that has all of its carbons in one continuous chain.

Sublimation (7.10) A phase change in which the solid phase enters the gas phase without passing through the liquid state.

Subshell (2.5) A sublevel within a shell designated by the letters *s, p, d,* or *f,* and containing one type of orbital.

Substitution reaction (13.13) A reaction in which an atom is replaced by another atom or a group of atoms.

Sulfate (3.6) An SO_4^{2-} ion.

Sulfhydryl group (14.1) An SH group.

Sulfonation (13.13) The substitution of SO_3H for a hydrogen.

Supersaturated solution (8.3) A solution that contains more than the predicted maximum amount of solute at a given temperature.

Surface tension (7.8) A measure of the resistance of a liquid to spread out.

Synapse (18.8) The gap between neurons across which neurotransmitters act.

T

Temperature (1.9) A measure of how hot or cold an object is.

Tertiary (3°) alcohol (14.2) An alcohol that has the general structure R_3COH.

Tertiary (3°) alkyl halide (14.9) An alkyl halide that has the general structure R_3CX.

Tertiary (3°) amide (17.1) A compound that has the general structure $RCONR'_2$.

Tertiary (3°) amine (18.1) A compound that has the general structure R_3N.

Tertiary (3°) carbon (12.2) A carbon atom that is bonded to three other carbons.

Tertiary structure (21.6) The three-dimensional shape adopted by an entire peptide chain.

Tetrose (20.2) A monosaccharide with four carbons.

Theoretical yield (5.7) The amount of product expected from a given amount of reactant based on the coefficients in the balanced chemical equation.

Thiol (14.1) A compound that contains a sulfhydryl group (SH group) bonded to a tetrahedral carbon atom; general structure RSH.

Titration (9.9) A technique for determining an unknown molarity of an acid by adding a base of known molarity to a known volume of acid.

Tollens reagent (16.5) An oxidizing agent that contains silver(I) oxide (Ag_2O) in aqueous ammonium hydroxide (NH_4OH).

Trace element (micronutrient, 2.1) An element required in the daily diet in small quantities—usually less than 15 mg.

Transamination (24.9) The transfer of an amino group from an amino acid to an α-keto acid.

Transcription (22.6) The process that synthesizes RNA from DNA.

Transfer RNA (tRNA, 22.5) The smallest type of RNA, which brings a specific amino acid to the site of protein synthesis on a ribosome.

Trans isomer (13.3) An alkene with two R groups on opposite sides of a double bond.

Transition metal element (2.4) An element contained in one of the 10 columns in the periodic table numbered 1B–8B.

Transition state (6.3) The unstable intermediate located at the top of the energy hill in an energy diagram.

Translation (22.8) The synthesis of proteins from RNA.

Triacylglycerol (17.9, 19.4) A triester formed from glycerol and three molecules of fatty acids.

Triol (14.3) A compound with three hydroxyl groups.

Triose (20.2) A monosaccharide with three carbons.

Tripeptide (21.4) A peptide that contains three amino acids joined together by two amide bonds.

Triple bond (4.2) A multiple bond that contains six electrons—that is, three two-electron bonds.

Triprotic acid (9.1) An acid that contains three acidic protons.

Tritium (2.3) A hydrogen atom that has one proton and two neutrons, giving it a mass number of three.

U

Universal gas constant (7.5) The constant, symbolized by R, that equals the product of the pressure and volume of a gas, divided by the product of the number of moles and Kelvin temperature; $R = PV/nT$.

Unpaired electron (2.6) A single electron.

Unsaturated fatty acid (19.2) A fatty acid that has one or more double bonds in its long hydrocarbon chain.

Unsaturated hydrocarbon (13.1) A compound that contains fewer than the maximum number of hydrogen atoms per carbon.

Unsaturated solution (8.2) A solution that has less than the maximum number of grams of solute.

Urea cycle (24.9) The process by which an ammonium ion is converted to urea, $(NH_2)_2C{=}O$.

V

Valence electron (2.7) An electron in the outermost shell that takes part in bonding and chemical reactions.

Valence shell electron pair repulsion (VSEPR) theory (4.6) A theory that predicts molecular geometry based on the fact that electron pairs repel each other; thus, the most stable arrangement keeps these groups as far away from each other as possible.

Vapor (7.8) Gas molecules formed from the evaporation of a liquid.

Vaporization (7.10) The conversion of a liquid to a gas.

Vapor pressure (7.8) The pressure above a liquid exerted by gas molecules in equilibrium with the liquid phase.

Vesicle (18.8) A small packet where neurotransmitters are stored, located in the filaments of the axon of a neuron near the synapse.

Virus (22.11) An infectious agent consisting of a DNA or RNA molecule that is contained within a protein coating.

Viscosity (7.8) A measure of a fluid's resistance to flow freely.

Vitamin (11.7) An organic compound that must be obtained in the diet and is needed in small amounts for normal cell function.

Volatile (8.7) Readily vaporized.

Volume/volume percent concentration (8.4) The number of milliliters of solute dissolved in 100 mL of solution.

W

Water-soluble vitamin (11.7) A vitamin with many polar bonds that dissolves in water.

Wax (19.3) An ester (RCOOR') formed from a fatty acid (RCOOH) and a high molecular weight alcohol (R'OH).

Weight (1.4) The force that matter feels due to gravity.

Weight/volume percent concentration (8.4) The number of grams of solute dissolved in 100 mL of solution.

X

X-ray (10.7) A high-energy form of radiation.

Z

Zaitsev rule (14.5) A rule that states that the major product in an elimination reaction is the alkene that has more alkyl groups bonded to the double bond.

Zwitterion (21.2) A neutral compound that contains both a positive and a negative charge.

Zymogen (21.9) The inactive precursor of an enzyme that is then converted to its active form when needed.

Credits

Chapter 1

Opener: Alexander S. Berk; **1.1a,b:** © The McGraw-Hill Companies, Inc./Jill Braaten, photographer; **1.2a:** © Bob Krist/Corbis; **1.2b:** © Corbis RF; **1.3a:** © Douglas Peebles Photography/Alamy; **1.3b:** Daniel C. Smith; **1.3c:** © Dr. Parvinder Sethi RF; **Page 6(sugar):** Daniel C. Smith; **(water, sugar dissolved in water):** © The McGraw-Hill Companies, Inc./Jill Braaten, photographer; **1.4a:** Daniel C. Smith; **1.4b:** © Richard T. Nowtiz/Photo Researchers, Inc.; **1.5a:** Daniel C. Smith; **1.5b:** © Keith Eng, 2008; **1.5c:** © The McGraw-Hill Companies, Inc./Jill Braaten, photographer; **1.5d:** Daniel C. Smith; **p. 9(top):** © Doug Wilson/Corbis; **(bottom):** © Jill Braaten; **p. 10(top):** © Chuck Savage/Corbis; **(bottom):** © PhotoDisc/Getty RF; **p. 11:** © PhotoDisc/Getty RF; **p. 12 (macadamia nuts):** Zachary D.-K. Smith; **(fish):** Daniel C. Smith; **p. 16:** © Stockbyte/Getty RF; **p. 17:** © Creative Studios/Alamy RF; **p. 20:** © The McGraw-Hill Companies, Inc./Elite Images; **p. 21:** © PhotoDisc/Getty RF; **p. 22, 24 & 26:** © The McGraw-Hill Companies, Inc./Jill Braaten, photographer; **p. 27:** © Photodisc/Getty RF.

Chapter 2

Opener: © Keith Eng. 2008; **p. 33:** © Michael S. Yamashita/Getty Images; **p. 39(top):** © Jill Braaten; **(bottom):** © The McGraw-Hill Companies, Inc./Charles D. Winters/Timeframe Photography, Inc.; **p. 43:** © Steve Snodgrass; **2.4b,c:** © Dr. A. Leger/Phototake; **p. 45:** © Anna Kari - Photojournalist; **p. 48:** © Jill Braaten; **2.6a-c:** © The McGraw-Hill Companies, Inc./Jill Braaten, photographer and Anthony Arena, chemistry consultant; **p. 53:** © Karen Kasmauski/Science Faction/Corbis; **p. 56:** © Dr. Parvinder Sethi; **p. 59:** © Peter Dench/Corbis.

Chapter 3

Opener: © Stockbyte/PunchStock RF; **3.1(Sodium metal & chlorine gas):** © The McGraw-Hill Companies, Inc./Stephen Frisch, photographer; **(sodium chloride crystals):** © Dane S. Johnson/Visuals Unlimited; **p. 69:** © Iconotec/Alamer and Cali, photographers RF; **p. 75:** © The McGraw-Hill Companies, Inc./Jill Braaten, photographer; **p. 79:** © James L. Amos/Photo Researchers, Inc.; **p. 80(both):** © The McGraw-Hill Companies, Inc./Jill Braaten, photographer; **p. 81:** © Digital Vision Ltd./SuperStock RF; **p. 83:** © BananaStock/PunchStock RF; **p. 85:** © The McGraw-Hill Companies, Inc./Jill Braaten, photographer; **p. 87(top):** © The McGraw-Hill Companies, Inc./Elite Images; **(bottom):** © CNRI/Photo Researchers, Inc.; **p. 88(oysters):** © Image Source/Corbis RF; **(tums, maalox, iron):** © The McGraw-Hill Companies, Inc./Jill Braaten, photographer; **p. 89(both):** © Steve Gschmeissner/Photo Researchers, Inc.

Chapter 4

Opener: © The McGraw-Hill Companies, Inc./Elite Images; **p. 96(top):** © Photodisc/Alamy RF; **(middle):** © Grant Heilman Photography/Alamy; **(bottom):** Photo by Tim McCabe, USDA Natural Resources Conservation Service; **p. 100:** U.S. Dept. of Commerce photoset Hawaii Volcanism: Lava Forms; **p. 103:** © Ted Nelson/Dembinsky Photo Associates; **p. 104 & 106:** © Jill Braaten; **p. 109(top):** Daniel C. Smith; **(bottom):** © Image Source Black/Alamy RF; **p. 116(top):** © The McGraw-Hill Companies, Inc./Jill, Braaten, photographer; **(bottom):** © Jill Braaten.

Chapter 5

Opener: © Jill Braaten; **p. 124:** Daniel C. Smith; **5.1(left):** © The McGraw-Hill Companies, Inc./Jill, Braaten, photographer and Anthony Arena, chemistry consultant; **(right):** Daniel C. Smith; **p. 128:** © BananaStock/Punchstock RF; **p. 130:** Scott Bauer/USDA; **5.2b:** © Jack Sullivan/Alamy; **p. 133 & 136:** © The McGraw-Hill Companies, Inc./Jill, Braaten, photographer and Anthony Arena, chemistry consultant; **p. 137:** © Science Photo Library/Getty RF; **p. 139:** © Hisham F. Ibrahim/Getty RF; **p. 140(top):** © Keith Eng, 2008; **(bottom):** © Comstock Images/Punchstock RF; **p. 142:** © Royalty Free/Corbis; **5.3:** © The McGraw-Hill Companies, Inc./Jill, Braaten, photographer and Anthony Arena, chemistry consultant; **p. 145:** © Bob Daemmrich/Stock Boston; **p. 146:** © The McGraw-Hill Companies, Inc./Jill, Braaten, photographer and Anthony Arena, chemistry consultant; **p. 147:** © Ryan McVay/Getty Images RF; **5.4(albuterol & fluoxetine):** © The McGraw-Hill Companies, Inc./Jill, Braaten, photographer; **(atorvastatin):** © Beaconstox/Alamy; **p. 152:** U.S. Department of Energy; **p. 156:** © Jill Braaten; **p. 158(left):** © Tony Cordoza/Alamy RF; **(right):** © Clair Dunn/Alamy; **5.7:** © Keigh Eng, 2008.

Chapter 6

Opener: © UpperCut Images/Alamy RF; **p. 168:** Daniel C. Smith; **p. 169:** © The McGraw-Hill Companies, Inc./Jill, Braaten, photographer; **p. 170:** © Royalty Free/Corbis; **p. 173(top):** © Digital Vision/PunchStock RF; **(bottom):** © Comstock/PunchStock RF; **p. 178:** © Jack Star/PhotoLink/Getty RF; **p. 179 & 6.3:** © The McGraw-Hill Companies, Inc./Jill, Braaten, photographer; **p. 181:** © Ingram Publishing/SuperStock RF; **p. 187:** © Royalty-Free/Corbis.

Chapter 7

Opener: Daniel C. Smith; **7.1:** © Doug Menuez/Getty Images RF; **p. 201:** Daniel C. Smith; **p. 206:** © Open Door/Alamy RF; **p. 209:** © Bill Aron/Photo Edit; **p. 211:** © Jill Braaten; **p. 216:** © National Geographic/Getty Images; **p. 217:** © Spencer Grant/Photo Edit; **p. 218(top):** © Martin Harvey/Corbis; **(bottom):** © Andrew Syred/Photo Researchers, Inc.; **p. 223(chloroethane):** Courtesy of Gebauer Company, Cleveland, Ohio; **(girl drinking):** Daniel C. Smith; **(liquid in a closed container):** © The McGraw-Hill Companies, Inc./Jill, Braaten, photographer; **7.8a:** © The McGraw-Hill Companies, Inc./Jill, Braaten, photographer and Anthony Arena, chemistry consultant; **7.8b:** © blickwinkel/Alamy; **7.9a-d:** © The McGraw-Hill Companies, Inc./Jill, Braaten, photographer; **p. 227(bikers):** © Royalty Free/Corbis; **(glass, ice, liquid water):** © The McGraw-Hill Companies, Inc./Jill, Braaten, photographer; **p. 228(both):** © The McGraw-Hill Companies, Inc./Jill, Braaten, photographer; **p. 229(all):** © The McGraw-Hill Companies, Inc./Jill, Braaten, photographer and Anthony Arena, chemistry consultant.

Chapter 8

Opener: Zachary D.-K. Smith; **p. 242(top):** © Jill Braaten; **8.1a:** © Brian Evans/Photo Researchers, Inc.; **8.1b:** © Digital Vision/Alamy RF; **8.1c:** © Keith Eng, 2008; **p. 243(both):** © The McGraw-Hill Companies, Inc./Jill Braaten, photographer and Anthony Arena, chemistry consultant; **8.3(both):** © The McGraw-Hill Companies, Inc./Jill Braaten, photographer; **p. 245:** © Royalty-Free/Corbis; **8.4:** © Tom Pantages; **p. 247:** © Keith Eng, 2008; **8.5(both):** © The McGraw-Hill Companies, Inc./Jill Braaten, photographer; **p. 249:** © Oliver Anlauf/Getty Images; **p. 250:** © The McGraw-Hill Companies, Inc./Suzie Ross, photographer; **8.6a,b:** © The McGraw-Hill Companies, Inc./Jill Braaten, photographer and Anthony Arena, chemistry consultant; **p. 251:** © BananaStock/PunchStock RF; **p. 252:** © David Hoffman Photo Library/Alamy; **p. 253:** © Comstock/PunchStock RF; **p. 258:** © Jill Braaten; **8.7(both):** © The McGraw-Hill Companies, Inc./Jill Braaten, photographer; **p. 261(top):** © Traverse City Record-Eagle, John L. Russell/AP/Wide World Photos; **(bottom):** © OSF/Doug Allan/Animals Animals; **8.8a-c:** © Dennis Kunkel Microscopy, Inc.

Chapter 9

Opener, p. 275(both): © The McGraw-Hill Companies, Inc./Jill Braaten, photographer and Anthony Arena, chemistry consultant; **9.1a:** © Jill Braaten; **9.1b:** © Photolink/Getty RF; **9.1c:** © BananaStock/PunchStock RF; **9.2a-c:** © The McGraw-Hill Companies, Inc./Jill Braaten, photographer; **p. 280:** © Charles D. Winters/Photo Researchers, Inc.; **9.4, 9.5(all):** © The McGraw-Hill Companies, Inc./Jill Braaten, photographer and Anthony Arena, chemistry consultant; **p. 287:** © Digital Vision Ltd./SuperStock RF; **p. 289:** © The McGraw-Hill Companies, Inc./Jill Braaten, photographer; **p. 291:** © Comstock Images/PictureQuest RF; **p. 293:** © Royalty-Free/Corbis; **9.6a:** © The McGraw-Hill Companies, Inc./Stephen Frisch, photographer; **9.6b:** © Sciencephotos/Alamy; **9.6c:** © Leslie Garland Picture Library/Alamy; **9.7(lemons):** © Humberto Olarte Cupas/Alamy RF; **(strawberries):** © Photolink/Getty RF; **(tomatoes):** © Burke/Triolo/Getty RF; **(milk):** © Mitch Hrdlicka/Getty RF; **(phillips):** © The McGraw-Hill Companies, Inc./Jill Braaten, photographer; **(ammonia):** © The McGraw-Hill Companies, Inc./Terry Wild Studio; **(Clorox):** © The McGraw-Hill Companies, Inc./Jill Braaten, photographer; **p. 295:** © Bruce Heinemann/Getty RF; **p. 298, 299, Fig. 9.9a-c:** © The McGraw-Hill Companies, Inc./Jill Braaten, photographer and Anthony Arena, chemistry consultant; **p. 303:** © Dr. Parvinder Sethi; **p. 309:** © JupiterImages/Brand X/Alamy RF.

Chapter 10

Opener: © Martin Dohrn/Photo Researchers, Inc.; **p. 319(top):** © AFP/Getty Images; **(bottom):** © Cordelia Molloy/Photo Researchers, Inc.; **p. 320:** © S. Wanke/PhotoLink/Getty RF; **10.2a:** © Owen Franken/Corbis; **10.2b,c:** © Custom Medical Stock Photo; **10.3:** © Science VU/Visuals Unlimited; **p. 327(top):** © Hank Morgan/Photo Researchers, Inc.; **(bottom):** Landauer Corporation; **10.4b:** © Living Art Enterprises, LLC/Photo Researchers, Inc.; **10.5a,b:** Daniel C. Smith; **p. 331:** Image courtesy of the Australian Nuclear Science and Technology Organization; **10.7a,c:** Daniel C. Smith; **10.8a:** © Martin Bond/Photo Researchers, Inc.; **10.9a:** © Royalty-Free/Corbis; **10.9b:** © Scott Camazine/Photo Researchers, Inc.; **10.9c:** With permission, Daniel C. Smith.

Chapter 11

Opener: © Corbis RF; **11.1a:** © Comstock/PunchStock RF; **11.1b:** © Corbis Premium RF/Alamy; **11.1c:** © Steven May/Alamy; **11.1d:** © Layna Kennedy/Corbis; **p. 343(methane):** © Ingram Publishing/SuperStock RF; **(ethanol):** © Goodshoot/PunchStock RF; **(capsaicin):** © The McGraw-Hill Companies, Inc./Jill Braaten, photographer; **(caffeine):** © Comstock/PunchStock RF; **p. 346(top):** © Vol. 129 PhotoDisc/Getty RF; **(bottom):** © PhotoDisc/Getty RF; **p. 347:** © Corbis/RF; **p. 350:** John Somerville; **p. 356:** © Ted Kinsman/Photo Researchers, Inc.; **11.3(cherries):** © Brand X Pictures/PunchStock RF; **(bananas):** © Ingram Publishing/SuperStock RF; **(oranges):** © Brand X Pictures/PunchStock RF; **(pineapple):** © Corbis RF; **p. 359:** © Jill Braaten; **p. 360:** © Graham Titchmarsh/Alamy RF; **p. 361:** © National Geographic Image Collection/Alamy RF; **Table 11.5(left):** © PIXTAL/PunchStock RF; **(right):** © Royalty-Free/Corbis; **p. 366:** © The McGraw-Hill Companies, Inc./Jill Braaten, photographer; **p. 367 (top):** © The McGraw-Hill Companies, Inc./John Flournoy, photographer; **(bottom):** Photo by Mary Clay Stensvold, courtesy of Smithsonian Institution.

Chapter 12

Opener: © Bettmann/Corbis; **p. 377(left):** God of Insects; **(right):** © Douglas Peebles/Corbis; **p. 378:** © Bloomberg/Getty Images; **p. 383:** © PhotoDisc Website RF; **p. 384:** © Jill Braaten; **p. 389(left):** © Brand X Pictures/PunchStock RF; **(right):** © The McGraw-Hill Companies, Inc./Suzie Ross, photographer; **12.1a:** © PhotoDisc RF; **p. 393:** © The McGraw-Hill Companies, Inc./Jill Braaten, photographer; **p. 394(top):** © Vince Bevan/Alamy; **(bottom):** © Jill Braaten; **p. 395:** PhotoLink/Getty RF.

Chapter 13

Opener, p. 403: © The McGraw-Hill Companies, Inc./Jill Braaten, photographer; **p. 410:** © Degginger E.R./Animals Animals/Earth Scenes; **p. 411:** © Jill Braaten; **p. 413 (top):** © The McGraw-Hill Companies, Inc./Jill Braaten, photographer; **(bottom):** © Sergio Piumatti; **p. 417:** © 1998 Richard Megna, Fundamental Photographs, NYC; **p. 419(top):** Ethanol Promotion and Information Council (EPIC); **(bottom):** © The McGraw-Hill Companies, Inc./Jill Braaten, photographer; **p. 420:** © Royalty-Free/Corbis; **13.5(both):** © The McGraw-Hill Companies, Inc./Jill Braaten, photographer; **p. 421(both):** © The McGraw-Hill Companies, Inc./Elite Images; **p. 422:** © Jill Braaten; **13.6(PVC):** © The McGraw-Hill Companies, Inc./John Thoeming, photographer; **(balls):** © Dynamicgraphics/Jupiterimages RF; **(blankets):** © Fernando Bengoechea/Corbis; **(styrofoam):** © The McGraw-Hill Companies, Inc./John Thoeming, photographer; **Table 13.2(blood bag):** © Image Source/Getty Images RF; **(syringes):** © Royalty Free/Corbis; **(dental floss):** © Jill Braaten; **p. 429(sunscreen):** © The McGraw-Hill Companies, Inc./John Thoeming, photographer; **(tobacco plant):** Photo by Bob Nichols, USDA Natural Resources Conservation Service; **(cigarette smoke):** © PhotoAlto/PictureQuest RF; **p. 430(tylenol):** © The McGraw-Hill Companies, Inc./John Thoeming, photographer; **(dentist):** © Mikael Karlsson/Arresting Images RF; **(blowing nose):** © Picture Partners/Alamy; **p. 431(vanilla bean):** © CD16/Author's Image RF; **(cloves):** © Peter Arnold, Inc./Alamy; **(tumeric):** Mr. Napat Kitipanangkul, Science School, Walailak University with financial support by Biodiversity; Research and training program (BRT); **(cell protector):** © The McGraw-Hill Companies, Inc./Elite Images; **p. 432:** © Royalty-Free/Corbis.

Chapter 14

Opener: © John A. Rizzo/Getty Images RF; **p. 444(coffee):** © Creatas/PunchStock RF; **(ether):** © Mira/Alamy; **(tree trunk):** © Greg Vaughn/Alamy; **p. 445:** © Iconotec.com/Pepiera Tom Canabi Hugo RF; **p. 446:** © The McGraw-Hill Companies, Inc./Jill Braaten, photographer; **p. 448:** © Jill Braaten; **14.1(grapes):** © Dynamic Grapics Group/PunchStock RF; **(barrels of wine):** © Goodshoot/PunchStock RF; **(wine bottles):** © BananaStock/RunchStock RF; **p. 450(wheat):** © Vol. 1 PhotoDisc/Getty RF; **(cotton):** © Corbis RF; **14.4:** © The McGraw-Hill Companies, Inc./Elite Images; **p. 457(top):** © BananaStock/PunchStock RF; **(bottom):** Gwinnet County Police Department/Centers for Disease Control and Prevention; **p. 458(top):** © Ed Reschke; **(bottom):** Peter J.S. Franks, Scripps Institution of Oceanography; **p. 461:** The Boston Medical Library in the Francis A. Countway Library of Medicine; **p. 462:** © Jill Braaten; **p. 465(top):** © The McGraw-Hill Companies, Inc./Jill Braaten, photographer; **(bottom):** NASA; **p. 466:** © Mark Downey/Getty Images RF; **14.7(both):** © The McGraw-Hill Companies, Inc./Suzi Ross, photographer.

Chapter 15

Opener: © The McGraw-Hill Companies, Inc./Elite Images; **p. 477:** Daniel C. Smith; **15.1a:** © The McGraw-Hill Companies, Inc./Jill Braaten, photographer; **15.1b:** © Claude Thouvenin/Peter Arnold, Inc.; **p. 482(grapes):** © PhotoDisc/Getty RF; **(ephedrine):** © Henriette Kress; **(greens):** © Comstock/PunchStock RF; **p. 485:** © John Fischer, About.com Hawaii Travel; **p. 486:** © The McGraw-Hill Companies, Inc./Jill Braaten, photographer; **p. 487:** © Nigel Cattlin/Alamy; **p. 492:** © GYRO PHOTOGRAPHY/amanaimages RF; **p. 496(caraway seeds):** © The McGraw-Hill Companies, Inc./Elite Images; **(spearmint leaves):** DAJ/Getty RF.

Chapter 16

Opener: © David Sieren/Visuals Unlimited; **p. 505:** © Iconotec/Alamer and Cali, photographers RF; **p. 507:** © TTH/a.collection/Getty/RF; **p. 510(both), 16.1, p. 511:** © The McGraw-Hill Companies, Inc./Jill Braaten, photographer; **p. 513:** © The McGraw-Hill Companies, Inc./Charles D. Winters/Timeframe Photography, Inc.; **p. 516:** © M.K. Ranjitsinh/Photo Researchers, Inc.; **p. 517(fluoxetine):** © The McGraw-Hill Companies, Inc./Jill Braaten, photographer; **(soybeans):** © PhotoDisc/Getty RF; **523(milk):** © The McGraw-Hill Companies, Inc./Elite Images; **(foxgrove):** © Richo Cech, Horizon Herbs, LLC.

Chapter 17

Opener: © Jill Braaten; **p. 536:** © The McGraw-Hill Companies, Inc./Jill Braaten, photographer; **p. 537:** © Photo Researchers, Inc.; **p. 543:** Photo by Forest and Kim Starr; **p. 544:** © The McGraw-Hill Companies, Inc./Jill Braaten, photographer; **p. 545(mangoes):** © CD16/Author's Image RF; **(apricots):** © Jupiterimages/ImageSource RF; **(wintergreen):** © Westend61 GmbH/Alamy; **(Melatonin & p. 546(both)):** © The McGraw-Hill Companies, Inc./Jill Braaten, photographer; **p. 550(ivory soap ad):** Ivory Soap Advertising Collection, Archives Center, National Museum of American History, Smithsonian Institution; **(willow tree):** © National Geographic/Getty Images; **(meadowsweet):** © Biopix. dkhttp://www.biopix.dk; **p. 553:** © Jill Braaten; **p. 554:** Coby Schal/NC State University; **p. 555:** Photo by Scott Bauer/USDA; **p. 558:** © The McGraw-Hill Companies, Inc./Jill Braaten, photographer; **p. 560(top):** Image courtesy of The Advertising Archives; **(bottom):** © Royalty-Free/Corbis; **p. 561(both):** © The McGraw-Hill Companies, Inc./Jill Braaten, photographer; **17.5a:** © SIU/Visuals Unlimited, Inc.; **17.5b:** © Antonia Reeve/Photo Researchers, Inc.; **p. 563(top):** © Jill Braaten; **(bottom):** Library of Congress.

Chapter 18

Opener: © Taxi/Getty; **p. 572(pepper plant):** © Maximilian Weinzierl/Alamy; **(hemlock):** © D. Hurst/Alamy RF; **p. 574:** © James Forte/Getty RF; **p. 579:** © BananaStock/PunchStock RF; **18.2(coffee plant):** © Mediacolor's/Alamy; **(cup):** © Nick Koudis/Gettty RF; **(coffee cherries):** © Inga Spence/Visuals Unlimited; **p. 580:** © Stockdisc/PunchStock RF; **18.3(tobacco plant):** © Flora Torrance/Life File RF; **(cigarette smoke):** © Nancy R. Cohen/Getty RF; **(dried tobacco leaves):** © Wayne Hutchinson/Alamy; **p. 582(poppy seeds):** © Stockbyte Silver/Getty RF; **(opium poppy):** © Scott Camazine/Photo Researchers, Inc.; **(cinchona tree):** Photo by Forest and Kim Starr; **p. 583(deadly nightshade):** © Werner Arnold; **p. 587:** © The McGraw-Hill Companies, Inc./Jill Braaten, photographer; **p. 591(bufo toad):** © Daniel C. Smith; **(mushrooms):** © IT Stock/age fotostock RF; **p. 593:** © The McGraw-Hill Companies, Inc./Jill Braaten, photographer; **p. 594:** Daniel C. Smith.

Chapter 19

Opener: © Jill Braaten; **p. 602:** © The McGraw-Hill Companies, Inc./Jill Braaten, photographer; **p. 606:** © Brand X Pictures/PunchStock RF; **p. 607(whale):** © Denis Scott/Corbis; **(leaf):** Daniel C. Smith; **(lip gloss):** © The McGraw-Hill Companies, Inc./Jill Braaten, photographer; **(bee's):** © Photodisc/Getty RF; **p. 608:** USDA, ARS, National Genetic Resources Program; **p. 609:** © The McGraw-Hill Companies, Inc./Jill Braaten, photographer; **p. 610(left):** © Ingo Jezierski/Corbis RF; **(right):** © Jupiterimages/ImageSource RF; **p. 611(top):** Daniel C. Smith; **p. 611 (bottom & 19.1(all)):** © The McGraw-Hill Companies, Inc./Jill Braaten, photographer; **p. 614:** Daniel C. Smith; **19.2:** © The McGraw-Hill Companies, Inc./Dennis Strete, photographer; **p. 615:** © AP/Wide World Photos; **p. 616(left):** © Jupiterimages/ImageSource RF; **(right):** David Buffington/Getty RF; **p. 624:** © Getty RF; **19.8 a,b:** © Ed Reschke; **p. 626:** © Andrew Brookes/Corbis; **p. 628:** © Comstock/JupiterImages RF; **p. 629:** © Jill Braaten; **p. 630(top):** © BananaStock RF; **(middle):** © Stockbyte/PunchStock RF; **(bottom):** © IT Stock/PunchStock RF; **p. 631:** © Jill Braaten.

Chapter 20

Opener: © Isabelle Rosenbaum & Frederic Cirou/PhotoAlto/PunchStock RF; **p. 641(top):** © Michelle Garrett/Corbis; **(bottom):** © ImageSource/Corbis RF; **p. 642(top):** Bauer/USDA; **(bottom):** Daniel C. Smith; **p. 643:** © The McGraw-Hill Companies, Inc./Elite Images; **p. 645:** © Photodisc Collection/Getty RF; **p. 647:** © Keith Brofsky/Getty RF; **p. 648(top):** © Comstock/PunchStock RF; **(bottom):** © Jill Braaten; **p. 657, 20.2:** © The McGraw-Hill Companies, Inc./Jill Braaten, photographer; **p. 658:** © Vol. 3/PhotoDisc/Getty RF; **p. 660(left):** © The McGraw-Hill Companies, Inc./Jill Braaten, photographer; **(right):** © D. Hurst/Alamy RF; **p. 661(left):** © David Muench/Corbis; **(right):** © The McGraw-Hill Companies, Inc./Elite Images; **20.3:** © The McGraw-Hill Companies, Inc./Jill Braaten, photographer; **p. 662:** © inga/Alamy; **20.4:** Biophoto Associates/Photo Researchers, Inc.; **20.5(stalks):** © Vol. 1 PhotoDisc/Getty RF; **(kernels):** © Borland/PhotoLink/Getty Images RF; **20.6:** © Dennis Kunkel/Visuals Unlimited; **667(top):** © Geldi/Alamy; **(bottom):** © The McGraw-Hill Companies, Inc./Jill Braaten, photographer; **p. 668:** Comstock Images/PictureQuest RF; **p. 669:** © Royalty-Free/Corbis.

Chapter 21

Opener: © Royalty-Free/Corbis; **p. 677:** © Jill Braaten; **p. 679(top):** © John A. Raineri; **(bottom):** © Jill Braaten; **p. 681:** © Comstock/PunchStock RF; **21.13:** © Image Source/PunchStock RF; **p. 698:** Daniel C. Smith; **p. 699:** © Eye of Science/Photo Researchers, Inc.; **p. 701:** © The McGraw-Hill Companies, Inc./Jill Braaten, photographer; **p. 702:** Daniel C. Smith.

Chapter 22

Opener: © Lawrence Lawry/Getty RF; **22.3a:** ©Photodisc/Jupiterimages RF; **p. 725:** Daniel C. Smith; **22.7b:** © Kenneth Eward/Photo Researchers, Inc.; **p. 738:** Cystic Fibrosis Trust; **22.12:** Courtesy Genelex Corp., www.HealthandDNA.com; **p. 743(top):** © The McGraw-Hill Companies, Inc./Jill Braaten, photographer; **(bottom):** © Time & Life Pictures/Getty Images.

Chapter 23

Opener: © David Stoecklein/Corbis; **23.2(left):** © Royalty-Free/Corbis; **(middle):** © Nancy R. Cohen/Getty RF; **(right):** © PhotoLink/Getty RF; **p. 761:** © Jill Braaten; **p. 764:** © The McGraw-Hill Companies, Inc./Jill Braaten, photographer; **p. 765:** © Digital Vision/Getty RF; **p. 772:** © Connie Brainsilver/Photo Researchers, Inc.; **p. 773:** © The McGraw-Hill Companies, Inc./Jill Braaten, photographer.

Chapter 24

Opener: © Dennis Gray/Cole Group/Getty RF; **p. 787(sugar beets):** © Corbis RF; **(milk):** © Isabelle Rozenbaum Frederic Cirou/PhotoAlto/PunchStock RF; **(cranberries):** © Burke/Triolo/Getty RF; **p. 789:** © Warren Morgan/Corbis; **p. 790:** © John A. Rizzo/Getty RF; **p. 798:** Daniel C. Smith; **p. 799(both):** © The McGraw-Hill Companies, Inc./Jill Braaten, photographer.

Index

Magnesium
  as alkaline earth element, 47
  as major mineral (macronutrient), 35*f*, 36
  oxidation of metal, 157–158
  properties, 47
  role in human body, 75, 76*f*
Magnesium cation, formation of, 70–71
Magnesium chloride, 82
Magnesium hydroxide, 87, 88, 277
Magnesium oxide antacid, 298, 298*f*
Magnesium sulfate, 89, 247
Magnetic resonance imaging (MRI), 335, 336*f*
Main group elements
  common ions formed, 74*f*
  covalent bonding and, 96, 97*f*
  electronegativity, 112, 112*f*
  ionic charge, 72–74, 73*t*, 74*f*
  octet rule, 71
  in periodic table, 45, 46*f*
Major minerals, 35*f*, 36
Malate, 703, 767*f*, 768
Maltose, 658–659, 658*mn*
Manganese, as trace element
    (micronutrient), 35*f*
Manganese dioxide, in batteries, 158, 159*f*
Mannose, 651, 787
Mannose 6-phosphate, 805
Manure, methane from, 393, 393*f*
Margarine, 420–421, 420*f*, 420*mn*
Markovnikov's rule, 418, 419
Mass. *See also* Molar mass
  atomic, 43
  atomic mass unit, 39
  calculations in chemical equations,
    140–146
  conservation of, 126
  definition, 10
  law of conservation, 126
  measuring, 10
  mole–mass conversions, 135–139
  number of molecules–mass conversions,
    138–139
  of subatomic particles, 38, 38*t*, 39
  units of measurement, 9*t*, 10, 11*t*, 12*t*
Mass number (*A*)
  definition, 40, 316
  of isotopes, 41–42
  in nuclear equation, 319–323
Mathematical operations
  scientific calculator use, A-4–A-6
  scientific notation, A-1–A-2
  significant figures, determining number of,
    A-2–A-4
Matrix, mitochondrial, 753, 753*f*
Matter
  chemical properties, 5
  classification of, 5–8, 6*f*, 7*f*, 8*f*, 244*f*
  definition, 2
  naturally occurring materials, 2, 2*f*, 3*f*
  physical properties, 4
  states of, 3–5, 4*f*, 199–200, 199*f*, 200*t*
  synthetic materials, 2, 2*f*, 3*f*

MDMA (Ecstasy), 370, 573
Meadowsweet, 550, 550*mn*
Measurement, 8–12
  conversion factors, 19–23
  English system, 9, 12*t*
  length, 9*t*, 10, 11*t*, 12*t*
  mass, 9*t*, 10, 11*t*, 12*t*
  metric system, 9–11, 9*t*, 10*t*, 11*t*, 12*t*
  reporting a value, 9
  rounding off numbers, 14–15, 14*t*, A-3
  scientific notation, 16–18, 17*f*, A-1–A-2
  significant figures, 12–16, A-2–A-4
  units, 9–11, 9*mn*, 9*t*, 10*t*, 11*t*
  volume, 9*t*, 11, 11*t*, 12*t*
Medicine, products of organic chemistry used
    in, 342*f*
Mega- (prefix), 10*mn*, 10*t*
Melatonin, 545
Melting
  definition, 227
  heat of fusion, 227, 228
  physical changes in state, 4–5
Melting point
  alcohols, 446
  alkanes, 394
  alkenes and alkynes, 403
  alkyl halides, 462
  amides, 542
  carboxylic acid, 541–542
  definition, 221
  ethers, 459
  fatty acid, 411*t*, 412, 606
  intermolecular forces and, 221–222
  ionic compounds, 85
  monosaccharides, 644
  organic compounds, 361
  thiols, 466
  triacylglycerols, 609
Membrane, 262–266, 266*f*
Membrane protein, 677
Mendeleev, Dmitri, 45
Menthol, 353, 529, 603
Menthone, 529
Meperidine, 573
Mercaptomethylfuran, 444
Mercury
  barometer, 201, 201*f*
  in dental filling, 242, 242*f*
  toxicity, 59*mn*
Mescaline, 593
Meselson, Matthew, 727
Messenger RNA (mRNA), 729–738, 732*t*,
    734*t*, 735*f*
Meta (prefix), 427
Metabolic acidosis, 309
Metabolic alkalosis, 309
Metabolic pathway
  coupled reactions in, 758–760, 759*f*
  cyclic, 752, 766
  definition, 752
  linear, 752
  spiral, 796

Metabolism, 751–777, 778–807
  amino acids, 799–803, 800*f*, 803*f*
  anabolism, 752
  anaerobic, 789, 789*mn*
  carbohydrate, 779, 782–794
    ATP yield from glucose, 791–792, 791*f*
    gluconeogenesis, 793–794, 793*f*
    glycolysis, 779, 782–788, 782*f*, 785*f*
  catabolism, 752, 753–756, 754*f*, 755*f*
  coenzymes in, 761–765, 764*t*
  common enzymes, 780–782, 780*t*
  definition, 752
  energy release, 642
  ketone bodies, 798–799, 799*mn*
  overview of, 753–756
  triacylglycerol catabolism, 794–799, 795*f*
  of triacylglycerols, 614–615, 615*f*
Metal(s)
  catalyst, 179, 181, 181*f*, 415*f*, 416
  cations, 71, 71*mn*, 72–73, 74–75, 74*f*, 75*f*, 78
    naming, 81, 82*t*
    naming ionic compounds from main
      group metals, 82–83
    naming ionic compounds with metals
      with variable charge, 83–84
  definition, 35
  ionic bonds, 68
  oxidation, 157
  in periodic table, 34*f*, 35
Metallic solid, 226, 226*f*
Metalloid(s)
  covalent bonds, 68, 96
  definition, 35
  in periodic table, 34*f*, 35
Met-enkephalin, 687–688
Meter (m) (unit of measurement), 9*t*, 10,
    11*t*, 12*t*
Meth- (prefix), 385
Methadone hydrochloride, 587
Methamphetamine, 362, 498, 574, 574*f*,
    584, 593
Methane
  boiling point, 221, 224
  combustion of, 124–125, 127, 159, 173,
    173*mn*, 393, 395
  covalent bonding, 96
  intermolecular forces, 221, 224
  London dispersion forces, 218
  from manure, 393, 393*f*
  melting point, 221
  molecular shape, 109
  in natural gas, 343, 392
  shape, 347
  structure, 343, 344, 378, 380*t*
  vapor pressure, 224
Methanethiol, 392*mn*
Methanoic acid, 538
Methanol
  addition to ethanol, 449
  combustion of, 164, 197
  Lewis structure for, 101
  polarity, 363

Common Functional Groups in Organic Chemistry

Type of Compound	General Structure	Example	Functional Group
Alcohol	R—ÖH	CH_3—ÖH	—OH hydroxyl group
Aldehyde	:O: R—C—H	:O: CH_3—C—H	C=O carbonyl group
Alkane	R—H	CH_3CH_3	— —
Alkene	C=C	C=C (H, H, H, H)	double bond
Alkyl halide	R—Ẍ: (X = F, Cl, Br, I)	CH_3—Br̈:	—X
Alkyne	—C≡C—	H—C≡C—H	triple bond
Amide	:O: R—C—N—H (or R) H (or R)	:O: CH_3—C—NH_2	—$CONH_2$, —CONHR, —$CONR_2$
Amine	R—N̈H_2 or R_2N̈H or R_3N̈	CH_3—N̈H_2	—NH_2 amino group
Aromatic compound	(benzene ring)	(benzene ring)	benzene ring
Carboxylic acid	:O: R—C—ÖH	:O: CH_3—C—ÖH	—COOH carboxyl group
Ester	:O: R—C—ÖR	:O: CH_3—C—ÖCH_3	—COOR
Ether	R—Ö—R	CH_3—Ö—CH_3	—OR
Ketone	:O: R—C—R	:O: CH_3—C—CH_3	C=O carbonyl group

Common Metric Prefixes

Prefix	Symbol	Numerical Value
mega-	M	10^6
kilo-	k	10^3
deci-	d	10^{-1}
centi-	c	10^{-2}
milli-	m	10^{-3}
micro-	μ	10^{-6}
nano-	n	10^{-9}

Useful Conversion Factors

Length	Mass	Volume
1 m = 100 cm = 1,000 mm	1 kg = 1,000 g	1 L = 1,000 mL
1 cm = 10 mm	1 g = 1,000 mg	1 mL = 1 cm^3 = 1 cc
2.54 cm = 1 in.	1 kg = 2.20 lb	946 mL = 1 qt
1 m = 39.4 in.	454 g = 1 lb	1 L = 1.06 qt
1 km = 0.621 mi	28.3 g = 1 oz	29.6 mL = 1 fl oz
Temperature	**Pressure**	**Energy**
°F = 1.8(°C) + 32	1 atm = 14.7 psi	1 kcal = 1,000 cal
°C = (°F − 32)/1.8	1 atm = 760 mm Hg	1 cal = 4.184 J
K = °C + 273	1 mm Hg = 1 torr	

Physical Constants

Avogadro's number	6.02×10^{23} particles/mol
Universal gas constant (R)	0.0821 L · atm/(mol · K)
Universal gas constant (R)	62.4 L · mm Hg/(mol · K)
Volume of one mole of gas at STP	22.4 L

Common Element Colors Used in Molecular Art

C   H   O   N   F   Cl   Br   I   S   P